NUMERICAL PROPERTIES AND METHODOLOGIES IN HEAT TRANSFER

SERIES IN COMPUTATIONAL METHODS IN MECHANICS AND THERMAL SCIENCES

W. J. Minkowycz and E. M. Sparrow, Editors

Baker **Finite Element Computational Fluid Mechanics**
Patankar **Numerical Heat Transfer and Fluid Flow**
Shih **Numerical Heat Transfer**

Proceedings

Shih, Editor **Numerical Properties and Methodologies in Heat Transfer: Proceedings of the Second National Symposium**

NUMERICAL PROPERTIES AND METHODOLOGIES IN HEAT TRANSFER

Proceedings of the Second National Symposium

Edited by

T. M. Shih

University of Maryland

HEMISPHERE PUBLISHING CORPORATION

Washington New York London

DISTRIBUTION OUTSIDE NORTH AMERICA

SPRINGER-VERLAG

Berlin Heidelberg New York Tokyo

NUMERICAL PROPERTIES AND METHODOLOGIES IN HEAT TRANSFER: Proceedings of the Second National Symposium

1 2 3 4 5 6 7 8 9 0 B C B C 8 9 8 7 6 5 4 3

Library of Congress Cataloging in Publication Data
Main entry under title:

Numerical properties and methodologies in heat transfer.

(Series in computational methods in mechanics and thermal sciences)
Bibliography: p.
Includes index.
1. Heat—Transmission—Congresses. 2. Numerical analysis—Congresses. I. Shih, T. M. II. National Symposium on Numerical Methodologies in Heat Transfer (2nd : 1981 : University of Maryland, College Park) III. Series.

QC319.8.N85 536'.2 82-6187
AACR2

ISBN 0-89116-309-3 Hemisphere Publishing Corporation
ISSN 0272-4804

DISTRIBUTION OUTSIDE NORTH AMERICA:
ISBN 3-540-12249-4 Springer-Verlag Berlin

Contents

*Invited reviewing papers.

HIGHER-ORDER SCHEMES

FREE CONVECTION IN ENCLOSURES

STREAMWISE-DIFFUSION FLOWS

LAMINAR AND TURBULENT EXTERNAL FLOWS

TWO-PHASE FLOWS

THERMAL RADIATION

COMBUSTION AND FIRES

LAMINAR AND TURBULENT EXTERNAL FLOWS

TWO-PHASE FLOWS

THERMAL RADIATION

COMBUSTION AND FIRES

Preface

This book includes invited lectures and contributed presentations delivered at the Second National Symposium on Numerical Methods in Heat Transfer, which was held September 28–30, 1981 at the University of Maryland, College Park, Maryland. The symposium was sponsored jointly by the National Science Foundation and the Office of Naval Research.

The material, after review and revision, is organized into eight parts. Part 1 deals with the important properties of various numerical schemes, including stability, consistency, convergence, accuracy and error bounds. Also presented are comparison of the existing methodologies, introduction of novel techniques, and improvement of existing schemes. The higher-order accurate difference schemes are described in Part 2. These schemes not only are subject to smaller truncation errors, but also stabilize the discretized convection-diffusion equation. The latter feature therefore is closely related to Part 3, which is devoted to investigation of the convection-diffusion flows. Part 4 examines the buoyancy-driven cavity flows. Interestingly, both the streamfunction-vorticity approach and the primitive-variables approach continue to be adopted, which suggests that perhaps the time has not yet come to assert which approach is convincingly more advantageous. From Part 5 to Part 8, this volume then is devoted to applications of various numerical schemes to important heat-transfer phenomena.

The organizing committee members who contributed tremendously to this symposium are: W. F. Ames, I. Babuska, J. deRis, D. K. Edwards, B. A. Finlayson, H. B. Keller, R. B. Kellogg, W. J. Minkowycz, S. V. Patankar, P. J. Roache, S. F. Shen, T. M. Shih, D. B. Spalding, E. M. Sparrow, C. L. Tien, and K. T. Yang.

On behalf of the organizing committee, I wish to express our gratitude to the following reviewers of the submitted manuscripts: R. K. Ahluwalia, L. L. Briggs, T. C. Chawla, Y. N. Chen, J. deRis, B. Gebhart, A. Haji-Sheikh, L. J. Hayes, N. D. Kararinoff, R. B. Kellogg, R. W. Knight, J. R. Lloyd, M. E. Palmer, III, G. D. Raithby, E. A. Thornton, A. T. Wassel, and S. S. Wang.

Finally, we gratefully acknowledge the contribution of the authors who promptly submitted their typed mats before enjoying the Christmas holiday. The symposium and its proceedings were made possible by the kind support of the aforementioned federal agencies and the Department of Mechanical Engineering at the University of Maryland. The personal interest and encouragement from Dr. W. Aung of NSF and Mr. M. K. Ellingsworth of ONR are also greatly appreciated.

T. M. Shih

NUMERICAL PROPERTIES AND METHODOLOGIES

A Survey of Finite Difference Schemes for Parabolic Partial Differential Equations

W.F. AMES
Georgia Institute of Technology
Atlanta, Georgia 30332

ABSTRACT

This evaluative survey introduces and discusses classical, predictor-corrector, fractional steps, hopscotch and lines methods for the numerical solution of parabolic partial differential equations. In addition a contracting interval scheme, which can be superimposed on other algorithms to give upper and lower bounds is described. Finally a brief discussion of six computer codes completes the paper.

1. INTRODUCTION

The strongly nonlinear parabolic differential dimensionless equation

$$\frac{\partial u}{\partial t} = \operatorname{div}[k(u) \operatorname{grad} u] + \phi(u) \tag{1.1}$$

governs classes of evolution type transport processes in diffusion and heat conduction. In this general lecture various forms of (1) will be used as a vehicle to describe numerical procedures based upon finite difference approximation.

To fix the notation we use the dimensionless equation

$$\left.\begin{array}{ll}
u_t = u_{xx} + u_{yy}, \quad u = u(x,y,t) & \\
0 < x < 1, \quad 0 < y < 1, \quad 0 < t \le T, & \\
\left.\begin{array}{l} u(0,y,t) = f_1(y,t) \\ u(1,y,t) = f_2(y,t) \end{array}\right\} & \text{on } 0 < y < 1,\ 0 < t \le T \\
\left.\begin{array}{l} u(x,0,t) = f_3(x,t) \\ u(x,1,t) = f_4(x,t) \end{array}\right\} & \text{on } 0 < x < 1,\ 0 < t \le T \\
u(x,y,0) = g(x,y) & \text{on } 0 < x < 1,\ 0 < y < 1
\end{array}\right\} \tag{1.2}$$

Development of a finite difference approximation for problem (2) necessitates the introduction of a grid (net) whose mesh (grid or net) points are denoted by $(x_i, y_j, t_n) = (i\Delta x, j\Delta y, n\Delta t)$, where $i = 0,1,2,\cdots,I$; $j = 0,1,2,\cdots,J$; $n = 0,1,2,\cdots,N$ with $\Delta x = 1/I$, $\Delta y = 1/J$ and $\Delta t = T/N$. The boundaries are specified by $i = 0$ and $i = I$, $j = 0$ and $j = J$. Any "false" boundaries will be labeled $i = -1,-2,\cdots$, $i = I+1,\cdots$, $j = J+1$ etc. The initial line is denoted by $n = 0$ and the discrete approximation for u at (x_i, y_j, t_n) is given by $U^n_{i,j}$. The exact value for u at the grid point is given by $u^n_{i,j}$. Sometimes it will be necessary to utilize mid-values such as $U^n_{i+\frac{1}{2},j+\frac{1}{2}}$. In addition the space and/or time increments can vary with the index, but this will not be so unless indicated.

If an approximate solution $U^n_{i,j}$ is assumed to be known at all grid points up to time t_n, a method must be specified to advance the solution to time t_{n+1}, subject to the boundary conditions. This method is our <u>numerical algorithm</u>. The values of $U^{n+1}_{0,j}$, $U^{n+1}_{I,j}$, $U^{n+1}_{i,0}$, $U^{n+1}_{i,J}$ are normally selected as

$$U^{n+1}_{0,j} = f_1(j\Delta y, (n+1)\Delta t) \tag{1.3}$$

- i.e. by means of the specified boundary conditions, etc. Algorithms will be called <u>explicit</u> or <u>implicit</u>. An explicit algorithm provides for a noniterative "marching" process for obtaining the solution at <u>each</u> present point in terms of known preceding (in time) and boundary points. On the other hand, implicit algorithms generally involve iterative calculations of many present values in terms of known preceding and boundary values.

Stability, consistency, convergence and discretization error are mathematical properties of algorithms that always concern us. Roughly speaking we say an algorithm is <u>stable</u> if errors generated in the computation, such as round-off and truncation errors, are dissipated as the propagation variable (time-like) increases. For analysis a more mathematical definition of stability is required (see Ames [1]). A finite difference scheme <u>converges</u> if U(P) converges to the exact solution u(P), with the same boundary values, as the net sizes go to zero. A finite difference algorithm is said to be consistent with the partial differential equation if the local <u>truncation errors</u> (the error involved when the Taylor series is truncated) tend to zero as $\Delta x, \Delta y$ and $\Delta t \to 0$. The <u>discretization error</u> is a combination of the equation truncation error and the boundary and initial truncation errors.

2. CLASSICAL METHODS

The classical methods (before 1955) for the linear problem

$$\left.\begin{aligned} &u_t = u_{xx},\ a_1 u(0,t) + a_2 u_x(0,t) = c(t), \\ &b_1 u(1,t) + b_2 u_x(1,t) = d(t),\ u(x,0) = g(x) \end{aligned}\right\} \tag{2.1}$$

are easily summarized in one expression with two parameters $r = \Delta t/(\Delta x)^2$, λ where $0 < r < \infty$ and $0 \le \lambda \le 1$. The algorithm equates a linear combination of three unknowns in the (n+1)st row to a linear combination of known values in the nth row by means of

$$-r\lambda U_{i-1}^{n+1} + (1+2r\lambda)U_i^{n+1} - r\lambda U_{i+1}^{n+1}$$
$$= r(1-\lambda)U_{i-1}^n + [1 - 2r(1-\lambda)]U_i^n + r(1-\lambda)U_{i+1}^n \tag{2.2}$$

with a local truncation error $O[(\Delta t)^2 + \Delta t(\Delta x)^2]$. The "O" is read as "big oh" and $O[k^2]$ means something which goes to zero as $k^2 \to 0$. Algorithm (2.2) is applied for $i = 0,1,2,\cdots,I$ with $\Delta x = 1/I$ and all $n = 0,1,2,\cdots,N$. The initial values follow from (2.1) as

$$U_i^0 = g(x_i) = g(i\Delta x) = g_i,\ i = 0,1,2,\cdots I.$$

At the boundaries ($x = 0$ and $x = 1$) we use a central difference to keep the local truncation error second order in space - i.e. $O[(\Delta x)^2]$, since the equation's local truncation error is second order in space. To do this "false" boundaries are introduced, indexed by $i = -1$ and $i = I+1$, at $x = 0$ and $x = 1$. Then the boundary conditions are approximated by

$$a_1U_0^n + a_2(U_1^n - U_{-1}^n)/2\Delta x = c^n,\ c^n = c(n\Delta t) \tag{2.3}$$

and

$$b_1U_I^n + b_2(U_{I+1}^n - U_{I-1}^n)/2\Delta x = d^n \tag{2.4}$$

When algorithm (2.2) is applied at $i = 0$ and $i = N$ the terms U_{-1}^n and U_{I+1}^n are computed, in terms of an interior grid point and a boundary grid point, by means of (2.3) and (2.4). The resulting system of tridiagonal equations can be computed iteratively (Ames [1]) or by means of a banded algorithm (see von Rosenberg [2]).

Crandall [3] has examined the stability, oscillation and truncation error of the two-level scheme given by (2.2). The results, as a function of r and λ are shown in Fig. 1. Each coordinate point (r,λ) represents a different algorithm. Precise values of stability and oscillation limits depend on the

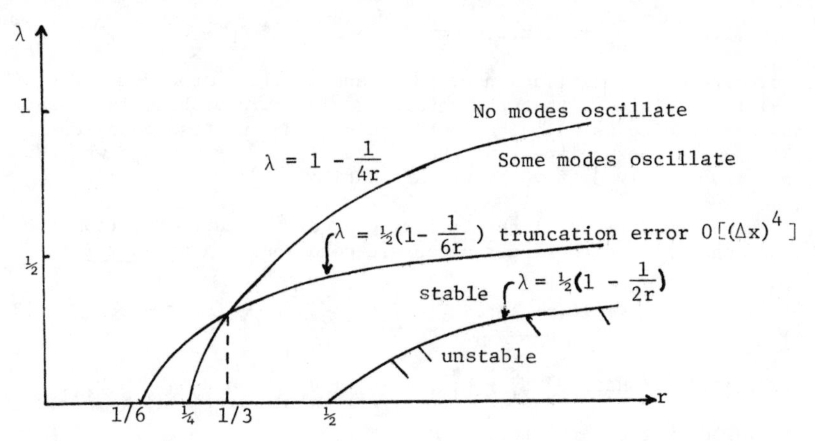

FIG. 1: Properties of algorithms for the diffusion equation

number of space subdivisions, I, and on the boundary conditions. As I increases there is a rapid approach to the limiting values shown in Fig. 1. If the boundary conditions are approximated to $O[(\Delta x)^4]$ then it follows from the truncation error expressions that superior accuracy can be expected from those $O[(\Delta x)^4]$ algorithms.

Stability of algorithms is analyzed by several methods (see Ames [1]) including the Fourier method which effectively ignores the boundary conditions and studies the growth or decay of a typical term $[\exp(\alpha jk)\exp(\sqrt{-1}\,\lambda ih)]$ as $j\to\infty$. A second procedure is called the amplification matrix method. Boundary data are included and one studies the eigenvalues of the matrix form $U^{n+1} = AU^n$ of the algorithm. If the eigenvalues of A are in absolute value less than or equal to 1 then stability is ensured.

3. PREDICTOR-CORRECTOR METHODS

When approximating nonlinear equations with classical finite differences nonlinear algebraic equations arise. Since their solution usually slows the computation drastically and introduces other errors it is desireable to choose an alternative. One means for doing this is to use a predictor-corrector method. These have been successfully used by many in the numerical solution of ordinary differential equations (see Hamming [4]). We describe several methods given by Douglas and Jones [5] to illustrate the method.

Consider

$$u_{xx} = \psi(x,t,u,u_x,u_t) \tag{3.1}$$

on $0 < x < 1$, $0 < t \le T$ with $u(x,0)$, $u(0,t)$, and $u(1,T)$ prescribed. If either

$$\psi = f_1(x,t,u)\frac{\partial u}{\partial t} + f_2(x,t,u)\frac{\partial u}{\partial x} + f_3(x,t,u) \tag{3.2}$$

or

$$\psi = g_1(x,t,u,\frac{\partial u}{\partial x})\frac{\partial u}{\partial t} + g_2(x,t,u,\frac{\partial u}{\partial x}) \tag{3.3}$$

a predictor-corrector modification of the Crank-Nicolson procedure (Eqn. (2.2) with $\lambda = \frac{1}{2}$) is possible so that the resulting algebraic problem is linear. Both classes are quite useful since both include the Burgers' equation $u_{xx} = u_t + uu_x$ and the nonlinear diffusion equation $u_{xx} = \alpha(u)u_t$, which can be obtained from $[K(v)v_x]_x = v_t$ by transformation.

If ψ is of the form (3.2) the following predictor-corrector (combined with u_i^0, u_0^n and u_I^n) leads to linear algebraic equations. A <u>predictor</u> is

$$\frac{1}{(\Delta x)^2}\delta_x^2 U_i^{n+\frac{1}{2}} = \psi[i\Delta x, (n+\tfrac{1}{2})\Delta t, U_i^n, \frac{1}{2\Delta x}\mu_x\delta_x U_i^n, \frac{2}{\Delta t}(U_i^{n+\frac{1}{2}} - U_i^n)] \tag{3.4}$$

for $i = 1,2,\cdots,I-1$. Here $\delta_x^2 U_i^n = U_{i+1}^n - 2U_i^n + U_{i-1}^n$ and $\mu_x\delta_x U_i^n = U_{i+1}^n - U_{i-1}^n$.

This is followed by the <u>corrector</u>

$$\frac{1}{2(\Delta x)^2} \delta_x^2[U_i^{n+1} + U_i^n] = \psi[i\Delta x, (n+\tfrac{1}{2})\Delta t, U_i^{n+\frac{1}{2}}, \frac{1}{4\Delta x}\mu_x\delta_x(U_i^{n+1}+U_i^n), \frac{1}{\Delta t}(U_i^{n+1} - U_i^n)]. \tag{3.5}$$

Equation (3.4) is a backward difference equation utilizing the intermediate points $(n+\frac{1}{2})\Delta t$. Since (3.2) only involves $\partial u/\partial t$ linearly, the calculation into the $n+\frac{1}{2}$ time row is a linear one. To move up to the (n+1)st time row use (3.5). By virtue of the linearity of (3.2) in $\partial u/\partial x$, this problem is also a linear algebraic one.

When ψ is given by (3.3) and the corrector is replaced by

$$\frac{1}{2(\Delta x)^2} \delta_x^2[U_i^{n+1} + U_i^n] = \psi[i\Delta x, (n+\tfrac{1}{2})\Delta t, U_i^{n+\frac{1}{2}}, \frac{1}{2\Delta t}\mu_x\delta_x U_i^{n+\frac{1}{2}}, \frac{1}{\Delta t}(U_i^{n+1} - U_i^n)] \tag{3.6}$$

then the predictor-corrector system (3.4) and (3.6)) generates linear algebraic equations for the evolution of the solution.

The results are known to converge. The truncation error is $O[(\Delta x)^2 + (\Delta t)^2]$ for (3.4) and (3.5) and it is $O[(\Delta x)^2 + (\Delta t)^{3/2}]$ for (3.4) and (3.6). Miller [6] has demonstrated the superiority of this method over the explicit method for the Burgers' problem $\nu u_{xx} = u_t + uu_x$, $0 < x < 1$, $0 < t \leq T$, $u(0,t) = u(1,t) = 0$, $u(x,0) = \sin \pi x$. A number of industrial applications have also demonstrated the utility of the method.

4. FRACTIONAL STEPS (SPLITTING).

In the method(s) of fractional steps the transition from one stage of the computation to the next (e.g. time step n to time step n+1) is divided into a series of intermediate steps. It is not required to satisfy conditions of consistency with the original equations and stability criteria at each step as is the case in ordinary difference schemes. Consequently, the fractional steps techniques permit a choice of parameters which makes possible the development of economical and efficient schemes. Beginning with the basic ADI (alternating direction implicit) method of Peaceman, Rachford [7] and Douglas [8], work on the method(s) has been extended and improved by many authors (see Yanenko [9]). The method of fractional steps is an essential element in the construction of schemes for solving complicated problems in several independent variables.

The multidimensional problem is reduced to a series of steps of which involves difference approximations in only one dimension. This idea will be introduced for the diffusion equation $u_t = u_{xx} + u_{yy} + u_{zz}$. A Crank-Nicolson implicit method for the equation with ADI imposed on it would be

$$\frac{1}{2(\Delta x)^2}\,\delta_x^2(\bar{U}^{n+1}+U^n)+\frac{1}{(\Delta y)^2}\,\delta_y^2\,U^n+\frac{1}{(\Delta z)^2}\,\delta_z^2\,U^n=\frac{\bar{U}^{n+1}-U^n}{\Delta t} \tag{4.1}$$

$$\frac{1}{2(\Delta x)^2}\,\delta_x^2\,(\bar{U}^{n+1}+U^n)+\frac{1}{2(\Delta y)^2}\,\delta_y^2\,(\bar{\bar{U}}^{n+1}+U^n)+\frac{1}{(\Delta z)^2}\,\delta_z^2\,U^n=\frac{\bar{\bar{U}}^{n+1}-U^n}{\Delta t} \tag{4.2}$$

$$\frac{1}{2(\Delta x)^2}\,\delta_x^2\,(\bar{U}^{n+1}+U^n)+\frac{1}{2(\Delta y)^2}\,\delta_y^2(\bar{\bar{U}}^{n+1}+U^n)+\frac{1}{2(\Delta z)^2}\,\delta_z^2(U^{n+1}+U^n)=\frac{U^{n+1}-U^n}{\Delta t} \tag{4.3}$$

where each U is U_{ijk} - i.e. the obvious subscripts are dropped and $\bar{U}$, $\bar{\bar{U}}$ denote intermediate values. These are locally second order in space and time, they are unconditionally stable and being implicit require the solution of a tridiagonal system of linear equations at each of the three steps. But each equation is in <u>one direction only</u>.

For various alternatives the reader is referred to Yanenko's book [9]. We terminate our discussion here with an analytic "splitting"scheme for the two-dimensional unsteady fluid equations (∇^2 is the Laplace operator, $p = a^2\rho^k$, ρ the density)

$$\left.\begin{aligned} u_t + uu_x + vu_y + \rho^{-1}p_x &= \nu\nabla^2 u \\ v_t + uv_x + vv_y + \rho^{-1}p_y &= \nu\nabla^2 v \\ p_t + u\,p_x + vp_y + kp(u_x + v_y) &= 0 \end{aligned}\right\} \tag{4.4}$$

A splitting scheme in coordinates x and y when applied to (4.4) approximates the system at the first half step $n\Delta t$ to $(n+\frac{1}{2})\Delta t$ by

$$\left.\begin{aligned} \tfrac{1}{2}u_t + uu_x + \rho^{-1}p_x &= \nu u_{xx} \\ \tfrac{1}{2}v_t + uv_x &= \nu v_{xx} \\ \tfrac{1}{2}p_t + up_x + kp\,u_x &= 0 \end{aligned}\right\} \tag{4.5}$$

The system is approximated at the second half step (in the y direction) by

$$\left.\begin{aligned} \tfrac{1}{2}u_t + vu_y &= \nu u_{yy} \\ \tfrac{1}{2}v_t + vv_y + \rho^{-1}p_y &= \nu v_{yy} \\ \tfrac{1}{2}p_t + vp_y + kpv_y &= 0 \quad . \end{aligned}\right\} \tag{4.6}$$

Fractional steps methods have considerable promise in both theoretical and numerical investigations. (Yanenko [9], Ames [10])

5. HOPSCOTCH ALGORITHMS

Motivated by papers of Gordon [11] and Gordon and Scala [12,13] Gourlay [14] introduced an alternating direction implicit (ADI) method which he labels of "hopscotch" type. This ADI method has a rather novel way of decomposing the problem into two simpler parts. Moreover there is always a two stage process no matter the number of space dimensions!

With L a linear elliptic operator in cartesian two space a hopscotch method will be described for

$$u_t = Lu + g(x,y,t) \tag{5.1}$$

in $R \times [0 \le t \le T]$ with R bounded. Let L_h be a finite difference replacement for L and define

$$\theta^n_{ij} = \begin{cases} 1 & n + i + j \quad \text{odd} \\ 0 & n + i + j \quad \text{even} . \end{cases}$$

Then the hopscotch algorithm is

$$U^{n+1}_{ij} = k\,\theta^{n+1}_{ij}[L_h\, U^{n+1}_{ij} + g^{n+1}_{ij}] + U^n_{ij} + k\theta^n_{ij}[L_h\, U^n_{ij} + g^n_{ij}]. \tag{5.2}$$

If n + i + j is odd then (5.2) is explicit and if n + i + j is even then (5.2) is implicit. The overall algorithm is therefore explicit requiring no tridiagonal computations.

Gourlay [14] considers many mathematical questions including questions of stability and convergence. He also compares this ADI method with that of Peaceman and Rachford [7] with a net favorable score for this method because of: a) economy of storage, b) increased speed of computation (3 to 4 times faster), c) ease in programming for both linear and nonlinear problems, and d) the two stage process regardless of the dimensionality. This procedure comes as close as any to being a general parabolic partial differential equation solver. Moreover, it is also applicable to hyperbolic partial differential equations (Ames [1, pp. 221 - 227]).

6. CONTRACTING INTERVAL ITERATION

Many algorithms while consistent, stable and convergent to the exact solution, as the grid parameters approach zero, give results which may be poor approximations to the exact solution. This occurs because we have no idea about how the successive values behave. Do they oscillate about the true solution, remain above it, remain below it or what? In one attempt to provide iterative finite difference algorithms for nonlinear parabolic equations which generate convergent upper and lower bounds at each grid point, and hence give automatic error estimates after every even number of iterations, Adams and Ames [15,16] have studied the concept of contracting interval iteration in R^n. The results of those lengthy papers remain to be fully implemented but it seems likely that they apply to some algorithms for the equations of fluid mechanics.

To illustrate the idea consider the equation

$$u_t - a(u)(u_{xx} + u_{yy}) - b(u)[u_x^2 + u_y^2] = 0 \tag{6.1}$$

On $0 < x < 1$, $0 < y < 1$, $0 < t \le T$ with the initial condition $u = \phi_0(x,y) \in C^2$ at $t = 0$ and boundary conditions, $u \equiv 0$ on the boundary of the spatial square for $0 < t \le T$. On an a priori interval for u, $I_0 = \{u | \underline{u} \le u \le \bar{u}, \bar{u} \in R^+\}$ with $\phi_0 \in I_0$ for every $(x,y) \in \overline{D} = \{(x,y), 0 \le x \le 1, 0 \le y \le 1\}$ it is required that $a(u) > 0$, $b(u) > 0$, $a \in C^1(I_0)$, $b(u) \in C^2(I_0)$. After adopting the usual grid

$$G = \{(x_i, y_j, t_n), x_i = i\Delta x, \ y_j = j\Delta y, \ t_n = n\Delta t,$$

$$i,j = 1,2,\cdots,I-1, \ n = 1,2,\cdots,N, \ \Delta x = \Delta y = 1/I, \ \Delta t = T/N,$$

consider the following finite difference approximation:

$$U_{ij}^n + \omega U_{ij}^n = \omega U_{ij}^n + U_{ij}^{n-1} \tag{6.2}$$

$$+ \Delta t[a_{ij}^n(\delta_{xx} + \delta_{yy})U_{ij}^n + b_{ij}^n((\delta_x U_{ij}^n)^2 + (\delta_y U_{ij}^n)^2)],$$

with $U_{0j}^n = U_{Ij}^n = U_{i0}^n = U_{iI}^n = 0$, $U_{ij}^0 = \phi_0(x_i, y_j)$. Here the notation a_{ij}^n means $a(U_{ij}^n)$. The operators are $\delta_x U_{ij}^n = (U_{i+1,j}^n - U_{i-1,j}^n)/2\Delta x$, $\delta_{xx} U_{ij}^n = (U_{i+1,j}^n - 2U_{ij}^n + U_{i-1,j}^n)/(\Delta x)^2$, with corresponding operators for δ_y and δ_{yy} (Note: These operators are slightly different from those used previously).

The introduction of the parameter ω (see equation (6.2)) and its choice so that the operator (call it g) on the right hand side of (6.2) is isotone is an important part of the method. An operator A is an inverse monotone operator when the inequality $Au \le Aw$ (using a partial ordering of the space U on which A operates) implies that $u \le w$. A is isotone if $u \le w$ implies $Au \le Aw$.

The results of Adams and Ames [16] are as follows: (A) the function g is isotone for every $U_{ij}^n \in I = I_0 \times I_0 \cdots \times I_0 \in R^m$ if ω is selected to satisfy

$$\omega - \tau \operatorname*{Max}_{u \in I_0} [4a(u) + 4d|a'(u)| + 2d^2|b'(u)|] \geq 0, \quad (6.3)$$

where $\tau = \Delta t/(\Delta x)^2$ and $d = \bar{\bar{u}} - \underline{\underline{u}}$, and I_0 is sufficiently small so that

$$\operatorname*{Min}_{u \in I_0} a(u) - (d/2) \operatorname*{Max}_{u \in I_0} |b(u)| \geq 0 \quad (6.4)$$

With the choice of ω the iterative method yields a sequence of nested intervals (ν is the iteration member)

$$H_\nu = \{U_{ij}^n | \underline{U}_{ij}^{n(\nu)} \leq U_{ij}^n \leq \bar{U}_{ij}^{n(\nu)}\} \quad (6.5)$$

by means of the procedure

$$\begin{aligned} (1+\omega)\bar{U}_{ij}^{n(\nu+1)} &= g(\bar{U}_{ij}^{n(\nu)}, \bar{U}_{ij}^{(n-1)(\nu)}, \cdots) \\ (1+\omega)\underline{U}_{ij}^{n(\nu+1)} &= g(\underline{U}_{ij}^{n(\nu)}, \underline{U}_{ij}^{(n-1)(\nu)}, \cdots) \end{aligned} \quad (6.6)$$

For starting values the following are suggested:

$$\begin{aligned} &-\underline{U}_{ij}^{n(0)} = \bar{U}_{ij}^{n(0)} = \varepsilon \exp(\alpha t_n), \ \varepsilon, \alpha \in \text{Positive reals}, \\ &\varepsilon \text{ such that } |\phi_0| < \varepsilon \quad (x,y) \text{ on initial line}, \\ &\quad \text{and } \alpha \text{ is sufficiently small such that} \\ &\quad \pm\varepsilon \exp(\alpha T) \in I_0. \end{aligned} \quad (6.7)$$

Under these conditions the sequences act as follows:

(B) The $\{\underline{U}_{ij}^{n(\nu)}\}$ are monotone increasing and the sequence $\{\bar{U}_{ij}^{n(\nu)}\}$ are monotone decreasing, such that $\underline{U}_{ij}^{n(\nu)} < \underline{U}_{ij}^{n(\nu+1)} < \cdots < \bar{U}_{ij}^{n(\nu+1)} < \bar{U}_{ij}^{n(\nu)}$.

These sequences have limits $\underline{U}_{ij}^{n*}$, $\bar{U}_{ij}^{n*}$ which are equal.

An example problem is detailed in Adams and Ames [16].

7. METHOD OF LINES

Strictly speaking the "method of lines" does not fall under the label of a finite difference method. Nevertheless, because of its considerable utility in parabolic problems, it warrants discussion.

The method is simple in concept - for a given system of partial differential equations discretize all but one of the independent variables. This semidiscrete procedure yields a coupled system of ordinary differential equations which are then numerically integrated with a digital scheme or perhaps an analog computer. To aid in the presentation consider the nonlinear diffusion (parabolic) equation

$$u_t = [D(x,t,u)u_x]_x + f(x,t,u,u_x), \quad 0 < x < 1, \quad 0 < t \le T \tag{7.1}$$

$$u(x,0) = F(x), \quad 0 \le x \le 1$$

$$\alpha_1(t)u(0,t) + \alpha_2(t)u_x(0,t) = \alpha_3(t), \quad 0 < t \le T$$

$$\beta_1(t)u(1,t) + \beta_2(t)u_x(1,t) = \beta_3(t), \quad 0 < t \le T$$

where $0 < m \le D < M$ for stability and $-\infty < u < \infty$.

The first step is to discretize the spatial variable in the partial differential equation to obtain the system of ordinary differential equations that also include the boundary conditions. The selected finite differences in the spatial derivative are self-evident. Let $\Delta x = h = 1/N$, with the left-hand boundary at $i = 0$ and the right-hand one at $i = N$, and $D_{i\pm1/2} = D(x_{i\pm1/2}, t, u_{i\pm1/2})$. Then, for $i = 0$,

$$\frac{du_0}{dt} = \begin{cases} 0 \quad \text{and} \quad u_0 = \alpha_3/\alpha_1 & \text{if } \alpha_2 = 0 \\ \frac{2}{h}\left[D_{1/2}\frac{u_1-u_0}{h} - D_0\frac{\alpha_3-\alpha_1 u_0}{\alpha_2}\right] + f\left(x_0, t, u_0 \frac{\alpha_3-\alpha_1 u_0}{\alpha_2}\right) & \text{if } \alpha_2 \ne 0 \end{cases}$$

for $i = 1,\cdots,N-1$,

$$\frac{du_i}{dt} = [D_{i+1/2}(u_{i+1}-u_i) - D_{i-1/2}(u_i - u_{i-1})]/h^2 + f\left(x_i, t, u_i, \frac{u_{i+1}-u_{i-1}}{2h}\right)$$

and for $i = N$,

$$\frac{du_N}{dt} = \begin{cases} 0 \quad \text{and} \quad u_N = \beta_3/\beta_1 & \text{if } \beta_2 = 0 \\ \frac{2}{h}\left[D_N\frac{\beta_3-\beta_1 u_N}{\beta_2} - D_{N-1/2}\frac{u_N-u_{N-1}}{h}\right] + f\left(x_N, t, u_N, \frac{\beta_3-\beta_1 u_N}{\beta_2}\right) & \text{if } \beta_2 \ne 0 \end{cases}$$

The initial data are $u_i(0,x_i)\ F(x_i)$, $i = 0,1,2,\cdots,N$.

For the numerical solution, the Gear-Hindmarsh integrators [17] have both nonstiff and stiff subroutines built into the same program. Unless one knows the system to be stiff a priori, the usual procedure is to use the less-complicated nonstiff integrator initially. If it proves ineffective, the stiff integrator is then used.

A variety of problems have been solved by lines. Here we only mention the paper of Chang and Madsen [18] on a two-dimensional chemical kinetics transport problem, and the papers of Madsen and Sincovec [19] who study a nonlinear diffusion problem for $u_t = [D(1-\alpha/\bar{u})u_x]_x$ and one-dimensional shallow water flow over an isolated obstacle. A useful survey paper is due to Liskovets [20].

One useful code (see Section 8) uses the eigenvalues of the thermal conductivity matrices thereby requiring only a few leading terms to approximate the full solution.

7. COMPUTER CODES

A number of general purpose codes for parabolic, and sometimes other types as well, have been prepared. Some of them of rather recent vintage will be generally discussed and addresses of knowledgeable individuals provided in the references. We do not restrict our attention to codes which use finite differences exclusively.

(A) DISPL was developed and written at Argonne National Laboratory. For details one good contact is Byrne [21] (see also Byrne [22]). DISPL is designed for nonlinear second order partial differential equations (parabolic, elliptic, hyperbolic (some cases) and parabolic - elliptic). Boundary conditions of a general nature and material interfaces are allowed. The spatial dimension can be either one or two and in Cartesian, cylindrical or spherical (one dimension only) geometry. The partial differential equations are reduced to ordinary differential equations by Galerkin discretization of the spatial variables. The resulting ordinary equations in the time-like variable is solved by an ODE software package (such as GEAR). Software features include graphics capabilities, printed output, dump/restart facilities and free format input. DISPL is intended to be an engineering and scientific tool and is not a finely tuned production code for a small set of problems.

DISPL makes no effort to control the spatial discretization errors. It has been used to successfully solve a variety of problems in chemical transport, heat and mass transfer, pipe flow etc.

(B) PDELIB was developed and written at Los Alamos Scientific Laboratory. For details write Hyman [23]. PDELIB is a library of subroutines to support the number solution of evolution equations with a time-like variable and one or two space variables. The routines are grouped into a dozen independent modules according to their function - i.e. accepting initial data, approximating spatial derivatives, advancing the solution in time etc. - each task is isolated in a distinct module. Within a module, the basic task is further refined into general purpose flexible lower level routines.

PDELIB can be understood and used at different levels. Within a small period of time a large class of problems can be solved by a novice. Moreover, he can provide a wide variety of outputs.

(C) DSS/2 is a differential systems simulator developed at Lehigh University as a transportable Numerical Method of Lines (NMOL) code. See also LEANS. For details write Schiesser [24].

(D) FORSIM is designed for the automated solution of sets of implicitly coupled partial differential equations of the form

$$\frac{\partial u_i}{\partial t} = \phi_i(x,t,u_i,u_j,\cdots,(u_i)_x,\cdots,(u_i)_{xx},(u_j)_{xx},\cdots,), \text{ for } i = 1,\cdots,N.$$

The user specifies the ϕ_i in a simple FORTRAN subroutine. Finite difference formulae of any order may be selected for the spatial discretization and the spatial grid need not be equidistant. The resulting system of time dependent ODE's is solved by the method of lines. For details write Carver [25] (See also Carver [26]).

(E) SLDGL is a program package for the self-adaptive solution of nonlinear systems of elliptic and parabolic partial differential equations in up to and including 3 space dimensions. Variable step size and variable order are permitted. The discretization error is estimated and used for the determination of the optimum grid and optimum orders. This is the most general of the codes described here (not for hyperbolic systems of course). For details write Schönauer [27] (see Schönauer et. al. [28]).

(F) CAVE is a program package [29] for conduction analysis via eigenvalues for three dimensional geometries using the method of lines. In many problems much time is saved since only a few terms suffice.

REFERENCES

1. Ames, W.F. 1977. Numerical Methods for Partial Differential Equations. Academic Press, New York, pp. 40-91.

2. Rosenberg, D.U. 1969. Methods for the Numerical Solution of Partial Differential Equations. Elsevier, New York, pp. 113-122.

3. Crandall, S.H. 1955. Quart. Appl. Math., Vol. 13, pp. 318-320.

4. Hamming, R.W. 1962. Numerical Methods for Scientists and Engineers. McGraw Hill, New York, pp. 194-209.

5. Douglas, J., Jr. and Jones, B.F. 1963. J. Soc. Ind. Appl. Math., Vol. 11, pp. 195-204.

6. Miller, E.L. 1966. Predictor-Corrector Studies of Burgers' Model of Turbulent Flow, M.S. Thesis, University of Delaware, Newark, Delaware.

7. Peaceman, D.W. and Rachford, H.H. 1955. J. Soc. Ind. Appl. Math., Vol. 3, pp. 28-41.

8. Douglas, J., Jr. 1955. J. Soc. Ind. Appl. Math., Vol. 3 pp. 42-65.

9. Yanenko, N.N. (Translated and Edited by M. Holt). 1971. The Method of Fractional Steps, Springer-Verlag, New York, pp. 17-33, pp. 106-110.

10. Ames, W.F. 1972. Nonlinear Partial Differential Equations in Engineering, Vol. II., Academic Press, New York, pp. 29-32, 261, 274-284.

11. Gordon, P. 1965. J. SIAM. Appl. Math., Vol. 13, pp. 667-684.

12. Scala, S.M. and Gordon, P. 1966. Phys. Fluids, Vol. 9, pp. 1158-1163.

13. Scala, S.M. and Gordon, P. 1968. AIAA J., Vol. 6, pp. 815-823.

14. Gourlay, A.R. 1970. J. Inst. Maths. Appls., Vol. 6, pp. 375-384.

15. Adams, E. and Ames, W.F. 1979. J. Nonlinear Anal. (Theory, Meth., Appl.) Vol. 3, pp. 773-794.

16. Adams, E. and Ames, W.F. 1981. J. Nonlinear Anal. (Theory, Meth., Appl.) Vol. 5, pp. 525-542.

17. Hindmarsh, A.C. 1972. GEAR, Ordinary differential equation system solver UCID-3001 Rev. 2. Lawrence Livermore Laboratory.

18. Chang, J.S. and Madsen, N.K. 1973. Global transport and kinetics models, UCRL-75062. Lawrence Livermore Laboratory.

19. Madsen, N.K. and Sincovec, R.F. 1974. Computational Methods in Nonlinear Mech. (J.T. Oden et. al., eds.). Texas Inst. for Comp. Mech., Austin Texas, pp. 371-380.

20. Liskovets, O.A. 1965. (Russian) J. Diff. Eqts. Vol. 1, pp. 1308-1317.

21. Byrne, G.D. Computing Technology and Service Div., Exxon Research and Engineering Co., P.O. Box 51, Linden, N.J. 07036.

22. Byrne, G.D. 1979. Adv. Comp. Methods Part. Diff. Eqts. III (R. Vichnevetsky and R.S. Stepleman, eds.), IMACS, pp. 40-42.

23. Hyman, J.M.: Theoretical Div., Los Alamos Scientific Lab., Los Alamos, N.M. 87545.

24. Schiesser, W.E.: Department of Chemical Engineering, Lehigh University, Bethlehem, PA 18015.

25. Carver, M.B.: Chalk River Nuclear Labs., Atomic Energy of Canada Ltd., Chalk river, Ontario, Canada.

26. Carver, M.B. 1975. Adv. Comp. Methods Part. Diff. Eqts. I (R. Vichnevetsky and R.S. Stepleman, eds.), IMACS, pp. 369-376.

27. Schönauer, W.: Rechenzentrum der Universität Karlsruhe, 7500 Karlsruhe, Federal Republic of Germany.

28. Schönauer, W., Routh, K. and Glotz, G. 1981. Adv. Comp. Methods Part. Diff. Eqts. IV (R. Vichnevetsky and R.S. Stepleman, eds.), IMACS, pp. 117-125.

29. CAVE. 1978. NASA CR-145290.

Variational Principles for Heat Transfer

BRUCE A. FINLAYSON
University of Washington
Seattle, Washington 98195

1. TERMINOLOGY

A variational principle is based on a functional, which is a correspondence assigning a real number to each function in a given class of functions. The functional is made stationary (preferably, but not always, a minimum) with respect to changes or variations in the function. This terminology agrees with the classical development (see [1,2,3]). In this paper, so-called variational principles which do not have a functional, or for which the functional is not stationary, are called quasi-variational principles or restricted variational principles.

This distinction is similar to the distinction between d'Alembert's principle and Hamilton's principle for the movement of a system of particles. D'Alembert's principle is

$$\widehat{\delta W} = \sum_{k=1}^{N} (\hat{F}_k - m_k \hat{A}_k) \cdot \delta \hat{R}_k = 0 \tag{1}$$

where $\hat{F}_k$ is the net force on the k-th particle, m_k and $\hat{A}_k$ are the mass and acceleration of the k-th particle. The virtual work $\widehat{\delta W}$ is a differential form, i.e., there is no W whose variation gives $\widehat{\delta W}$. The $\delta \hat{R}_k$ is an infinitesimal displacement. Hamilton's principle is obtained by integrating over time.

$$A \equiv \int_{t_1}^{t_2} L dt, \quad L \equiv T - V. \tag{2}$$

$$\int_{t_1}^{t_2} \widehat{\delta W} dt = \delta \int_{t_1}^{t_2} (T - V) dt. \tag{3}$$

Here T is the kinetic energy, V is the potential energy, L is the Lagrangian and A is the action integral. Such a formulation is possible if the forces are derivable from a potential. Note that in Hamilton's principle a functional, A, exists and is made stationary. Hamilton's principle is thus a true variational principle whereas d'Alembert's principle is a quasi-variational principle.

2. FRÉCHET DERIVATIVES

The scientist and engineer usually have a differential or integral equation and the question arises whether or not a variational principle exists for that equation. Fréchet derivatives are used to answer this question [4]. Consider the differential equation, possibly nonlinear

$$N(u) = 0. \tag{4}$$

The Fréchet differential of the operator N in the direction ϕ is

$$N'_u \phi \equiv \lim_{\varepsilon \to 0} \frac{N(u+\varepsilon\phi) - N(u)}{\varepsilon} = \frac{\partial}{\partial \varepsilon} [N(u+\varepsilon\phi)] \Big|_{\varepsilon=0} \tag{5}$$

N'_u is the Fréchet derivative of the operator N. A variational principle exists if the operator N'_u is symmetric.

$$\int \psi \, N'_u \, \phi \, dV = \int \phi N'_u \, \psi \, dV. \tag{6}$$

This condition is applied below to answer the question of whether a variational principle exists for various forms of the heat transfer equations. The application is described in detail elsewhere [4].

3. VARIATIONAL PRINCIPLES

3.1 Steady-State, Linear Heat Conduction

The equations for temperature, T, are

$$\nabla\cdot(k\nabla T) = f(\underset{\wedge}{x}) \text{ in } V, \tag{7}$$

$$T = T_1 (\underset{\wedge}{x}) \text{ on } S_1, \tag{8}$$

$$-k\underset{\wedge}{n}\cdot\nabla T = q_2(x) \text{ on } S_2, \tag{9}$$

$$-k\underset{\wedge}{n}\cdot\nabla T = h(T-T_3(\underset{\wedge}{x})) \text{ on } S_3, \tag{10}$$

where the thermal conductivity, k, and heat transfer coefficient, h, are functions of position, but not temperature. The functions, T_1, q_2, and T_3 are specified on their respective boundaries, which may be null. The variational principle is

$$\Phi(T) = \int_V [1/2 k\nabla T\cdot\nabla T + Tf(\underset{\sim}{x})]\, dV + \int_{S_2} q_2 T dS + 1/2 \int_{S_3} h(T-T_3)^2 dS, \qquad (11)$$

and the function Φ is to be made stationary among functions T satisfying $T = T_1$ on S_1 and which are continuous with piecewise continuous first derivatives. Note that for each function T there is a real number Φ, making Φ a functional, and the variations of Φ with respect to T lead to Eq. (7) as Euler equation and Eq. (9-10) as natural boundary conditions. The variations give:

$$\delta\Phi = \left.\frac{d\Phi(T + \varepsilon\delta T)}{d\varepsilon}\right|_{\varepsilon=0} = \int_V [k\nabla T\cdot\nabla\delta T + \delta T\, f(\underset{\sim}{x})]dV + \int_{S_2} q_2\, \delta T dS + \int_{S_3} h\,(T-T_3)\delta T dS. \qquad (12)$$

Using the divergence theorem and setting $\delta\Phi = 0$ gives

$$\int_V \delta T\, [-\nabla\cdot(k\nabla T) + f(\underset{\sim}{x})]dV + \int_{S_2} \delta T\, [q_2 + k\underset{\sim}{n}\cdot\nabla T]dS + \int_{S_3} \delta T[h(T-T_3) + k\underset{\sim}{n}\cdot\nabla T]dS + \int_{S_1} \delta T\, k\underset{\sim}{n}\cdot\nabla T dS = 0. \qquad (13)$$

Since $\delta T = 0$ on S_1 (the trial function must satisfy $T = T_1$ on S_1) the last integral vanishes. The remaining integrands in Eq. (13) are the desired differential equation (7), and natural boundary conditions (9-10).

3.2 Steady-State, Nonlinear Heat Conduction

When k and h depend on temperature, we make the transformation

$$\phi = \int_{T_o}^{T} k(\xi)d\xi, \quad \nabla\phi = k\nabla T. \tag{14}$$

This leads to equations of the form Eq. (7-10) except that Eq. (10) becomes

$$-\hat{n}\cdot\nabla\phi = h(\phi)[g(\phi) - g(\phi_3)] \text{ on } S_3. \tag{15}$$

$g(\phi)$ is the inverse transformation of Eq. (14). The boundary term on S_3 in Eq. (11) is then

$$\int_{S_3}\int_{\phi_3}^{\phi} h(\xi)[g(\xi) - g(\phi_3)]\, d\xi dS. \tag{16}$$

Thus nonlinear functions k(T) and/or h(T) can be handled.

If the boundary condition is a radiation condition

$$-k(\hat{x})\hat{n}\cdot\nabla T = h(\hat{x})(T^n - T_3^n), \tag{17}$$

then the boundary term on S_3 is

$$\int_{S_3}\int_{T_3}^{T} h(\xi^n - T_3^n)d\xi dS = \int_{S_3} [\frac{h}{n+1}(T^{n+1} - T_3^{n+1}) - hT_3^n(T - T_3)]dS. \tag{18}$$

Thus, simple radiation boundary conditions can be handled with variational principles.

If the heat generation term is nonlinear, as in reaction-diffusion problems or combustion problems, a variational principle also exists. For example, consider the following equation.

$$\nabla^2 T = e^T. \tag{19}$$

By letting $N(T) = \nabla^2 T - e^T$ we obtain the Fréchet differential from Eq. (5).

$$N'_T\ \phi = \nabla^2\phi - e^T\phi. \tag{20}$$

Equation (6) then becomes

$$\int [\psi \nabla^2 \phi - e^T \psi \phi] dV \overset{?}{=} \int [\phi \nabla^2 \psi - e^T \phi \psi] dV. \tag{21}$$

The divergence theorem can be used to show that these are the same under appropriate boundary conditions. For the more general equation,

$$\nabla \cdot (k \nabla T) = f(\underset{\sim}{x}, T), \tag{22}$$

the variational integral is an extension of Eq. (11), with the term Tf(x) replaced by

$$\int_{T_o}^{T} f(\underset{\sim}{x}, \xi) d\xi, \tag{23}$$

with T_o an arbitrary reference temperature.

The Euler equation comes from

$$\int_V \delta T \; [\nabla \cdot (k \nabla T) - f(\underset{\sim}{x}, T)] dV = 0. \tag{24}$$

3.3 Steady-State, Linear Heat Convection

The equation for combined heat conduction and convection is

$$\underset{\wedge}{u} \cdot \nabla T = \alpha \nabla^2 T, \tag{25}$$

where u is a known velocity field and α is the thermal diffusivity. Frechet derivatives show that no variational principle exists for Eq. (25). Equation (6) applied to the troublesome convection term is

$$\int \psi \underset{\sim}{u} \cdot \nabla \phi dV \neq \int \phi \underset{\sim}{u} \cdot \nabla \psi dV. \tag{26}$$

The Fréchet derivative is not symmetric.

If an integrating factor is used,

$$g(T, \nabla T) [\underset{\wedge}{u} \cdot \nabla T - \alpha \nabla^2 T] = 0, \tag{27}$$

then Fréchet derivatives give a variational principle only if the velocity is derivable from a potential [4],

$$\underset{\wedge}{u} = -\nabla \Omega. \tag{28}$$

The integrating factor is $g = \exp(\Omega/\alpha)$ and the variational integral is

$$\Phi(T) = -\tfrac{1}{2} \int_V \exp(\Omega/\alpha)\nabla T \cdot \nabla T dV$$

$$-\tfrac{1}{2} \int \exp(\Omega/\alpha) \frac{h}{\rho Cp} (T-T_s)^2 dS. \quad (29)$$

Since velocity fields are given by Eq. (28) only in unusual cases, a variational principle seldom applies to heat convection. Even this transformation does not work if the thermal conductivity depends on temperature [4].

3.4 Unsteady-State, Linear Heat Conduction

Another complication is the unsteady-state problem:

$$\frac{\partial T}{\partial t} = \alpha \nabla^2 T, \quad (30)$$

$$T = T_o \text{ at } t = 0, \quad (31)$$

$$T = T_1 \text{ on } S_1. \quad (32)$$

Fréchet derivatives show that a variational principle does not exist for the equation in this form [4]. The Laplace transform can be taken, and then a variational principle exists.

With $\bar{T} \equiv L[T]$ (33)

the Laplace transform of Eq. (30-31) is

$$s\bar{T} - T_o = \alpha \nabla^2 \bar{T}, \quad (34)$$

$$\bar{T} = \bar{T}_1 \text{ on } S_1. \quad (35)$$

We divide by s and provide a variational functional

$$\Phi(\bar{T}) = \int_V [\frac{1}{2} \frac{\alpha}{s} \nabla\bar{T} \cdot \nabla\bar{T} + \frac{1}{2} \bar{T}^2 - \frac{1}{s} \bar{T}\, T_o] dV. \quad (36)$$

The variation gives

$$\delta\Phi = \int_V \delta\bar{T} \; [- \frac{\alpha}{s} \nabla^2 \bar{T} + \bar{T} - \frac{1}{s} T_o] dV = 0. \quad (37)$$

Gurtin [5] used convolution integrals to provide a variational principle:

$$\Phi(T;t) = \tfrac{1}{2} \int_V [T*T + \alpha*\nabla T*\nabla T - 2T_o*T] dV. \quad (38)$$

The convolution is defined as

$$\int_V u*v \, dV = \int_V \int_0^t u(t-\tau,\underset{\wedge}{x})v(\tau,\underset{\wedge}{x})d\tau dV, \tag{39}$$

and the variation of Eq. (38) gives the Euler equation

$$T-T_o = \int_0^t \alpha\nabla^2 T(\tau,\underset{\wedge}{x})d\tau \equiv \alpha*\nabla^2 T. \tag{40}$$

Eq. (40) is the integral version of Eq. (30).

Filippov and Skorokhodov [6] provide a variational integral involving spatial integrals rather than temporal integrals for one-dimensional problems:

$$\Phi(T) = \tfrac{1}{2}\int_o^t \int_a^b [\frac{1}{\alpha}\frac{\partial(T^2)}{\partial t} + (\frac{1}{\alpha}\int_0^x \frac{\partial T}{\partial t}(\xi,t)d\xi)^2 + (\frac{\partial T}{\partial x})^2]dxdt. \tag{41}$$

These last variational integrals, Eq. (38,41) are so specialized that their extensions to nonlinear problems are not at all clear.

Equation (30) has an adjoint problem, and the techniques to find it are described elsewhere [4].

$$-\frac{\partial T^*}{\partial t} = \alpha\nabla^2 T^*, \tag{42}$$

$$T^* = T_o \text{ at } t = t_f, \tag{43}$$

$$T^* = T_1^* \text{ on } S_1. \tag{44}$$

The "final" time is t_f. A variational principle for the combined problem, Eq. (30-32,42-44) was given by Morse and Feshback [7].

$$\Phi[T,T^*] = \int_0^{t_f}\int_V [\alpha\nabla T\cdot\nabla T^* + \frac{1}{2}(T^*\frac{\partial T}{\partial t} - T\frac{\partial T^*}{\partial t})]dV$$

$$+ \frac{1}{2}\int [T_o(T^* - T)]_o^{t_f} dV. \tag{45}$$

Taking variations with respect to T gives the following equation.

$$\delta_T \Phi = \int_0^{t_f} \int_V \delta T \, [-\alpha \nabla^2 T^* - \frac{\partial T^*}{\partial t}] dV + \frac{1}{2} \int_V \delta T \, [T^* - T_o] \Big|_o^{t_f} dV. \quad (46)$$

Since $\delta T = 0$ at $t = 0$ and $T^* = T_o$ at $t = t_f$ we get Eq. (42). Taking variations with respect to T* gives another equation.

$$\delta_{T^*} \Phi = \int_0^{t_f} \int_V \delta T^* \, [-\alpha \nabla^2 T + \frac{\partial T}{\partial t}] dV + \frac{1}{2} \int_V \delta T^* \, [T_o - T] \Big|_o^{t_f} dV. \quad (47)$$

Since $\delta T^* = 0$ at $t = t_f$ and $T = T_o$ at $t = 0$ we get the Euler equation (30).

3.5 Applications to Unsteady-State Heat Conduction

We have thus provided four variational principles for the unsteady-state heat conduction equation (30). In application these can be shown to give identical results. When we apply Laplace transforms, Eq. (36), we expand in a trial function

$$\bar{T}^N = \frac{1}{s} T_1 + \sum_{j=1}^{N} \bar{a}_j(s) T_j(\underset{\sim}{x}). \quad (48)$$

(We consider only the case of T_1 a constant, for simplicity.) Eq. (37) becomes

$$\int_V T_i(\underset{\sim}{x}) \, [-\frac{\alpha}{s} \nabla^2 \bar{T}^N + \bar{T}^N - \frac{1}{s} T_o] dV = 0. \quad (49)$$

Since

$$L^{-1} \, [\bar{u} \, \bar{v}] = \int_0^t u(t-\tau) \, v(\tau) \, d\tau \quad (50)$$

we can take the inverse transform of Eq. (49) to get

$$\int_V T_i(\underset{\sim}{x}) \, [-\alpha \int_0^t 1 \cdot \nabla^2 T(\underset{\sim}{x},\tau) d\tau] dV + \int_V T_i(\underset{\sim}{x}) \, [T^N(\underset{\sim}{x},t) - T_o] dV = 0, \quad (51)$$

Differentiating this once with respect to time gives

$$\int_V T_i(\underset{\sim}{x}) \left[\frac{\partial T^N}{\partial t} (\underset{\sim}{x},t) - \alpha\nabla^2 T^N(\underset{\sim}{x},t)\right] dV = 0. \tag{52}$$

This is identical to the Galerkin method applied to the same problem (30).

When we apply convolution integrals in Eq. (38), we use the trial function

$$T^N = T_1 + \sum_{j=1}^{N} a_j(t)\, T_j(x). \tag{53}$$

The variation of Eq. (38) gives

$$\delta\Phi = \int_V \delta T* [T - \alpha*\nabla^2 T - T_o] dV = 0. \tag{54}$$

Using Eq. (53) gives

$$\delta\Phi = \int_V T_j(x) * [T^N - \alpha*\nabla^2 T^N - T_o] dV = 0 \tag{55}$$

$$= \int_V \int_o^t T_j(\underset{\sim}{x}) \left[T^N(\underset{\sim}{x},\tau) - \int_o^\tau \alpha\nabla^2 T^N(\underset{\sim}{x},\xi)d\xi - T_o(\underset{\sim}{x})\right] dV. \tag{56}$$

Differentiation of this twice with respect to t gives Eq. (52).

Next we apply the variational principle (41). This case is restricted to one dimension, $a \le x \le b$. The first variation gives

$$\delta\Phi = \int_o^t \int_a^b \left[\frac{1}{\alpha}\frac{\partial}{\partial t}(T\delta T) + \frac{1}{\alpha^2}\int_o^x \frac{\partial T}{\partial t}(\xi,t)d\xi \int_o^x \frac{\partial \delta T}{\partial t}(\xi,t)d\xi\right.$$

$$\left. + \frac{\partial T}{\partial x}\frac{\partial \delta T}{\partial x}\right] dxdt. \tag{57}$$

Henceforth we use $w(x,t) \equiv \delta T(x,t)$. To obtain the correct Euler equations we first prove some identities. The identification B.T. denotes terms which can be evaluated on the boundary using the divergence theorem after integration over x and/or t.

$$f(\theta,t) \equiv \int_a^\theta \frac{\partial w}{\partial t}(\xi,t)d\xi \quad , \quad \frac{\partial f(x,t)}{\partial x} = \frac{\partial w}{\partial t}(x,t). \tag{58}$$

The following term is integrated by parts several times.

$$\int_a^b \frac{\partial^2 T}{\partial x^2} \int_b^x f(\theta,t)d\theta\ dx = -\int_a^b \frac{\partial T}{\partial x} f(x,t)dx + B.T.$$

$$= \int_a^b T \frac{\partial f}{\partial x} dx + B.T. = \int_a^b T \frac{\partial w}{\partial t} dx. \qquad (59)$$

Next define a function h:

$$\frac{\partial h}{\partial x} = \frac{\partial T}{\partial t}(x,t) \ ; \quad h(x,t) = \int_a^x \frac{\partial T}{\partial t}(\xi,t)d\xi. \qquad (60)$$

Then the following integral can be integrated by parts several times.

$$\int_a^b \frac{\partial T}{\partial t}(x,t) \int_b^x f(\theta,t)d\theta dx = \int_a^b \frac{\partial h}{\partial x} \int_b^x f(\theta,t)d\theta dx \qquad (61)$$

$$= \int_a^b \frac{\partial}{\partial x}\left[h \int_b^x f(\theta,t)d\theta\right]dx - \int_a^b h\ f(x,t)dx \qquad (62)$$

$$= -\int_a^b \int_a^x \frac{\partial T}{\partial t}(\xi,t)d\xi \int_a^x \frac{\partial w}{\partial t}(\xi,t)d\xi\ dx + B.T. \qquad (63)$$

Finally we use

$$\int_o^t \frac{\partial}{\partial t}(Tw)dt = \int_o^t \frac{\partial T}{\partial t} w\ dt + \int_o^t T \frac{\partial w}{\partial t} dt \qquad (64)$$

and

$$\int_a^b \frac{\partial T}{\partial x}\frac{\partial w}{\partial x} dx = -\int_a^b w \frac{\partial^2 T}{\partial x^2} dx + B.T. \qquad (65)$$

We now put these into Eq. (57). The first term uses Eq. (64) and Eq. (59). The second term uses Eq. (63) while the third term uses Eq. (65).

$$\delta\Phi = \int_0^t \int_a^b \left[\frac{1}{\alpha}\frac{\partial T}{\partial t} w + \frac{1}{\alpha}\frac{\partial^2 T}{\partial x^2} \int_b^x f(\theta,t)d\theta \right.$$

$$\left. - \frac{1}{\alpha^2}\frac{\partial T}{\partial t}(x,t) \int_b^x f(\theta,t)d\theta - w\frac{\partial^2 T}{\partial x^2}\right] dxdt + \text{B.T.} \tag{66}$$

Rearrangement of Eq. (66) gives the Euler equation.

$$0 = \delta\Phi = \int_0^t \int_a^b \left[\frac{1}{\alpha}\frac{\partial T}{\partial t} - \frac{\partial^2 T}{\partial x^2}\right] \left[w - \frac{1}{\alpha}\int_b^x f(\theta,t)d\theta\right] dxdt \tag{67}$$

$$= \int_0^t \int_a^b \left[\frac{1}{\alpha}\frac{\partial T}{\partial t} - \frac{\partial^2 T}{\partial x^2}\right] \left[w - \frac{1}{\alpha}\int_b^x \int_a^\theta \frac{\partial w}{\partial t}(\xi,t)d\xi d\theta\right] dxdt. \tag{68}$$

If we use an expansion of the type in Eq. (53), where $T_j(x)$ is known but $a_j(t)$ is not, then $w = T_j(x)$ and we get from Eq. (68)

$$\int_0^t \int_a^b \left[\frac{1}{\alpha}\frac{\partial T^N}{\partial t} - \frac{\partial^2 T^N}{\partial x^2}\right] T_j(x)\, dxdt = 0. \tag{69}$$

This is also equivalent to a Galerkin method.

Finally, in applying the fourth variational principle, the adjoint variational principle, we expand T as in Eq. (53) and write a similar expansion for T*.

$$T^{*N} = T_1^* + \sum_{j=1}^{N} a_j^*(t)\, T_j(x). \tag{70}$$

Equation (47) then becomes

$$\int_0^{t_f} \int_V T_j(\underset{\sim}{x}) \left[-\alpha\nabla^2 T^N + \frac{\partial T^N}{\partial t}\right] dV = 0 \tag{71}$$

or the same as Eq. (52). Thus all four variational principles lead to the same equations, and these are the same as applications of Galerkin's method.

4. VARIATIONS ON THE VARIATIONAL PRINCIPLES

Sometimes the search for a variational principle is fruitless. If a principle does not exist for the equation in one form, it may for another form of the same equation, such as Eq. (27), or Eq. (36, 38, 41, 45). If all these approaches fail a variational principle in the form of least-squares principle of the Method of Weighted Residuals always holds. For example, for Eq. (30) the variational integral can be taken as

$$\Phi(T) = \int_0^t \int_V \left[\frac{\partial T}{\partial t} - \alpha\nabla^2 T \right]^2 dV dt. \qquad (72)$$

The trial functions must be smooth since higher derivatives appear in Eq. (72) than Eq. (45), for example.

Reciprocal variational principles are sometimes useful for giving error bounds or special meaning to the variational integral. Minimum variational principles for eigenvalues can be used to give quite close upper and lower bounds on eigenvalues. A variational principle may lead to error bounds on the solution or proofs of uniqueness.

In applications the variational method will lead to symmetric matrices, and the linear algebra problem is more quickly solved than one with unsymmetric matrices. This is an important advantage over the Galerkin method. If there is a variational method applicable to a problem, the Galerkin method should be applied in a way that leads to equivalence with the variational method which is usually achieved by appropriate integration by parts. The variational principle also identifies the natural and essential boundary conditions. By contrast, the Galerkin method must be properly formulated to insure the boundary conditions are physically meaningful.

The heat conduction equation has led to a variety of quasi-variational principles and restricted variational principles. Rosen [8] and Glansdorff and Prigogine [local potential, 9] and Gyarmati [10] have constructed restricted variational principles--called restricted because certain variables are held constant during the variation but then allowed to be variable.

For Eq. (30) in one-dimension their restricted principles give

$$\Phi(T(x,t),\ T_o(x,t)) = \int_a^b \left[T \frac{\partial T_o}{\partial t} + \alpha\left(\frac{\partial T}{\partial x}\right)^2 \right] dx. \qquad (73)$$

Formal variation of T, keeping To fixed, and use of integration by parts, gives

$$\delta_T\Phi = \int_a^b \delta T \left(\frac{\partial T_o}{\partial t} - \alpha \frac{\partial^2 T}{\partial x^2}\right) dx + \text{B.T.} \tag{74}$$

This is clearly not the required equation, so now we set $T_o = T$, even though we could not do this in Eq. (73). If T_o were a given, known function, then Eq. (74) would make Φ stationary. Use of $T_o = T$, however, destroys the stationary character, as described by Finlayson and Scriven [11,4]. Thus the functional is not even stationary. The same formal operations can be used on any equation. The advantages attributed above to variational principles do not hold for such variational principles.

Biot [12] provides an alternative which is analogous to d'Alembert's principle in that no functional exists. For Eq. (30) he introduces a new heat-flow vector, defined such that

$$T = -\nabla \cdot \underset{\sim}{H}. \tag{75}$$

The quasi-variational principle is stated as

$$\int_V \delta \underset{\sim}{H} \cdot \left[\nabla T + \frac{1}{\alpha} \frac{\partial \underset{\sim}{H}}{\partial t}\right] dV = 0. \tag{76}$$

The Euler equation is

$$\nabla T + \frac{1}{\alpha} \frac{\partial \underset{\sim}{H}}{\partial t} = 0 \tag{77}$$

and if one takes the divergence of this equation and uses Eq. (75) one gets Eq. (30). Biot uses this quasi-variational principle in some innovative ways, as is also done in the heat integral method [13]. For heat conduction in a slab, when the wall temperature has suddenly jumped, a heat penetration distance is defined, and the approximate solution is defined over that distance.

$$T = \left(1 - \frac{x}{q(t)}\right)^2$$

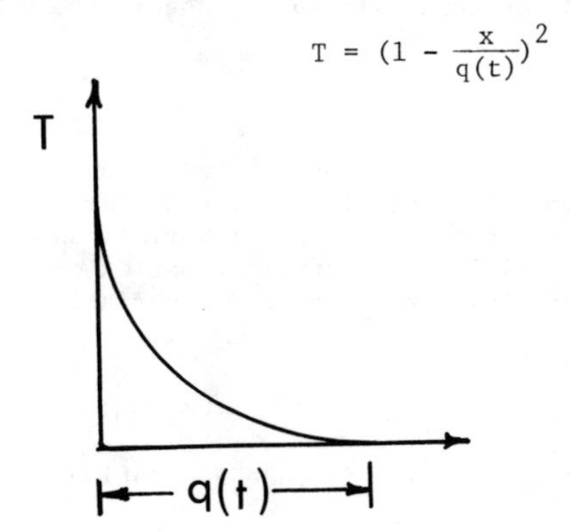

Use of the quasi-variational principle gives an equation for q(t). Approaches such as these, which can be done with Galerkin, integral and other methods, are quite useful for engineering purposes.

Another attempt to obtain a variational principle is provided by Vujanovic [14]. He adds a term to Eq. (30).

$$m \frac{\partial^2 T}{\partial t^2} + \frac{\partial T}{\partial t} = \alpha \frac{\partial^2 T}{\partial x^2}. \tag{79}$$

The variational integral is then

$$\Phi(T) = \frac{1}{2} \int_o^t \int_a^b [m (\frac{\partial T}{\partial t})^2 - \alpha (\frac{\partial T}{\partial x})^2] e^{t/m} dxdt. \tag{80}$$

The first variation gives

$$\delta\Phi = \int_o^t \int_a^b \partial T [-m \frac{\partial^2 T}{\partial t^2} - \frac{\partial T}{\partial t} + \alpha \frac{\partial^2 T}{\partial x^2}] e^{t/m} dxdt + B.T. \tag{81}$$

thus giving the right Euler equation, (79). Then Vujanovic sets m=0 to turn Eq. (79) into Eq. (30) and uses Eq. (81) with $m \to 0$. No consideration is given to the fact that this procedure creates a singular perturbation problem, the number of boundary conditions changes for a well-posed problem, and the solution T actually depends on m and no proof is given that the second and third integrals in Eq. (81) actually dominate the first integral (they do if the solution of Eq. (79) is independent of m). In any case, the variational integral (80) is undefined for m=0 and applications again are equivalent to Galerkin's method.

All these "principles" lead to methods which are identical to Galerkin methods, yet have no functional which is made stationary. They have not led to new insights. Their main impact is in the imaginative use of trial functions, such as Biot's treatment of heat conduction involving a heat penetration distance. Usually they are introduced and used to solve simple problems, in contrast to the Galerkin method which has found widespread use in the past decade.

5. CONCLUSIONS

Variational principles exist for some, but not all, heat transfer problems. The important ones are given and compared to quasi-variational principles and restricted variational principles. In applications Galerkin methods are often equivalent, and are certainly preferred if no variational principle exists.

ACKNOLWEDGEMENT

This research was supported in part by National Science Foundation Grant No. 80-11035.

REFERENCES

1. Courant, R. and Hilbert, D., Methods of Mathematical Physics, Interscience, New York, 1953.

2. Gelfand, I. M. and Fomin, S. V., Calculus of Variations (tr. R. A. Silverman), Prentice-Hall, Englewood Cliffs, New Jersey, 1963.

3. Serrin, J., Handbuch der Physik, Vol. 8, Part 1, ed. S. Flugge, Springer-Verlag, Berlin, 1959, p. 144.

4. Finlayson, B. A., The Method of Weighted Residuals and Variational Principles, Academic Press, New York, 1972, pp. 300-307, 312-319, 335-347.

5. Gurtin, M. E., Variational Principles for Linear Initial-Value Problems, Quart. Appl. Math, Vol. 22, 1964, pp. 252-256.

6. Filippov, V. M. and Skorokhodov, A. N., A Quadratic Functional for the Heat-Conduction Equation, Diff. Eqn., Vol. 13, 1977, pp. 770-776.

7. Morse, P. M. and Feshbach, H., Methods of Theoretical Physics, Vol. I, McGraw-Hill, New York, 1953, p. 313.

8. Rosen, P., On Variational Principles for Irreversible Processes, J. Chem. Phys., Vol. 21, 1953, pp. 1220-1221.

9. Glansdorff, P. and Prigogine, I., On a General Evolution Criterion in Macroscopic Physics, Physica, Vol. 30, 1964, pp. 351-374.

10. Gyarmati, I., On the Governing Principle of Dissipative Processes and its Extension to Non-Linear Problems, Ann. Phys., Vol. 23, 1969, pp. 353-378.

11. Finlayson, B. A. and Scriven, L. E., On the Search for Variational Principles, Int. J. Heat Mass Transfer, Vol. 10, 1967, pp. 799-821.

12. Biot, M. A., New Methods in Heat Flow Analysis with Applications to Flight Structures, J. Aero. Sci., Vol. 24, 1957, pp. 857-873.

13. Goodman, T. R., The Heat-Balance Integral and Its Application to Problems Involving a Change in Phase, Trans. ASME, Vol. 80, 1958, pp. 335-342.

14. Vujanovic, B., An Approach to Linear and Nonlinear Heat-Transfer Problem Using a Lagrangian, AIAA J., Vol. 9, 1971, pp. 131-134.

Comparison of Finite Difference Method and Finite Element Method

T.M. SHIH and Y.N. CHEN*
Department of Mechanical Engineering
University of Maryland
College Park, Maryland 20742

1. INTRODUCTION

In this paper we shall attempt to make comparisons of the two most powerful numerical methods, i.e., finite difference and finite element, in terms of smoothness, instability, accuracy (or error bound), higher-order scheme, irregular geometry, nonlinearity, non-Dirichlet boundary conditions and nonuniform grid. Unless the merit is evidently clear, we shall avoid mentioning the authors' subjective viewpoints and leave to the readers the judgement of choosing the better scheme in certain aspects.

2. SMOOTHNESS

One of the major differences between the finite difference method and the finite element method is the smoothness of the approximate solution to the differential equation. The former method generally requires that the approximate solution belong to C^{2k}, where 2k is the order of the differential equation, whereas the latter only requires that its approximate solution belong to W_2^k, a Sobolev space [1] in which all the elements $\phi(x)$ satisfy

$$\int_a^b [\phi^2 + (\frac{d\phi}{dx})^2 + \ldots + (\frac{d^\alpha\phi}{dx^\alpha})^2]dx < \infty, \text{ for all } \alpha \leq k. \tag{1}$$

We shall illustrate this difference by considering the following two linear ordinary differential equations:

$$L_1\phi = -\frac{d^2\phi}{dx^2} + f_1(\frac{d\phi}{dx}, \phi, x) = 0, \quad x \in [a,b] \tag{2a}$$

and

$$L_2\phi = \frac{d^4\phi}{dx^4} + f_2(\frac{d^3\phi}{dx^3}, \frac{d^2\phi}{dx^2}, \frac{d\phi}{dx}, \phi, x) = 0 \tag{2b}$$

subject to certain prescribed boundary conditions.

(a) Finite Difference Methods

To approximate the second derivative $d^2\phi/dx^2$ by the finite difference method, we first expand $\phi(x_{j\pm1})$ about $\phi(x_j)$ by

* Permanent address: Department of Mechanics, Zhejiang University, Hangzhou, China

$$\phi(x_{j\pm 1}) = \phi(x_j) \pm \left(\frac{d\phi}{dx}\right)_{x_j} h + \left(\frac{d^2\phi}{dx^2}\right)_{x_j} \frac{h^2}{2} \pm \text{higher-order terms.}$$

Truncating the higher-order terms leads to the approximate solution

$$\tilde{\phi}(x_{j\pm 1}) \simeq \tilde{\phi}(x_j) \pm \left(\frac{d\tilde{\phi}}{dx}\right)_{x_j} h + \left(\frac{d^2\tilde{\phi}}{dx^2}\right)_{x_j} \frac{h^2}{2}, \tag{3a,b}$$

which suggests that $\tilde{\phi}(x) \in C^2 [a,b]$ must have at least second derivative. Then, rearranging Eqs. (3a,b) leads to the familiar three point relation ($\phi_j = \tilde{\phi}_j(x_j)$, etc)

$$\frac{d^2\tilde{\phi}}{dx^2} \simeq \frac{1}{h^2} (\phi_{j-1} - 2\phi_j + \phi_{j+1}).$$

To approximate the fourth derivative $d^4\phi/dx^4$, we write

$$\tilde{\phi}(x_{j\pm k}) = \tilde{\phi}(x_j) \pm \left(\frac{d\tilde{\phi}}{dx}\right)_{x_j} (kh) + \left(\frac{d^2\tilde{\phi}}{dx^2}\right)_{x_j} \frac{(kh)^2}{2} \pm \left(\frac{d^3\tilde{\phi}}{dx^3}\right)_{x_j} \frac{(kh)^3}{6}$$

$$+ \left(\frac{d^4\tilde{\phi}}{dx^4}\right)_{x_j} \frac{(kh)^4}{24}, \quad k=1,2. \tag{4a,b,c,d}$$

It can be seen from Eqs. (4a-d) that $C^4 [a,b]$ continuity of $\tilde{\phi}(x)$ is required. Eliminating $(d^\nu\phi/dx^\nu)_{x_j}$, $\nu=1,2,3$ from Eqs. (4a-d) eventually yields the five-point relation

$$\left(\frac{d^4\phi}{dx^4}\right)_{x_j} \simeq \frac{1}{h^4} (\phi_{j-2} - 4\phi_{j-1} + 6\phi_j - 4\phi_{j+1} + \phi_{j+2}) . \tag{5}$$

It is noteworthy that, after the nodal unknowns are computed, the approximate solution in the entire domain other than at those discrete points remains unavailable.

(b) Finite Element Methods

We shall exclusively speak of the Galerkin formulation here. Let the approximate function $\tilde{\phi}(x)$ be expressed by

$$\tilde{\phi}(x) = \sum_{j=0}^{J} v_j(x)\phi_j, \qquad v_j(a) = v_j(b) = 0 \quad \text{if} \quad v_j \in W_2^1$$

$$v_j(a) = \frac{dv_j(a)}{dx} = v_j(b) = \frac{dv_j(b)}{dx} = 0 \quad \text{if} \quad v_j \in W_2^2 .$$

Integrating the inner product $(L_1\tilde{\phi}, v_j)$ by parts yields the weak equation

$$(L_1\tilde{\phi}, v_j) = \int_a^b \frac{d\tilde{\phi}}{dx} \frac{dv_j}{dx} dx + \int_a^b f_1 v_j dx = 0 . \tag{6}$$

It is seen from Eq. (6) that the requirement of the smoothness of $\tilde{\phi}(x)$ is much relaxed; $\tilde{\phi}(x)$ only needs to be such that $d\tilde{\phi}/dx$ is integrable; i.e.,

$\phi(x) \in W_2^1 [a,b]$.

Next, we integrate the inner product $(L_2\phi, v_j)$ by parts twice and yield

$$(L_2\phi, v_j) = \int_a^b \frac{d^4\phi}{dx^4} v_j dx + \int_a^b f_2 v_j dx$$

$$= \int_a^b \frac{d^2\phi}{dx^2} \frac{d^2 v_j}{dx^2} dx + \int_a^b f_2 v_j dx^{\dagger}$$

$$= 0 \,, \tag{7}$$

which dictates that $d^2\phi/dx^2$ is integrable; i.e., $\phi \in W_2^2[a,b]$. A typical element in $W_2^2[a,b]$ is the quadratic spline defined as

$$S(x) = \begin{cases} x^2 & , x \in [0,1] \\ 1+2(x-1) - (x-1)^2 & , x \in [1,2] \\ 2 - (x-2)^2 & , x \in [2,3] \\ (4-x)^2 & , x \in [3,4] \,. \end{cases} \tag{8}$$

Remarks:

(i) The finite element method that incorporates the evaluation of the inner-product integral enables us to seek the approximate solution in the large spaces. We are provided with more admissible functions in the larger spaces and therefore are in an easier position to seek approximate solutions.

(ii) In the finite element method, the approximate solution throughout the entire domain automatically becomes available as soon as the nodal variables are obtained. In the finite difference method, however, the solution is strictly discrete; we are seeking the unknowns only at the grid points, but not throughout the entire domain. To obtain the solution within a computational molecule, we need to use, for example, interpolation and perform additional calculation.

3. NUMERICAL INSTABILITY

There are at least two types of numerical instability that may arise due to discretization. One is associated with a large convective term in the streamwise-diffusion equation. The other concerns the adoption of an improper mesh-size ratio in the transient equation. We shall compare the instabilities of both the finite difference equation and the finite element equation in terms of these two types subsequently.

(a) Convective Numerical Instability

---

† If $d^3\phi/dx^3$ is contained in the function f_2, it must be also integrated by parts at least once.

It has been reported [2-5] that, when the one-dimensional streamwise-diffusion equation

$$\frac{d^2\phi}{dx^2} - \frac{u}{\alpha}\frac{d\phi}{dx} = 0 \tag{9}$$

was discretized by the central finite difference scheme

$$\frac{d\phi}{dx} = \frac{1}{2h}(\phi_{j+1} - \phi_{j-1}) + O(h^2), \tag{10}$$

the numerical instability arose if $Pe>2$ where $Pe = uh/\alpha$. This instability can be detected by a simple analysis. Substituting Eq. (10) into Eq. (9) and replacing the second derivative by the three-point formula, we obtain

$$\phi_j - \phi_{j-1} = \frac{2-Pe}{2+Pe}(\phi_{j+1} - \phi_j). \tag{11}$$

Clearly, if $Pe>2$, the value of ϕ will oscillate as the index j varies. To remove this instability, some researchers proposed the upwind finite difference scheme [6-9]

$$\frac{d\phi}{dx} = \frac{1}{h}(\phi_j - \phi_{j-1}) + \frac{h}{2}\frac{d^2\phi}{dx^2}. \tag{12}$$

The counterpart of Eq. (11) for the upwind scheme becomes

$$\phi_j - \phi_{j-1} = \frac{1}{1+Pe}(\phi_{j+1} - \phi_j), \tag{13}$$

which suggests that $\phi_{j+1} - \phi_j$ and $\phi_j - \phi_{j-1}$ have the same sign. But unfortunately the accuracy of this scheme, as shown in Eq. (12), is only of $O(h)$, although an artificial viscosity [10], identified by the second term of the R.H.S. of Eq. (12), can be introduced to raise the accuracy. Other finite difference treatments [2, 11, 12] have been developed to achieve both accuracy and stability, but they appear to work well only for some ideally-designed equations.

On the other hand, through the finite element formulation with the use of asymmetric weighting functions [13] defined as

$$W_j(x) = \begin{cases} N_j(x) + \mu n_j(x), & x \in [x_{j-1}, x_j] \\ N_j(x) - \mu n_j(x), & x \in [x_j, x_{j+1}] \\ 0 & \text{elsewhere} \end{cases}, \tag{14}$$

the first derivative can be discretized into

$$\int_{x_{j-1}}^{x_{j+1}} \frac{d\tilde{\phi}}{dx} W_j\,dx \Big/ \int_{x_{j-1}}^{x_{j+1}} W_j\,dx = -\frac{1}{2h}(1+\mu)\phi_{j-1} + \frac{\mu}{h}\phi_j + \frac{1}{2h}(1-\mu)\phi_{j+1}, \tag{15}$$

where $n_i(x) = 3(x-x_{i-1})(x_{i+1}-x)/h^2$ and μ is a constant to be optimally chosen to achieve both stability and accuracy. If μ is chosen to be 0 and 1, Eq. (15) degenerates to Eq. (10) and Eq. (12), respectively, Therefore, Eq. (15) appears to be more general than the other two. In fact, it was shown [13] that, as long as

$$\mu > (Pe - 2)/Pe \quad ,$$

the discretized form of Eq. (9) is stable. Thus, there may exist an optimal value of μ, other than zero and unity, such that both the accuracy and the stability of the discretization scheme are achieved. This optimal value can be determined by Eq. (9) and generally lies between 0 and 1. However, under the choice of Eq. (14), the weighting function sometimes exceed unity (e.g., $\mu = 0.5$, $x = x_{i-1} + 0.8h$), which is physically impossible in the absence of source term. Alternatives to the selection of proper basis functions and weighting functions are summarized in Table 1, and their corresponding discretization equations of Eq. (9) (h=1) and solutions ($\phi_0 = 0$, $\phi_4 = 1$) are listed in Table 2 , and Table 3, respectively. We shall omit the details.

Remarks:

It appears that the finite element upwind schemes are more flexible in accounting for the characteristics of the convection-diffusion equations. By properly choosing the basis function and weighting functions, the finite element methods generally are able to derive the same discretized equations as those derived by the finite difference schemes if one wishes.

(b) Transient Instability

When the one-dimensional transient heat-conduction equation

$$\frac{\partial \phi}{\partial t} = \alpha \frac{\partial^2 \phi}{\partial x^2}$$

is discretized, the stability criterion was derived [14] to be

$$r = \frac{\alpha \Delta t}{h^2} \leq \frac{1}{2}$$

for the explicit finite difference scheme, and is

$$r \leq \frac{1}{6}$$

for the "explicit" finite element scheme as indicated in Ref. [5]. Since this latter criterion is subject to rather severe restriction on r and the corresponding scheme is not really explicit, we generally adopt the implicit finite element method to discretize a transient equation.

For the two-dimensional transient problems described by

$$\frac{\partial \phi}{\partial t} = \alpha \left(\frac{\partial^2 \phi}{\partial x^2} + \frac{\partial^2 \phi}{\partial y^2}\right),$$

the explicit finite difference scheme with uniform mesh size is stable if

$$r \leq \frac{1}{4} ,$$

and the "explicit" finite element method using the square elements is stable if

Scheme	Characteristics (j − 2, j − 1, j, j + 1, j + 2 ; ———> convection)	
Central	$(d\phi/dx)_j = (\phi_{j+1}-\phi_{j-1})/2h + 0(h^2)$	
Upwind 1	$(d\phi/dx)_j = (\phi_j-\phi_{j-1})/h + 0(h)$	
Upwind 2	$(d\phi/dx)_j = (\frac{3}{2}\phi_j-2\phi_{j-1} + \frac{1}{2}\phi_{j-2})/h + 0(h^2)$	
Hybrid	Central if Pe $\leq$ Pe*; upwind 1 if Pe > Pe*	
Exponential	Using the exponential profile and equating the momentum fluxes	
Galerkin	Basis function = Weighting function	
Quadratic Assym. Wt.	Weighting function 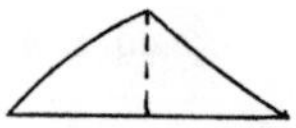	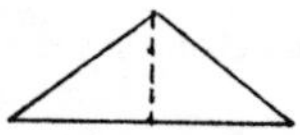 Basis function
Exponential Assym. Basis	Weighting function 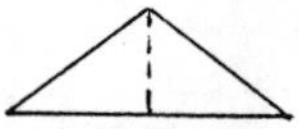	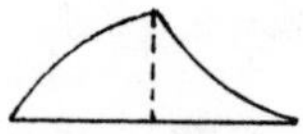 Basis function
Collocated Basis	Weighting function 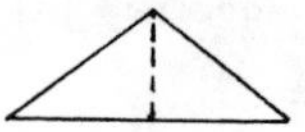	Basis function satisfying $\tilde{\phi}(x_{j-1}) = \phi_{j-1}$, $\tilde{\phi}(x_j) = \phi_j$, $L\tilde{\phi}(x_{j-\frac{1}{2}}) = f(x_{j-\frac{1}{2}})$

Table 1 Characteristics of Various Schemes

Scheme	Discretization Equation
Central	$-(Pe+2)\phi_{j-1} + 4\phi_j - (2-Pe)\phi_{j+1} = 0$
Upwind 1	$-(Pe+1)\phi_{j-1} + (Pe+2)\phi_j - \phi_{j+1} = 0$
Upwind 2	$\frac{Pe}{2}\phi_{j-2} - (2Pe+1)\phi_{j-1} + (\frac{3}{2}Pe+2)\phi_j - \phi_{j+1} = 0$
Hybrid	Central if $Pe \leq 2$; Upwind 1 if $Pe > 2$
Exponential	$-e^{Pe}\phi_{j-1} + (1+e^{Pe})\phi_j - \phi_{j+1} = 0$
Galerkin	The same as Central Difference
Quadratic Assymetric Weighting	$-[1+\frac{Pe}{2}(\mu+1)]\phi_{j-1} + (2+Pe\mu)\phi_j - [1+\frac{Pe}{2}(\mu-1)]\phi_{j+1} = 0$
Exponential Assymetric Basis	The same as Exponential Difference
Collocated Basis	$-(1+\frac{Pe}{2} + \frac{Pe^2}{12})\phi_{j-1} + (2+\frac{Pe^2}{6})\phi_j - (1-\frac{Pe}{2} + \frac{Pe^2}{12})\phi_{j+1} = 0$

Table 2 Discretized form of Eq. (9) by means of various schemes

	Pe = 0.2			Pe = 1			Pe = 3			Pe = 6		
Scheme	ϕ_1	ϕ_2	ϕ_3	ϕ_1	ϕ_2	ϕ_3	ϕ_1	ϕ_2	ϕ_3	ϕ_1	ϕ_2	ϕ_3
Exact	.1807	.4013	.6708	.0321	.1192	.3561	.00012	.00248	.04979	.00	.00001	.00248
Central	.1804	.4009	.6705	.0250	.10	.3250		Unstable			Unstable	
Upwind 1	.1366	.4099	.6781	.0667	.20	.4667	.0118	.0588	.2471	.0025	.020	.1425
Upwind 2	.1839	.4045	.6730	.0563	.1689	.4225	.0076	.0378	.1929	.0014	.011	.1036
Hybrid	.1804	.4009	.6705	.0250	.10	.3250	.0118	.0588	.2471	.0025	.020	.1425
Exponential	The same as the exact solution to the fourth digit											
Galerkin	The same as the central - difference solution											
Quadratic Assy-metric Weighting	.1806	.4011	.6707	.0321	.1192	.3561	.00012	.0025	.0498	$.516 \times 10^{-7}$	$.613 \times 10^{-5}$	.00248
Exponential Assy-metric Basis	The same as the exact solution to the fourth digit											
Collocated Basis	.1807	.4013	.6708	.0322	.1195	.3565	.00042	.00589	.07689	.0025	.020	.1425

Table 3 Numerical solutions to Eq. (9) obtained by various schemes

$$r \le \frac{1}{12} .$$

Remarks:

(i) The finite element "explicit" schemes generally are subject to more strict stability criteria than the finite difference counterparts.

(ii) After Galerkin formulation with the pyramid weighting function, the one-dimensional transient equation can be discretized into

$$\frac{1}{6}\frac{d\phi_{j-1}}{dt} + \frac{2}{3}\frac{d\phi_j}{dt} + \frac{1}{6}\frac{d\phi_{j+1}}{dt} = (\phi_{j-1} - 2\phi_j + \phi_{j+1})\frac{\alpha}{h^2}. \tag{16}$$

Using the implicit scheme, we can further discretize Eq. (16) into

$$(1-6r)\phi_{j-1}^{(n)} + (4+12r)\phi_j^{(n)} + (1-6r)\phi_{j+1}^{(n)} = \phi_{j-1}^{(n-1)} + 4\phi_j^{(n-1)} + \phi_{j+1}^{(n-1)} , \tag{17}$$

of which the matrix form is by no means more complicated than that of the "explicit" scheme. Furthermore, letting

$$\phi_j^{(n)} = A_m \xi^n \exp(imj\pi h)$$

in the von Neumann stability analysis, we can derive

$$-1 \le \xi = \frac{2 + \cos\theta}{(1-6r)\cos\theta + 2 + 6r} \le 1,$$

where $\theta = m\pi h$. Since the above equation is valid for any r, Eq. (17) is unconditionally stable. For these two reasons, it is preferable that the semi-discrete Galerkin equation (16) be discretized using the implicit scheme. Of course, other types of time differencing [15], methods of lines or Eigenvalue method [16] can also be used to solve Eq. (16).

4. ACCURACY AND ERROR BOUNDS

In the finite difference method, the accuracy of the scheme is judged by the truncation error of the Taylor's series expansions. The scheme

$$L\phi = \tilde{L}\phi_{j,k}^{(n)} + O(h^{\nu}, (\Delta t)^{\mu}) \tag{18}$$

is said to be accurate if the magnitude of the second term $O(\cdot)$ is small. The accuracy can be increased by the following ways:

(a) reducing the mesh sizes h and Δt (if the difference scheme is consistent). But this reduction is clearly penalized by the increase of the computer-memory storage and the round-off error.

(b) choosing proper interval-size ratios such that the higher-order derivatives are nearly or completely cancelled by each other. For example, the truncation error of the explicit scheme for the one-dimensional transient conduction equation is

$$L\phi - \tilde{L}\tilde{\phi} = \frac{\alpha h^2}{2} \frac{\partial^4 \phi}{\partial x^4} \left(\frac{1}{6} - r\right) + \frac{\alpha h^4}{6} \frac{\partial^6 \phi}{\partial x^6} \left(\frac{1}{60} - r^2\right) + \ldots, \tag{19}$$

If r is chosen to be 1/6, the error is reduced.

(c) adopting higher-order analyses by considering many-point relations such as the five-point relation for the second ordinary derivatives

$$\frac{d^2\phi}{dx^2} = \frac{1}{12h^2}(-\phi_{j-2}+16\phi_{j-1} - 30\phi_j + 16\phi_{j+1} - \phi_{j+2}) + O(h^4), \tag{20}$$

and the nine-point and twenty-one-point relations for the Laplace equation (25).

(d) adopting higher-order analyses by requiring smoother continuities and considering more nodal unknowns. The number of the nodal points, however, remains the same as that in the second-order analyses. Generally, the discretized equation is arranged in the block matrix system in order to be solved efficiently by a block-matrix solver. Other alternatives are Operator Compact Implicit (OCI) schemes [17, 18, 19], which are sometimes called "Mehrstellen" schemes.

For the finite element methods, we can no longer speak of the truncation errors. Instead, we judge the accuracy of the finite element solution $\tilde{\phi}$ by the error bounds measured by a certain type of norms

$$|| e || = || \phi - \tilde{\phi} || \leq Mh^{\nu} , \tag{21}$$

where M is a higher-order derivative independent of h. This error bound can be decreased by

(a) subdividing the domain into finer mesh systems;

(b) raising the power ν by means of higher-order C^0 and C^1 elements.

This treatment also increases the rate of convergence.

Remarks:

(i) It is possible to compare the accuracy of a finite difference scheme with that of another finite difference scheme simply based on the magnitude of the truncation error. It is also straightforward to compare the error bound of a finite element scheme with that of another finite element method. For example, Eq. (20) is more accurate than the three-point relation, if the error bound equation such as Eq. (21) can be derived. Also, the error bound

$$|| \phi - \tilde{\phi} || \leq M_1 h^2$$

obtained using one-dimensional quadratic elements has higher power of h than the error bound

$$|| \phi - \tilde{\phi} || \leq M_2 h$$

obtained using one-dimensional linear elements.

(ii) It is, however, difficult to compare the accuracy of a finite difference scheme with that of a finite element scheme unless the exact solution is available.

5. DISCRETIZATION SCHEMES OF HIGHER-ORDER ACCURACY

It is known that the twenty-one-point relation can be derived from either the finite difference formulation or the finite element formulation. In this section, we shall present both formulations for discretization of the Laplace equation. Although the use of the 21-point relation may be impractical, such a derivation can be readily extended to relations of less points. The finite difference formulation is to be described first.

(a) Finite Difference Formulation

Figure 1 shows the computational molecule containing the central grid point j and the twenty surrounding grid points. A typical nodal unknown ϕ_{NW} can be expanded about ϕ_j in Taylor's series as

$$\phi_{NW} = \phi_j + [h(-\frac{\partial}{\partial x} + \frac{\partial}{\partial y}) + \frac{h^2}{2}(-\frac{\partial}{\partial x} + \frac{\partial}{\partial y})^2 + \frac{h^3}{6}(-\frac{\partial}{\partial x} + \frac{\partial}{\partial y})^3 + \frac{h^4}{24}(-\frac{\partial}{\partial x} + \frac{\partial}{\partial y})^4 + \frac{h^5}{120}(-\frac{\partial}{\partial x} + \frac{\partial}{\partial y})^5]\phi(x,y) + O(h^6). \quad (22)$$

Multiplying Eq. (22) by a constant a_1 and rearranging the result leads to

$$a_1(\phi_{NW} - \phi_j) = -a_1 h\frac{\partial\phi}{\partial x} + a_1 h\frac{\partial\phi}{\partial y} + \frac{a_1 h^2}{2}\frac{\partial^2\phi}{\partial x^2} + \frac{a_1 h^2}{2}\frac{\partial^2\phi}{\partial y^2} - \frac{a_1 h^2}{2}\frac{\partial^2\phi}{\partial x\partial y} + \ldots - \frac{a_1 h^5}{120}\frac{\partial^5\phi}{\partial x^5} + \frac{a_1 h^5}{120}\frac{\partial^5\phi}{\partial y^5}. \quad (23a)$$

Similarly,

$$a_2(\phi_{NWW} - \phi_j) = -a_2 h\frac{\partial\phi}{\partial x} + \frac{a_2 h}{2}\frac{\partial\phi}{\partial y} + \frac{a_2 h^2}{2}\frac{\partial^2\phi}{\partial x^2} + \frac{a_2 h^2}{8}\frac{\partial^2\phi}{\partial y^2} - \frac{a_2 h^2}{4}\frac{\partial^2\phi}{\partial x\partial y} + \ldots - \frac{a_2 h^5}{120}\frac{\partial^5\phi}{\partial x^5} + \frac{a_2 h^5}{120\times 32}\frac{\partial^5\phi}{\partial y^5}, \quad (23b)$$

$$a_3(\phi_W - \phi_j) = -a_3 h\frac{\partial\phi}{\partial x} + 0 + \frac{a_3 h^2}{2}\frac{\partial^2\phi}{\partial x^2} + 0 + 0 + \ldots - \frac{a_3 h^5}{120}\frac{\partial^5\phi}{\partial x^5} + 0, \quad (23c)$$

. . . . . .

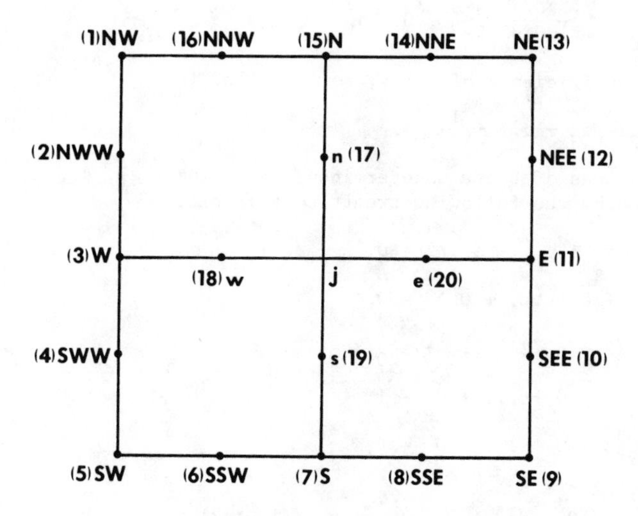

Fig. 1 The quadratic square element involving 21 grid points.

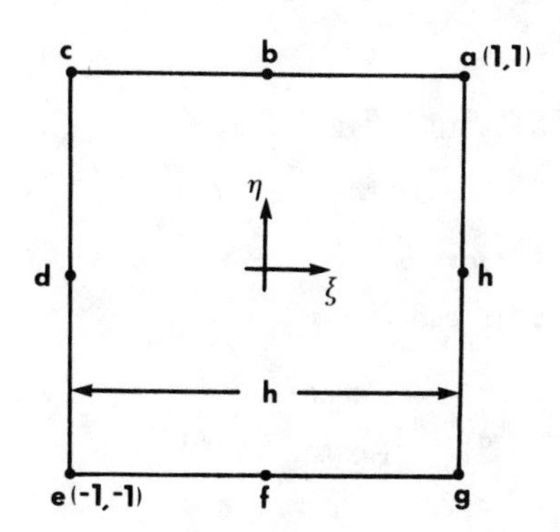

Fig. 2 The isoparametric quadratic square element.

$$a_{20}(\phi_e - \phi_j) = a_{20}\frac{h}{2}\frac{\partial\phi}{\partial x} + 0 + \frac{a_{20}h^2}{8}\frac{\partial^2\phi}{\partial x^2} + 0 + 0 + \ldots + \frac{a_{20}h^5}{120\times 32}\frac{\partial^5\phi}{\partial x^5} + 0 \quad . \tag{23t}$$

The sum of the coefficients of $\partial\phi/\partial x$, for example, is

$$h(-a_1 - a_2 - a_3 + \ldots + \tfrac{1}{2}a_{20}).$$

The numerical values of these undetermined coefficients $a_1, a_2, a_3, \ldots, a_{20}$ can be evaluated by the following twenty constraints:

$$\begin{aligned}
-a_1 - a_2 - a_3 + \ldots + a_{20}/2 &= 0,\\
a_1 + a_2/2 + 0 + \ldots + 0 &= 0,\\
a_1/2 + a_2/2 + a_3/2 + \ldots + a_{20}/8 &= 1,\\
a_1/2 + a_2/8 + 0 + \ldots + 0 &= 1,\\
-a_1/2 - a_2/4 + 0 + \ldots + 0 &= 0,\\
\ldots \qquad \ldots &\\
-a_1/120 - a_2/120 - a_3/120 + \ldots + a_{20}/(120\times 32) &= 0,
\end{aligned} \tag{24}$$

and

$$a_1/120 + a_2/(120x32) + 0 + \ldots + 0 = 0.$$

Only the coefficients of $\partial^2\phi/\partial x^2$ and $\partial^2\phi/\partial y^2$ are set to unity; others are forced to vanish. The calculation can be facilitated by letting

$$a_1 = a_5 = a_9 = a_{13},$$

$$a_3 = a_7 = a_{11} = a_{15},$$

$$a_2 = a_4 = a_6 = a_8 = a_{10} = a_{12} = a_{14} = a_{16},$$

and

$$a_{17} = a_{18} = a_{19} = a_{20}.$$

Utilization of this set of equations leads to

$$[a_1\sum_{p=NW}^{NE}\phi_p + a_3\sum_{q=W}^{N}\phi_q + a_2\sum_{r=NWW}^{NNW}\phi_r + a_{17}\sum_{t=w}^{n}\phi_t - 4(a_1+a_3+2a_2+a_{17})\phi_j]/h^2$$
$$= \frac{\partial^2\phi}{\partial x^2} + \frac{\partial^2\phi}{\partial y^2} + O(h^4), \tag{25}$$

where

$$a_1 = \frac{2}{3}, \; a_2 = -\frac{4}{3}, \; a_3 = 1 \text{ and } a_{17} = 8.$$

By means of the method of undetermined coefficients, any discretization scheme representing an n-point relation can be, in principle, obtained. We also note that the sum of the coefficients in the L.H.S. of Eq. (25) should be equal to zero because Eq. (25) remains valid in the case of uniform ϕ.

(b) Finite Element Formulation

Next, we shall turn our attention to the finite element formulation that leads to the twenty-one-point relations.

If we approximate the interpolant inside the isoparametric element shown in Fig. 2 in terms of the eight nodel values as

$$\tilde{\phi}(x,y) = \sum_{m=a}^{h} N_m(x,y)\phi_m, \qquad (26)$$

it can be derived after considerable algebra [20] that

$$N_p = (1+\xi\xi_p)(1+\eta\eta_p)(\xi\xi_p+\eta\eta_p-1)/4 \ , \ p=a,c,e,g \qquad (27a\sim d)$$

$$N_q = (1-\xi^2)(1+\eta\eta_q)/2 \ , \ q=b,f \qquad (27e,f)$$

and

$$N_r = (1+\xi\xi_r)(1-\eta^2)/2 \ , \ r=d,h \qquad (27g,h)$$

where $\xi=2(x-x^*)/h$ and $\eta=2(y-y^*)/h$ are the isoparametric coordinates ranging from -1 to 1; x^* and y^* are the coordinates of the element center. After lengthy algebra, we obtain the following inner product

$$(-\nabla^2\tilde{\phi},N_j) = K_{NW} + K_{SW} + K_{SE} + K_{NE} = 0, \qquad (28)$$

where

$$K_p = \iint_{e_p} \left(\frac{\partial\tilde{\phi}}{\partial x}\frac{\partial N_j}{\partial x} + \frac{\partial\tilde{\phi}}{\partial y}\frac{\partial N_j}{\partial y}\right)dxdy, \ p=NW,SW,SE,NE. \qquad (29)$$

For the sake of bookkeeping, these integrals are derived and expressed in terms of the nodal unknowns and the result is listed in Table 4. Using this table, we finally obtain

$$\begin{aligned}(-\nabla^2\tilde{\phi},N_j) &= 4A_{aa}\phi_j + 2A_{ag}(\phi_W + \phi_S + \phi_E + \phi_N) \\ &+ 2A_{hg}(\phi_w + \phi_s + \phi_e + \phi_n) + A_{ae}(\phi_{NW} + \phi_{SW} + \phi_{SE} + \phi_{NE}) \\ &+ A_{bg}(\phi_{NWW} + \dots + \phi_{NNW}) \\ &= 0. \end{aligned} \qquad (30)$$

In order to compare Eq. (30) with Eq. (25), we evaluate

$$(1,N_j) = \iint_{e_{supp}} N_j dxdy = -h^2/3. \qquad (31)$$

Then dividing Eq. (30) by Eq. (31) for normalization yields

$$\iint_{e_{NW}} E\,dxdy \quad A_{ag}\phi_N + A_{bg}\phi_{NNW} + A_{cg}\phi_{NW} + A_{dg}\phi_{NWW}$$
$$+ A_{eg}\phi_W + A_{fg}\phi_w + A_{gg}\phi_j + A_{hg}\phi_n$$

$$\iint_{e_{SW}} E\,dxdy \quad A_{aa}\phi_j + A_{ba}\phi_w + A_{ca}\phi_W + A_{da}\phi_{SWW}$$
$$+ A_{ea}\phi_{SW} + A_{fa}\phi_{SSW} + A_{ga}\phi_S + A_{ha}\phi_s$$

$$\iint_{e_{SE}} E\,dxdy \quad A_{ac}\phi_E + A_{bc}\phi_e + A_{cc}\phi_j + A_{dc}\phi_s$$
$$+ A_{ec}\phi_S + A_{fc}\phi_{SSE} + A_{gc}\phi_{SE} + A_{hc}\phi_{SEE}$$

$$\iint_{e_{NE}} E\,dxdy \quad A_{ae}\phi_{NE} + A_{be}\phi_{NNE} + A_{ce}\phi_N + A_{de}\phi_n$$
$$+ A_{ee}\phi_j + A_{fe}\phi_e + A_{ge}\phi_E + A_{he}\phi_{NEE}$$

A_{aa}, A_{cc}, A_{ee}, A_{gg}	52/45
A_{ag}	1/2
A_{hg}	-37/45
A_{ae}	23/45
A_{bg}	-23/45

Table 4 Convenient result which may be used in deriving the twenty-point discretized equation. $E = \frac{\partial\phi}{\partial x}\frac{\partial N_j}{\partial x} + \frac{\partial\phi}{\partial y}\frac{\partial N_j}{\partial y}$ and

$$A_{pq} = \int_{-1}^{1}\int_{-1}^{1} \left(\frac{\partial N_p}{\partial\xi}\frac{\partial N_q}{\partial\xi} + \frac{\partial N_p}{\partial\eta}\frac{\partial N_q}{\partial\eta}\right) d\xi d\eta.$$

$$(\nabla^2\tilde{\phi},N_j)/(1,N_j) = (\frac{23}{15}\sum_{p=NW}^{NE}\phi_p + 3\sum_{q=W}^{N}\phi_q - \frac{23}{15}\sum_{r=NWW}^{NNW}\phi_r$$

$$- \frac{74}{15}\sum_{t=n}^{W}\phi_t + \frac{208}{15}\phi_j)/h^2$$

$$= 0, \qquad (32)$$

which is different from Eq. (25). Again, the sum of the coefficients should be equal to zero; i.e.,

$$4 \times \frac{23}{15} + 4 \times 3 - 8 \times \frac{23}{15} - 4 \times \frac{74}{15} + \frac{208}{15} = 0.$$

Remarks:

(i) Any n-point relation can be, in principle, obtained using the method of undetermined coefficients and the Galerkin finite element scheme.

(ii) The accuracy of the finite difference scheme can be readily judged from the truncation error. The error bound of the finite element scheme, however, requires elaborate derivation.

6. IRREGULAR GEOMETRY OF THE SYSTEM

When the geometry of the system is irregular such as shown in Fig. 3, some special treatments are needed to account for the irregularity of the boundary. In this section, we shall assume that $\phi(x,y)$ is prescribed on the boundary and the partial differential equation is linear.

(a) Finite Difference Method

One way to account for the irregularity of the boundary is to expand $\phi(x,y)$ in Taylor's series about the j point, temporarily taken to be the origin as

$$\phi(x,y) = \phi_j + x(\frac{\partial\phi}{\partial x})_j + y(\frac{\partial\phi}{\partial y})_j + \frac{x^2}{2}(\frac{\partial^2\phi}{\partial x^2}) + \frac{y^2}{2}(\frac{\partial^2\phi}{\partial y^2}) + \dots \qquad (33)$$

Substituting the coordinates of the points W, S, E and N into Eq. (33) yields

$$\begin{bmatrix} -h_W & 0 & \frac{1}{2}h_W^2 & 0 \\ 0 & -h & 0 & \frac{1}{2}h^2 \\ h & 0 & \frac{1}{2}h^2 & 0 \\ 0 & h_N & 0 & \frac{1}{2}h_N^2 \end{bmatrix} \begin{Bmatrix} (\frac{\partial\phi}{\partial x})_j \\ (\frac{\partial\phi}{\partial y})_j \\ (\frac{\partial^2\phi}{\partial x^2})_j \\ (\frac{\partial^2\phi}{\partial y^2})_j \end{Bmatrix} = \begin{Bmatrix} \phi_W - \phi_j \\ \phi_S - \phi_j \\ \phi_E - \phi_j \\ \phi_N - \phi_j \end{Bmatrix} . \qquad (34)$$

The matrix system can be inverted to yield the expressions of $(\partial\phi/\partial x)_j$, $(\partial\phi/\partial y)_j$, $(\partial^2\phi/\partial x^2)_j$ and $(\partial^2\phi/\partial y^2)_j$ in terms of five nodal functions. For example,

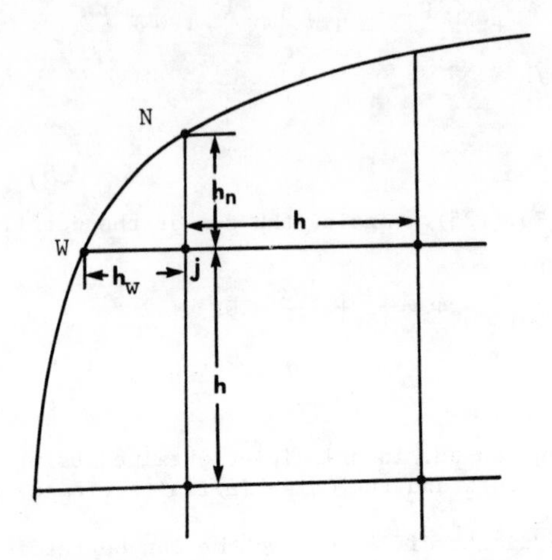

Fig. 3 Mesh system near the irregular boundary.

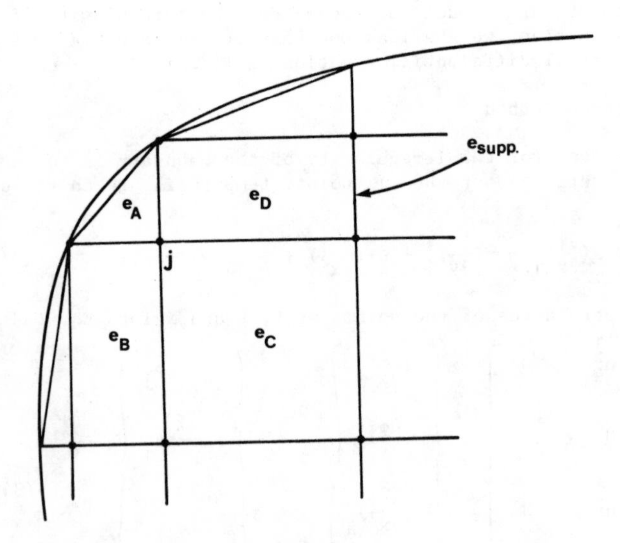

Fig. 4 Partially-triangulated irregular region. e_{supp} includes e_A, e_B, e_C and e_D.

$$(\frac{\partial\phi}{\partial x})_j = \frac{h_W}{h^2+hh_W}\phi_E + \frac{h-h_W}{hh_W}\phi_j - \frac{h}{h_W^2+hh_W}\phi_W \tag{35a}$$

and

$$(\frac{\partial^2\phi}{\partial x^2})_j = \frac{2}{h^2+hh_W}\phi_E - \frac{2}{hh_W}\phi_j + \frac{2}{h_W^2+hh_W}\phi_W. \tag{35b}$$

Observe that Eqs. (35a,b), respectively, reduce to the familiar central-difference scheme and three-point relation if $h=h_W$. Therefore, for finite difference discretization of the differential equations at the nodal points adjacent to the boundary, Eqs. (35a,b) can be used.

(b) Finite Element Method

In the finite element formulation, when there exist irregular boundaries around the physical domain, the triangular elements can be used to triangulate the region near the boundary since the triangular elements possess high conformity in fitting the irregular domain. A typical partially-triangulated irregular region is shown in Fig. 4. We shall demonstrate the Galerkin discretization of the Laplace equation for the grid point j surrounded by three regular rectangular elements and one triangular element.

A weak Galerkin form of the Laplace equation can be written as

$$(-\nabla^2\tilde{\phi}, N_j) = \iint_{e_{supp}} (\frac{\partial\tilde{\phi}}{\partial x}\frac{\partial N_j}{\partial x} + \frac{\partial\tilde{\phi}}{\partial y}\frac{\partial N_j}{\partial y})\,dxdy = 0 , \tag{36}$$

where $N_j(x,y)$ is a piecewise basis function having local support in elements e_A, e_B, e_C and e_D. The double integral in Eq. (36) can be evaluated separately in the four elements. For example, in the triangular element e_A, we derive

$$\iint_{e_A} (\frac{\partial\tilde{\phi}}{\partial x}\frac{\partial N_j}{\partial x} + \frac{\partial\tilde{\phi}}{\partial y}\frac{\partial N_j}{\partial y})\,dxdy$$

$$= B_{bb}\phi_j + B_{cb}\phi_N + B_{ab}\phi_W , \tag{37}$$

where

$$B_{pb} = \iint_{e_A} (\frac{\partial N_p}{\partial x}\frac{\partial N_b}{\partial x} + \frac{\partial N_p}{\partial y}\frac{\partial N_b}{\partial y})\,dxdy, \quad p=a,b,c. \tag{38a,b,c}$$

7. DISCRETIZATION OF NONLINEAR TERMS

Although the nonlinearity can arise due to infinitely many possible arrangements, we shall consider only two typical nonlinear terms

$\frac{d}{dx}(\phi\frac{d\phi}{dx})$ and $(\frac{d\phi}{dx})(\frac{d^2\phi}{dx^2})$.

(a) Finite Difference Methods

In the finite difference formulation, the discretizations of these two terms are similar and straightforward. Immediately, we may write

$$\frac{d}{dx}\left(\tilde{\phi}\frac{d\tilde{\phi}}{dx}\right)_{x_j} = \phi_j\left(\frac{d^2\tilde{\phi}}{dx^2}\right)_{x_j} + \left(\frac{d\tilde{\phi}}{dx}\right)^2_{x_j}$$

$$= \phi_j(\phi_{j-1} - 2\phi_j + \phi_{j+1})/h^2 + (\phi_{j+1} - \phi_{j-1})^2/4h^2 \qquad (39)$$

and

$$\left(\frac{d\tilde{\phi}}{dx}\right)\left(\frac{d^2\tilde{\phi}}{dx^2}\right) = \left(\frac{\phi_{j+1}-\phi_{j-1}}{2h}\right)\left(\frac{\phi_{j+1}-2\phi_j+\phi_{j-1}}{h^2}\right), \qquad (40)$$

and the discretization is accomplished.

(b) Finite Element Methods

In the Galerkin finite element formulation, significant distinction is observed between the discretizations of these two nonlinear terms. To discretize $\frac{d}{dx}(\phi\frac{d\phi}{dx})$, we approximate $\phi(x)$ by $\sum_{j=0}^{J} v_j(x)\phi_j$ and integrate the inner product

$$\left(\frac{d}{dx}\left(\tilde{\phi}\frac{d\tilde{\phi}}{dx}\right), v_j\right) = \int \frac{d}{dx}\left(\tilde{\phi}\frac{d\tilde{\phi}}{dx}\right)v_j\,dx$$

by parts to yield

$$\left(\frac{d}{dx}\left(\tilde{\phi}\frac{d\tilde{\phi}}{dx}\right), v_j\right) = -\int \tilde{\phi}\frac{d\tilde{\phi}}{dx}\frac{dv_j}{dx}dx + \text{boundary terms.} \qquad (41)$$

It is seen from Eq. (41) that the differentiability of $\tilde{\phi}(x)$ is weakened; i.e., $\phi(x)$ belongs to C^2, whereas $\tilde{\phi}(x)$ belongs to W_2^1.

Regarding the discretization of $(\frac{d\phi}{dx})(\frac{d^2\phi}{dx^2})$, the situation becomes different. We find that the computation of the inner product

$$\left(\frac{d\tilde{\phi}}{dx}\frac{d^2\tilde{\phi}}{dx^2}, v_j\right) = \int \frac{d\tilde{\phi}}{dx}\frac{d^2\tilde{\phi}}{dx^2}v_j\,dx \qquad (42)$$

cannot weaken the differentiability of $\tilde{\phi}$ by integration by parts. Under such circumstances, the Galerkin method may not be advantageous over the finite difference method.

Remarks:

(i) The discretization procedure of the finite element method generally required lengthier algebra than the finite difference method. If the differentiability of the approximate solution can be weakened such as shown in Eq. (41), then it may be worthwhile to adopt the Galerkin method for discretization. Otherwise, it may be wise to use the finite difference method.

(ii) Sometimes the discretized nonlinear result obtained by the Galerkin method is identical to that obtained by the finite difference method.

8. INCORPORATION WITH MIXED BOUNDARY CONDITIONS

Consider again the classical equation (9), but now subject to

$$\phi(0) = 1 \quad \text{and} \quad 2\,\phi'(4) = \phi(4). \tag{43}$$

As aforementioned, both the central difference scheme and the Galerkin scheme will both yield the following discretized equation

$$\left(1 + \frac{Pe}{2}\right)\phi_{j-1} - 2\phi_j + \left(1 - \frac{Pe}{2}\right)\phi_{j+1} = 0 \quad , \quad j=1,2,\ldots,J-1. \tag{44}$$

However, at the boundary point (j=J) major differences exist between the finite difference equation and the finite element equation. In the central difference scheme, a fictitious nodal unknown, ϕ_{J+1}, must be introduced for the discretization of Eq. (43). Then eliminating ϕ_{J+1} from the discretized result and Eq. (44) yields

$$\phi_J = \frac{4}{2+Pe}\phi_{J-1}. \tag{45}$$

On the other hand, at j=J, the Galerkin scheme gives

$$(L\hat{\phi},N_J) = \int_0^4 \left(\frac{dN_J}{dx} + \frac{u}{\alpha}N_J\right)\left(\frac{d\hat{\phi}}{dx}\right)dx - N_J(4)\frac{d\phi(4)}{dx}\ . \tag{46}$$

After simplification, Eq. (46) becomes

$$\phi_J = \left(\frac{2+Pe}{1+Pe}\right)\phi_{J-1}\ , \tag{47}$$

which <u>naturally</u> takes into account the influence of Pe via integration by parts.

Remark:

When the boundary conditions are <u>not</u> of Dirichlet type, the finite element schemes that generate weak equations incorporate the boundary conditions into discretization spontaneously. Consequently, the characteristics of the original differential equation is better preserved.

9. NONUNIFORM GRID

When rapid change of the field variable exists in the thin boundary layers, adoption of a uniform grid may not be suitable because, for adequate resolution, several mesh points are required and the entire domain of the system may be orders of magnitude larger than the boundary-layer thickness. In this case, a nonuniform grid that is fine within the boundary layer and coarse elsewhere may provide accurate results while keeping the computation inexpensive.

In this section we shall use both uniform grid and nonuniform grid to solve a simple one-dimensional convection-diffusion equation by the central difference scheme and the Galerkin scheme. Consider

$$-\ \frac{1}{4}\phi'' - \phi' + 8\phi = 0,\ \phi(0) = 0 \text{ and } \phi(1) = 1, \tag{48}$$

of which the exact solution is

$$\phi(t) = (e^{4t} - e^{-8t})/(e^4 - e^{-8}). \tag{49}$$

(a) Central Difference

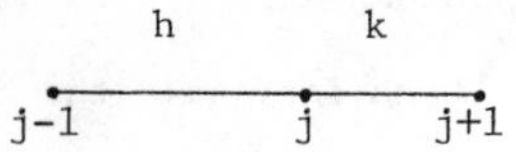

Using the Taylor's series expansion with some algebra, we can obtain

h k

j-1 j j+1

Fig.5 Nonuniform grid.

$$\phi_j' = [-\sigma^2\phi_{j-1} + \phi_j(\sigma^2-1) + \phi_{j+1}]/h\sigma(1+\sigma) + \text{H.O.T.} \tag{50a}$$

and

$$\phi_j'' = 2[\sigma\phi_{j-1} - \phi_j(\sigma+1) + \phi_{j+1}]/h^2\sigma(1+\sigma) + h(1-\sigma)\phi_j'''/3 - h^2(1-\sigma+\sigma^2)\phi_j''''/12 + \text{H.O.T.}, \tag{50b}$$

where $\sigma = k/h$ (see Fig. 5). For uniform grid (σ=1), Eq. (50b) reduces to

$$\phi_j'' = (\phi_{j-1} - 2\phi_j + \phi_{j+1})/h^2 - h^2\phi_j''''/12 . \tag{51}$$

The magnitudes of the truncation errors in Eqs. (50a, 51) are problem-dependent. It is likely that, with the proper choice of a nonuniform grid applied to certain problems, the truncation error in Eq. (50b) will be smaller than that in Eq. (51). For example, consider the solution to Eq. (48). At t = 0.75, we may approximate

$$\phi(0.75) \approx 0.0183e^3 \approx \phi'(0.75) \approx \phi''(0.75) \approx \phi'''(0.75) \approx \phi''''(0.75).$$

With these approximations, the truncation error of the nonuniform grid case with h = 1.25 and σ = 0.6 is calculated to be 0.02488, whereas the error in the uniform grid case with h = 1 is 0.03062. The numerical results are listed in Table 5. It is seen that, at t = 0.75, the solution of the non-uniform grid is more accurate than that of the uniform grid.

(b) Galerkin Finite Element

In the finite element formulation, we should not speak of the truncation error. Instead, we shall present a very elementary example to illustrate the advantage of adopting a nonuniform grid. Suppose it is desired to approximate the function $\phi(x) = x^2(1-x)$, $x\epsilon[0,1]$ by a pyramid function

$$\tilde{\phi}(x) = \begin{cases} x\phi^*/h = N^-(x)\phi^* , & x\epsilon[0,h] \\ (1-x)\phi^*/(1-h) = N^+(x)\phi^*, & x\epsilon[h,1]. \end{cases}$$

Forcing the residual orthogonal to the basis functions, we obtain

$$\int_0^h [\phi(x) - \tilde{\phi}(x)]N^-(x)dx + \int_h^1 [\phi(x) - \tilde{\phi}(x)]N^+(x)dx = 0 . \tag{52}$$

Substitution of $\phi^* = h^2 - h^3$ into Eq. (52) yields

$$\frac{h^2}{3} - \frac{7}{12}h^3 + \frac{1}{5}h^4 - \frac{1}{1-h}\left(\frac{1}{30} - \frac{h^3}{3} + \frac{h^4}{2} - \frac{h^5}{5}\right) = 0,$$

of which one of the roots is h ≈ 2/3 (and not 1/2). The discretized equation of Eq. (48) takes the following form

Scheme	t = .25	t = .4375	t = .5	t = .75	t = .9375
Exact	.0473	.1049	.1350	.3678	.7788
F. D. (Uniform grid)	.0582	-	.1552	.3944	-
F. D. (Nonuniform grid)	-	.1184	-	.3720	.7740
F. E. (Uniform grid)	.044	-	.1269	.3563	-
F. E. (Nonuniform grid)	-	.09134	-	.3486	.770

Table 5 Numerical solutions to Eq. (48) for uniform and nonuniform grids. At t = .75, solutions for both grids are available for comparison.

$$-\left(\frac{1}{h}-\frac{1}{2}-\frac{h}{3}\right)\phi_{j-1} + \left[\frac{1}{h}+\frac{1}{k}+\frac{2}{3}(h+k)\right]\phi_j - \left(\frac{1}{k}+\frac{1}{2}-\frac{k}{3}\right)\phi_{j+1} = 0$$

and its solutions of both the uniform and nonuniform grids are also listed in Table 5. Again, we find that the nonuniform grid solution appears to be more accurate.

10. CONCLUSION

In this paper we have attempted, in a rather elementary way, to identify the similarities and differences between the finite difference schemes and the finite element schemes in several aspects. Much work remains in comparing these two powerful methods in a rigorous and conclusive manner.

REFERENCES

1. Adams, R.A. 1975. Sobolev Spaces, Academic Press, New York.

2. Spalding, D.B. 1972. A novel finite difference formulation for differential expressions involving both first and second derivatives, Int. J. Numerical Methods Eng., Vol. 4, pp. 551-559.

3. Zienkiewicz, O.C. and Heinrich, J.C. 1978. The finite element method and convection problems in fluid mechanics, Finite Elements in Fluids, Wiley Interscience, New York, Vol. 3, pp. 1-22.

4. Patankar, S.V. 1980. Numerical Heat Transfer and Fluid Flow, Hemisphere/McGraw-Hill, New York.

5. Shih, T.M. 1982. Numerical Heat Transfer, Hemisphere/McGraw-Hill, New York.

6. Courant, R., Isaacson, E. and Rees, M. 1952. On the solution of nonlinear hyperbolic differential equations by finite differences, Comm. Pure Appl. Math., Vol. 5, p. 243.

7. Gentry, R.A., Martin, R.E. and Daly, B.J. 1966. An Eulerian differencing method for unsteady compressible flow problems, J. of Comp. Phys., Vol. 1, pp. 87-118.

8. Gosman, A.D., Pun, W.M., Runchal, A.K., Spalding, D.B. and Wolfshtein, M. 1969. Heat and Mass Transfer in Recirculating Flows, Academic Press, New York.

9. Roache, P.J. 1972. Computational Fluid Dynamics, Hermosa Press, Albuquerque.

10. Roache, P.J. 1972. On artificial viscosity, J. of Comp. Physics, Vol. 10, pp. 169-184.

11. Leonard, B.P. 1979. A stable and accurate convective modelling procedure based on quadratic upstream interpolation, Comp. Meth. Appl. Mech. & Eng., Vol. 19, pp. 59-98.

12. Patankar, S.V. and Spalding, D.B. 1970. Heat and Mass Transfer in Boundary Layers, Intertext, London.

13. Heinrich, J.C., Huyakorn, P.S., Zienkiewicz, O.C. and Mitchell, A.R. 1977. An "upwind" finite element scheme for two dimensional convective transport equation, Int. J. Num. Methods in Eng., Vol. 11, pp. 131-143.

14. Crandall, S.H. 1956. Engineering Analysis, McGraw-Hill, New York.

15. Gottlieb, D. and Orszag, S.A. 1977. Numerical Analysis of Spectral Methods: Theory and Applications, SIAM, Chap. 9.

16. Rathjen, K.A. 1977. CAVE: A computer code for two-dimensional transient heating analysis of conceptual thermal protection systems for hypersonic vehicles, NASA Contractor Report 2897.

17. Krause, E., Hirschel, E.H. and Kordulla, W. 1976. Fourth order "Mehrstellen"-integration for three-dimensional turbulent boundary layers, Computers and Fluids, Vol. 4, pp. 77-92.

18. Ciment, M., Leventhal, S.H. and Weinberg, B.C. 1978. The operator compact implicit method for parabolic equations, J. of Comp. Physics, Vol. 28, pp. 135-166.

19. Berger, A.E., Soloman, J.M., Ciment, M., Leventhal, S.H. and Weinberg, B.C. 1980. Generalized OCI schemes for boundary layer problems, Math. of Computation, Vol. 35, pp. 695-731.

20. Huebner, K.H. 1975. The Finite Element Method for Engineers, John Wiley & Sons, New York.

An Application of Two-Stage, Two-Level Finite Difference Schemes in Nonlinear Heat Diffusion

PETER C. MEEK and JOHN NORBURY
Oxford University Computing Laboratory
Oxford, England

ABSTRACT

This paper is concerned with four, two-stage, two-level finite difference schemes for approximating the solution of a single nonlinear parabolic partial differential equation. The schemes are derived from second-order Newton schemes and obtain comparable accuracy without having to iterate systems of nonlinear algebraic equations. A convergence proof for one of the schemes is given together with stability restrictions which arise when the diffusion coefficient assumes a separable form. The schemes are compared with, and concluded to be generally better than (with respect to accuracy and stability), some recently published second-order, three-level schemes and a method of lines package.

1. INTRODUCTION

We take as our standard equation the nonlinear heat diffusion equation

$$u_t = K(x,t,u)u_{xx} + S(x,t,u,u_x) \quad , \tag{1}$$

in the region $0 \leqslant x \leqslant 1$, $t \geqslant 0$, with $u(0,t)$, $u(1,t)$ and $u(x,0)$ all prescribed (these boundary conditions can be generalised in the usual way to u_x or a linear combination of u and u_x prescribed at $x = 0$, etc.). We also consider a special energy conserving form of Eq.(1)

$$u_t = (K(x,u)u_x)_x \quad , \tag{2}$$

with the same domain and form of boundary conditions. We assume that Eqs.(1,2) each have a unique solution and that $K(x,t,u)$ and $K(x,u)$ are strictly positive functions.

Many numerical schemes have been suggested for solving equations such as Eq.(1). The particular finite difference schemes that we will suggest perform much better than most others, and never worse than any other, in terms of accuracy and stability.

The relative accuracy of any particular scheme does depend on the problem considered as the numerical evidence in Sec. 3 will show. On balance we suggest that for problems in the form of Eq. (1) the MPC scheme, as described in Eqs. (21, 24), is best (it has unconditional stability and is almost second-order convergent in time, second-order in space, with low values for the actual error constants), while for problems such as those outlined in Eq. (2) the CPC scheme, as described by Eqs. (4,6) following, is best (it has unconditional stability and similar accuracy to the MPC scheme). Note that because of the low values of the error constants these schemes are often much more accurate than fully second-order, in space and time, schemes that are quoted in the literature (Varah [1]).

We use the standard Δx, Δt rectangular mesh in space and time, and denote the finite difference solution $v(i\Delta x, j\Delta t)$ by v_i^j. We assume that

$$\Delta x = 1/N \quad \text{and} \quad \Delta t = T/M, \text{ for integer } M,\ N > 0. \tag{3}$$

The following discretisations of Eq. (2) (where we omit the space subscript unless it is important) will be considered:

Scheme 1 - NPC (Newton predict and correct)

1st Stage

$$\frac{2}{\Delta t}\left(v^{j+\frac{1}{2}} - v^j\right) = \left(K_{v+}^j \left(v^{j+\frac{1}{2}}\right)_{\underline{x}}\right)_{\bar{x}}, \quad i = 1, 2, \ldots, N-1, \tag{4}$$

2nd Stage

$$\frac{1}{\Delta t}\left(v^{j+1} - v^j\right) = \left(K_{v+}^{j+\frac{1}{2}} \left(v^{\frac{1}{2}((j+1)+j)}\right)_{\underline{x}}\right)_{\bar{x}} +$$

$$+ \frac{1}{4\Delta x}\left\{\frac{\partial K}{\partial u}{}_{v+}^{j+\frac{1}{2}}\left(v^{j+\frac{1}{2}}\right)_{\underline{x}}\left(v^{j+\frac{1}{2}}\right)_{t\bar{t}+} - \frac{\partial K}{\partial u}{}_{v-}^{j+\frac{1}{2}}\left(v^{j+\frac{1}{2}}\right)_{\bar{x}}\left(v^{j+\frac{1}{2}}\right)_{t\bar{t}-}\right\},$$

$$i = 1, 2, \ldots, N-1. \tag{5}$$

Scheme 2 - CPC (Conservative predict and correct)

1st Stage as in Eq. (4)

2nd Stage

$$\frac{1}{\Delta t}\left(v^{j+1} - v^j\right) = \left(K_{v+}^{j+\frac{1}{2}}\left(v^{\frac{1}{2}((j+1)+j)}\right)_{\underline{x}}\right)_{\bar{x}}, \quad i = 1, 2, \ldots, N-1. \tag{6}$$

In Eqs. (4-6), we define

$$\left(v^j\right)_{\bar{x}} = \frac{1}{\Delta x}\left(v_i^j - v_{i-1}^j\right), \quad \left(v^{\frac{1}{2}((j+1)+j)}\right)_{\underline{x}} = \frac{1}{2\Delta x}\left(v_{i+1}^{j+1} + v_{i+1}^j - v_i^{j+1} - v_i^j\right),$$

$$\left(v^{j+\frac{1}{2}}\right)_{t\bar{t}\pm} = \left(v_{i\pm1}^{j+1} + v_i^{j+1} - 2v_{i\pm1}^{j+\frac{1}{2}} - 2v_i^{j+\frac{1}{2}} + v_{i\pm1}^j + v_i^j\right),$$

$K_{v\pm}^s = K\left(x_{i\pm\frac{1}{2}}, \frac{1}{2}\left(v_{i\pm1}^s + v_i^s\right)\right)$ and similarly for $\frac{\partial K}{\partial u}{}_{v\pm}^s$.

We use two-stage schemes in Eqs. (4-6) so that we only have to solve systems of linear algebraic equations, by inverting tri-diagonal matrices, at each stage, rather than iterate (repeatedly, which is costly in terms of computing time) systems of nonlinear algebraic equations which arise when we implicitly discretise Eq. (2).

A derivation of Eqs. (4-6) will be given in Sec. 2, together with a similar analysis for Eq. (1). In Sec. 3 we outline some three time-level schemes used by Varah [1], and give details of a method of lines package currently used in the NAG (Numerical Algorithms Group) library. These four schemes are then compared with our schemes, using four specially chosen examples. Finally in Sec. 3, we give numerical evidence of second-order convergence in time for the NPC scheme, as defined in Eqs. (4,5), together with evidence to show that the CPC scheme has an order of convergence between 1.5 and 2 (typically 1.99) in the time-direction. It will be seen from the numerical evidence presented that our schemes have good stability properties, and accuracies which compare favourably with those of all the other schemes outlined in Sec. 3.

In Sec. 4 a convergence proof for the CPC scheme is given. The proof follows the outline given by Douglas and Jones [2] and uses energy estimates which are derived in two appendices. These energy estimates are extensions of those given by Lees [3] and apply to problems in the form of Eq. (2). Finally in Sec. 5 we state stability restrictions, which arise when considering a special form of Eq. (1), with the first stage being either implicit (CPC) or fully explicit.

2. DERIVATION OF THE NPC AND NMPC (NEWTON MODIFIED PREDICT AND CORRECT) SCHEMES

Consider the solution of a system of n nonlinear algebraic equations

$$f_s(\underline{w}) = 0, \quad s = 1, 2, \ldots, n, \tag{7}$$

in the n unknowns

$$\underline{w}^T = (w_1, w_2, \ldots, w_n).$$

Suppose that we try to solve Eq. (7) using Newton's method as follows:

$$\underline{w}^{(r+1)} = \underline{w}^{(r)} - J^{-1}F(\underline{w}^{(r)}), \quad r = 0, 1, 2, \ldots, \tag{8}$$

where $J(\underline{w}^{(r)})$, the Jacobian matrix, is defined by

$$J = \begin{pmatrix} \frac{\delta f_1}{\delta w_1} & \frac{\delta f_1}{\delta w_2} & \cdot & \cdot & \cdot & \frac{\delta f_1}{\delta w_n} \\ \cdot & & & & & \cdot \\ \frac{\delta f_n}{\delta w_1} & \frac{\delta f_n}{\delta w_2} & \cdot & \cdot & \cdot & \frac{\delta f_n}{\delta w_n} \end{pmatrix} \tag{9}$$

Convergence of the sequence of approximations $\underline{w}^{(r)}$, to the true solution $\underline{w}^*$, is well known to be second-order (see Conte & de Boor [4]), provided that $\underline{w}^{(o)}$ is a good enough initial guess and $|J(\underline{w}^{(r)})|$ is nowhere zero in a suitable ball centred at $\underline{w}^*$. It is easy to show that, if $\underline{w}^{(o)}$ is a first-order approximation to $\underline{w}^*$ and J is non-singular (at zero'th order) in a ball centred at $\underline{w}^*$, then one application of Eq. (8) will produce a second-order approximation to $\underline{w}^*$.

Consider the standard Crank-Nicolson discretisation of Eq.(2)

$$\frac{1}{\Delta t}(v^{j+1} - v^j) = (K_{v+}^{\frac{1}{2}((j+1)+j)}(v^{\frac{1}{2}((j+1)+j)})_{\underline{x}})_{\overline{x}}, \quad i=1,2,\ldots,N-1. \quad (10)$$

For ease of notation in the subsequent analysis, we refer to the right-hand side of Eq. (10) as (α). To calculate the Jacobian matrix J, one has to perturb, separately, each of the three unknowns $v_{i\pm1}^{j+1}$ and v_i^{j+1}, in each equation of the form of Eq. (10). Perturbing v_{i+1}^{j+1} to $v_{i+1}^{j+1} + \delta v_{i+1}^{j+1}$, expanding in powers of δv_{i+1}^{j+1} and ignoring terms of $O(\delta v_{i+1}^{j+1})^2$, we have

$$\frac{1}{\Delta t}(v^{j+1} - v^j) = (\alpha) + \{\frac{1}{4\Delta x}\frac{\partial K^+}{\partial u}(v^{\frac{1}{2}((j+1)+j)})_{\underline{x}} +$$

$$+\frac{1}{2(\Delta x)^2}K^{\frac{1}{2}((j+1)+j)}\}\delta v_{i+1}^{j+1} + O(\delta v_{i+1}^{j+1})^2, \quad (11)$$

where $\frac{\partial K^+}{\partial u}$ is evaluated at a point called for by the Mean Value Theorem (a corresponding equation results when perturbing v_{i-1}^{j+1}. Similarly perturbing v_i^{j+1}, we deduce

$$\frac{1}{\Delta t}(v^{j+1} - v^j) = (\alpha) + \left\{\frac{1}{4\Delta x}\left[\frac{\partial K^{++}}{\partial u}(v^{\frac{1}{2}((j+1)+j)})_{\underline{x}} - \frac{\partial K^{--}}{\partial u}(v^{\frac{1}{2}((j+1)+j)})_{\overline{x}}\right]\right.$$

$$\left. - \frac{1}{2(\Delta x)^2}\left[K_{v+}^{\frac{1}{2}((j+1)+j)} + K_{v-}^{\frac{1}{2}((j+1)+j)}\right]\right\}\delta v_i^{j+1} - \delta v_i^{j+1} + O(\delta v_i^{j+1})^2. \quad (12)$$

As mentioned earlier we are, in theory, going to have to iterate Eq. (10). To avoid this (repeated) iteration, we define

$$\underline{v}^{j+1} = \underline{\beta}^{j+1} + \underline{\xi}^{j+1}, \quad (13)$$

where $\underline{\beta}^{j+1}$ is assumed small, actually $O(\Delta t)$ and $\underline{\xi}^{j+1}$ is assumed to be known, first-order approximation to $\underline{v}^{j+1}$. We aim to solve Eq. (10) in the form of Eq. (7) for $\underline{w}^* = \underline{\beta}$. This is accomplished, to $O(\underline{\beta})^2$ if $\underline{\beta}$ is small, by solving

$$\underline{0} = F(\underline{0}) + J(\underline{0})\underline{\beta}. \quad (14)$$

The form of $F(\underline{\beta})$ is given by

$F(\underline{\beta}^{j+1})$ = Left-hand side of Eq.(10) - Right-hand side of Eq.(10), with v_p^{j+1} everywhere replaced by $\beta_p^{j+1} + \xi_p^{j+1}$, for all p.

For clarity in later work we drop the j+1 superscripts. Using Eqs. (10-14) we deduce that solving Eq.(14) is equivalent to solving

$$0 = \xi_i - v_i^j - \frac{\Delta t}{2\Delta x}\{K(x_{i+\frac{1}{2}}, g_i^+)(\xi_i + v_i^j)_x - K(x_{i-\frac{1}{2}}, g_i^-)(\xi_i + v_i^j)_{\bar{x}}\}$$

$$- \frac{\Delta t}{4(\Delta x)^2}\{2K(x_{i-\frac{1}{2}}, g_i^-) - \frac{\Delta x}{2}\frac{\partial K^-}{\partial u}(\xi_i + v_i^j)_{\bar{x}}\}\beta_{i-1} +$$

$$+ \left\{1 - \frac{\Delta t}{4(\Delta x)^2}\left[\frac{\Delta x}{2}\left(\frac{\partial K^{++}}{\partial u}(\xi_i + v_i^j)_{\underline{x}} - \frac{\partial K^{--}}{\partial u}(\xi_i + v_i^j)_{\bar{x}}\right) + - 2(K(x_{i+\frac{1}{2}}, g_i^+) + K(x_{i-\frac{1}{2}}, g_i^-))\right]\right\}\beta_i +$$

$$- \frac{\Delta t}{4(\Delta x)^2}\{2K(x_{i+\frac{1}{2}}, g_i^+) + \frac{\Delta x}{2}\frac{\partial K^+}{\partial u}(\xi_i + v_i^j)_{\underline{x}}\}\beta_{i+1}, \qquad (15)$$

where

$$g_i^{\pm} = \tfrac{1}{4}(\xi_{i\pm1}^{j+1} + v_{i\pm1}^j + \xi_i^{j+1} + v_i^j).$$

Recall that we defined earlier in Eq. (13) $v_i = \beta_i + \xi_i$, for all i. Thus, rewriting Eq.(15) we have

$$v_i^{j+1} - v_i^j = \frac{\Delta t}{2\Delta x}\{K(x_{i+\frac{1}{2}}, g_i^+)(v_i^{j+1} + v_i^j)_{\underline{x}} - K(x_{i-\frac{1}{2}}, g_i^-)(v_i^{j+1} + v_i^j)_{\bar{x}}\}$$

$$+ \frac{\Delta t}{8\Delta x}\{-\frac{\partial K^-}{\partial u}(\xi_i^{j+1} + v_i^j)_{\bar{x}}\beta_{i-1}^{j+1} + \frac{\partial K^{++}}{\partial u}(\xi_i^{j+1} + v_i^j)_{\underline{x}}\beta_i^{j+1} +$$

$$- \frac{\partial K^{--}}{\partial u}(\xi_i^{j+1} + v_i^j)_{\bar{x}}\beta_i^{j+1} + \frac{\partial K^+}{\partial u}(\xi_i^{j+1} + v_i^j)_{\underline{x}}\beta_{i+1}^{j+1}\}. \qquad (16)$$

Up to now we have not defined $\underline{\xi}^{j+1}$, and so we define

$$\underline{\xi}^{j+1} = 2\underline{v}^{j+\frac{1}{2}} - \underline{v}^j, \qquad (17)$$

where $\underline{v}^{j+\frac{1}{2}}$ satisfies

$$\frac{2}{\Delta t}(v^{j+\frac{1}{2}} - v^j) = (K_{v+}^j(v^{j+\frac{1}{2}})_{\underline{x}})_{\bar{x}}, \quad i = 1, 2, \ldots, N-1. \qquad (18)$$

The specific choice of $\underline{\xi}^{j+1}$ in Eq.(17) is made not only to ensure that systems of <u>linear</u> algebraic equations are to be solved at each stage, but also because it can be shown that the scheme given in Eq.(18) is unconditionally stable. Substituting into Eq.(16), for $\underline{\xi}^{j+1}$, and using Eqs.(17,18), we deduce

$$v^{j+1} - v^j = \Delta t (K_{v+}^{j+\frac{1}{2}} (v^{\frac{1}{2}((j+1)+j)})_{\underline{x}})_{\bar{x}} +$$
$$+ \frac{\Delta t}{4\Delta x} \{ - \frac{\partial K^{-}}{\partial u} (v^{j+\frac{1}{2}})_{\bar{x}} \beta_{i-1}^{j+1} + \frac{\partial K^{++}}{\partial u} (v^{j+\frac{1}{2}})_{\underline{x}} \beta_i^{j+1} +$$
$$- \frac{\partial K^{--}}{\partial u} (v^{j+\frac{1}{2}})_{\bar{x}} \beta_i^{j+1} + \frac{\partial K^{+}}{\partial u} (v^{j+\frac{1}{2}})_{\underline{x}} \beta_{i+1}^{j+1} \}. \quad (19)$$

We know that

$$\frac{\delta K^{\pm}}{\delta u} = \frac{\delta K}{\delta u}{}_{v\pm}^{j+\frac{1}{2}} + O(\Delta t) = \frac{\delta K^{\pm\pm}}{\delta u} ,$$

and by ignoring the $O(\Delta t)$ term we are led to the NPC scheme, as defined in Eqs. (4,5).

<u>Remark</u>. β_i^{j+1} is evaluated using Eqs. (13,17) as

$$\beta_i^{j+1} = v_i^{j+1} - \xi_i^{j+1} = v_i^{j+1} - 2v_i^{j+\frac{1}{2}} + v_i^j. \quad (20)$$

NPC is a two-stage, two-level scheme and bears a resemblance to predictor-corrector ideas as used in the case of ordinary differential equations, by Lambert [5] . The ideas of predictor-corrector methods being used to approximate solutions of parabolic partial differential equations were first introduced by Douglas and Jones [2] .

Following a similar analysis for the problem given in Eq.(1), we derive a scheme which we call NMPC (Newton modified predict and correct).

1st Stage

$$\frac{2}{\Delta t} (v^{j+\frac{1}{2}} - v^j) = K(x,t_{j+\frac{1}{2}},v^j)(v^{j+\frac{1}{2}})_{\underline{x}\bar{x}} + S(x,t_{j+\frac{1}{2}},v^j,(v^j)_{\hat{x}}), \quad (21)$$

2nd Stage

$$\frac{1}{\Delta t} (v^{j+1}-v^j) = K(x,t_{j+\frac{1}{2}},v^{j+\frac{1}{2}})(v^{\frac{1}{2}((j+1)+j)})_{\underline{x}\bar{x}} + S(x,t_{j+\frac{1}{2}},v^{j+\frac{1}{2}},(v^{j+\frac{1}{2}})_{\hat{x}})$$
$$+ \{\tfrac{1}{2} \frac{\partial K}{\partial u}{}_{v}^{j+\frac{1}{2}} (v^{j+\frac{1}{2}})_{\underline{x}\bar{x}} + \tfrac{1}{2} \frac{\partial S}{\partial u}{}_{v}^{j+\frac{1}{2}}\}\beta_i^{j+1} +$$
$$+ \tfrac{1}{2} \frac{\partial S}{\partial u_x}{}_{v}^{j+\frac{1}{2}} (\beta_i^{j+1})_{\hat{x}} , \quad (22)$$

$$i = 1,2,\ldots,N-1,$$

where $(v^j)_{\underline{x}\bar{x}} = \frac{1}{(\Delta x)^2} (v_{i+1}^j - 2v_i^j + v_{i-1}^j)$,

$(v^j)_{\hat{x}} = \frac{1}{2\Delta x} (v_{i+1}^j - v_{i-1}^j)$ and $\underline{\beta}^{j+1}$ is as defined in Eq. (20).

In practice the forms of $K(x,t,u)$, $S(x,t,u,u_x)$ and $K(x,u)$

are invariably complicated, and partial differentiation of these quantities can add to the complications. To avoid differentiation of these quantities we consider the following two schemes:

CPC - (simplified NPC)

$$\frac{1}{\Delta t}\left(v^{j+1}-v^{j}\right)=\left(K_{v+}^{j+\frac{1}{2}}\left(v^{\frac{1}{2}((j+1)+j)}\right)_{\underline{x}}\right)_{\bar{x}}, \qquad (23)$$

where $\underline{v}^{j+\frac{1}{2}}$ satisfies Eq. (18).

MPC - (simplified NMPC)

$$\frac{1}{\Delta t}\left(v^{j+1}-v^{j}\right)=K(x,t_{j+\frac{1}{2}},v^{j+\frac{1}{2}})\left(v^{\frac{1}{2}((j+1)+j)}\right)_{\underline{x}}\Big)_{\bar{x}}+$$

$$+\;S\left(x,t_{j+\frac{1}{2}},v^{j+\frac{1}{2}},(v^{j+\frac{1}{2}})_{\hat{x}}\right), \qquad (24)$$

where $\underline{v}^{j+\frac{1}{2}}$ satisfies Eq. (21).

The penalty that we pay for using Eqs. (23,24), instead of Eqs. (5,22), is that convergence in the time-direction is no longer second-order (in practice it is usually $O(\Delta t)^{2-\varepsilon}$ for some small $\varepsilon > 0$). A convergence proof for the MPC scheme is given in Meek and Norbury [6] , where convergence in time is shown to be at least at a rate of $O(\Delta t)^{3/2}$. In practice the CPC and MPC schemes are sometimes better, in terms of accuracy of approximation, than the corresponding NPC and NMPC schemes. This is explained by considering local truncation errors for each scheme. We substitute the exact solution $u(x,t)$ of the governing partial differential equation given in Eq. (1) or Eq. (2), into the appropriate difference equation. We expand in Taylor Series centred at (x_i, t_j) and equate coefficients of like powers of Δx and Δt. It is found that the local truncation error at the first stage of each scheme is $O((\Delta x)^2+\Delta t)$ and at the second stage it is $O((\Delta x)^2+(\Delta t)^2)$. Hence as the mesh-lengths tend to zero, so do the local truncation errors (provided the appropriate derivatives are uniformly bounded), and, by definition, we have consistency of each scheme. For certain problems the actual error constants (multiplying the mesh-lengths) in the truncation errors for the CPC and MPC schemes are smaller than the corresponding ones for the NPC and NMPC schemes, and hence higher accuracy is attained. Examples to illustrate this point are given in Sec. 3.

3. A COMPARISON WITH SOME OTHER FINITE DIFFERENCE SCHEMES

First we describe four other schemes with which to compare our schemes against. We then compare the schemes with our schemes, using four examples with known exact solutions. Finally we give numerical evidence of second-order time convergence for the NPC scheme described in Sec. 2 and corresponding evidence to show that the CPC scheme is not quite second-order convergent in time.

The main idea of using our schemes is to avoid the (repeated) iteration of systems of nonlinear algebraic equations, which can be costly in terms of computing time. We have compared our schemes with typical finite element, Galerkin, collocation and finite difference methods. For the sort of problem we have in mind, where the nonlinearity is in the diffusion space-derivative terms, finite difference methods are generally superior, and so we consider examples of these, and their performances on our "test problems". Three of the schemes which we compare our schemes against are given in Varah [1] . Two of these schemes are special cases of the following general three time-level finite difference scheme:

$$\frac{1}{\Delta t}\left((\theta+\tfrac{1}{2})v_i^{j+1} - 2\theta v_i^j + (\theta-\tfrac{1}{2})v_i^{j-1}\right) = K(x_i,t_j,b(v_i))(c(v_i))_{\underline{x}\bar{x}} + \\ + S(x_i,t_j,b(v_i),\ (b(v_i))_{\hat{x}}), \tag{25}$$

where $b(v_i) = -\theta v_i^{j-1} + (1+\theta)v_i^j$ and $c(v_i) = \theta v_i^{j+1} + (1-\theta)v_i^j$.

The two special cases that we consider are:

(a) Extrapolated Crank-Nicolson (ECN), (26)

which is defined by taking $\theta=\frac{1}{2}$ in Eq. (25), and

(b) Extrapolated Gear (EGEAR), (27)

which is defined by taking $\theta=1$ in Eq. (25).

The third scheme, again a three time-level scheme, is defined by

$$\frac{1}{2\Delta t}(v_i^{j+1}-v_i^{j-1}) = K(x_i,t_j,v_i^j)\left(v^{\frac{1}{3}((j+1)+j+(j-1))}\right)_{\underline{x}\bar{x}} + \\ + S(x_i,t_j,v_i^j,\ (v_i^j)_{\hat{x}}), \tag{28}$$

and is referred to as the Averaged Crank-Nicolson scheme (AVCN). All three schemes are second-order accurate in both space and time. Convergence proofs for Eqs. (26,28) are given by Lees [7,8] .

As a further test of our schemes we compare them with a time-method of lines package (DO3PGF). This package appears in mark 8 of the NAG library. It reduces the original partial differential equation to a system of coupled ordinary differential equations in time by discretising in space only. These ordinary differential equations are then solved using an updated version of Gear's variable-step, variable-order, ordinary differential equation package. Mesh-points in space are user specified and are chosen to correspond exactly with those used in all other schemes. The time-step Δt is chosen by the routine in order to satisfy local error tolerances in the time-direction specified by the user (the error in space is not controlled).

The four examples, two smooth, one with a rapid time-variation and one with a rapid space variation, are described as follows:

Example 1.

$$u_t = (K(x,u)u_x)_x, \quad 0\leqslant x\leqslant 1, \quad 0.5\leqslant t\leqslant 4.5, \tag{29}$$

where

$$K(x,u) = \frac{16}{5\pi^2} \frac{(\sin^2((\pi/4)(x+1))-u^2)^{\frac{1}{2}}}{u} .$$

(We take $0<t<5\pi/2$ to ensure $0<K(x,u)<\infty$). An exact solution is given by

$$u = \cos(t/5)\sin((\pi/4)(x+1)). \tag{30}$$

Example 2 (a form of the percolation equation).

$$u_t = (uu_x)_x \ , \quad 0\leqslant x\leqslant 1, \quad 0\leqslant t\leqslant 3.8. \tag{31}$$

An exact solution (with a finite time "blow-up") is given by

$$u = (x+2)^2/(6(4-t)) \quad . \tag{32}$$

Example 3 (a form of Burgers' equation).

$$u_t = \nu u_{xx} - uu_x, \quad 0\leqslant x\leqslant 1, \quad 0\leqslant t\leqslant 5, \tag{33}$$

where ν is a positive constant. An exact solution, with a rapid space-variation, is given by

$$u = 1 - \frac{(0.9r_1 + 0.5r_2)}{(r_1 + r_2 + r_3)} \ , \tag{34}$$

where

$$r_1 = \exp(-((x-\tfrac{1}{2})/20\nu)-(99t/400\nu)),$$

$$r_2 = \exp(-((x-\tfrac{1}{2})/4\nu)-(3t/16\nu))$$

and

$$r_3 = \exp(-((x-\tfrac{3}{8})/2\nu)).$$

For this example we take $\nu = 0.01$.

Example 4.

$$u_t = ((2/3)(x+1)^{\frac{5}{2}} u^{-\frac{1}{4}}u_x)_x, \quad 0\leqslant x\leqslant 1, \quad 0.5\leqslant t\leqslant 2.5. \tag{35}$$

An exact solution is given by

$$u = t^4(x+1)^2. \tag{36}$$

This example was specifically chosen to show that for certain problems the MPC scheme is more accurate than the NMPC scheme. Similarly it is possible to construct examples for which the NPC scheme is more accurate than the CPC scheme (see Meek & Norbury

[6]).

In Tables 1-4 below, we compare absolute errors between exact and computed solutions for each scheme, using $|| \quad ||_\infty$ at fixed points im time.

Remark 1. Errors are expressed in the form 0.a-b, which is used to represent $0.a*10^{-b}$.

Remark 2. In each application of the method of lines package we specify a tolerance of 10^{-5}, since this is the approximate accuracy attained using all other schemes.

Finally in this section we give numerical evidence to show that the NPC scheme is second-order convergent in time. To do this we consider the following example:

Example 5.

$$u_t = (K(x,u)u_x)_x, \quad 0 \leq x \leq 1, \quad 0 \leq t \leq 5, \tag{37}$$

where

$$K(x,u) = e^x(2x+e^{-x})\left(1+\frac{(e^{-x}-2)}{u}\right).$$

An exact solution of Eq.(37) is given by

$$u = (1+e^t)(2-e^{-x}). \tag{38}$$

We choose Δt much larger than Δx, so that the major contribution to the truncation errors arising from the use of our discretisation schemes, comes from the $O(\Delta t)$ and $O(\Delta t)^2$ terms appearing in the expressions given earlier. We proceed by repeatedly halving Δx and Δt and observe a factor of 4 decrease in the magnitude of the errors, between successive approximations at fixed points in space and time. Results are given in Table 5, where absolute errors at specific mesh-points are quoted. A corresponding set of results for the CPC scheme, are given in Table 6, and these show that the CPC scheme is almost second-order convergent in time.

Remark 3. For both the NPC and CPC schemes we take, initially, $\Delta x=1/50$ and $\Delta t=10\Delta x$. We then halve these values three times recording results at each halving in the Tables below. Results in Tables 5 and 6 are given in the form of absolute errors at the mesh-point $x=\frac{1}{2}$ for chosen time-levels.

From the results given in Tables 1-4 we conclude that our schemes compare favourably with all other schemes considered in terms of accuracy and stability. Results in Table 5 reveal second-order convergence in time for the NPC scheme. Similarly results given in Table 6 show that the order of convergence in time for the CPC scheme is better than 3/2 (factor of decrease then given as $8^{\frac{1}{2}}$), but not quite 2 (factor of 4 decrease of the errors when we halve mesh-lengths, as with the NPC scheme). However, note that at "practical" values of $\Delta x=1/50$ to $\Delta x=1/100$ the ratios for the NPC and CPC schemes are virtually indistinguishable. As mentioned earlier, sometimes, because of smaller error constants, the CPC scheme can be more accurate than the NPC scheme even though its order of convergence, in time, is not as high. This phenomenon is clearly shown in Tables 1 and 2 (where we can also see that the NMPC scheme is more accurate than the MPC scheme because of smaller error constants).

Table 1(Example 1) $\Delta x=1/16$, $\Delta t=1/32$.

Scheme / time t =	AVCN	ECN	EGEAR	D03PGF	NPC	CPC	MPC	NMPC
1.0	0.1076-3	0.1139-3	0.1264-3	0.1380-3	0.2694-3	0.2525-3	0.1064-3	0.9966-4
1.5	0.1239-3	0.1353-3	0.1560-3	0.3082-4	0.3027-3	0.2975-3	0.1235-3	0.1166-3
2.0	0.1073-3	0.1180-3	0.1372-3	0.2129-3	0.2414-3	0.2396-3	0.1081-3	0.1020-3
2.5	0.7924-4	0.8722-4	0.1019-3	0.8000-5	0.1660-3	0.1611-3	0.8047-4	0.7619-4
3.0	0.5430-4	0.5950-4	0.6929-4	0.5281-5	0.1018-3	0.1016-3	0.5554-4	0.5269-4
3.5	0.3642-4	0.3963-4	0.4597-4	0.4677-5	0.5756-4	0.5711-4	0.3755-4	0.3579-4
4.0	0.2551-4	0.2747-4	0.3162-4	0.7231-4	0.3200-4	0.3121-4	0.2653-4	0.2544-4
4.5	0.1907-4	0.2032-4	0.2317-4	0.9870-5	0.1909-4	0.1752-4	0.2002-4	0.1935-4

Table 2 (Example 2) $\Delta x = \Delta t = 1/20$.

Scheme / time t =	AVCN	ECN	EGEAR	D03PGF	NPC	CPC	MPC	NMPC
0.2	0.1681-5	0.2359-5	0.9868-5	0.4717-4	0.1079-5	0.6664-6	0.7429-6	0.4243-6
0.6	0.4273-5	0.7310-5	0.6656-5	0.1711-4	0.3159-5	0.1852-5	0.2034-5	0.1322-5
1.0	0.6887-5	0.1210-4	0.1115-4	0.8581-4	0.4666-5	0.2491-5	0.3285-5	0.2194-5
1.4	0.1077-4	0.1898-4	0.1748-4	0.3357-5	0.6422-5	0.2994-5	0.5120-5	0.3456-5
1.8	0.1780-4	0.3127-4	0.2872-4	0.1217-4	0.9256-5	0.3570-5	0.8404-5	0.5727-5
2.2	0.3249-4	0.5666-4	0.5177-4	0.1527-4	0.1477-4	0.4369-5	0.1515-4	0.1046-4
2.6	0.6896-4	0.1189-3	0.1078-3	0.9278-5	0.2776-4	0.5619-5	0.3153-4	0.2224-4
3.0	0.1887-3	0.3189-3	0.2852-3	0.1204-3	0.6861-4	0.7866-5	0.8333-4	0.6104-4
3.4	0.8643-3	0.1400-2	0.1217-2	0.3596-4	0.2933-3	0.1311-4	0.3546-3	0.2826-3
3.8	0.2094-1	0.2935-1	0.2297-1	0.7536-4	0.7235-2	0.3933-4	0.6962-2	0.7476-2

Table 3 (Example 3) (CPC & NPC not applicable), $\Delta t=\Delta x=1/10$.

Scheme / time t =	AVCN	ECN	EGEAR	DO3PGF	MPC	NMPC
1.0	0.5269	0.8788	0.5801	0.8912	0.4253	0.3889
2.0	0.1905	0.2680+2	0.8464+2	0.8441	0.9750-1	0.4900-1
3.0	METHODS BECOME UNSTABLE			0.5746	0.3786-1	0.5969-2
4.0				0.2961-1	0.1294-1	0.1452-2

Note that this example is not used for accuracy considerations, but to show the effect of stability restrictions on the numerical solutions.

Table 4 (Example 4) $\Delta x=1/20$; $\Delta t=\Delta x/2$.

Scheme / time t =	AVCN	ECN	EGEAR	DO3PGF	NPC	CPC	MPC	NMPC
1.00	0.1346-3	0.6306-3	0.1123-2	0.1114-3	0.3965-3	0.4354-3	0.9333-4	0.3544-3
1.25	0.2109-3	0.9942-3	0.1783-2	0.1072-3	0.6563-3	0.6951-3	0.1438-3	0.5537-3
1.50	0.3037-3	0.1440-2	0.2596-2	0.4329-3	0.1010-2	0.1039-2	0.2045-3	0.7974-3
2.00	0.5400-3	0.2578-2	0.4676-2	0.1323-2	0.2089-2	0.2067-2	0.3562-3	0.1418-2
2.25	0.6835-3	0.3271-2	0.5944-2	0.2484-2	0.2869-2	0.2807-2	0.4471-3	0.1794-2
2.50	0.8438-3	0.4045-2	0.7364-2	0.3749-2	0.3853-2	0.3738-2	0.5480-3	0.2259-2

Table 5 (NPC ; $\Delta t=10x$)

time t =	$\Delta x=1/50$	Ratio	$\Delta x=1/100$	Ratio	$\Delta x=1/200$	Ratio	$\Delta x=1/400$
0.4	0.5317-3	3.883	0.1337-3	4.023	0.3320-4	4.000	0.8300-5
0.8	0.6896-3	3.980	0.1714-3	4.000	0.4289-4	3.997	0.1073-4
1.2	0.9150-3	3.987	0.2285-3	3.994	0.5726-4	3.998	0.1432-4
1.6	0.=254-2	3.986	0.3142-3	3.993	0.7872-4	3.998	0.1969-4
2.0	0.1763-2	3.985	0.4423-3	3.993	0.1108-3	3.998	0.2771-4
2.4	0.2524-2	3.985	0.6335-3	3.994	0.1586-3	3.998	0.3967-4
2.8	0.3660-2	3.985	0.9188-3	3.995	0.2300-3	3.999	0.5752-4
3.2	0.5356-2	3.986	0.1345-2	3.995	0.3365-3	3.999	0.8415-4
3.6	0.7887-2	3.986	0.1980-2	3.996	0.4954-3	3.999	0.1239-3
4.0	0.1166-1	3.987	0.2927-2	3.996	0.7324-3	3.999	0.1832-3
4.4	0.1730-1	3.987	0.4340-2	3.997	0.1086-2	3.999	0.2716-3
4.8	0.2571-1	3.988	0.6449-2	3.997	0.1614-2	3.999	0.4035-3
5.0	0.3135-1	3.988	0.7865-2	3.997	0.1968-2	3.999	0.4921-3

Table 6 (CPC ; $\Delta t=10\Delta x$.)

time t =	$\Delta x=1/50$	Ratio	$\Delta x=1/100$	Ratio	$\Delta x=1/200$	Ratio	$\Delta x=1/400$
0.4	0.2114-3	3.850	0.5511-4	3.910	0.1439-4	3.843	0.3729-5
0.8	0.3790-3	3.924	0.9916-4	3.882	0.2614-4	3.821	0.6819-5
1.2	0.6160-3	3.944	0.1604-3	3.898	0.4201-4	3.845	0.1093-4
1.6	0.9636-3	3.957	0.2486-3	3.922	0.6445-4	3.878	0.1666-4
2.0	0.1477-2	3.967	0.3781-3	3.943	0.9710-4	3.910	0.2491-4
2.4	0.2242-2	3.974	0.5701-3	3.959	0.1453-3	3.935	0.3702-4
2.8	0.3381-2	3.978	0.8558-3	3.971	0.2169-3	3.955	0.5496-4
3.2	0.5079-2	3.981	0.1282-2	3.979	0.3235-3	3.968	0.8165-4
3.6	0.7612-2	3.984	0.1917-2	3.985	0.4824-3	3.978	0.1214-3
4.0	0.1139-1	3.985	0.2864-2	3.989	0.7195-3	3.985	0.1807-3
4.4	0.1702-1	3.986	0.4278-2	3.992	0.1073-2	3.990	0.2691-3
4.8	0.2543-1	3.987	0.6387-2	3.993	0.1601-2	3.993	0.4011-3
5.0	0.3107-1	3.987	0.7803-2	3.994	0.1955-2	3.993	0.4896-3

4. CONVERGENCE OF THE CPC SCHEME

For the convergence proof that follows we assume that a solution of Eq.(2) exists and has bounded fourth derivatives in $0 \leq x \leq 1$, $0 < t \leq T$. Moreover, we assume that $K(x,u)$ has continuous derivatives with respect to x and u, and that all second derivatives are uniformly bounded. It follows from these hypotheses that u satisfies Eq.(4) with a local error that is $O((\Delta x)^2+\Delta t)$, and Eq.(6) with a local error that is $O((\Delta x)^2+(\Delta t)^2)$.

Define

$$z_i^j = u_i^j - v_i^j \text{ , for all } i,j, \tag{39}$$

to be the error between u, the exact solution of the partial differential equation, and v, the exact solution of the corresponding difference equation. From Eqs.(4,6), using the assumed boundedness of the appropriate derivatives, we deduce

1st Stage

$$\frac{2}{\Delta t}(u^{j+\frac{1}{2}}-u^j) = (K^j_{u+}(u^{j+\frac{1}{2}})_{\underline{x}})_{\bar{x}} + O((\Delta x)^2+\Delta t), \tag{40}$$

2nd Stage

$$\frac{1}{\Delta t}(u^{j+1}-u^j) = (K^{j+\frac{1}{2}}_{u+}(u^{\frac{1}{2}((j+1)+j)})_{\underline{x}})_{\bar{x}} + O((\Delta x)^2 + (\Delta t)^2), \tag{41}$$

$$i = 1,2,\ldots,N-1.$$

Subtracting Eq.(6) from Eq.(41) and using Eq.(39), we deduce

$$\frac{1}{\Delta t}(z^{j+1}-z^j) = (K^{j+\frac{1}{2}}_{v+}(z^{\frac{1}{2}((j+1)+j)})_{\underline{x}})_{\bar{x}} + \tfrac{1}{2}\{\frac{\partial K}{\partial u}u_{xx} + \frac{\partial K}{\partial u}{}_x u_x\}z^{j+\frac{1}{2}} + $$

$$+ \tfrac{1}{2}\frac{\partial K}{\partial u}u_x(z^{j+\frac{1}{2}})_{\hat{x}} + O((\Delta x)^2 + (\Delta t)^2), \tag{42}$$

where $\frac{\delta K}{\delta u}$, $\frac{\delta K}{\delta u}{}_x$, u_{xx} and u_x are evaluated at points called for by the Mean Value Theorem, and

$$K_x = \frac{\delta K}{\delta u}u_x + \frac{\delta K}{\delta x} = \frac{dK}{dx} .$$

Rewriting Eq.(42), we have

$$\frac{1}{\Delta t}(z^{j+1}-z^j) = (K^{j+\frac{1}{2}}_{v+}(z^{\frac{1}{2}((j+1)+j)})_{\underline{x}})_{\bar{x}} + G^{j+1}, \tag{43}$$

where

$$|G^{j+1}| \leq L|z^{j+\frac{1}{2}}| + \widetilde{L}|(z^{j+\frac{1}{2}})_{\hat{x}}| + O((\Delta x)^2 + (\Delta t)^2), \qquad (44)$$

L and $\widetilde{L}$ being constants, dependent on the assumed boundedness of the appropriate derivatives. We introduce norms appropriate to the functions defined on the finite difference grid $R_{\Delta x,\Delta t}$ ($R_{\Delta x,\Delta t}$ is the rectangular mesh determined by the intersection of the grid lines $x=i\Delta x$ $(i=0,1,2,...,N)$, $t=j\Delta t$ $(j=0,1,2,...,M)$).

$$(||\phi||^j)^2 = \Delta x \sum_{\substack{i=1\\ t=j\Delta t}}^{N-1} (\phi_i^j)^2 ,$$

$$(||\phi||_1^j)^2 = \Delta x \sum_{\substack{i=1\\ t=j\Delta t}}^{N} (\phi_i^j)^2 . \qquad (45)$$

Taking norms in Eq.(44) and using the Schwarz inequality, we deduce that

$$(||G||^{j+1})^2 \leq L_1((||z||^{j+\frac{1}{2}})^2+(||z_{\hat{x}}||^{j+\frac{1}{2}})^2)+O(((\Delta x)^2+(\Delta t)^2)^2). \qquad (46)$$

It was shown, Lees [3], that

$$(||\phi||^j) \leq \tfrac{1}{2}(||\phi_{\bar{x}}||_1^j),$$

and

$$(||\phi_{\hat{x}}||^j) \leq (||\phi_{\bar{x}}||_1^j). \qquad (47)$$

Using Eq.(47) and an energy estimate, given in the corollary of Appendix 2, we deduce that

$$(||G||^{j+1})^2 \leq L_2 \, (||z_{\bar{x}}||_1^j)^2+O(\Delta t((\Delta x)^2+\Delta t)^2)+O(((\Delta x)^2+(\Delta t)^2)^2),$$

$$= L_2(||z_{\bar{x}}||_1^j)^2+O((\Delta x)^4+(\Delta t)^3). \qquad (48)$$

Applying an energy estimate, given in Appendix 1, to Eq.(43), we have by using Eq.(48)

$$(||z_{\bar{x}}||_1^{j+1})^2 \leq L_3\sum_{1}^{j+1} \Delta t(||G||^r)^2,$$

$$\leq L_4\sum_{r=0}^{j} \Delta t\{(||z_{\bar{x}}||_1^r) + O((\Delta x)^4+(\Delta t)^3)\}. \qquad (49)$$

Using the discrete Gronwall Lemma (Lees [3]) in Eq.(49), we obtain

$$(||z||^{j+1})^2 \leq \tfrac{1}{4}(||z_{\bar{x}}||_1^{j+1})^2 \leq S\,\exp(L_4\Delta t(j+1)). \qquad (50)$$

Since $(j+1)\Delta t \leq T$, we deduce

$$4(||z||^{j+1})^2 \leq (||z_{\bar{x}}||_1^{j+1})^2 \leq 4S\,\exp(L_4 T), \qquad (51)$$

where

$$4S = L_4 \Delta t \sum_{r=0}^{j} P((\Delta x)^4 + (\Delta t)^3), \text{ constant } P,$$

$$= L_5 T((\Delta x)^4 + (\Delta t)^3).$$

It is shown, in Appendix 3, that

$$(||z||_\infty) = \max_{i,j} |u_i^j - v_i^j| = \max_{i,j} |z_i^j| \leq \tfrac{1}{2}\max_j (||z_{\bar{x}}||_1^j), \tag{52}$$

Using Eq.(52) in Eq.(51), we deduce

$$||z||_\infty = O((\Delta x)^2 + (\Delta t)^{3/2}),$$

and we have proved convergence, in the infinity norm, of the CPC scheme.

A convergence proof for the MPC scheme is more complicated, but follows the same reasoning, and will appear in Meek and Norbury [6].

5. STABILITY FOR A SPECIAL KIND OF EQUATION

The stability analysis given in this section is an extension of the work by Douglas [9]. The analysis only applies to an equation in the form:

$$r(x,t,u)u_t = (K(x,t,u)u_x)_x + Q(x,t,u), \tag{53}$$

where $K(x,t,u)$ is a separable function

$$K(x,t,u) = P_1(x,t)\ P_2(u). \tag{54}$$

Define

$$\omega = \int^u P_2(z)\, dz,$$

so that Eq.(53) transforms into

$$r_1(x,t,\omega)\omega_t = (P_1(x,t)\omega_x)_x + Q_1(x,t,\omega). \tag{55}$$

Douglas [9] concludes that, by using Eq.(6) suitably adjusted to cope with Eq.(55), but with a <u>fully explicit</u> 1st Stage, then stability is restricted by

$$\Delta t/\Delta x < (\min_{x,t,\omega} r_1)^{\frac{1}{2}} (\max_{x,t,\omega} |a| P_1)^{-\frac{1}{2}}, \tag{56}$$

where

$$a = \frac{-1}{r_1}\left(\frac{\partial Q_1}{\partial \omega} + \frac{\partial r_1}{\partial \omega}\frac{\partial \omega}{\partial t}\right).$$

If we use the original 1st Stage for Eq.(6) which is given in Eq.(4) then, following a similar analysis, we deduce unconditional stability for the CPC scheme. To give numerical evidence to support this theory, we consider the following example:

Example 6.

$$u_t = ((1/6)(x+1)^{\frac{1}{2}}u^{\frac{1}{2}}u_x)_x, \quad 0\leqslant x\leqslant 1, \quad 0\leqslant t\leqslant 3. \tag{57}$$

An exact solution is given by

$$u = (x+1)^3(4-t)^{-2}. \tag{58}$$

From Eq.(56), we deduce that

$$a = \frac{1}{3\omega}\frac{\partial\omega}{\partial t} = \frac{3}{2(4-t)} \quad \text{and} \quad \frac{\Delta t}{\Delta x} < 1.2247, \tag{59}$$

and that if we integrate as far as $t = T^* < 4$, then stability is restricted by

$$\Delta t/\Delta x < 1.2247(4-T^*). \tag{60}$$

We take $\Delta x = 1/320$ and vary the ratio $\Delta t/\Delta x$, with results as shown below in Tables 7 and 8.

Remark. $\|\ \|_\infty$ of errors at specific time-levels is quoted.

Table 7 (Eq.(6) with a fully explicit 1st Stage)

Δt/Δx / time t=T*	1	2	4	Douglas bound 0⩽t⩽3	Bound for t⩽T*
0.2	0.4727-7	0.4068-7	0.3962-7	1.2247	4.6540
0.4	0.9497-7	0.8236-7	0.7803-7	"	4.4091
0.6	0.1451-6	0.1253-6	0.1679-6	"	4.1641
0.8	0.1979-6	0.1691-6	0.3424-6	"	3.9192
1.0	0.2544-6	0.2139-6	0.4361-1	"	3.6742
1.2	0.3162-6	0.2602-6	-	"	3.4293
1.4	0.3858-6	0.3082-6	-	"	3.1843
1.6	0.4663-6	0.3579-6	-	"	2.9394
1.8	0.5623-6	0.4096-6	-	"	2.6944
2.0	0.6796-6	0.5462-5	-	"	2.4495
2.2	0.8268-6	0.2140-3	-	"	2.2045
2.4	0.1015-5	0.7674-1	-	"	1.9596
2.6	0.1257-5	-	-	"	1.7146
2.8	0.1559-5	-	-	"	1.4697
3.0	0.1885-5	-	-	"	1.2247

- denotes values > $0.9*10^1$.

Table 8 (Eq.(6), with the original 1st Stage, Eq.(4).)

$\Delta t/\Delta x$ / time t =	1	8	32	128
0.4	0.1124-6	0.9312-6	0.1237-4	0.1691-3
0.8	0.2374-6	0.2105-5	0.2851-4	0.3958-3
1.2	0.3930-6	0.4001-5	0.5503-4	0.7589-3
1.6	0.6155-6	0.7597-5	0.1059-3	0.1448-2
2.0	0.9938-6	0.1562-4	0.2198-3	0.2966-2
2.4	0.1785-5	0.3732-4	0.5280-3	0.6977-2
2.8	0.3993-5	0.1148-3	0.1622-2	0.2065-1

Remark. Note that the penalty for having an unconditionally stable scheme is a slight loss of accuracy when $\Delta t = \Delta x$.

6. CONCLUSION

We have seen in Sec.3 that our four schemes compare favourably with some currently used finite difference schemes, including a method of lines. In three of the four "test examples" considered at least one of our schemes is more accurate than all other schemes mentioned. Stability properties are very good and in practice it has not been possible to "blow-up" any of our schemes, provided that $K(x,t,u)$ in Eq.(1) and $K(x,u)$ in Eq.(2) is nonlinear.

As noted earlier, the slight loss in the order of convergence of the CPC and MPC schemes compared to the NPC and NMPC schemes, does not necessarily mean a similar loss in accuracy. The major advantage, in terms of computing time, is that all four of our schemes avoid the (repeated) iteration of systems of nonlinear algebraic equations, while they still attain sufficiently high accuracy. If estimates of the derivatives of $u, K(x,t,u)$, $S(x,t,u,u_x)$ and $u, K(x,u)$ in Eqs. (1,2) are available, then the choice of which of our schemes to use is influenced by the error constants appearing in the local truncation errors. For ease of practical implementation we would recommend use of the CPC and MPC schemes. The CPC scheme is only applicable, but is particularly effective, when the governing partial differential equation is in an energy conserving form.

The CPC and MPC schemes have been extended easily (together with their convergence proofs) to two-dimensional problems, and also to approximate Eq.(2) with discontinuous $K(x,u)$ in layered media.

ACKNOWLEDGEMENTS

P.C. Meek would like to thank the Science and Engineering Research Council for supplying the grant for his research work and also for subsidising his trip to America to present this paper. J. Norbury would like to thank the Central Electricity Generating Board for funding his research fellowship in Oxford.

REFERENCES

1. Varah, J.M. 1980. Stability restrictions on second-order three-level finite difference schemes for parabolic equations. SIAM J. Numer. Anal., Vol.17, pp.300-309.

2. Douglas, J.Jr. and Jones, B.F. 1963. Predictor-Corrector methods for nonlinear parabolic differential equations. J.Soc.Ind.Appl.Math., Vol. 11, pp. 195-204.

3. Lees, M. 1959. Approximate solutions of parabolic equations. J.Soc.Ind.Appl.Math., Vol. 7, pp. 167-183.

4. Conte, S.D. and de Boor, C. 1972. Elementary Numerical Analysis. McGraw-Hill, New York, pp. 58-61.

5. Lambert, J.D. 1973. Computational Methods in Ordinary Differential Equations. Wiley, New York, pp. 85-88.

6. Meek, P.C. and Norbury, J. Two-stage, two-level finite difference schemes for nonlinear parabolic partial differential equations, to appear in I.M.A. Journal of Numerical Analysis.

7. Lees, M. 1966. A linear, three-level difference scheme for quasi-linear parabolic equations. Math. Comp., Vol. 20, pp. 516-522.

8. Lees, M. 1967. An extrapolated Crank-Nicolson scheme for quasi-linear parabolic equations. Nonlinear Partial Differential Equations. Ames, W.F. (ed), Academic Press, New York, pp. 193-203.

9. Douglas, J. Jr. 1959. The application of stability analysis in the numerical solution of quasi-linear parabolic differential equations. Trans. Amer. Math. Soc., Vol. 89, pp. 484-518.

APPENDIX 1 (AN ENERGY ESTIMATE).

Lemma 1 Let ϕ be a solution of the difference equation

$$\phi_{\bar{t}}(x,t) \equiv \frac{1}{\Delta t}(\phi(x,t)-\phi(x,t-\Delta t)) = (D(x,t,\phi)\phi_{\underline{x}}(x,t))_{\bar{x}} + G(x,t,\phi), \tag{61}$$

in $R_{\Delta x,\Delta t}$.

We assume that $D_* = \min_{x,t,\phi} D(x,t,\phi) > 0$ and that $\left|\frac{dD}{dx}\right| \leq \tilde{A}$. If ϕ vanishes on x=0, x=1 and t=0, then there exists a constant S, depending only on $T, D_*, \tilde{A}$ and $D^* = \max_{x,t,\phi} D(x,t,\phi)$, such that

$$(||\phi_{\bar{x}}||_1^m)^2 \leq S \sum_{r=1}^{m} \Delta t(||G||^r)^2, \tag{62}$$

for all m such that $0 \leq m \leq M$.

Proof

Since

$$(D\phi_{\underline{x}})_{\bar{x}} = D\phi_{\underline{x}\bar{x}} + \frac{dD}{dx}\phi_{\hat{x}}, \tag{63}$$

Eq. (61) can be written in the form

$$F\phi_{\bar{t}} = \phi_{\underline{x}\bar{x}} + \bar{G}, \tag{64}$$

where

$$F = \frac{1}{D} > 0 \quad \text{and} \quad \bar{G} = \frac{1}{D}\left(G + \frac{dD}{dx}\phi_{\hat{x}}\right). \tag{65}$$

Multiplying Eq. (64) through by $\Delta x \Delta t \phi_{\bar{t}}$ and summing over all interior mesh-points of $R_{\Delta x,\Delta t}$, we obtain

$$\Delta x\Delta t \sum_{R_{\Delta x,\Delta t}} \phi_{\bar{t}}\bar{G} = \Delta x\Delta t \sum_{R_{\Delta x,\Delta t}} F(\phi_{\bar{t}})^2 - \Delta x\Delta t \sum_{R_{\Delta x,\Delta t}} \phi_{\bar{t}}\phi_{\underline{x}\bar{x}}. \tag{66}$$

Since ϕ vanishes on the boundary, $\phi_{\bar{t}}$ vanishes on x=1. Therefore, we do not alter the value of the second summation on the right-hand side of Eq.(66) if we extend the region of summation to $H_{\Delta x,\Delta t} = R_{\Delta x,\Delta t} \cup (1, j\Delta t)$, j=1,2,...,M. Hence Eq.(66) becomes

$$\Delta x\Delta t \sum_{R_{\Delta x,\Delta t}} \phi_{\bar{t}}\bar{G} = \Delta x\Delta t \sum_{R_{\Delta x,\Delta t}} F(\phi_{\bar{t}})^2 - \Delta x\Delta t \sum_{H_{\Delta x,\Delta t}} \phi_{\bar{t}}\phi_{\underline{x}\bar{x}}. \tag{67}$$

It is easily verified that

$$\phi_{\bar{t}}\phi_{\underline{x}\bar{x}} = (\phi_{\bar{t}}\phi_{\underline{x}})_{\bar{x}} - \tfrac{1}{2}(\phi_{\bar{x}}^2)_{\bar{t}} - \tfrac{1}{2}\Delta t(\phi_{\bar{x}\bar{t}})^2. \tag{68}$$

Using Eq.(68) in Eq.(67), we deduce

$$\Delta x\Delta t \sum_{R_{\Delta x,\Delta t}} \phi_{\bar{t}}\bar{G} = \Delta x\Delta t \sum_{R_{\Delta x,\Delta t}} F(\phi_{\bar{t}})^2 - \Delta x\Delta t \sum_{H_{\Delta x,\Delta t}} (\phi_{\bar{t}}\phi_{\underline{x}})_{\bar{x}} + $$
$$+ \tfrac{1}{2}\Delta x\Delta t \sum_{H_{\Delta x,\Delta t}} (\phi_{\bar{x}}^2)_{\bar{t}} + \tfrac{1}{2}\Delta x(\Delta t)^2 \sum_{H_{\Delta x,\Delta t}} (\phi_{\bar{x}\bar{t}})^2. \tag{69}$$

Since ϕ vanishes on x=0 and x=1, it follows that

$$\Delta x\Delta t \sum (\phi_{\bar{t}}\phi_{\underline{x}})_{\bar{x}} = \Delta t \sum_{t=\Delta t}^{T} \{\phi_{\bar{t}}\phi_{\underline{x}}\big|_{1,t} - \phi_{\bar{t}}\phi_{\underline{x}}\big|_{0,t}\} = 0. \tag{70}$$

Therefore, using the assumed positiveness of D, Eq.(69) becomes:

$$\Delta x\Delta t \sum_{R_{\Delta x,\Delta t}} \phi_{\bar{t}}\bar{G} \geq \frac{\Delta x\Delta t}{D^*} \sum_{R_{\Delta x,\Delta t}} \phi_{\bar{t}}^2 + \tfrac{1}{2}\Delta x\Delta t \sum_{H_{\Delta x,\Delta t}} (\phi_{\bar{x}}^2)_{\bar{t}} . \tag{71}$$

It follows from Eq. (71) that

$$\sum_{R_{\Delta x,\Delta t}} \phi_{\bar{t}}^2 \leq D^* \sum_{R_{\Delta x,\Delta t}} \phi_{\bar{t}}\bar{G} .$$

Applying Schwarz's inequality, we have

$$\sum_{R_{\Delta x,\Delta t}} \phi_{\bar{t}}^2 \leq D^*\Big(\sum_{R_{\Delta x,\Delta t}} \phi_{\bar{t}}^2\Big)^{\frac{1}{2}}\Big(\sum_{R_{\Delta x,\Delta t}} \bar{G}^2\Big)^{\frac{1}{2}},$$

so that

$$\Big(\Delta x\Delta t \sum_{R_{\Delta x,\Delta t}} \phi_{\bar{t}}^2\Big)^{\frac{1}{2}} \leq D^*\Big(\Delta x\Delta t \sum_{R_{\Delta x,\Delta t}} \bar{G}^2\Big)^{\frac{1}{2}} . \tag{72}$$

Returning to Eq. (71), we find that

$$\Delta x\Delta t \sum_{H_{\Delta x,\Delta t}} (\phi_{\bar{x}}^2)_{\bar{t}} = \Delta x \sum_{\substack{i=1\\ t=M\Delta t=T}}^{N} (\phi_{\bar{x}}^2) = (||\phi_{\bar{x}}||_1^M)^2 \leq 2\Delta x\Delta t \sum_{R_{\Delta x,\Delta t}} \phi_{\bar{t}}\bar{G} ,$$

which, after a further application of Schwarz's inequality, becomes

$$(||\phi_{\bar{x}}||_1^M)^2 \leq 2\Big(\Delta x\Delta t \sum_{R_{\Delta x,\Delta t}} \phi_{\bar{t}}^2\Big)^{\frac{1}{2}}\Big(\Delta x\Delta t \sum_{R_{\Delta x,\Delta t}} \bar{G}^2\Big)^{\frac{1}{2}}. \tag{73}$$

It follows from Eqs.(72,73) that

$$(||\phi_{\bar{x}}||_1^M)^2 \leqslant 2D^*\Delta x\Delta t \sum_{R_{\Delta x,\Delta t}} \bar{G}^2,$$
$$= 2D^*\Delta t \sum_{r=1}^{M} (||\bar{G}||^r)^2. \quad (74)$$

Using Eq. (65) and the triangle inequality, we have

$$(||\bar{G}||^r)^2 \leqslant \frac{2}{D_*^2} \left((||G||^r)^2 + \tilde{A}^2(||\phi_{\hat{x}}||^r)^2 \right). \quad (75)$$

It is easily verified (Lees [3]) that

$$(||\phi_{\hat{x}}||^r) \leqslant (||\phi_{\bar{x}}||_1^r). \quad (76)$$

Hence, using Eqs. (74-76), we have

$$(||\phi_{\bar{x}}||_1^M)^2 \leqslant \frac{4D^*}{D_*^2} \Delta t \sum_{r=1}^{M} \left((||G||^r)^2 + \tilde{A}^2(||\phi_{\bar{x}}||_1^r)^2 \right). \quad (77)$$

That is

$$\left(1 - \frac{4D^*\tilde{A}^2\Delta t}{D_*^2}\right) (||\phi_{\bar{x}}||_1^M)^2 \leqslant \frac{4D^*}{D_*^2} \Delta t \left[\sum_{r=1}^{M} (||G||^r)^2 + \sum_{r=1}^{M-1} \tilde{A}^2(||\phi_{\bar{x}}||_1^r)^2 \right]. \quad (78)$$

By choosing Δt sufficiently small, $\Delta t < \dfrac{D_*^2}{4D^*\tilde{A}^2}$, we are able to deduce that

$$(||\phi_{\bar{x}}||_1^M)^2 \leqslant A\Delta t \sum_{r=1}^{M} (||G||^r)^2 + B\Delta t \sum_{r=0}^{M-1} (||\phi_{\bar{x}}||_1^r)^2, \quad (79)$$

where A and B are independent of r. Applying the discrete Gronwall Lemma (Lees [3]) to Eq. (79), we deduce finally

$$(||\phi_{\bar{x}}||_1^M)^2 \leqslant A\Delta t \sum_{r=1}^{M} (||G||^r)^2 \exp(B\Delta t M)$$
$$= S\Delta t \sum_{r=1}^{M} (||G||^r)^2. \quad (80)$$

Since M is arbitrary the result follows immediately.

APPENDIX 2 (A SECOND ENERGY ESTIMATE).

Lemma 2. Let ϕ be a solution of the difference equation

$$(D(x,t,\phi)\phi_{\underline{x}}(x,t))_{\bar{x}} = \phi_{\bar{t}}(x,t) + \tilde{H}(x,t,\phi), \quad (81)$$

in $R_{\Delta x,\Delta t}$. If ϕ vanishes on x=0 and x=1, but ϕ is arbitrarily prescribed on t=0, then

$$(||\phi_{\bar{x}}||_1^m)^2 \leq 2(||\phi_{\bar{x}}||_1^o)^2 + C_1 \Delta t \sum_{r=1}^{m} (||\widetilde{H}||^r)^2, \quad (82)$$

for some constant C_1 depending on T, D_*, D^* and $\left|\frac{dD}{dx}\right|$.

Proof.

As before we rewrite Eq.(81) as

$$\bar{H} + \phi_{\underline{x}\bar{x}} = F\phi_{\bar{t}}. \quad (83)$$

We simplify Eq. (83) by writing

$$\phi = \omega + \eta, \quad (84)$$

where

$$\bar{H} + \omega_{\underline{x}\bar{x}} = F\omega_{\bar{t}}, \quad (85)$$

with

$$\omega(0,j\Delta t) = \omega(1,j\Delta t) = \omega(i\Delta x,0) \equiv 0, \text{ for all } i,j,$$

and where

$$\eta_{\underline{x}\bar{x}} = F\eta_{\bar{t}}, \quad (86)$$

with

$$\eta(0,j\Delta t) = \eta(1,j\Delta t) \equiv 0, \text{ for all } j,$$

and

$$\eta(i\Delta x,0) = \phi(i\Delta x,0), \text{ for all } i.$$

Using Lemma 1 of Appendix 1 for Eq.(85), we deduce that (for sufficiently small Δt)

$$(||\omega_{\bar{x}}||_1^m)^2 \leq C_o \sum_{r=1}^{m} \Delta t(||\widetilde{H}||^r)^2. \quad (87)$$

The method used in Appendix 1 may be applied in a slightly modified form to estimate $||\eta_{\bar{x}}||_1^m$. It is sufficient to multiply Eq.(86) through by $\Delta x\Delta t\eta_{\bar{t}}$, and use Eq.(68), in order to deduce that

$$\Delta x\Delta t(\eta_{\bar{t}}\eta_{\underline{x}})_{\bar{x}} - \frac{\Delta x\Delta t}{2}(\eta_{\bar{x}}^2)_{\bar{t}} - \frac{\Delta x(\Delta t)^2}{2}(\eta_{\bar{x}\bar{t}})^2 = F\Delta x\Delta t\eta_{\bar{t}}^2. \quad (88)$$

Summing over time-level $t=m\Delta t$ $(m\geq 1)$, we have

$$\Delta x\Delta t \sum_{i=1}^{N} (\eta_{\bar{t}}\eta_{\underline{x}})_{\bar{x}} - \frac{\Delta x\Delta t}{2}\sum_{i=1}^{N} (\eta_{\bar{x}}^2)_{\bar{t}} - \frac{\Delta x(\Delta t)^2}{2}\sum_{i=1}^{N} (\eta_{\bar{x}\bar{t}})^2 = \Delta x\Delta t\sum_{i=1}^{N-1}\frac{1}{D}\eta_{\bar{t}}^2. \quad (89)$$

As in Appendix 1, the first term in Eq.(89) vanishes, the third is non-positive and the term on the right-hand side is non-negative. Thus,

$$\frac{\Delta x \Delta t}{2} \sum_{i=1}^{N} (\eta_{\bar{x}}^2)_{\bar{t}} \leqslant 0;$$

that is

$$\Delta x \sum_{\substack{i=1 \\ t=m\Delta t}}^{N} \eta_{\bar{x}}^2 \leqslant \Delta x \sum_{\substack{i=1 \\ t=(m-1)\Delta t}}^{N} \eta_{\bar{x}}^2 . \tag{90}$$

Using Eq.(90) iteratively, we have

$$(||\eta_{\bar{x}}||_1^m)^2 \leqslant (||\eta_{\bar{x}}||_1^{m-1})^2 \leqslant \ldots \leqslant (||\eta_{\bar{x}}||_1^o)^2 = (||\phi_{\bar{x}}||_1^o)^2 . \tag{91}$$

It follows from Eqs.(87,91) and the triangle inequality that

$$(||\phi_{\bar{x}}||_1^m)^2 \leqslant 2(||\phi_{\bar{x}}||_1^o)^2 + C_1 \Delta t \sum_{r=1}^{m} (||\tilde{H}||^r)^2 ,$$

as required.

Corollary. If in Eq.(82), we take m=1, $\phi^o = z^j$, $\phi^1 = z^{j+\frac{1}{2}}$ and $||\tilde{H}||^1 = O((\Delta x)^2 + \Delta t)$, then

$$(||z_{\bar{x}}||_1^{j+\frac{1}{2}})^2 \leqslant 2(||z_{\bar{x}}||_1^j)^2 + C_2 \Delta t((\Delta x)^2 + \Delta t)^2 ,$$

$$\leqslant C\{(||z_{\bar{x}}||_1^j)^2 + \Delta t((\Delta x)^2 + \Delta t)^2\}, \tag{92}$$

where C is a positive constant independent of j, Δx and Δt.

APPENDIX 3

Lemma 3. Using the definitions of the norms given in Eq.(45)

$$(||z||_\infty) = \max_{i,j} |z_i^j| \leqslant \tfrac{1}{2} \max_j (||z_{\bar{x}}||_1^j). \tag{93}$$

Proof.

Using the definitions given in Sec. 1, we deduce

$$2z_1^j = \Delta x \sum_{r=1}^{i} (z_r^j)_{\bar{x}} - \Delta x \sum_{r=i+1}^{N} (z_r^j)_{\bar{x}} ,$$

$$= \Delta x \sum_{r=1}^{N} \operatorname{sgn}(i-r)\ (z_r^j)_{\bar{x}} , \tag{94}$$

where

$$\operatorname{sgn}(b) = -1,\ b<0,$$

and

$$\operatorname{sgn}(b) = 1,\ b \geqslant 0.$$

We assume that $z_o^j = z_N^j = 0$, and that $N\Delta x = 1$. Using the generalised Schwarz inequality in Eq.(94), we deduce

$$(2z_i^j)^2 \leq \Delta x \sum_{r=1}^{N} (\operatorname{sgn}(i-r))^2 \Delta x \sum_{r=1}^{N} (z_r^j)_{\bar{x}}^2$$

$$= \Delta x \sum_{r=1}^{N} (z_r^j)_{\bar{x}}^2 . \qquad (95)$$

Since Eq. (95) holds for arbitrary i, we have

$$\max_i |z_i^j|^2 \leq \tfrac{1}{4}\Delta x \sum_{r=1}^{N} (z_r^j)_{\bar{x}}^2 ,$$

that is

$$\max_i |z_i^j| \leq \tfrac{1}{2}(||z_{\bar{x}}||_1^j),$$

and the result follows immediately.

Mixed Time Integration Schemes for Transient Conduction Forced-Convection Analysis

WING KAM LIU and JERRY I. LIN
The Technological Institute
Northwestern University
Evanston, Illinois 60201

ABSTRACT

A current research topic in coupled-field problems is to develop effective transient algorithms which permit different time integration methods with different time steps to be used simultaneously in various regions of the coupled-field problems. The implicit-explicit approach seems to be very successful in structural, fluid and fluid-structure problems. This paper presents a summary of this research direction. A family of mixed time integration schemes, which accommodates the above mentioned capabilities, is also introduced for transient conduction forced-convection analysis. A stability analysis and the computer implementation of this technique are also presented. In particular, it is shown that the mixed time implicit-explicit methods provide a natural framework for the further development of efficient, clean and modularized computer codes.

1. INTRODUCTION

Design by analysis of actively cooled engine and airframe structures for hyersonic flight requires effective coupled thermal-fluid and stress analyses techniques. Finite element methods enable the modeling of such complicated problems. However, when the resulting semi-discrete equations are solved by direct time integration methods, due to the different finite element types, the selection of a time integration method can be a critical factor in the efficient solution of such problems.

A current research topic is to develop mixed time integration schemes which permit different time integration methods with different time steps to be used simultaneously in various regions of the modeling problem. The aim of this approach is to achieve the attributes of the various time integration methods.

For example, Thornton and Wieting [1] proposed a "zero capacitance nodes" method for the transient conduction forced-convection analysis. In their approach, the coolant capacitance nodes are "statically" condensed, and the resulting equations are then solved by a conditionally stable explicit method. However, this approach is restricted to the zero capacitance assumption and the "static" condensation procedure is not straightforward.

An alternate approach to the above problem is to employ the implicit-explicit method proposed by Hughes and Liu [2,3]. This implicit-explicit method has been proven to be very successful in structural, fluid and fluid-structure interaction problems (see e.g. [3,4]). Recent developments along this line can be found in [4-8] and references therein.

In [8] Liu and Belytschko proposed a mixed time integration method for structural problems. In this approach the mesh is partitioned into two element groups: explicit group and implicit group. The explicit group is integrated with a time step of Δt, while the implicit group is integrated with a time step of $m\Delta t$. This partition technique can provide significant savings in computer time and storage.

In this paper, we present a partition procedure for forced-convection conduction transient problems. The coolant capacitance equations are integrated explicitly m times with a time step Δt while the structural capacitance equations are integrated implicitly with a time step of $m\Delta t$. An alternate approach is to integrate the coolant and structural capacitance equations implicitly with a time step of $m\Delta t$ and explicitly m times with a time step of Δt respectively. A similar m explicit-explicit partition is also possible for this type of problem.

In these mixed time partitions, the complete coupled conduction force-convection matrix equations are discretized by an implicit integration method. A general mixed time integration technique is then derived from this implicit integration method. This general partition procedure is amenable to a unified stability analysis and incorporates the mentioned algorithms as special cases. To simplify the presentation of this technique, we describe the m-explicit-implicit (mE-I) partition and the m-explicit-explicit (mE-E) partition in detail herein. However, it is intuitively obvious that the general mixed time schemes will be a combination of the two.

An outline of the remainder of the paper is as follows. In Sec. 2, a finite element model for a convectively cooled panel is disucssed. The governing equations arising from a finite element spatial discretization are summarized. In Sec. 3, the mixed time partition procedures are described. The implicit integration method used is the generalized trapezoidal rule [9]. The mE-I partition and mE-E partition are presented. In Sec. 4, the critical time step restrictions for the general mixed time schemes are described. In Sec. 5, the computer implementation aspects of mixed time integration are presented. Numerical examples are presented in Section 6 and conclusions are presented in Section 7.

2. GOVERNING EQUATIONS

A finite element model of a convectively cooled panel (see [10] for a discussion) consists of a panel which is cooled by fluid flow through tubes bonded to the panel. The panel can be modeled with two dimensional conduction elements and the fluid/tube can be modeled with one-dimensional conduction forced-convection coolant elements. In finite element computer implementation, we separate the model into two element groups; the two dimensional conduction element group which has one degree of freedom per node (solid temperature) and the one dimensional flow passage element group which has two degrees of freedom per node (fluid bulk temperature and solid temperature). The interface conditions between the panel and the fluid/tube are automatically satisfied by the standard finite element assembly procedures.

The general transient finite element formulations for heat conduction and for a typical conduction forced-convection coolant have been described in [9] and [11] respectively. To simplify the presentation, we write the resulting discretized finite element matrix equations.

$$\underset{\sim}{M}\dot{\underset{\sim}{\theta}} + \underset{\sim}{K}\underset{\sim}{\theta} = \underset{\sim}{Q} \ , \quad (2.1)$$

$$\underset{\sim}{M} = \underset{\sim}{M}^s + \underset{\sim}{M}^f \ , \quad (2.2)$$

$$\underset{\sim}{K} = \underset{\sim}{K}^s + \underset{\sim}{K}^f + \underset{\sim}{K}^v + \underset{\sim}{K}^{sf} \ , \quad (2.3)$$

$$\theta = \begin{Bmatrix} \underset{\sim}{\theta}^s \\ \underset{\sim}{\theta}^f \end{Bmatrix} \ , \quad (2.4)$$

and

$$\underset{\sim}{Q} = \begin{Bmatrix} \underset{\sim}{Q}^s \\ \underset{\sim}{Q}^f \end{Bmatrix} \ , \quad (2.5)$$

Equations (2.1) to (2.5) are derived from the energy balances on the panel and tube (all quantities with a superscript "s") and fluid (all quantities with a superscript "f") for a typical convectively cooled panel (see [11,12] for details). The thermal energy of the fluid is represented by average temperature $\underset{\sim}{\theta}^f$ which varies only in the flow direction. A superposed dot denotes t (time) differentiation. The matrices $\underset{\sim}{M}^f$ and $\underset{\sim}{M}^s$ are the capacitance matrices of the fluid and solid respectively, and for low-density coolants such as gases, $\underset{\sim}{M}^f$ is usually several orders of magnitude smaller than $\underset{\sim}{M}^s$. $\underset{\sim}{K}^s$ and $\underset{\sim}{K}^f$ are the conductance matrices for the panel and tube, and the fluid respectively; $\underset{\sim}{K}^v$ is the mass flow rate convective matrix, $\underset{\sim}{K}^{sf}$ is the convective heat transfer matrix between the fluid and the tube; $\underset{\sim}{Q}^s = \underset{\sim}{Q}^s(t)$ and $\underset{\sim}{Q}^f = \underset{\sim}{Q}^f(t)$ are given vectors for the solid and fluid respectively.

If the standard Galerkin finite element method is applied to the energy balance on the solid and fluid coupled partial differential equations to yield equation (2.1) $\underset{\sim}{K}^v$ is nonsymmetric and all other matrices are symmetric. If a consistent Petrov-Galerkin method (see [13] for a discussion) is employed, all the matrices can be nonsymmetric. However, for discussion purposes here, we assume a Galerkin finite element method is employed and the upwind scheme described in [4] is used to generate the convective heat transfer matrix $\underset{\sim}{K}^v$. Henceforth, $\underset{\sim}{M}$ is positive definite, and the upwind scheme used to generate the matrix $\underset{\sim}{K}^v$ can avoid spatial mesh instability (see [4,14] for a discussion). The initial value problem for (2.1) consists of finding a function $\underset{\sim}{\theta} = \underset{\sim}{\theta}(t)$ satisfying the discretized transport equation (2.1) and the initial condition

$$\underset{\sim}{\theta}(0) = \underset{\sim}{R}_o \ , \quad (2.6)$$

where $\underset{\sim}{R}_o$ is given data.

3. MIXED TIME PARTITION PROCEDURES

In this section, equations (2.1) to (2.3) are to be integrated by a mE-I partition based on similar concepts introduced by Liu and Belytschko [8]. A similar mE-E partition can easily be derived from this mE-I partition procedure. Let n be the time step number; $\underset{\sim}{\theta}_n$, $\underset{\sim}{V}_n$ and $\underset{\sim}{Q}_n$ be the approximations to $\underset{\sim}{\theta}(t_n)$, $\dot{\underset{\sim}{\theta}}(t_n)$ and $\underset{\sim}{Q}(t_n)$ respectively. Let Δt be the time step used in the explicit group (e.g., the two dimensional heat conduction element), and $m\Delta t$, where m is an integer greater or equal to 1, is the time step used in the implicit group (e.g., the one dimensional fluid/tube conduction convection element).

For the purpose of describing these partition time integration procedures, all the matrices with the implicit and explicit groups are designated by a superscript "I" and "E" respectively. Hence it follows that any assembled global matrix is the sum of the implicit and explicit matrices, cf. $\underset{\sim}{M} = \underset{\sim}{M}^I + \underset{\sim}{M}^E$ and $\underset{\sim}{K} = \underset{\sim}{K}^I + \underset{\sim}{K}^E$. Nodes associated with only explicit elements are denoted by superscript "E", whereas those which are in contact with at least one implicit element are denoted by superscript "I"; nodes which are connected to both implicit and explicit elements are designated by "B", so "B" is a subset of "I". All vectors are then partitioned accordingly into explicit and implicit parts, cf. $\underset{\sim}{\theta} = (\underset{\sim}{\theta}^I\ \underset{\sim}{\theta}^E)^T$, $\underset{\sim}{V} = (\underset{\sim}{V}^I\ \underset{\sim}{V}^E)^T$ and $\underset{\sim}{Q} = (\underset{\sim}{Q}^I\ \underset{\sim}{Q}^E)^T$. The superscript "T" denotes the transpose. The vectors $\underset{\sim}{V}$ and $\underset{\sim}{\theta}$ are sometimes redefined by augmented vectors, $\underset{\sim}{V} = \underset{\sim}{V}^{*I} + \underset{\sim}{V}^{*E}$ and $\underset{\sim}{\theta} = \underset{\sim}{\theta}^{*I} + \underset{\sim}{\theta}^{*E}$ where $\underset{\sim}{V}^{*I} = (\underset{\sim}{V}^I\ \underset{\sim}{0})^T$, $V^{*E} = (\underset{\sim}{0}\ \underset{\sim}{V}^E)^T$, $\underset{\sim}{\theta}^{*I} = (\underset{\sim}{\theta}^I\ \underset{\sim}{0})^T$ and $\underset{\sim}{\theta}^{*E} = (\underset{\sim}{0}\ \underset{\sim}{\theta}^E)^T$. In any computation of a vector $\underset{\sim}{P}^{*E}$ which leads to nonzero terms in the zero partition, these nonzero terms are neglected; they are assumed to be zero.

With these definitions, the mE-I partition at step n+m is given as follows.

• Governing equation

$$\underset{\sim}{M}\underset{\sim}{V}_{n+m} + \underset{\sim}{K}^I \underset{\sim}{\theta}^I_{n+m} + \underset{\sim}{K}^E \underset{\sim}{\tilde{\theta}}^E_{n+m} = \underset{\sim}{Q}_{n+m} \tag{3.1}$$

• Modified generalized trapezoidal rule for j=1,...,m

$$\underset{\sim}{\tilde{\theta}}^E_{n+j} = \underset{\sim}{\theta}^E_{n+j-1} + (1-\alpha)\Delta t\ \underset{\sim}{V}^E_{n+j-1} , \tag{3.2}$$

$$\underset{\sim}{\tilde{\theta}}^I_{n+j} = \underset{\sim}{\theta}^I_n + (1-\alpha)j\Delta t\ \underset{\sim}{V}^I_n , \text{ for } 1 \leqslant j < m \text{ define the subset "B" only} \tag{3.3}$$

$$\underset{\sim}{\theta}^E_{n+j} = \underset{\sim}{\tilde{\theta}}^E_{n+j} + \alpha\Delta t\ \underset{\sim}{V}^E_{n+j} , \tag{3.4}$$

and

$$\underset{\sim}{\theta}^I_{n+m} = \underset{\sim}{\tilde{\theta}}^I_{n+m} + \alpha m\Delta t\ V^I_{n+m} . \tag{3.5}$$

Where α is a free parameter which governs the stability and accuracy of the method, and $\underset{\sim}{\tilde{\theta}}^E_{n+j}$ and $\underset{\sim}{\tilde{\theta}}^I_{n+j}$ are predictors. If a mE-E partition is desired, let the superscript "I" be replaced by the superscript "E_m" in the above equations. The mE-E partition at step n+m is given as follows:

• Governing equation

$$\underset{\sim}{M}\underset{\sim}{V}_{n+m} + \underset{\sim}{K}^{E_m} \underset{\sim}{\tilde{\theta}}^{E_m}_{n+m} + \underset{\sim}{K}^E \underset{\sim}{\tilde{\theta}}^E_{n+m} = \underset{\sim}{Q}_{n+m} \tag{3.6}$$

• Modified generalized trapezoidal rule for j=1,...,m

$$\underset{\sim}{\tilde{\theta}}_{n+j} = \underset{\sim}{\theta}^E_{n+j-1} + (1-\alpha)\Delta t\ \underset{\sim}{V}^E_{n+j-1} , \tag{3.7}$$

$$\tilde{\underset{\sim}{\theta}}^{E_m}_{n+j} = \underset{\sim}{\theta}^{E_m}_{n} + (1-\alpha)j\Delta t\ \underset{\sim}{V}^{E_m}_{n} \quad , \text{ for } 1 \leq j < m \text{ define the subset "B" only} \tag{3.8}$$

$$\underset{\sim}{\theta}^{E}_{n+j} = \tilde{\underset{\sim}{\theta}}^{E}_{n+j} + \alpha\Delta t\ \underset{\sim}{V}^{E}_{n+j} \quad , \tag{3.9}$$

and

$$\underset{\sim}{\theta}^{E_m}_{n+m} = \tilde{\underset{\sim}{\theta}}^{E_m}_{n+m} + \alpha m\Delta t\ \underset{\sim}{V}^{E_m}_{n+m} \quad . \tag{3.10}$$

In the above equations, we have employed the modified generalized trapezoidal rule to carry out the time temporary discretization of equation (2.1). For our purpose, $\alpha = 1/2$ is employed in order to achieve second order accuracy.

4. STABILITY ANALYSIS

In this section, we assumed $\underset{\sim}{Q} = \underset{\sim}{0}$ and all mass matrices are lumped. We employed an energy balance technique (see [2] for a discussion) to carry out the stability analysis. The following notations will be used.

$$[\underset{\sim}{x}_{n+m}] = \underset{\sim}{x}_{n+m} - \underset{\sim}{x}_{n} \quad , \tag{4.1}$$

$$\langle \underset{\sim}{x}_{n+m} \rangle = (\underset{\sim}{x}_{n+m} + \underset{\sim}{x}_{n})/2 \quad , \tag{4.2}$$

$$[\underset{\sim}{x}_{n+j}] = \underset{\sim}{x}_{n+j+1} - \underset{\sim}{x}_{n+j} \quad , \tag{4.3}$$

and $\qquad j=0,1,\ldots,m-1$

$$\langle \underset{\sim}{x}_{n+j} \rangle = (\underset{\sim}{x}_{n+j+1} + \underset{\sim}{x}_{n+j})/2 \quad . \tag{4.4}$$

Using the above definitions, eqs. (3.4) and (3.5) can be written as follows.

• Explicit nodes for $j=1,\ldots,m$

$$[\underset{\sim}{\theta}^{*E}_{n+j}] = \Delta t\ \langle \underset{\sim}{V}^{*E}_{n+j} \rangle + (\alpha-1/2)\Delta t[\underset{\sim}{V}^{*E}_{n+j}] \tag{4.5}$$

• Implicit nodes

$$[\underset{\sim}{\theta}^{*I}_{n+m}] = m\Delta t\ \langle \underset{\sim}{V}^{*I}_{n+m} \rangle + (\alpha-1/2)m\Delta t[\underset{\sim}{V}^{*I}_{n+m}] \tag{4.6}$$

4.1 mE-I Partition

Using eqs. (3.4) and (3.5), equation (3.1) can be rewritten as follows:

$$\underset{\sim}{M}^{*I}\ \underset{\sim}{V}^{*I}_{n+m} + \underset{\sim}{K}\underset{\sim}{\theta}^{*I}_{n+m} = \underset{\sim}{0} \tag{4.7}$$

and

$$\underset{\sim}{M}^{*E}\ \underset{\sim}{V}^{*E}_{n+j} + \underset{\sim}{K}^{E}\underset{\sim}{\theta}^{*E}_{n+j} + \underset{\sim}{K}^{E}\tilde{\underset{\sim}{\theta}}^{*I}_{n+j} = \underset{\sim}{0} \qquad j=1,\ldots,m \tag{4.8}$$

where

$$\underset{\sim}{M}^{*I} = \underset{\sim}{M}^{I} + \underset{\sim}{M}^{E} - \alpha m\Delta t\ \underset{\sim}{K}^{E} \tag{4.9}$$

and

$$\underset{\sim}{M}^{*E} = \underset{\sim}{M}^{E} - \alpha\Delta t\ \underset{\sim}{K}^{E} \tag{4.10}$$

An energy identity can be established by taking the difference between steps n+j+1 and n+j of equation (4.8) and premultiplying the resulting equation by $\langle \underset{\sim}{V}^{*I}_{n+m} \rangle^T + \langle \underset{\sim}{V}^{*E}_{n+j} \rangle^T$ for j=0,1,...,m-1. The energy expression of this mE-I partition can be obtained by summing up the mentioned energy identities, and it is:

$$\langle \underset{\sim}{V}^{*I}_{n+m} \rangle^T \underset{\sim}{M}^{*I} [\underset{\sim}{V}^{*I}_{n+m}] + \langle \underset{\sim}{V}^{*I}_{n+m} \rangle^T \underset{\sim}{K} [\underset{\sim}{\theta}^{*I}_{n+m}] + \langle \underset{\sim}{V}^{*I}_{n+m} \rangle^T \underset{\sim}{K}^E [\underset{\sim}{\tilde{\theta}}^{*E}_{n+m}]$$

$$+ \sum_{j=0}^{m-1} \left\{ \langle \underset{\sim}{V}^{*E}_{n+j} \rangle^T \left(\underset{\sim}{M}^{*E} [\underset{\sim}{V}^{*E}_{n+j}] + \underset{\sim}{K}^E [\underset{\sim}{\theta}^{*E}_{n+j}] + \underset{\sim}{K}^E [\underset{\sim}{\tilde{\theta}}^{*I}_{n+j}] \right) \right\} = 0 \tag{4.11}$$

Using eqs. (4.5) and (4.6), equation (4.11) can be reduced to (see Appendix A for details and assumptions)

$$\underset{\sim}{V}^{*I^T}_{n+m} (\underset{\sim}{B}^I + \underset{\sim}{B}^{mE}) \underset{\sim}{V}^{*I}_{n+m} + \underset{\sim}{V}^{*E^T}_{n+m}\ \underset{\sim}{B}^E\ \underset{\sim}{V}^{*E}_{n+m}$$

$$\geqslant \underset{\sim}{V}^{*I^T}_{n} (\underset{\sim}{B}^I + \underset{\sim}{B}^{mE}) \underset{\sim}{V}^{*I}_{n} + \underset{\sim}{V}^{*E^T}_{n}\ \underset{\sim}{B}^E\ \underset{\sim}{V}^{*E}_{n}$$

$$- 2m\Delta t \langle \underset{\sim}{V}^{*I}_{n+m} \rangle^T \underset{\sim}{K}^I \langle \underset{\sim}{V}^{*I}_{n+m} \rangle - 2\Delta t \sum_{j=0}^{m-1} \langle \underset{\sim}{V}^{*E}_{n+j} \rangle^T \underset{\sim}{K}^E \langle \underset{\sim}{V}^{*E}_{n+j} \rangle \tag{4.12}$$

where

$$\underset{\sim}{B}^I = \underset{\sim}{M}^I + (\alpha - 1/2) m\Delta t\ \underset{\sim}{K}^I \tag{4.13}$$

and

$$\underset{\sim}{B}^{jE} = \underset{\sim}{M}^E - 1/2\ j\Delta t\ \underset{\sim}{K}^E \qquad j=1 \text{ and } m \tag{4.14}$$

4.2 mE-E Partition

The above procedures for mE-I partition can be repeated on eqs. (3.6) to (3.10) to yield the energy expression of the mE-E partition. This energy expression is exactly the same as in equation (4.12) with the superscript "I" replaced by the superscript "E_m" and

$$\underset{\sim}{B}^{E_m} = \underset{\sim}{M}^{E_m} - 1/2\ m\Delta t\ \underset{\sim}{K}^{E_m} \tag{4.15}$$

4.3 Stability Analysis Results

The mE-I partition is stable if the symmetric parts of $\underset{\sim}{B}^I + \underset{\sim}{B}^{mE}$ and $\underset{\sim}{B}^E$ are both positive definite. Since $\alpha = 1/2$ is assumed and $\underset{\sim}{C}$ which is the symmetric part of $\underset{\sim}{K}$, is positive definite; the stability of this partition depends only on the explicit elements. Similarly the mE-E partition is stable if the symmetric parts of $\underset{\sim}{B}^{E_m} + \underset{\sim}{B}^{mE}$ and $\underset{\sim}{B}^{E}$ are both positive definite. Its stability is governed by both explicit element groups. A summary of the results is as follows:

4.4 mE-I Partition

$$\Omega^{E*}_{crit} \equiv 2 \qquad (4.16)$$

and

$$\Omega^{E}_{crit} \equiv 2 \ ; \qquad (4.17)$$

are the $m\Delta t$ and Δt restrictions for the explicit elements where

$$\Omega^{E*}_{crit} = m\Delta t \ \lambda^{E*}_{crit} \qquad (4.18)$$

$$\Omega^{E}_{crit} = \Delta t \ \lambda^{E}_{crit} \qquad (4.19)$$

λ^{χ} denotes a typical eigenvalue of the eigenproblem

$$\underset{\sim}{M}^{\chi}\dot{\underset{\sim}{\theta}} + \underset{\sim}{C}^{\chi}\underset{\sim}{\theta} = \underset{\sim}{0} \qquad (4.20)$$

In equation (4.20) if χ is picked to be E*, λ^{E*}_{crit} is the maximum eigenvalue among <u>only</u> those elements in the explicit group which are in contact with at least one implicit element. Similarly, λ^{E}_{crit} is the maximum eigenvalue among the explicit elements.

4.5 mE-E Partition

$$\Omega^{E_m}_{crit} = m\Delta t \ \lambda^{E_m}_{crit} = 2 \qquad (4.21)$$

is the $m\Delta t$ time step restriction for the E_m explicit element group, and equations (4.16) and (4.17) are the critical time steps restrictions for the other explicit element group.

Furthermore, if a mE-E-I partition and/or other combinations are required, the critical time steps restrictions are governed by each individual explicit element group only since we restrict ourselves to $\alpha = 1/2$.

5. IMPLEMENTATION ASPECTS OF MIXED TIME INTEGRATION

The mE-I partition time integration is to proceed over the time interval [0,T]. The solution procedures are as follows:

1. Initialization n=0, $\underset{\sim}{\theta}_o = \underset{\sim}{R}_o$.

2. Determine $\underset{\sim}{V}_o$.

$$\underset{\sim}{V}_o = \underset{\sim}{M}^{-1}(\underset{\sim}{Q}_o - \underset{\sim}{K}\theta_o) \qquad (5.1)$$

3. Form and factorize $\underset{\sim}{K}^*$.

$$\underset{\sim}{K}^{*I} = \underset{\sim}{M}^{I} + \alpha m \Delta t \, \underset{\sim}{K}^{I} \tag{5.2}$$

$$\underset{\sim}{K}^{*E} = \underset{\sim}{M}^{E} \quad \text{which is a diagonal matrix} \tag{5.3}$$

4. Loop on number of substeps $j=1,\ldots,m$.

5. Define predictor values:

$$\tilde{\underset{\sim}{\theta}}^{E}_{n+j} = \underset{\sim}{\theta}^{E}_{n+j-1} + (1-\alpha)\Delta t \, \underset{\sim}{V}^{E}_{n+j-1} \tag{5.4}$$

$$\tilde{\underset{\sim}{\theta}}^{I}_{n+j} = \underset{\sim}{\theta}^{I}_{n} + (1-\alpha) j \Delta t \, \underset{\sim}{V}^{I}_{n} \quad \text{for } 1 \leq j < m \text{ define subset "B" only} \tag{5.5}$$

6. Form $\underset{\sim}{F}^{*E}_{n+j}$.

$$\underset{\sim}{F}^{*E}_{n+j} = \underset{\sim}{M}^{E} \tilde{\underset{\sim}{\theta}}_{n+j} + \alpha \Delta t \underset{\sim}{W} (\underset{\sim}{Q}^{E}_{n+j} - \underset{\sim}{K}^{E} \tilde{\underset{\sim}{\theta}}_{n+j}) \tag{5.6}$$

$$\underset{\sim}{W} = \begin{bmatrix} m^2 \underset{\sim}{1} & \underset{\sim}{0} \\ \underset{\sim}{0} & \underset{\sim}{1} \end{bmatrix} \begin{matrix} \text{I rows} \\ \text{E rows} \end{matrix} \tag{5.7}$$

I columns E columns

$$\underset{\sim}{1} = \text{identity matrix} \tag{5.8}$$

7. Form $\underset{\sim}{F}^{*I}_{n+m}$.

$$\underset{\sim}{F}^{*I}_{n+m} = \alpha m \Delta t \, \underset{\sim}{Q}^{I}_{n+m} + \underset{\sim}{M}^{I} \tilde{\underset{\sim}{\theta}}_{n+m} \tag{5.9}$$

8. Solve for $\underset{\sim}{\theta}^{E}_{n+j}$ if $1 \leq j < m$.

$$\underset{\sim}{K}^{*E} \underset{\sim}{\theta}^{*E}_{n+j} = \underset{\sim}{F}^{*E}_{n+j} \tag{5.10}$$

9. Solve for $\underset{\sim}{\theta}_{n+m}$ if $j = m$.

$$\underset{\sim}{K}^{*} \underset{\sim}{\theta}_{n+m} = \underset{\sim}{F}^{*}_{n+m} \tag{5.11}$$

10. Determine $\underset{\sim}{V}^{E}_{n+j}$.

$$\underset{\sim}{V}^{E}_{n+j} = (\underset{\sim}{\theta}^{E}_{n+j} - \tilde{\underset{\sim}{\theta}}^{E}_{n+j}) / \alpha \Delta t \tag{5.12}$$

11. If $j < m$, $\underset{\sim}{\theta}^{E}_{n}$ and $\underset{\sim}{V}^{E}_{n}$ are replaced by $\underset{\sim}{\theta}^{E}_{n+j}$ and $\underset{\sim}{V}^{E}_{n+j}$ respectively.

12. if $j=m$ determine $\underset{\sim}{V}^{I}_{n+m}$.

$$\underset{\sim}{V}^{I}_{n+m} = (\underset{\sim}{\theta}^{I}_{n+m} - \tilde{\underset{\sim}{\theta}}_{n+m}) / \alpha m \Delta t \tag{5.13}$$

13. If $j < m$ goes to 5 .

14. If $(n+1) m \Delta t \geq T$ stop; otherwise replace n by n+m and go to 4 .

Remarks:

(a) In step 3, the factorization of $\tilde{K}^{*} = \tilde{L}\tilde{D}\tilde{U}$ includes $\tilde{K}^{*E}$ which is equal to $\tilde{D}^{E}$ and it is uncoupled to $\tilde{L}$ and $\tilde{U}$. The nonsymmetric version of the equation solver used in [8] can handle this nicely and efficiently.

(b) In step 8, the solution for $\tilde{\theta}^{E}_{n+j}$, j=1,...,m-1 is purely a divide operation during the backsubsituations if the beginning and ending addresses of $\tilde{K}^{*}$ corresponding to the "E" nodes are given.

(c) The potential saving in computation is considerable for the explicit elements are executed m times while the implicit elements are executed only once during each time step of step size mΔt (see Liu and Belytschko [8] for a comparison discussion).

(d) The mE-E partition time integration method can be implemented with the same procedures described above. In this partition, "I" is to be replaced by "E_m" and

$$\tilde{K}^{*E_m} = \tilde{M}^{E_m} \text{ which is a diagonal matrix} \quad , \tag{5.14}$$

and

$$\tilde{F}^{*E_m}_{n+m} = \tilde{M}^{E_m}\tilde{\tilde{\theta}}_{n+m} + \alpha m\Delta t(\tilde{Q}^{E_m}_{n+m} - \tilde{K}^{E_m}\tilde{\tilde{\theta}}_{n+m}) \quad . \tag{5.15}$$

(e) A very general mixed time partition can be obtained by combining the above procedures. It permits different time integration methods and/or different time steps to be used simultaneously in different parts of the mesh. The degeneration of this approach to various special cases such as implicit-explicit, implicit-explicit operator splitting, implicit or explicit are intuitively obvious.

6. NUMERICAL EXAMPLES

A one dimensional heat conduction program is written to confirm the stability and accuracy of these mixed time integration methods. The finite element mesh shown in figure 1, consists of a rod which is insulated at the right end and is subject to a constant initial temperature of 0.1 for $x > 0.0$. The temperature at the left end of the rod (x=0.0) is kept at 0.0 for all time. This finite element model consists of 18 explicit elements, each has a length $\ell_1 = 10.0$; 10 implicit or explicit elements, each has a length $\ell_2 = 100.0$; and 2 explicit elements, each has a length $\ell_3 = 90.0$ (see figure 1 for details). Lumped mass matrices are used throughout, and all computations are based on m=10 in these examples.

In order to demonstrate the advantages of this mE-I partition, the thermal diffusivity ν (which is the ratio of the thermal conductivity to the specific heat times density) of the material is set to 2.0×10^5 for the implicit elements ($\ell_2 = 100.0$); and is set to 200.0 for the rest of the explicit elements ($\ell_1 = 10.0$ and $\ell_3 = 90.0$). From the stability analysis, the critical time step among the explicit elements is 0.25. The results of a 10E-I partition with time steps of 2.5 and 0.25 for the implicit and explicit elements respectively are presented in figure 1. The above calculation is performed with $\alpha = 0.5$.

In the second analysis, a 10E-E integration procedure is performed. In this example, all elements (explicit) have the same $\nu = 200.0$. A time step of 2.5 is used for the explicit elements which have lengths of $\ell_2 = 100.0$ and a time step of 0.25 is used for the rest of the explicit elements ($\ell_1 = 10.0$ and $\ell_3 = 90.0$). The calculation is performed with $\alpha = 0.5$. The computed results are compared to the exact solutions and are shown in figure 2. They are almost identical.

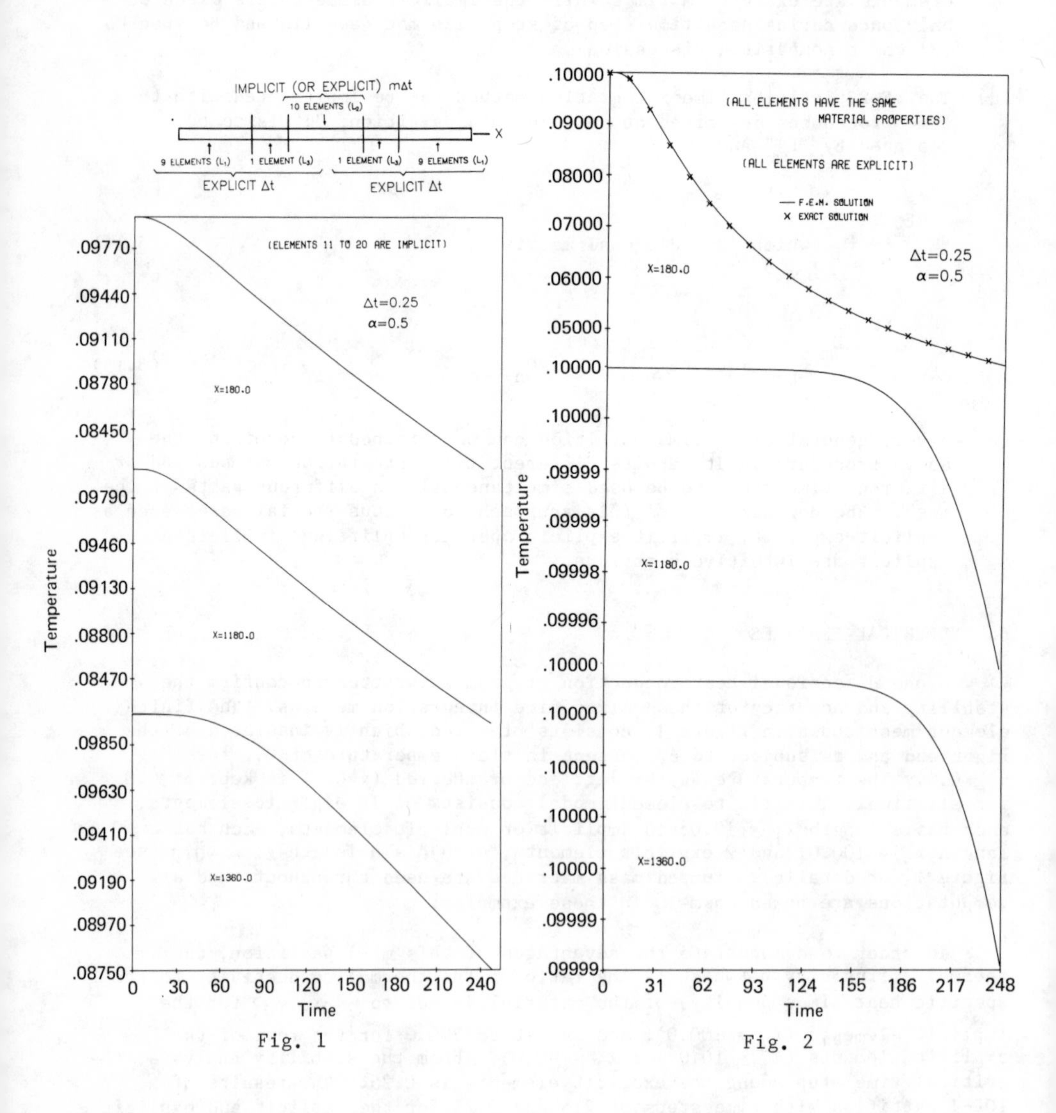

Fig. 1 Fig. 2

A drawback of this mE-I partition is the time-step restriction of eq. (4.16). In order to ascertain this time-step restriction, the above two analysis are repeated with m=10, $\ell_1 = 10.0$, $\ell_2 = 100.0$ and variable ℓ_3(10.0 to 100.0). According to eq. (4.16), stability can be achieved only if $\ell_3 = 100.0$. As may be seen in table 1, equation (4.16) is somewhat conservative for all the cases. Further stability analysis and numerical experiments are required.

TABLE 1

10E-I	$\nu_{imp} = 2.0 \times 10^5$	$\nu_{exp} = 200.0$
Δt	ℓ_3	stability
0.25	90.0	yes
0.25	70.0	yes
0.25	50.0	yes
0.25	30.0	yes
0.25	10.0	yes
10E-E	$\nu = 200.0$	
0.25	90.0	yes
0.25	70.0	yes
0.25	50.0	yes
0.25	20.0	yes
0.25	10.0	yes

7. CONCLUSION

In this paper, we have presented a family of mixed time integration schemes for transient conduction forced-convection analysis. Both the stability analysis and the implementation aspects of these schemes are described. Numerical examples are also presented to support the stability theory as well as the effectiveness of this new approach. In particular, from the standpoint of improved calculational efficiency, it is shown that this mixed time technique provides significant saving in computation. One drawback of the mE-I partition is the time-step restriction of eq. (4.16). Current research is now being actively pursued to eliminate that time step constraint and will be reported in a separate communication [15].

Finally, a word of caution is in order regarding the ability of the present capabilities to solve nonlinear forced-convection conduction problems. Unconditional stability for the implicit group is lost with the exception of the case $\alpha=1$ which is only first order accurate. Much research remains in this case.

ACKNOWLEDGEMENT

We wish to thank Professor T. B. Belytschko for his many helpful discussions during the course of the present study. We also wish to express our gratitude to the computer center at Northwestern University, for providing computing services.

The partial support of NASA under grant No. NAG-1-210 to this research is gratefully acknowledged.

REFERENCES

1. E. A. Thornton and A. R. Wieting, "Evaluation of finite-element formulations for transient conduction forced-convection analysis," Numerical Heat Transfer, vol. 3, 1980, pp. 281-295.

2. T. J. R. Hughes and W. K. Liu, "Implicit-explicit finite elements in transient analysis: stability theory," J. Applied Mech., vol. 45, 1978, pp. 371-374.

3. T. J. R. Hughes and W. K. Liu, "Implicit-explicit finite elements in transient analysis: implementation and numerical examples," J. Applied Mech., vol. 45, 1978, pp. 375-378.

4. W. K. Liu, "Development of finite element procedures for fluid-structure interactions," EERL 80-06, California Institute of Technology, Pasadena, California, August 1980.

5. T. Belytschko, H. J. Yen and R. Mullen, "Mixed methods for time integration," Computer Methods in Applied Mechanics and Engineering, 17/18 (1979) 259-275.

6. K. C. Park, "Partitioned transient analysis procedure for coupled-field problems: stability analysis," J. Applied Mech., vol. 47, 1980, pp. 370-376.

7. J. P. Wright, "Mixed time integration schemes," Computers and Structures, 10, (1979) 235-238.

8. W. K. Liu and T. Belytschko, "Mixed time implicit-explicit finite elements in transient analysis," in preparation.

9. T. J. R. Hughes, "Unconditionally stable algorithms for nonlinear heat conduction," Computer Methods in Applied Mechanics and Engineering, 10, (1977) 135-139.

10. H. N. Kelley, A. R. Wieting, C. P. Shore, and R. J. Nowak, "Recent advances in convectively cooled engine and airframe structures for hypersonic flight," presented at the 11th Congress of the International Council of the Aeronautical Sciences, Lisbon, Portugal, Sept. 10-16, 1978.

11. E. A. Thornton and A. R. Wieting, "Finite element methodology for transient conduction/forced-convection thermal analysis," AIAA paper 79-100, presented at AIAA 14th Thermophysics Conferences, Orlando, FL., June 4-6, 1979.

12. E. A. Thornton and A. R. Wieting, "Finite element methodology for thermal analysis of convectively-cooled structures," AIAA paper 77-187, presented at the AIAA 15th Aerospace Sciences Meeting, Los Angeles, CA., Jan. 24-26, 1977; in L. S. Fletcher (ed.), Heat Transfer and Thermal Control Systems, Prog. Astronaut. Aeronaut., vol. 60, 1978, pp. 171-189.

13. T. J. R. Hughes (editor), "Finite element methods for convection-dominated flows," ASME Winter Annual meeting, New York, Dec. 1979.

14. T. J. R. Hughes, W. K. Liu and A. Brooks, "Review of finite element analysis of incompressible viscous flows by the penalty function formulation," J. Computational Phys. 30, (1979), 1-60.

15. W. K. Liu, "Staggered mixed time solution procedures for coupled-field problems," in preparation.

APPENDIX A - DERIVATION OF EQUATION (4-12)

At the present time, we assume $\underset{\sim}{K}^E$ is positive definite, i.e., the coolant capacitance equations are treated implicitly. Furthermore we will need the following property for positive definite matrices:

If $\underset{\sim}{A}$ is positive definite then

$$\pm \underset{\sim}{x}^T \underset{\sim}{A} \underset{\sim}{y} \leqslant \frac{1}{2\varepsilon} \underset{\sim}{x}^T \underset{\sim}{A} \underset{\sim}{x} + \frac{\varepsilon}{2} \underset{\sim}{y}^T \underset{\sim}{A} \underset{\sim}{y} \tag{A.1}$$

for arbitrary vectors $\underset{\sim}{x}$ and $\underset{\sim}{y}$, $\varepsilon > 0$.

Applying equation (A.1) to the two coupling terms of equation (4.11) and assuming

1. $\langle \underset{\sim}{V}^{*I}_{n+m} \rangle^T \underset{\sim}{K}^E \langle \underset{\sim}{V}^{*I}_{n+m} \rangle / \underset{\sim}{z}^{*E^T} \underset{\sim}{K}^E \underset{\sim}{z}^{*E} \geqslant 1/m^2$, where $\underset{\sim}{z}^{*E} = \underset{\sim}{v}^{*E}_n + \sum_{j=1}^{m-2} \langle \underset{\sim}{V}^{*E}_{n+j} \rangle$;

2. $\langle \underset{\sim}{V}^{*E}_n \rangle^T \underset{\sim}{K}^E \langle \underset{\sim}{V}^{*E}_n \rangle / \underset{\sim}{V}^{*I^T}_n \underset{\sim}{K}^E \underset{\sim}{V}^{*I}_n \geqslant (1+(m-1)\alpha)^2$; and

3. $\langle \underset{\sim}{V}^{*E}_{n+j} \rangle^T \underset{\sim}{K}^E \langle \underset{\sim}{V}^{*E}_{n+j} \rangle / \underset{\sim}{V}^{*I^T}_n \underset{\sim}{K}^E \underset{\sim}{V}^{*I}_n \geqslant (1-\alpha)^2$ for $j=1,\ldots,m-1$;

equation (4.12) can be obtained after carrying out some tedious algebraic manipulation.

A New Explicit Method for the Numerical Solution of Parabolic Differential Equations

NOBUYUKI SATOFUKA
Ames Research Center
NASA
Moffett Field, California

ABSTRACT

A new method is derived for solving parabolic partial differential equations arising in transient heat conduction or in boundary-layer flows. The method is based on a combination of the modified differential quadrature (MDQ) method with the rational Runge-Kutta time-integration scheme. It is fully explicit, requires no matrix inversion, and is stable for any time-step for the heat equations. Burgers equation and the one- and two-dimensional heat equations are solved to demonstrate the accuracy and efficiency of the proposed algorithm. The present method is found to be very accurate and efficient when results are compared with analytic solutions.

1. INTRODUCTION

Many important physical phenomena arising in transient mass and heat transfer or in boundary-layer flows are governed by parabolic partial differential equations (PDEs). Because of their immense practical importance, many finite-difference schemes have been developed during the last decade [1]. Numerical procedures for the solution of these equations fall into two categories, explicit and implicit. The explicit scheme possesses conceptual and practical simplicity, but becomes unstable whenever the time-step exceeds the limit imposed by the so-called stability criterion; the implicit scheme has the advantage of unconditional stability but requires the solution of tridiagonal sets of simultaneous equations at each time-step. If one can devise a new scheme that possesses the conceptual simplicity of an explicit scheme as well as the property of unconditional stability, the scheme will have immense practical importance. The purpose of this paper is to present such a scheme and to demonstrate its application to some relevant problems.

The new method consists of the modified differential quadrature (MDQ) method combined with a rational Runge-Kutta (RRK) time-integration scheme [2]. The MDQ method is an extension of the differential quadrature (DQ) method proposed originally by Bellman et al. [3]. In the present method, spatial derivatives are approximated by a weighted sum of the values of an unknosn function at properly chosen neighboring points to generate a set of ordinary differential equations (ODEs) in time, whereas in the original DQ method these are approximated by using values at all mesh points in the computational domain. As a result, computational efficiency is significantly improved. The resulting set of ODEs is then solved by using an explicit A_0-stable RRK time integration scheme. It should be noted that the present method is computationally explicit and yet unconditionally stable for some class of parabolic PDEs.

The present paper is organized in the following way. The numerical procedure of the present method for a nonlinear scalar model equation, that is, Burgers equation, is described briefly in Sec. 2; the accuracy and stability properties of the method are discussed in Sec. 3; and some numerical results for Burgers equation and the heat equation are presented in Sec. 4 to demonstrated the accuracy and efficiency of the present method.

2. DESCRIPTION OF THE METHOD

In this section we will describe the basic elements of the present method when it is applied to the following nonlinear scalar model equation, viz., Burgers equation,

$$\frac{\partial u}{\partial t} = -u \frac{\partial u}{\partial x} + \nu \frac{\partial^2 u}{\partial x^2} , \tag{1}$$

with the initial condition

$$u(x,0) = f(x) , \tag{2}$$

and boundary conditions

$$B_j u(x,t) = 0 , \quad j = 1,2. \tag{3}$$

2.1. Spatial Discretization

If the function u satisfying Eq. (1) is sufficiently smooth, we can write the approximate relation

$$\frac{\partial u_i(t)}{\partial x} \cong \sum_{j=1}^{N} a_{ij} u_j(t) , \qquad i = 1,2,\ldots,N , \tag{4}$$

where we adopt the notation $u_i(t) = u(x_i,t)$. Viewing Eq. (4) as a linear transformation of u, we see that the second-order derivatives can be approximated by

$$\frac{\partial^2 u_i(t)}{\partial x^2} \cong \sum_{j=1}^{N} b_{ij} u_j(t) , \tag{5}$$

where $b_{ij} = \sum_{j=1}^{N} a_{ik} a_{kj}$. In this paper we have modified the approximate relations, Eqs. (4) and (5), to use the values of u at the nearest M mesh points centered around x_i, instead of using those at all mesh points in the computational domain, as is the case in the original DQ method [3]. By using these values of u, the number of arithmetic operations to be performed for every mesh point is significantly reduced; moreover, in the case of a uniform mesh, the weighting coefficients a_{ij} become independent of index i. therefore, the approximate relations, Eqs. (4) and (5), can be rewritten as

$$\frac{\partial u_i(t)}{\partial x} \simeq \sum_{j=1}^{M} a_j u_{i+j-\alpha}(t) \equiv D_M(u_i) , \tag{6}$$

$$\frac{\partial^2 u_i(t)}{\partial x^2} \simeq \sum_{j=1}^{M} b_j u_{i+j-\alpha}(t) \equiv D_M^2(u_i) , \tag{7}$$

where $a_j = a_{\alpha j}$, $b_j = b_{\alpha j}$, and $\alpha = (M + 1)/2$. For example,

$D_5(u_i) = (-u_{i+2} + 8u_{i+1} - 8u_{i-1} + u_{i-2})/12\Delta x$,

$D_5^2(u_i) = (-u_{i+2} + 16u_{i+1} - 30u_i + 16u_{i-1} - u_{i-2})/12\Delta x^2$.

2.2. Determination of Weighting Coefficients

There are many ways of determining the coefficients a_{ij}. In the DQ method, Bellman et al. determined a_{ij} explicitly, choosing x_i to be the root of shifted Legendre polynomial of gegree N, $P_N^*(x)$. In this paper we have determined a_{ij} numerically, similarly to Lagrangian interpolation and choose the test function in the following form,

$$p_j(x) = P(x)/[(x - x_j)P'(x_j)] , \tag{8}$$

where $P(x)$ is a polynomial of degree N,

$$P(x) = (x - x_1)(x - x_2)\ldots(x - x_N) . \tag{9}$$

It follows that $p_j(x)$ is a polynomial of degree $N - 1$ such that $p_j(x_i) = \delta_{ij}$ and $P(x_i) = 0$, where δ_{ij} denotes the classical Kronecker delta. If the values of $u(x)$ are known at N points, $x = x_1, x_2, \ldots, x_N$, a polynomial of degree $N - 1$, $\tilde{u}(x)$, which coincides with $u(x)$ at these collocation points, can be written as

$$\tilde{u}(x) = \sum_{j=1}^{N} p_j(x)u(x_j) . \tag{10}$$

By differentiating Eq. (10) with respect to x, we have the relation,

$$\tilde{u}'(x) = \sum_{j=1}^{N} p_j'(x)u(x_j) . \tag{11}$$

Using the fact that such a relation as Eq. (4) is to be exact for $u(x) = p_j(x)$, we see that

$$a_{ij} = P'(x_i)/[(x_i - x_j)P'(x_j)] , \quad i \neq j . \tag{12}$$

For the case $i = j$, use of l'Hospital's rule gives

$$a_{jj} = P''(x_j)/[2P'(x_j)] . \tag{13}$$

Using Eqs. (12) and (13), the coefficients b_{ij} in Eq. (5) can be calculated.

Then the coefficients a_j and b_j in Eqs. (6) and (7) are determined, using the relations $a_j = a_{\alpha j}$ and $b_j^j = b_{\alpha j}$ in which $\alpha = (M + 1)/2$. The coefficients a_i and b_i^j are computed once and for all at the beginning of the calculation and stored

2.3. Time Integration

Substitution of the approximate relations, Eqs. (6) and (7), into Eq. (1) yields the set of N ODEs in time,

$$u_i'(t) = -u_i(t)D_M(u_i) + \nu D_M^2(u_i) = F(u) , \tag{14}$$

where the prime denotes differentation with respect to time. The numerical solution of such a system, Eq. (14), is a simple task, using an apprpriate time-integration scheme. In this paper we adopt the rational Runge-Kutta (RRK) method [2]. As applied to Eq. (14), the scheme can be written in the following two-stage form,

$$\begin{aligned} g_1 &= \Delta t F(u^n) , \\ g_2 &= \Delta t F(u^n + c_2 g_1) , \\ u^{n+1} &= u^n + g^2/(b_1 g_1 + b_2 g_2) , \end{aligned} \tag{15}$$

where $b_1 + b_2 = 1$, c_2 is a constant parameter and subscript i is omitted throughout. The accuracy of the scheme is generally of the order of Δt but is of the oder of $(\Delta t)^2$ if, in addition, $b_2 c_2 = -1/2$. The scheme is really explicit and is A_0-stable if $b_2 c_2 \leq -1/2$. Therefore, for the heat equation, the method is free from the severe stability restriction to which most explicit schemes are subject.

3. ACCURACY AND STABILITY PROPERTIES OF THE METHOD

3.1. Formal Accuracy for Spatial Derivatives

We denote by I, the identity operator $IU(x) = U(x)$ and by E, the translation operator $EU(x) = U(x + \Delta x)$. We denote by D_0, D_+, D_-, the usual central-, forward-, and backward-difference approximations to the differential operator $\partial/\partial x$, that is, $2\Delta x D_0 = E - E^{-1}$, $\Delta x D_+ = E - I$, and $\Delta x D_- = I - E^{-1}$, respectively. The central-difference approximation D to the differential operator $\partial/\partial x$, accurate to the order M - 1, can be written in the form

$$D = \sum_{\mu=-m}^{m} \gamma_\mu E^\mu U(x)/2\Delta x, \tag{16}$$

where $m = (M - 1)/2$ and $E^\mu U(x) = U(x + \mu\Delta x)$. Inthis representation, the coefficients γ_μ can be expressed explicitly in terms of μ and m as show by Kreiss and Oliger [4] and Fornberg [5], as

$$\gamma_\mu = \frac{2(m!)^2(-1)^{\mu+1}}{\mu(m+\mu)!(m-\mu)!} , \quad \gamma_0 = 0 . \tag{17}$$

It can be shown easily that for a uniform mesh, $\gamma_\mu = 2\,\Delta x a_{\alpha+\mu}$. As the number of points M used to approximate $\partial/\partial x$ is increased, the values of coefficients γ_μ approach the limit $(2/\mu)(-1)^{\mu+1}$. In this limit, the method is clearly identical to the Fourier method [5]. Analysis of the second-order derivative, $\partial^2/\partial x^2$ parallels that for $\partial/\partial x$. Therefore, it should be noted that the approximations with $M = 3$, 5, and 7 correspond to second, fourth, and sixth-order central-difference schemes, and the limit $M = \infty$ corresponds to the Fourier method, which is of infinite order of accuracy.

3.2. Stability Considerations

In this section we investigate the stability properties of the time-integration scheme (16) for the linearized version of Burgers equation,

$$\frac{\partial u}{\partial t} = -c\,\frac{\partial u}{\partial x} + \nu\,\frac{\partial^2 u}{\partial x^2}\,. \tag{18}$$

Using the MDQ method for spatial discretization, Eq. (18) can be written as

$$\bar{U}' = A\bar{U}\,, \tag{19}$$

where $\bar{U} = (u_1, u_2, \ldots, u_{N-1})^T$ and A is a constant $(N-1)\times(N-1)$ matrix. For the case of $M = 3$ with periodic boundary condition, the eigenvalues β_k of matrix A, which is composed of two parts A_h and A_p can be written as [8]

$$\beta_k = -(4\nu/\Delta x^2)\sin[\pi k/(N-1)] - \hat{i}(c/\Delta x)\sin[2\pi k/(N-1)]\,, \tag{20}$$

The elements of A_h and A_p can be written as

$$A_h = -\frac{c}{2\Delta x}\begin{bmatrix} 0 & 1 & \cdot & \cdot & \cdot & \cdot & \cdot & -1 \\ -1 & 0 & 1 & \cdot & \cdot & \cdot & \cdot & \\ 0 & -1 & 0 & 1 & & & & \\ & & & \cdot & \cdot & & & \\ & & & & & \cdot & \cdot & \\ 1 & & & & & & -1 & 0 \end{bmatrix} \tag{21}$$

$$A_p = \frac{\nu}{\Delta x^2}\begin{bmatrix} -2 & 1 & \cdot & \cdot & \cdot & \cdot & \cdot & 1 \\ 1 & -2 & 1 & & & & & \\ 0 & 1 & -2 & 1 & & & & \\ & & & \cdot & \cdot & & & \\ & & & & & \cdot & \cdot & \\ 1 & & & & & & 1 & -2 \end{bmatrix} \tag{22}$$

For the stability behavior of the RRK method, it is sufficient to consider the system

$$\bar{U}' = \Lambda\bar{U}\,, \qquad \Lambda = \mathrm{diag}(\beta_1, \beta_2, \ldots, \beta_{N-1})\,, \tag{23}$$

instead of Eq. (19). For the scalar test equation, $U' = \beta U$, the stability domain of the RRK method (15) is determined by the inequality

$$\left| \frac{1 + \xi(1 + b_2c_2) + \xi^2(1/2 + b_2c_2) + \xi^3 c_2/2(1/2 + b_2c_2)}{1 + b_2c_2\xi} \right| \leq 1 , \quad (24)$$

where $\xi = \beta\Delta t$. If we put $b_2c_2 = -1/2$ in (24), the stability interval is determined as

$$\left| \frac{1 + \xi/2}{1 - \xi/2} \right| \leq 1. \quad (25)$$

The left-hand side of this inequality is always less than 1 in the whole left half plane. therefore, method (15) is unconditionally stable. For a system of equations, the situation is somewhat different. However, Hairer [6] has proved that scheme (15) is A_0-stable if $b_2c_2 \leq -1/2$ and $A(\alpha)$-stable if $b_2c_2 \leq -1/[2 \cos \alpha(2 - \cos \alpha)]$. According to his stability definition, a method is said to be A_0-stable if $\{x \in R | x \leq 0\}$ is the stability region and $A(\alpha)$-stable if $\{z || \pi - \arg z | \leq \alpha\}$ is the stability region. In the case of the heat equation, the eigenvalues of A are real and negative. Therefore, the RRK method (15) is unconditionally stable. Details of the stability analysis of RRK can be seen in [6].

4. NUMERICAL RESULTS

4.1. Burgers Equation

The present method was first applied to the nonlinear Burgers equation (1), written in terms of a transformed coordinate, $x' = x - t/2$. for the sake of convenience, we will hereinafter drop the prime for the transformed coordinate. The initial condition was specified such that

$$f(x) = \begin{cases} 0 & x > 0 , \\ 1/2 & x = 0 , \\ 1 & x < 0 , \end{cases} \quad (26)$$

with the boundary conditions

$$u \to 1 \text{ as } x \to -\infty ; \quad u \to 0 \text{ as } x \to \infty \quad (27)$$

A steady-state solution of the Burgers equation subject to these boundary condition is known to be

$$U(x) = [1 - \tanh(x/4\nu)]/2 , \quad (28)$$

which gives a measure of the accuracy of the numerical results.

The results for the case of $\nu = 0.5$ obtained by the present method with $M = 9$, $c_2 = 1/2$, and $b_2c_2 = -1/2$, which is of second-order accuracy in time and of eighth-order accuracy in space, are compared in Fig. 1 with the steady-state analytical solution, Eq. (28). The numerical solutions were obtained for a uniform mesh with $\Delta x = 1.0$, which contained 17 points in the computational domain, $-8 \leq x \leq 8$. The boundary conditions at these finite locations were assigned values predicted from the exact solution, Eq. (28). In Fig. 1, the abscissa is the spatial coordinate x and the ordinate is the velocity U. The exact steady-state solution is shown by a solid line, and the numerical solutions at two different time cycles are identified by symbols (O for $n = 20$ and Δ for $n = 200$). With $\lambda = \Delta t/\Delta x = 4.0$, which corresponds to a CFL

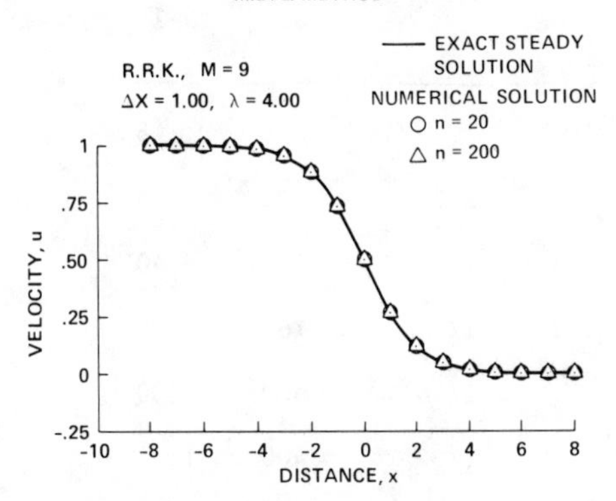

Fig. 1 Comparison of numerical solution with exact solution of Burgers equation.

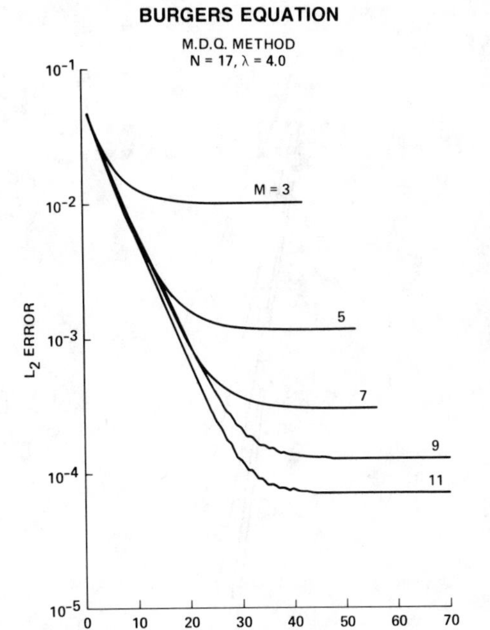

Fig. 2 Comparison of accuracy of the MDQ method with M = 3, 5, 7, 9, and 11.

number equal to 6.0, only 20 time cycles were needed to reach a steady state, starting from the initial condition, Eq. (26).

To investigate the effect of the order of the spatial derivative approximations on the accuracy of numerical solutions, the L_2 errors, defined by

$$L_2 \text{ error} = \left[\sum_{i=1}^{N-1} (\delta u_i)^2/(N-1) \right]^{1/2} , \qquad (29)$$

are plotted in Fig. 2 for $M = 3, 5, 7, 9$, and 11. In Eq. (29), the δu_i denote the difference between the analytic and numerical solution. The results were obtained for the same problem as that shown in Fig. 1, using the same values of parameters. It should be noted that at staeady state the L_2 error of the fourth-order method ($M = 5$) is an order of magnitude smaller than that of the second-order method ($M = 3$). The error of the sixth-order method ($M = 7$) is about half of the corresponding value of the method with $M = 5$. Since computational time increases proportionally with the order of the method, we can see that little is to be gained by an accuracy greater than $M = 7$.

Figure 3 is a log-log plot of the L_2 errors versus $N - 1 (\propto \Delta x^{-1})$ for the present method with $M = 3, 5, 7, 9$, and 11. Each computation was carried out to a converged steady-state solution with a fixed ratio λ. The computations were repeated successively with twice the number of mesh points as in the previous case, starting from $N - 1 = 8$. For a pth order method without machine roundoff error, the slope of the graph should be $-p$. Since the accuracy of the M-point MDQ method is of the order of $M - 1$ in space, the slope for the case with $M = 3$ should be -2; likewise with $M = 5$, it should be -4, and so on. The results confirm that the present method is of the order of $M - 1$ accurate in space. The results also show that if the given tolerance of L_2 errors is less than 5.0×10^{-4}, the second-order method ($M = 3$) needs

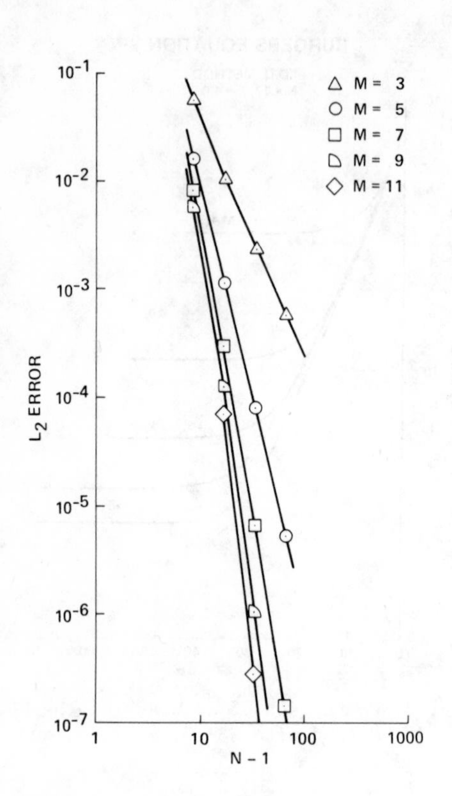

Fig. 3 Plot of L_2 errors vs N - 1 for the MDQ method with M = 3, 5, 7, 9, and 11.

c_2 \ b_2c_2	-1/2	-1
1	8	8
1/2	32	36
1/4	40	40
1/8	160	400
1/16	400	800
1/32	400	1600

Table 1 Experimental maximum stable CFL number for Burgers equation.

65 mesh points, and that the method with M = 7 requires only 17 points. The superiority of the higher-order method is clearly demonstrated in Fig. 3 and is even greater in higher dimensions.

Stability properties of the present time-integration scheme (15) were investigated for Burgers equation by repeating the caluculations for a series of fixed CFL numbers, defined as

$$\mathrm{CFL} = (|u| + 2\nu/\Delta x)\lambda \ . \tag{30}$$

The results of numerical stability investigations for the first-order (b_2c_2 = -1) and the second-order (b_2c_2 = -1/2) RRK methods with various values of c_2 are summarized in Table 1. It is remarkable that although the present method is explicit, it gives stable solutions with Cfl numbers up to $O(10^3)$.

4.2. Heat Equation

When the convection term is absent from Eq. (1), that equation reduces to the one-dimensional, unsteady heat-conduction or diffusion equation

$$\frac{\partial u}{\partial t} = \nu \frac{\partial^2 u}{\partial x^2} \ . \tag{31}$$

With an initial condition,

$$u(x,0) = b \sin \pi x + d \ , \tag{32}$$

where b and d are constants, and boundary conditions

$$u(0,t) = u(1,t) = d, \tag{33}$$

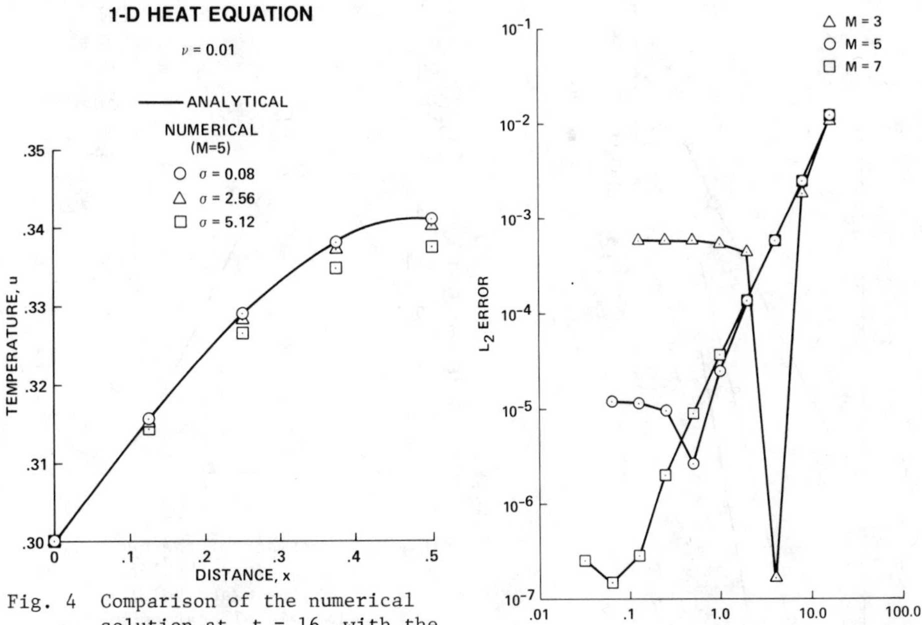

Fig. 4 Comparison of the numerical solution at $t = 16$ with the exact solution of one dimensional heat equation.

Fig. 5 Plot of L_2 error vs Δt for a fixed value of $\Delta x = 0.125$.

Eq. (31) has the analytic solution,

$$U(x,t) = b\, e^{-\nu \pi^2 t} \sin \pi x + d\ , \qquad (34)$$

which gives again a measure of the accuracy of the numerical results. The values of the constants are taken to be $\nu = 0.01$, $b = 0.2$, and $d = 0.3$.

The numerical solutions at $t = 16$ for the present method with $M = 5$ and $N = 9$, and calculated for various values of mesh ratio, $\sigma (= \nu\, \Delta t/\Delta x^2)$, are compared in Fig. 4 with the exact analytic solution (34). It is well known that the stability condition for the usual explicit, centered-space, forward-time, finite-difference scheme is $\sigma \leq 1/2$. It is clearly demonstrated in Fig. 4 that the present method gives very accurate solutions without any oscillations, even for much larger time-steps than the explicit stability limit.

Figure 5 shows log-log plots of the L_2 errors versus Δt for the second-, fourth-, and sixth-order MDQ methods combined with the RRK time-integration scheme. The parameters c_2 and $b_2 c_2$ in the RRK scheme were chosen to be 1/2 and -1/2, respectively. In this case, the RRK scheme is of second-order accuracy in time. Each computation was carried out to a given time ($t = 16.0$) with a fixed value of $x = 0.125$. The computations were repeated with successively smaller values of Δt so that the L_2 rate could be computed. The L_2 rate is defined to be the slope of a log-log graph of the L_2 error versus Δt [7]. When Δt is large (the largest value of Δt corresponds to $\sigma = 10.24$), the dominant part of the L_2 error is that of the RRK time integration scheme, so that the curves plotted for $M = 3$, 5, and 7 merge into one with a slope equal to 2. When Δt becomes smaller, the L error for each value of M decreases and finally becomes a constant that depends on the order of the MDQ method. Since Δx is fixed, the L_2 errors for small Δt are governed by the accuracy of spatial discretization.

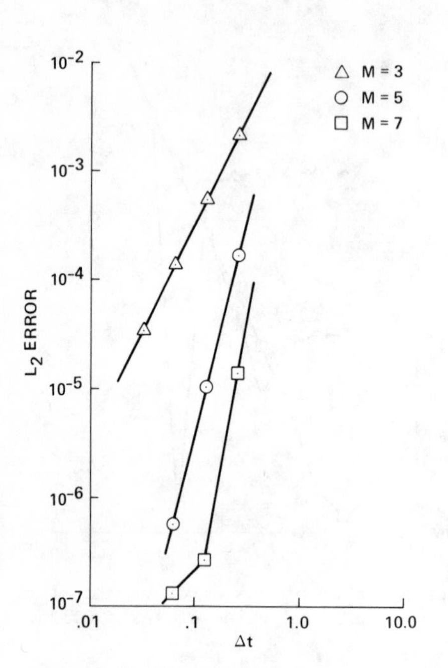

Fig. 6 Plot of L_2 errors vs Δt for a fixed value of $\lambda = 1.0$.

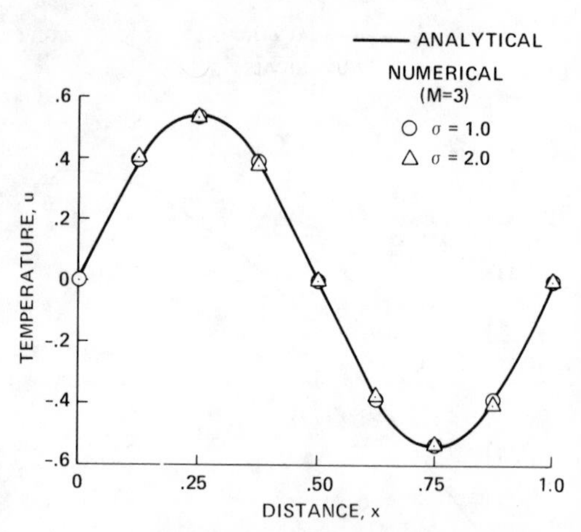

Fig. 7 Comparison of the numerical solution along the line $y = x$ with the exact solution of two-dimensional heat equation.

It should be noted that for each value of M, there exists an optimum value of Δt for which the time and spatial discretization errors cancel each other.

Figure 6 also shows log-log plots of the L_2 errors versus $\Delta t(= \Delta x)$ for the second-, fourth-, and sixth-order MDQ method combined with the second-order RRK scheme. In this case, each computation was carried out to a given time $(t = 5.0)$ with a fixed ratio of $\lambda = 1.0$. The computations were repeated successively for smaller values of $\Delta t(= \Delta x)$. Since Δx is not fixed in this case, for small values of Δt, the L_2 rate should be 2, 4, and 6 for the present method with $M = 3$, 5, and 7, respectively. The graphs clearly confirm this except for the case of $M = 7$. This discrepancy is not a result of the machine roundoff error. For the smallest value of $\Delta t(= \Delta x) = 0.0625$, the value of σ is 0.16, and the corresponding value of Δt in Fig. 5 that gives the same value of σ is 0.25. For this value of Δt, we can see that the L_2 rate for $M = 7$ is not constant but 2, which means that the dominant part of the error is that of the RRK method. Therefore, the L_2 rate for $M = 7$ should be 6 for computations with small values of λ, for which corresponding values of σ give a constant L_2 rate in Fig. 5.

As a preliminary test, the present method was then used to solve the two-dimensional heat equation,

$$\frac{\partial u}{\partial t} = \nu\left(\frac{\partial^2 u}{\partial x^2} + \frac{\partial^2 u}{\partial y^2}\right) \tag{35}$$

together with the initial condition

$$u(x,y,0) = \sin \pi(x + y) \ , \quad 0 \leq x, \ y \leq 1 \ , \tag{36}$$

and the boundary conditions

$$u(o,y,t) = e^{-2\nu\pi^2 t} \sin \pi y ,$$

$$u(1,y,t) = -e^{-2\nu\pi^2 t} \sin \pi y ,$$

$$u(x,0,t) = e^{-2\nu\pi^2 t} \sin \pi y , \tag{37}$$

and

$$u(x,1,t) = -e^{-2\nu\pi^2 t} \sin \pi x .$$

For these initial and boundary conditions, the analytic solution of Eq. (35) is known to be

$$U(x,y,t) = e^{-2\nu\pi^2 t} \sin \pi(x + y) . \tag{38}$$

Numerical calculations using the present method with $M = 3$, $c_2 = 1/2$, $b_2c_2 = -1/2$, and $\Delta x(= \Delta y = \Delta) = 0.125$ were carried out for two values of mesh ratio, $\sigma = 1.0$ and 2.0. Numerical solutions for $\nu = 1.0$ along the diagonal line $y = x$ at a fixed time, $t = 0.03125$, are compared in Fig. 7 with the analytical solution (38). We applied in this case, the present method only in its second-order form ($M = 3$), since for large values of Δt, the accuracy is determined predominantly by the time-integration scheme. There is no reason for using the higher-order methods to approximate spatial derivatives. Agreement of the numerical solution with the analytical solution is excellent, even for large values of σ.

5. CONCLUSIONS

A new explicit method has been presented for solving parabolic differential equations arising in transient heat conduction or in boundary-layer flows. The method is based on a combination of the modified differential quadrature (MDQ) method with the rational Runge-Kutta time-integration scheme and has the following features:

1. It is fully explicit and requires no matrix inversion
2. It is stable at any time-step for the heat equation
3. It is first- or second-order accurate in time
4. It is of arbitrary order of accuracy in space
5. It is simple and straightforward to program
6. It should be easy to adapt it for current and future computer

architectures.

A nonlinear model equation, that is, Burgers equation, and the one- and two-dimensional heat equations are solved to demonstrate the accuracy and efficiency of the proposed algorithm.

Even though the present method has been applied in detail only for relatively simple problems, it is clearly quite general. With no added complexity, it can be readily applied to three-dimensionsl problems and systems with an irregular boundary. The method is also applicable to other equations such as the boundary-layer equation.

ACKNOWLEDGMENTS

The research for this paper was conducted while the author was an NRC-NASA Senior Research Associate at Ames Research Center, Moffett Field, California. The author wishes to thank R. W. MacCormack for his encouragement and support, and also to thank M. Inouye for his careful reading of the manuscript.

REFERENCES

1. Richtmyer, R. D. and Morton, K. W., Difference Methods for initial-Value Problems, 2nd Ed., Interscience, New York, 1967.

2. Wambecq, A., Rational Runge-Kutta methods for solving systems of ordinary differential equations, Computing, Vol. 20, 1978, pp. 333-342.

3. Bellman, R., Kashef, B. G., and Casti, J., Differential quadrature: A technique for the rapid solution of nonlinear partial differential equations, J. Comp. Phys., Vol. 10, 1972, pp. 40-52.

4. Kreiss, H. D. and Oliger, J., Comparison of accurate methods for the integration of hyperbolic methods, Tellus, Vol. 14, 1972, pp. 199-215.

5. Fornberg, B., On a Fourier method for the integration of hyperbolic equations, SIAM J. Numer. Anal., Vol. 12, 1975, pp. 509-526.

6. Hsirer, E., Unconditionally stable explicit methods for parabolic equations, Numer. Math., Vol. 35, 1980, pp. 57-68.

7. Beam, R. M. and Warming, R. F., Alternating direction implicit methods for parabolic equations with a mixed derivative, SIAM J. Sci. Stat. Comput., Vol. 1, 1980, pp. 131-159.

8 Warming, R. F. and Beam, R. M., Implicit methods for stiff systems of ordinary and partial differential equations, Lecture notes on " Advances in Computational Fluid Dynamics " at the University of Tennessee Space Institute, Tullahoma, Tennessee, Dec. 8-12, 1980.

Evaluation of a New Iterative Solution Procedure for Conduction Heat Transfer Problems

D.O. BLACKKETTER and R.O. WARRINGTON
Montana State University
Bozeman, Montana 59717

RODNEY HORNING
Boeing Corporation
Seattle, Washington 78118

ABSTRACT:

A recently developed method for solving simultaneous linear algebraic equations will be discussed in the context of heat transfer problems. This new technique is an iterative method which reduces the number of equations and then solves the reduced set by conventional methods. While the mathematical formulation of the new method described below dictates convergence, the rate of convergence is dependent upon using knowledge of the physical system to select successive trial solutions which can result in very rapid computer solutions for physical problems, in particular, transient heat transfer problems. The new method was compared with the Alternating Direction Explicit Procedure (ADEP) for a transient three-dimensional heat transfer problem. The new method was significantly faster than ADEP.

1. INTRODUCTION

A new method for solving sets of simultaneous equations was recently presented by the authors [1]. The new method falls into the broad category of iterative or indirect solution techniques. The method uses a linear combination of trial solution vectors with each trial solution having an unknown scalar weighting coefficient. The weighting coefficients are obtained by solving a reduced set of equations which are obtained by minimizing the variance. The reduced set is solved using an exact or direct method. The trial solution vectors are different at each iteration and the iterative process is continued until the desired level of convergence has been obtained or the method stops converging. An appropriate name for this technique is the Reduced Coordinate Iterative Procedure which we will hereafter refer to as the RCIP method.

The RCIP described above is similar to the conjugate direction method [2, 3] (and appropriate conjugate gradient methods) in that both techniques involve a minimization problem at each step. The RCIP method is also similar to the least-squares method which minimizes the sum of the squares of the errors [4]. The method has been shown to be different from and perhaps more flexible than these techniques [1].

This new technique can utilize as much information about the solution as is known. Hence, the RCIP method will find its greatest application in the solution of engineering problems where there generally is considerable information about the form of the solution before the solution is attempted. In this study, the effect on convergence of the form and number of trial solution vectors will be investigated. A procedure for selecting the trial solution vectors will be proposed and the method will be compared with conventional methods for solving both steady-state and transient three-dimensional heat conduction problems.

2. ANALYSIS

2.1 Theory of the RCIP method

Let $KX = F$ (1)

be a system of n equations in n unknowns.
Initially choose m vectors

$$X_{01}, X_{02}, \ldots, X_{0m}$$

where $m < n$, and set

$$X_0 = \sum_{j=1}^{m} \alpha_j X_{0j}, \tag{2}$$

where the scalars $(\alpha_1, \alpha_2, \ldots, \alpha_m)$ are to be determined. Let

$$V_0 (\alpha_1, \ldots, \alpha_m) = \langle KX_0 - F, KX_0 - F \rangle = \| KX_0 - F \|^2, \tag{3}$$

be the inner product and the square of the norm of the residual ($R_0 = KX_0 - F$), respectively. Find the Solution $(\alpha_{01}, \ldots, \alpha_{0m})$ to the system

$$\frac{\partial V_0}{\partial \alpha_\ell} = 0, \ \ell = 1, \ldots, m. \tag{4}$$

Designate

$$\overline{V}_0 = V(\alpha_{01}, \ldots, \alpha_{0m}) \tag{5}$$

and let

$$X_{11} = \sum_{j=1}^{m} \alpha_{0j} X_{0j}. \tag{6}$$

Select the vectors $X_{12}, \ldots, X_{1m}$ and let

$$X_1 = \sum_{j=1}^{m} \alpha_j X_{1j}. \tag{7}$$

Then

$$V_1 (\alpha_1, \ldots, \alpha_m) = \| KX_1 - F \|^2. \tag{8}$$

Solve the system

$$\frac{\partial V_1}{\partial \alpha_\ell} = 0, \ \ell = 1, \ldots, m \tag{9}$$

and if $(\alpha_{11}, \ldots, \alpha_{1m})$ is the solution, designate

$$\overline{V}_1 = V_1 \ (\alpha_{11}, \ldots, \alpha_{1m}) \tag{10}$$

and let

$$X_{21} = \sum_{j=1}^{m} \alpha_{1j} \ X_{1j}. \tag{11}$$

At the i-th stage,

$$X_{i1} = \sum_{j=1}^{m} \alpha_{i-1,j} \ X_{i-1,j}. \tag{12}$$

Select vectors $X_{i2}, \ldots, X_{im}$, and let

$$X_i = \sum_{j=1}^{m} \alpha_j \ X_{ij}. \tag{13}$$

Then

$$V_i \ (\alpha_1, \ldots, \alpha_m) = \| KX_i - F \|^2. \tag{14}$$

Again solve the system

$$\frac{\partial V_i}{\partial \alpha_\ell} = 0, \ell = 1, \ldots, m. \tag{15}$$

If this solution is $(\alpha_{i1}, \ldots, \alpha_m)$, then

$$\overline{V}_i = V_i \ (\alpha_{i1}, \ldots, \alpha_{im}). \tag{16}$$

The algorithm continues with

$$X_{i+1,1} = \sum_{j=1}^{m} \alpha_{ij} \ X_{ij}, \tag{17}$$

a selection of $X_{i+1,2}, \ldots, X_{i+1,m}$,

$$X_{i+1} = \sum_{j=1}^{m} \alpha_j \ X_{i+1,j}, \tag{18}$$

and a subsequent minimization of

$$V_{i+1} \ (\alpha_1, \ldots, \alpha_m) = \| KX_{i+1} - F \|^2. \tag{19}$$

The solution of the original system is derived from

$$X = \lim_{i \to +\infty} X_{i1}. \tag{20}$$

As alluded to above, information derived from the physical setting may contribute to a strategic selection of the vectors $\{X_{i2}, \ldots, X_{im}\}$, i=0, 1, ... The influence of the number and form of the trial solution vectors is described below.

2.2 Influence of the Trial Solution Vectors, An Example

The following simple boundary value problem

$$\frac{d^2u}{dx^2} - u + x = 0 \text{ on } 0 < x < 1, \tag{21}$$

with

$$u(0) = 0 \text{ and } u(1) = 0, \quad (u_{exact} = x - \sinh(x)/\sinh(1)), \tag{21a}$$

was used to illustrate the effect of the trial solutions on the convergence rate of the new method. Equations (21) and (21a) were reduced to the following set of linear algebraic equations using central differences and a step size of 0.1,

$$\begin{bmatrix} 2.01 & -1 & 0 & \ldots & 0 \\ -1 & 2.01 & -1 & \ldots & 0 \\ \vdots & & & & \vdots \\ 0 & 0 & \ldots & -1 & 2.01 \end{bmatrix} \begin{bmatrix} u_1 \\ \vdots \\ \\ u_9 \end{bmatrix} = \begin{bmatrix} .001 \\ .002 \\ \vdots \\ .009 \end{bmatrix}. \tag{22}$$

This set of equations was solved using the new method and different trial solution vectors (except for the first iteration). The results are shown in Table 1 and in Fig. 1. The trial solution vectors consisted of:

1) The residual vector ($R_i = KX_i - F$),

2) The residual vector squared,

3) The set of conditions that if the residual were greater than zero, less than zero, or equal to zero at any particular node than that location in the trial solution vector was set to +1, -1, or zero, respectively,

4) The sum of the residuals one node away, and

5) The sum of the residuals two nodes away.

In Table 1, the second trial solution vector (X_{i2}) was always 1) except for runs number 2 and 3 where the second trial solution vectors were constructed using 2) and 3), respectively (as was shown above, the first trial solution vector, X_{i1}, is always the last best solution). The third trial solution vectors (X_{i3}) were 2), 3), and 4) for run numbers, 4, 5, and 6, respectively. The third and fourth trial solution vectors for run number 7 were 4) and 5), respectively. Each run in Table 1 converged until the mean square norm was less than .0004 with the exception of run number 2 which had not converged at 100 iterations. Clearly shown in Table 1 is the strong influence of the form of the trial solution vectors, and to a somewhat lesser extent, the influence of the number of trial solution vectors.

Table 1. Influence of the Trial Solution Vectors

Run Number	Number of Trial Solution Vectors	Number of Iterations	Mean Square Norm $(\sum_{i=1}^{n} (u_{exact}-u)^2)^{\frac{1}{2}}$	User Exec. Time (Sec)
1	2	19	.00035	.70
2	2	didn't converge at 100	.0098	2.57
3	2	63	.00035	1.71
4	3	20	.00038	.90
5	3	13	.00036	.68
6	3	7	.00035	.58
7	4	5	.00025	.58

Five of the computer runs listed in Table 1 are also shown in Figure 1. Conditions 1), 4), and 5) for selecting the trial solution vectors result in significant decreases in the number of iterations required to obtain a desired lower limit for the mean square norm. These conditions will be discussed below.

Although not shown here, the form and number of the trial solution vectors will affect the absolute convergence of the method. Certain choices for the trial solution vectors will cause the method to stop converging (in fact, if two trial solution vectors at any iteration are not independent, the method will not converge). An earlier study [1] pointed out that, in the general case, a systematic procedure for selecting $\{X_{i2}, \ldots, X_{im}\}$ that always guarantees convergence of the algorithm has not yet been realized. Thus far procedures guaranteeing convergence have not yet been computationally feasible. Independent of this choice, it has been established that $\overline{V}_{\ell+1} \leq \overline{V}_{\ell}$ and consequently $\lim_{\ell\to\infty} V_{\ell}$ exists; however, a necessary condition for convergence of the algorithm is that the sequence of the error functions, $\{V_i\}_{i=1}^{\infty}$, converge to zero.

2.3 Comments on the Selection of the Trial Solution Vectors

The selection of trial solution vectors $\{X_{i2}, X_{i3}, \ldots, X_{im}\}$ which are based on the iterative procedure and can relate to the physical problem being studied offer excellent potential for rapid convergence of the new method.

One method that has worked extremely well was to use the previous residual vector (R_{i-1}) for the second trial solution vector (X_{i2}) and the following trial solution vectors would be a linear superposition of the previous residuals one, two, ..., up to m nodes away. The residual at nodes where the dependent variable was specified was set equal to zero. For the example above the third trial solution vector (run numbers 6 and 7) would be:

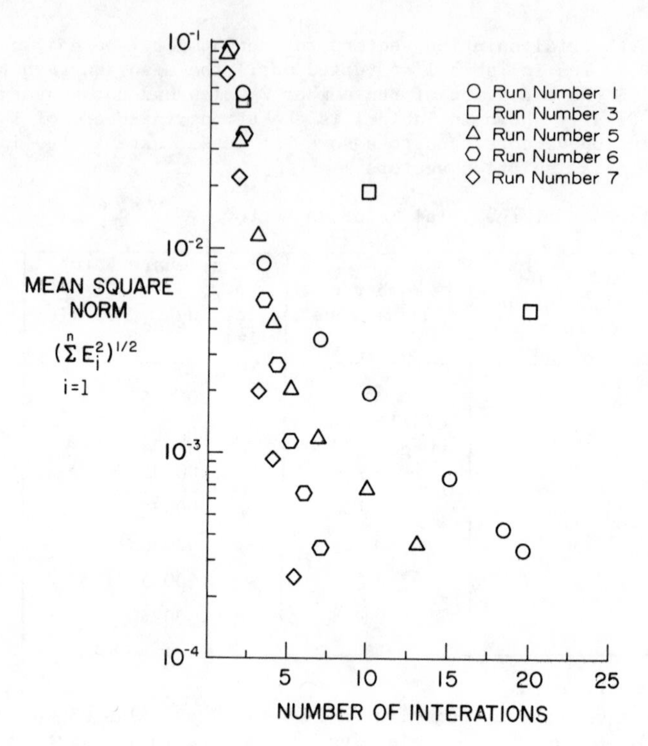

Fig.1. Convergence Rates for Different Trial Solution Vectors

$$X_{i+1,3} = \begin{bmatrix} 0 + R_{i,2} \\ R_{i,1} + R_{i,3} \\ R_{i,2} + R_{i,4} \\ \vdots \\ R_{i,n-2} + 0 \end{bmatrix} \tag{23}$$

With $R_i = KX_i - F$ and if we let $KX_i^! = R_i$ then $K(X_i - X_i^!) - F = 0$ and $(X_i - X_i^1)$ is the desired solution. Therefore, the method is similar to perturbation methods. The method described above will be used to generate the trial solution vectors in the applications to follow.

3. HEAT TRANSFER APPLICATIONS

3.1 A Three-Dimensional Steady-State Problem

A three-dimensional linear partial differential equation of the elliptic type was solved with the new RCIP technique and compared with the successive over-relaxation technique (SOR). The problem solved is

$$\frac{\partial^2 T}{\partial x^2} + \frac{\partial^2 T}{\partial y^2} + \frac{\partial^2 T}{\partial z^2} = 0 \tag{24}$$

over the region $0 < z < 1$, $0 < y < 1$ and $0 < x < z$ with boundary conditions

$$T(x,y,1) = T(x,1,z) = 0,\ T(x,y,.5) = T(x,.5,z) = 1 \tag{24a}$$

and

$$\left.\frac{\partial T}{\partial x}\right|_{(0,y,z)} = \left.\frac{\partial T}{\partial y}\right|_{(x,0,z)} = \left.\frac{\partial T}{\partial z}\right|_{(x,y,0)} = 0 \tag{24b}$$

with the final condition that

$$\left.\frac{\partial T}{\partial x}\right|_{(x=z,y)} = \left.\frac{\partial T}{\partial z}\right|_{(x=z,y)} . \tag{24c}$$

This problem represents conduction heat transfer between concentric, isothermal cubes where, due to symmetry, only a sixteenth of the region was used (Fig.2).

The results are shown in Table 2 for a grid spacing of $\Delta x = \Delta y = \Delta z = 0.1$ (330 equations). The algorithm for the interior points using SOR was

$$T^{n+1}_{i,j,k} = \gamma(T^n_{i+1,j,k} + T^n_{i-1,j,k} + T^n_{i,j+1,k} + T^n_{i,j-1,k} + T^n_{i,j,k+1} + T^n_{i,j,k-1} - (6. - \frac{1}{\gamma})\, T^n_{i,j,k}) \tag{25}$$

where γ is the over-relaxation factor. An optimum value of $\gamma = 0.31$ was determined by trial and error. For $\gamma = 0.1667$ the method is the same as Gauss Seidel and for $\gamma > 0.35$ the method diverged. For the new method, the trial solution vectors were selected as described in section 2.3 above.

Table 2. Comparison of SOR and the RCIP Method for Steady-State 3-D Heat Transfer

Method	Number of Trial Solution Vectors	γ	Number of Iterations	Exec. Time (percent greater than SOR, Optimum γ)
SOR	not applicable	0.1667 (Gauss-Seidel)	105	301.
	not applicable	0.2000	70	230.
	not applicable	0.3100	29	0.
RCIP Method	2	not applicable	88	1312
	3	not applicable	30	698
	4	not applicable	20	659
	5	not applicable	19	823

As shown in Table 2, SOR is significantly faster than the RCIP Method, particularly with the optimum over-relaxation factor. For both methods the criteria for convergence was that the inner and outer surface heat fluxes were the same (an exact solution is not available for this problem). Although the new method was slower, the results obtained for this problem were encouraging

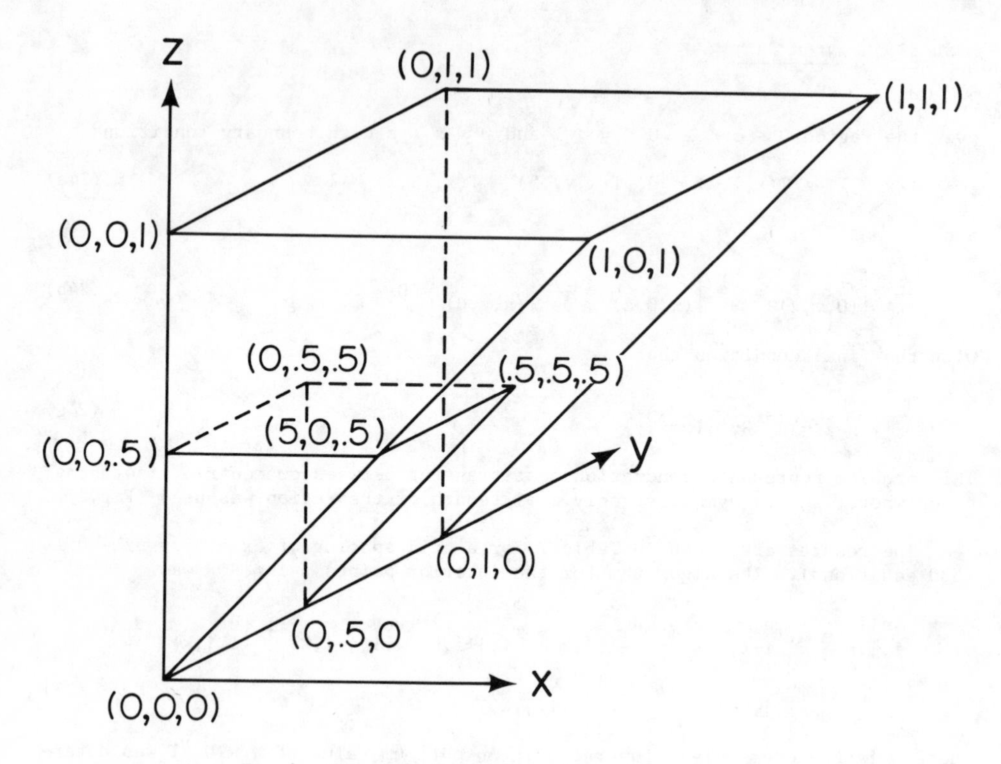

Fig.2. Geometry for Steady-State Heat Transfer

and the method was applied to transient conduction heat transfer problems where the form of the solution does not change significantly between time steps.

3.2 A Three-Dimensional Transient Problem

A three-dimensional linear partial differential equation of the parabolic type was also solved with the RCIP Method and compared with the Alternating Direction Explicit Procedure (ADEP). The problem solved is

$$\frac{\partial T}{\partial t} = \frac{\partial^2 T}{\partial x^2} + \frac{\partial^2 T}{\partial y^2} + \frac{\partial^2 T}{\partial z^2} \tag{26}$$

with boundary conditions

$$T = 0 \text{ at } x = y = z = 1 \tag{26a}$$

$$\frac{\partial T}{\partial x} = \frac{\partial T}{\partial y} = \frac{\partial T}{\partial z} = 0 \quad \text{at } x = y = z = 0$$

and initial condition

$$T = 1 \text{ at } t = o$$

The Crank-Nicolson method was used to generate 1331 equations for the cube at each time step and the RCIP Method was used to solve this set of equations.

In the solution of the problem, the initial temperature distribution in the cube was assumed to be 1.0 and four trial solution vectors, identical to those in the previous problem, were used to generate the solution using the RCIP Method. The results are shown in Figs. 3, 4, and 5 for t = 0.1, 0.5, and 1.0, respectively. As can be seen in these figures for larger time steps, the RCIP Method is clearly superior to ADEP. At t = .1, the results are similar to the steady-state example. The average percent error is defined by

$$\sum_{i=1}^{n} \left| \frac{(T_{i,exact} - T_{i,approx.})}{N} \right| \qquad (27)$$

where the exact solution was determined by Newman [5]. The dips in the curves in Figs. 4 and 5 are due to the variance (V) being much lower than the desired value of $1. \cdot 10^{-6}$ which was used to establish convergence. The lower variance was achieved because the next to last iteration produced a variance slightly above the desired value which required another iteration that reduced the variance considerably below this value. The increase in error with execution time was due to round-off. All of the computer runs just described were done in double precision on a Zerox Sigma 7 computer.

Allada and Quon [6] solved this same problem using ADEP and other implicit and explicit solution techniques. Their results showed ADEP to be an order of magnitude faster than the other techniques. We have achieved results better than ADEP.

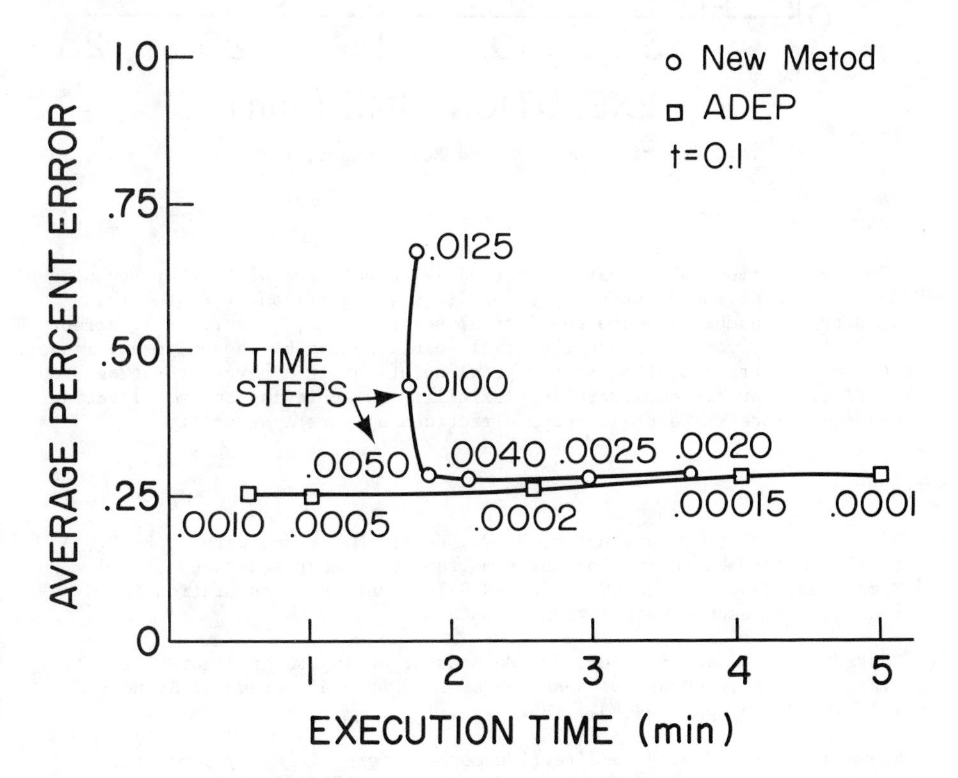

Fig.3. Comparison of ADEP and the RCIP Method, t = 0.1

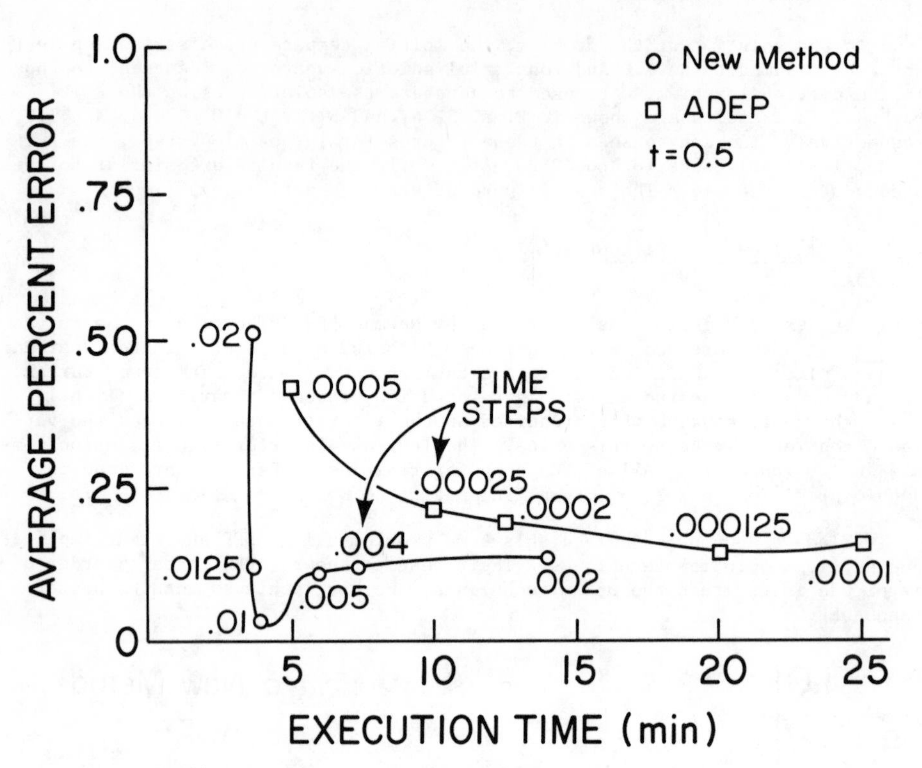

Fig.4. Comparison of ADEP and RCIP Method, t = 0.5

4. CONCLUSION

The applications show that the method is competitive with other techniques and in the case of the transient problems it was significantly faster than ADEP. Both the number and choice of trial solutions $\{X_{i,2}, \ldots, X_{i,m}\}$ effect the rate of convergence. Since the trial solutions can be chosen in any manner, with the one restriction that no two trial solutions in a given iteration step be identical, there is considerable flexibility in achieving and accelerating convergence. More research in these directions appears appropriate.

REFERENCES

1. Blackketter, D. O., Warrington, R. O., Henry, M.S., and Garner, E. R., A new iterative method for solving simultaneous linear equations, Third Symposium, June 20-22, pp. 70-72, 1979 International Association for Mathematics and Computer Simulations (IMACS).

2. Hestenes, M. R. and Stiefel, E., Methods of conjugate gradients for solving linear systems, Journal of Research of the National Bureau of Standards, Vol. 49, No. 6, pp. 409-434, 1952.

3. Steward, G. W., Conjugate direction methods for solving systems of linear equations, Numerische Mathematik, Vol. 21, pp. 285-297, 1973.

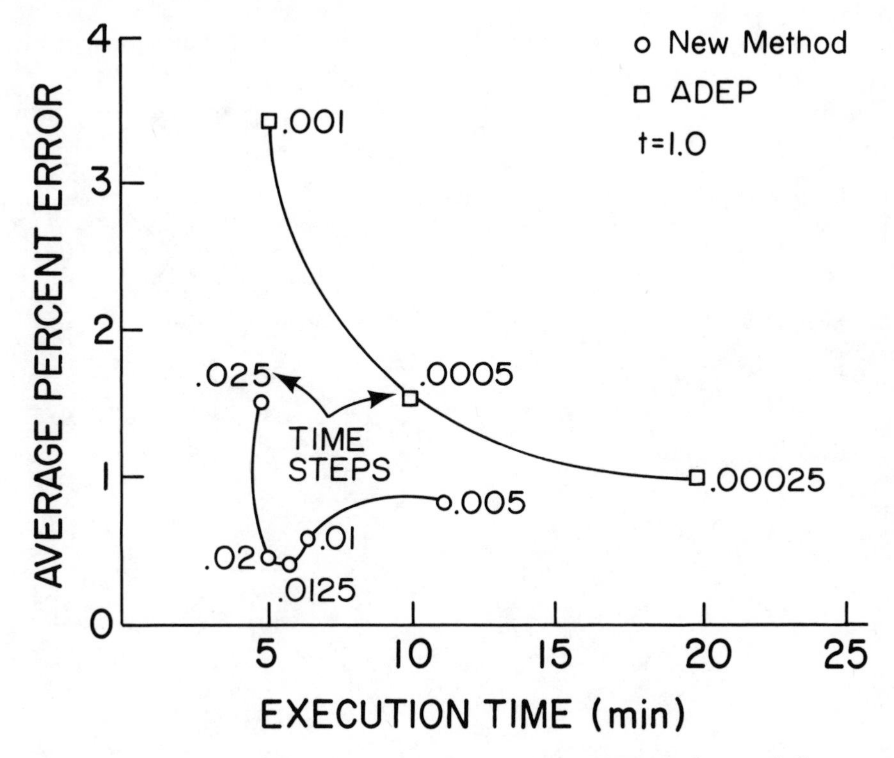

Fig.5. Comparison of ADEP and the RCIP Method, t = 1.0

4. Rust, B. W. and Burrus, W. R., Mathematical Programming and the Numerical Solution of Linear Equations, American Elsevier Publishing Co., New York, 1972.

5. Newman, A. B., Drying of porous solids: diffusion calculations, Transactions American Institute of Chemical Engineers, Vol. 27, 1931.

6. Allada, S. R. and Quon, D., A stable, explicit numerical solution of the conduction equation for multi-dimensional nonhomogeneous media, Chemical Engineering Progress Symposium Series, Vol. 62, No. 64, pp. 151-156, 1965.

Coordinate Transformation Method for Heat Conduction in 3-D

A.K. AGRAWAL
Brookhaven National Laboratory
Upton, New York 11973

R.S. PECKOVER
UKAEA Culham Laboratory
Abingdon, Oxfordshire, England

ABSTRACT

A method based on the coordinate transformation is developed to solve the heat conduction equation for an irregular, three-dimensional geometry. Basic equations for thermohydraulics are first noted. Then a change of coordinates is used to transform the irregular topography into a regularized ('cubic') shape. The resulting equations are then subjected to a second transformation which allows for fine meshes near the boundary surface without affecting interior region. This two-stage method is illustrated by applying it to heat conduction from a golf-ball shaped geometry.

1. INTRODUCTION

A common problem in the thermal and hydraulic analyses of irregular geometries has to do with the accurate specification of the boundary surfaces, since the region in the immediate vicinity of boundaries usually exhibits large gradients in flow and temperature fields, and these large gradients must be accurately accounted for. In conventional finite-difference methods, numerical solutions are obtained by approximating the irregular body shape with equivalent computational cells. Alternately, the effects due to minor deviations from approximate regular shapes are either neglected or ignored. In either case, the resulting solution is not very accurate unless the size of the computational cells is considerably reduced. Another alternative method is to employ some finite-element technique which is perhaps more suited for irregular geometries than the finite-difference method. In this paper we employ the method of coordinate transformation to solve the applicable conservation equations in a generalized three-dimensional topography.

Recently, Gal-Chen and Somerville [1] have employed a method of coordinate transformation by finding a suitable change of variables such that the irregular surfaces are regularized. We have extended [2] this method to allow for adequate resolution of boundary-layers without penalizing mesh structure in the interior region. In that paper the geometry under consideration was expressed in terms of the Cartesian coordinates, and then a suitable boundary regularization transformation was developed such that the irregular surfaces in the physical coordinate system were "ironed out" and thereby the body was reshaped into "cube" in the transformed coordinates. This method appears to work best when the body shape is readily expressible in terms of the Cartesian coordinates. For those problems where use of some other coordinates (such as cylindrical or spherical polar coordinates) facilitates expression of irregular surfaces, appropriate intermediate transformations must be developed.

This paper deals specifically with the extension of our previous work to allow for an intermediate transformation.

This paper is organized in a few parts. We begin with a general formulation of the conservation equations for incompressible, single phase fluid in non-orthogonal, generalized curvilinear coordinates. The derivation of these equations can be found in text books, such as [3], and elsewhere [2]. In order for the intermediate transformation to work, we must develop connections for various quantities such as the metric tensor, the Jacobian and the Christoffel symbol through the intermediate transformation. The resulting relationships are noted. Subsequently, we employ another change of variables to permit fine resolution inside the boundary layer without introducing unwarranted finer meshes in the interior region. A specific illustration is then given for golf ball-shaped geometry. Note that such a surface is readily expressible in terms of the spherical polar coordinates rather than the Cartesian system. The surface perturbations are treated in terms of an arbitrary function -- we have used spherical harmonics in our example. All of the intermediate quantities are then evaluated for this illustration. The complete set of equations thus obtained can then be solved for both fluid velocities and thermal heat conduction from a closed cavity.

A further simplification results when one is interested only in thermal heat conduction from solid bodies. The energy conservation equation, in the generalized coordinates, is shown to be quite simple as the Christoffel symbols do not appear in here. The metric tensor is evaluated. The resulting equation can be solved using some finite-difference method. Two types of boundary conditions are used and their equivalent forms in the transformed coordinates are also given. Finally, the paper is summarized.

2. GENERAL FORMULATION

2.1 Transformation for Generalized Coordinates

The motion of an incompressible fluid [4] in the Boussinesq approximation is represented [2,3] in a non-orthogonal curvilinear coordinate system by the following equations for continuity, momentum and energy:

$$\frac{1}{J}\frac{\partial}{\partial\xi^j}(J\rho_o w^j) = 0, \tag{1}$$

$$\frac{\partial}{\partial t}(\rho_o w^i) + \frac{1}{J}\frac{\partial}{\partial\xi^j}(J\rho_o w^i w^j) + \left\{ {i \atop m\;n} \right\} \rho_o w^m w^n$$

$$= \rho g \frac{\partial\xi^i}{\partial y^3} - g^{ij}\frac{\partial p}{\partial\xi^j} + \frac{1}{J}\frac{\partial(J\Gamma^{ij})}{\partial\xi^j} + \left\{ {i \atop m\;n} \right\} \Gamma^{mn}, \tag{2}$$

$$c_p\frac{\partial}{\partial t}(\rho_o T) + c_p\frac{1}{J}\frac{\partial}{\partial\xi^j}(J\rho_o w^j T) = \frac{1}{J}\frac{\partial}{\partial\xi^j}\left(Jg^{ij}k\frac{\partial T}{\partial\xi^i}\right) + q, \tag{3}$$

where the stress tensor Γ^{ij} is defined as

$$\Gamma^{ij} = 2\mu\, e^{ij}, \tag{4}$$

$$e^{ij} = \frac{1}{2}\left[g^{jn}\frac{\partial w^i}{\partial \xi^n} + g^{in}\frac{\partial w^j}{\partial \xi^n} - w^n\frac{\partial g^{ij}}{\partial \xi^n}\right], \tag{5}$$

ξ^i's and y^i's ($i = 1,2,3$) denote the coordinates of a point in the generalized, non-orthogonal curvilinear coordinate system and the Cartesian system, respectively, and all other symbols are defined in the nomenclature. It should be noted that the direction of gravity is taken to be parallel but in the opposite direction of y^3, and the Einstein convention for summation on repeated suffices is used.

The functional relationships for the metric tensor, g_{mn}, and its conjugate tensor, g^{mn}, are given by [5]

$$g_{mn} = \frac{\partial y^i}{\partial \xi^m}\frac{\partial y^i}{\partial \xi^n} \tag{6}$$

and

$$g^{mn} = \frac{\partial \xi^m}{\partial y^i}\frac{\partial \xi^n}{\partial y^i} \quad . \tag{7}$$

The Jacobian, J, is defined as

$$J \equiv \left|\frac{\partial y^r}{\partial \xi^s}\right|$$

$$= \left|g_{mn}\right|^{\frac{1}{2}} = \left|g^{mn}\right|^{-\frac{1}{2}} \quad , \tag{8}$$

and the Christoffel symbol of the second kind, $\left\{ {r \atop m\;n} \right\}$, is given by

$$\left\{ {r \atop m\;n} \right\} = \frac{\partial \xi^r}{\partial y^i}\,\frac{\partial^2 y^i}{\partial \xi^m \partial \xi^n} \quad . \tag{9}$$

Equations (1)-(5) take their more familiar forms in orthogonal coordinates. For example, in the Cartesian coordinate system the metric tensor g^{mn} becomes δ^{mn} (the Kronecker delta), all Christoffel symbols of the second kind reduce to zero. Equations (1)-(3) then reduce to the conservation equations in the Cartesian system.

We can now apply a transformation of coordinates, i.e., a functional relationship between the ξ^i's and y^i's, such that the irregular boundary surfaces are regularized to planar ones in the transformed space. Consider, for example, an irregular, simply connected region, as shown in Fig. 1. In the Cartesian system it can be represented as

$$0 \leq y^1 \leq D_1 , \tag{10}$$

$$0 \leq y^2 \leq D_2 , \tag{11}$$

and

$$0 \leq \phi(y^1,y^2) \leq y^3 \leq \psi(y^1,y^2), \tag{12}$$

where $\phi(y^1,y^2)$ and $\psi(y^1,y^2)$ represent, respectively, the lower and upper topographies. With the following transformation, suggested in an earlier paper [2]

$$\xi^1 = y^1/D_1 , \tag{13}$$

$$\xi^2 = y^2/D_2 , \tag{14}$$

and

$$\xi^3 = [y^3 - \phi(y^1,y^2)]/[\psi(y^1,y^2) - \phi(y^1,y^2)] , \tag{15}$$

the irregular shape of Fig. 1 is transformed into a cubic shape. The transformed conservation equations, Eqs. (1)-(3), can be solved using regularized boundaries.

2.2 Method of Successive Transformation

The transformation of variables, as given by Eqs. (13)-(15), relates the Cartesian coordinates to the generalized coordinates, and it is particularly suitable when the boundary surfaces, i.e., $\phi(y^1,y^2)$ and $\psi(y^1,y^2)$, are readily expressable in terms of the Cartesian variables. In many instances, however, it would be much more convenient to express boundary surfaces in some other coordinate system. For example, the surface of a golf ball could more easily be expressed in terms of the spherical polar coordinates along with perturbations. It is, therefore, desirable to introduce an intermediate coordinate transformation which will "bridge" the Cartesian system with the generalized curvilinear system.

Let us denote the intermediate coordinates by η^i's (i = 1,2,3). Then the transformation $\mathcal{C}$ from y^i to ξ^i can be considered as a combination of transformation $\mathcal{A}$ from y^i to η^i and transformation $\mathcal{B}$ from η^i to ξ^i. It is further assumed that all of these transformations are reversible. Then it can be shown that the transformation from one set of curvilinear coordinates to another is functional transformation. Appropriate expressions for the intermediate quantities like g_{mn}, J, and the Christoffel symbol can be obtained in terms of their counterparts in $\mathcal{A}$ and $\mathcal{B}$ spaces. We find

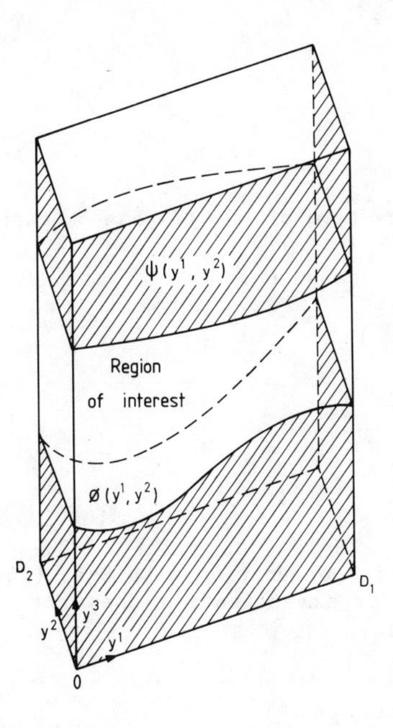

Fig. 1. General topography of the system considered.

$$g_{mn} = b^{\ell}_{m} \, g^{(A)}_{\ell r} \, b^{r}_{n} , \tag{16}$$

$$J = \left| \frac{\partial y^{r}}{\partial \xi^{s}} \right| = J_{A} J_{\mathcal{B}}, \tag{17}$$

and the Christoffel symbol of the second kind in "C" space is given by

$$\left\{ {r \atop m\ n} \right\} = \left\{ {r \atop m\ n} \right\}_{\mathcal{B}} + \mathcal{B}^{r}_{k} \, b^{\ell}_{n} \, b^{p}_{m} \left\{ {k \atop \ell\ p} \right\}_{A} \tag{18}$$

where

$$b^{i}_{j} = \frac{\partial \eta^{i}}{\partial \xi^{j}} , \tag{19}$$

$$\mathcal{B}^{i}_{j} = \frac{\partial \xi^{i}}{\partial \eta^{j}} , \tag{20}$$

$$\left\{ {k \atop \ell\ p} \right\}_{A} = \frac{\partial \eta^{k}}{\partial y^{i}} \, \frac{\partial^{2} y^{i}}{\partial \eta^{\ell} \partial \eta^{p}} , \tag{21}$$

and

$$\left\{ {r \atop m\ n} \right\}_{\mathcal{B}} = \frac{\partial \xi^r}{\partial \eta^k} \frac{\partial^2 \eta^k}{\partial \xi^m \partial \xi^n} \quad . \tag{22}$$

Finally, $\frac{\partial \xi^i}{\partial y^3}$ in the gravity term of Eq. (2) can be expressed as

$$\frac{\partial \xi^i}{\partial y^3} = \mathcal{B}^i_j \ A^j_3 \tag{23}$$

where

$$A^i_j = \frac{\partial \eta^i}{\partial y^j} \quad . \tag{24}$$

Thus, Eqs. (1) through (3) in conjunction with Eqs. (16)-(18) and (23) can be solved when body shape under investigation does not readily conform to the Cartesian coordinate system.

2.3 Boundary-Layer Resolution

In most problems of interest, there exists a large gradient of temperatures and velocities near the boundary surfaces which require incorporation of, at least, a few meshes within the boundary-layer thickness. At the same time, a uniform grid is desirable by most finite-difference schemes. As a result one ends up wasting substantial computing storage and time in the region where not needed. We, therefore, employ a method of spatial coordinate transformation which will broaden the boundary layer region without affecting the interior region. Amongst the variety of transformations that have been used [6], we recommend the following change of variables to resolve the boundary layer structures at both walls ($\xi^i = 0$ and $\xi^i = 1$):

$$x^i = \frac{c_i}{2}\left[1 + \frac{\tanh 2\alpha_i \xi^i}{\tanh 2\alpha_i} - \frac{\tanh 2\beta_i (1-\xi^i)}{\tanh 2\beta_i}\right] + (1-c_i)\xi^i \tag{25}$$

where α_i and β_i are determined by requiring that there be a desired number of meshes within the boundary layers and are given by

$$\alpha_i \simeq \frac{1}{2\delta_{oi}} \tanh^{-1}\left(\frac{2n_{oi}}{c_i N}\right) , \tag{26}$$

and

$$\beta_i \simeq \frac{1}{2\delta_{1i}} \tanh^{-1}\left(\frac{2n_{1i}}{c_i N}\right) , \tag{27}$$

where δ_{oi} and δ_{1i} are, respectively, the normalized boundary-layer thicknesses at $\xi^i = 0$ and $\xi^i = 1$, and c_i is an importance factor which determines the number of nodes in the interior region.

The conservation equations [Eqs. (1)-(3)] can now be written in the computational coordinates x^i. We get

Continuity

$$\frac{1}{J}\frac{1}{d_j}\frac{\partial}{\partial x^j}\left(J\rho_o d_j v^j\right) = 0 , \tag{28}$$

Momentum

$$\frac{\partial}{\partial t}\left(\rho_o d_i v^i\right) + \frac{1}{J}\frac{1}{dj}\frac{\partial}{\partial x^j}\left(J\rho_o d_i d_j v^i v^j\right) + \left\{ {i \atop m\ n} \right\} \rho_o d_m d_n v^m v^n = \rho g \frac{\partial \xi^i}{\partial y^3} - g^{ij}\frac{1}{d_j}\frac{\partial p}{\partial x^j} + \frac{1}{J}\frac{1}{d_j}\frac{\partial}{\partial x^j}\left(J\tau^{ij}\right) + \left\{ {i \atop m\ n} \right\} \tau^{mn}, \tag{29}$$

Energy

$$c_p \frac{\partial}{\partial t}\left(\rho_o T\right) + c_p \frac{1}{J}\frac{1}{d_j}\frac{\partial}{\partial x^j}\left(J\rho_o d_j v^j T\right) = \frac{1}{J}\frac{1}{d_j}\frac{\partial}{\partial x^j}\left(J g^{ij} k \frac{1}{d_i}\frac{\partial T}{\partial x^i}\right) + q, \tag{30}$$

where τ^{ij} denotes the stress tensor in the computational space as

$$\tau^{ij} = \mu \frac{1}{d_n}\left[g^{jn}\frac{\partial}{\partial x^n}\left(d_i v^i\right) + g^{in}\frac{\partial}{\partial x^n}\left(d_j v^j\right) - d_n v^n \frac{\partial g^{ij}}{\partial x^n} \right] \tag{31}$$

and

$$\frac{1}{d_j} = \frac{dx^j}{d\xi^j} = 1 + c_j\left[a_j \frac{\operatorname{sech}^2 2a_j\xi^j}{\tanh 2a_j} + b_j \frac{\operatorname{sech}^2 2b_j(1-\xi^j)}{\tanh 2b_j} - 1 \right] . \tag{32}$$

2.4 Inverse Transformation

So far we have presented two stages of transformations -- one from the physical space (y^i- or η^i- system) to transformed space (ξ^i-system), and the other from the transformed space to the computational space (x^i-system). While the first change of coordinates is, in general, non-orthogonal, the second one is chosen to be orthogonal. When the conservation equations

(28)-(30) are solved, the velocity components are obtained in x^i space. These results must then be transformed back into the physical space.

The contravariant components of the velocity vector in the transformed and computational spaces are related by

$$w^i = d_i v^i \tag{33}$$

since this transformation is orthogonal. If u^i denote the velocity vectors in the physical space (η^i-system), then we have

$$u^i = b^i_j w^j \tag{34}$$

where b^i_j is given by Eq. (19). Together, these two equations relate the velocity components in the computational space to the physical space.

3. EXAMPLE

We illustrate the method of successive transformation developed in the previous section by applying it to the fluid flow problem inside a golf ball-shaped cavity (Fig. 2). The surface of the golf ball can be easily characterized, in spherical coordinates, by the use of surface harmonics [7], $Y^{\ell}_m(\theta,\phi)$. Thus, the surface is expressed as

$$r = r_o \left[1 + \Sigma\, \varepsilon^{\ell}_m Y^{\ell}_m (\theta,\phi) \right] , \tag{35}$$

Fig. 2. Schematic of a golf ball-shaped cavity.

where ε_m^ℓ denotes the amplitude and it includes the normalization constant. Alternately, Eq. (35) can be written as

$$r = r_o\left[1 + f(\theta,\phi)\right] \quad . \tag{36}$$

Let (x,y,z) denote the Cartesian coordinates (y^1, y^2, y^3), the spherical coordinates (r, θ, ϕ) be the intermediate coordinates (η^1, η^2, η^3) and the generalized coordinates by (η, θ', ϕ'). Then the boundary regularization transformation, as given by Eqs. (13)-(15), becomes

$$\eta = \frac{r}{r_o[1 + f(\theta,\phi)]} \quad , \tag{37}$$

$$\theta' = \theta \; , \tag{38}$$

and

$$\phi' = \phi \; . \tag{39}$$

Then the Jacobians from the Cartesian to spherical and spherical to the transformed coordinates are given, respectively, by

$$J_A = r^2 \sin\theta \tag{40}$$

and

$$J_B = r_o(1 + f). \tag{41}$$

Using Eq. (17), the Jacobian from the Cartesian to the transformed coordinates is

$$J = r_o r^2 \sin\theta (1 + f) \tag{42}$$

The metric g_{mn} is calculated from Eq. (16). The result is

$$g_{mn} = \begin{pmatrix} \gamma_1^{\,2} & \gamma_1\gamma_2 & \gamma_1\gamma_3 \\ \gamma_1\gamma_2 & r^2+\gamma_2^{\,2} & \gamma_2\gamma_3 \\ \gamma_1\gamma_3 & \gamma_2\gamma_3 & r^2\sin^2\theta+\gamma_3^{\,2} \end{pmatrix} \tag{43}$$

where

$$\gamma_1 = r/\eta \quad , \tag{44}$$

$$\gamma_2/f_\theta = \gamma_3/f_\phi = \frac{r}{1+f} \quad , \tag{45}$$

and

$$f_\theta = \partial f/\partial\theta, \; f_\phi = \partial f/\partial\phi \; . \tag{46}$$

The calculations of the Christoffel symbols of the second kind are a bit more involved, but closed form results can be obtained by using Eq. (18). We find that out of a total of 27, only 15 are non-zero. Their expressions are given in the Appendix. Finally, from Eq. (23),

$$\frac{\partial\xi^i}{\partial y^3} = \left(\left[\frac{1}{r_o(1+f)\cos\theta} + \frac{f_\theta}{r_o(1+f)^2\sin\theta} \right], -\frac{1}{r\sin\theta} \; , \; 0 \right) \tag{47}$$

The contravarant components of the velocity vector in (r,θ,ϕ) coordinates can be related to those in the computational space from Eqs. (33) and (34). The result is

$$\begin{pmatrix} u^1 \\ u^2 \\ u^3 \end{pmatrix} = \begin{pmatrix} \gamma_1 d_1 v^1 + \gamma_2 d_2 v^2 + \gamma_3 d_3 v^3 \\ d_2 v^2 \\ d_3 v^3 \end{pmatrix} \tag{48}$$

4. HEAT CONDUCTION

The application of the coordinate transformation method to heat conduction problem from irregular solid bodies is considerably simplified, since the Christoffel symbols do not appear in the energy conservation equation. This equation, in the generalized curvilinear coordinates (ξ^i-space), is obtained from Eq. (3) as

$$c_v \frac{\partial}{\partial t} (\rho_o T) = \frac{1}{J} \frac{\partial}{\partial \xi^j} \left(J g^{ij} \, k \, \frac{\partial T}{\partial \xi^i} \right) + q. \tag{49}$$

For the case of golf ball, the desired transformation, which will make it appear like a parallelepiped ($0 \leq \eta \leq 1$, $0 \leq \theta \leq \pi$, $0 \leq \phi \leq 2\pi$) is given by Eqs. (37)-(39). The conjugate metric, g^{ij}, can be obtained from Eq. (43). We find

$$g^{ij} = \begin{pmatrix} \dfrac{1 + r^{-2}\gamma_2^2 + r^{-2}\sin^{-2}\theta\,\gamma_3^2}{\gamma_1^{\,2}} & -\dfrac{\gamma_2}{r^2\gamma_1} & -\dfrac{\gamma_3}{r^2\sin^2\theta\,\gamma_1} \\ -\dfrac{\gamma_2}{r^2\gamma_1} & \dfrac{1}{r^2} & 0 \\ -\dfrac{\gamma_3}{r^2\sin^2\theta\,\gamma_1} & 0 & \dfrac{1}{r^2\sin^2\theta} \end{pmatrix} \quad (50)$$

where γ_1, γ_2 and γ_3 are given by Eqs. (44) and (45). The Jacobian, J, is given by Eq. (42).

We now need to transform the boundary conditions. Two types of boundary conditions are considered:

(a) surface temperature specified, i.e., T is known at the surface $r = r_o[1 + f(\theta,\phi)]$,

(b) heat flux normal to the surface specified, i.e., $\partial T/\partial n$ is known at the surface.

Alternately, a linear combination of the two can be specified. The first type of condition is readily implemented by requiring temperatures at the surface $\xi^3 = \eta = 1$. For the second type, we calculate the contravariant components of the temperature gradient. It is given by $g^{ij}(\partial T/\partial \xi^j)$. Since we are interested in the normal temperature gradient and normal is in the ξ^3 direction, the quantity of interest is $g^{3j}(\partial T/\partial \xi^j)$. The heat conduction equation [Eq. (49)] can now be solved by using, for example, a standard Crank-Nicolson differencing scheme.

5. DISCUSSION AND SUMMARY

In this paper we have extended our previously described two-stage method to solve the incompressible Navier-Stokes equation for an irregular, three-dimensional geometry. The extension of the method allows consideration of an irregular, simply connected body even if it is not readily expressible in terms of the Cartesian coordinate system. This is done through an intermediate transformation which can be similarly extended to include a series of intermediate transformations. Needless to say that additional steps in the successive transformation will make the governing equations considerably more complicated.

The method developed here was then applied to a gold ball-shaped system and analytical expressions for the intermediate quantities were noted. It was pointed out that many of the additional terms in the conservation equation were in the momentum equation due to non-zero values for the Christoffel symbols. This resulted from the fact that the actual boundary regularization transformation is, in general, non-orthogonal. (Christoffel symbols of the second kind are identically zero for Cartesian coordinates.)

For the case of heat conduction from solids, only the energy conservation equation is involved. This equation does not involve any Christoffel symbol -- additional terms are still introduced due to the non-diagonal character of the metric tensor.

Although no numerical results were obtained, the most desirable feature of this technique appears to be the applicability of the method to any irregular body shape. In other words, once a computer program is written for an irregular geometry in the generalized coordinates, it can be used for a whole range of geometries by inputting the geometry shape thorugh data statements. It should also be added that the method can be further extended to multiply connected geometries by subdividing into several simply-connected regions.

ACKNOWLEDGEMENTS

This work was sponsored partly by the U.S. Nuclear Regulatory Commission and partly by the U.K. Safety and Reliability Directorate.

APPENDIX

Analytical expressions for all Christoffel symbols of the second kind have been obtained by using Eq. (18). Out of a total of 27, only the following 15 have non-zero values:

$$\begin{Bmatrix} 1 \\ 2\;2 \end{Bmatrix} = -\eta - \frac{2\eta}{(1+f)^2} f_\theta^2 + \frac{\eta}{1+f} f_{\theta\theta} \qquad (A.1)$$

$$\begin{Bmatrix} 1 \\ 3\;2 \end{Bmatrix} = \begin{Bmatrix} 1 \\ 2\;3 \end{Bmatrix} = -\frac{2\eta}{(1+f)^2} f_\theta f_\phi - \frac{\eta}{1+f} f_\phi \cot\theta + \frac{\eta}{1+f} f_{\theta\phi} \qquad (A.2)$$

$$\begin{Bmatrix} 1 \\ 3\;3 \end{Bmatrix} = -\eta\sin^2\theta - \frac{2\eta}{(1+f)^2} f_\phi^2 + \frac{\eta}{1+f} f_{\phi\phi} + \frac{\eta}{1+f} \sin\theta\cos\theta f_\theta \qquad (A.3)$$

$$\begin{Bmatrix} 2 \\ 2\;1 \end{Bmatrix} = \begin{Bmatrix} 2 \\ 1\;2 \end{Bmatrix} = \begin{Bmatrix} 3 \\ 1\;3 \end{Bmatrix} = \begin{Bmatrix} 3 \\ 3\;1 \end{Bmatrix} = \frac{1}{\eta} \qquad (A.4)$$

$$\begin{Bmatrix} 2 \\ 2\;2 \end{Bmatrix} = \frac{2f_\theta}{1+f} \qquad (A.5)$$

$$\begin{Bmatrix} 2 \\ 2\;3 \end{Bmatrix} = \begin{Bmatrix} 3 \\ 3\;2 \end{Bmatrix} = \frac{f_\phi}{1+f} \qquad (A.6)$$

$$\begin{Bmatrix} 2 \\ 3\;3 \end{Bmatrix} = -\sin\theta\cos\theta \qquad (A.7)$$

$$\begin{Bmatrix} 3 \\ 3\;2 \end{Bmatrix} = \begin{Bmatrix} 3 \\ 2\;3 \end{Bmatrix} = \frac{f_\theta}{1+f} + \cot\theta \qquad (A.8)$$

$$\left\{ {3 \atop 3\ 3} \right\} = \frac{2f_\phi}{1+f} \tag{A.9}$$

REFERENCES

1. Gal-Chen, T. and Somerville, R.C.J., On the use of a coordinate transformation for the solution of the Navier-Stokes equations, J. Comp. Phys., Vol. 17, 1975, pp. 209-228.
2. Agrawal, A.K. and Peckover, R.S., A coordinate transformation method for thermohydraulics in irregular 3-D geometries, Nucl. Sci. and Eng. (to be published).
3. Eringen, A.C., Mechanics of Continua, Robert E. Kriger Publishing Co., Huntington, New York, 1980.
4. Batchelor, G.K., An Introduction to Fluid Dynamics, Cambridge University Press, 1967.
5. McConnell, A.J., Applications of Tensor Analysis, Dover Publications, New York, 1957 (1931).
6. Agrawal, A.K. and Peckover, R.S., Nonuniform grid generation for boundary layer problems, Computer Phys. Comm., Vol. 19, 1980, pp. 171-178.
7. Morse, P.M. and Feshbach, H., Methods of Theoretical Physics, McGraw Hill, New York, 1953, p. 1264.

NOMENCLATURE

c_p	specific heat at constant pressure
c_v	specific heat at constant volume
g	acceleration due to gravity
g_{ij}	metric tensor
J	Jacobian
p	deviation in fluid pressure
q	external heat source per unit volume
u^i	fluid velocity components in the physical system
v^j	fluid velocity components in x^i-system
w^j	fluid velocity components in ξ^j-system
x^i	coordinates in the computational system (i=1,2,3)
y^i	Cartesian coordinates (i=1,2,3)
$Y^\ell_m(\theta,\phi)$	spherical harmonics
Γ^{ij}	stress tensor in ξ^i-system
η^i	intermediate coordinates (i=1,2,3)
θ,ϕ	spherical polar coordinates
μ	fluid viscosity
ξ^i	generalized coordinates (i=1,2,3)
ρ	deviation in fluid density
ρ_o	hydrostatic equilibrium fluid density
τ^{ij}	stress tensor in x^i-system
$\left\{ {i \atop j\ k} \right\}$	Christoffel symbol of the second kind

Two-Dimensional Analysis of Fin Assembly Heat Transfer: A Comparison of Solution Techniques

D.B. INGHAM
Department of Applied Mathematical Studies
University of Leeds
Leeds LS2 9JT, England

P.J. HEGGS
Department of Chemical Engineering
University of Leeds
Leeds LS2 9JT, England

M. MANZOOR
Department of Applied Mathematical Studies
University of Leeds
Leeds LS2 9JT, England

P.R. STONES
British Nuclear Fuels Ltd.
Windscale and Cumbria Works
Cumbira, England

ABSTRACT

The two-dimensional analysis of the heat flow within a finned heat exchanger which comprises longitudinal rectangular fins attached to a plane wall requires the solution of a Laplacian mixed boundary-value problem. This can be achieved by various numerical techniques, e.g. the finite-difference, finite-element and boundary integral equation methods. In addition, this particular fin assembly problem is also susceptible to treatment by a series truncation method. In this study the relative performances of the finite-difference, finite-element, boundary integral equation and series truncation methods in determining the fin assembly heat transfer rate are investigated. The capabilities and limitations of each method are also discussed.

1. INTRODUCTION

The theoretical study of the heat flow within finned heat exchangers is of considerable practical importance because of the extensive utilisation of fins for heat transfer enhancement in applications varying from gas liquefacation plant to heat rejection equipment in motor vehicle engines. The accurate prediction of the thermal performance of finned heat exchangers is essential for compact and efficient design. However, in the analysis of such systems, it is conventionally assumed that the heat flow is one-dimensional because this, in general, facilitates an analytical treatment, e.g. [1,2] . The early investigations into the applicability of the one-dimensional approximation restricted attention solely to the fin and concluded that two-dimensional effects are negligible provided the transverse Biot number, based on the fin-base thickness, is much less than unity, e.g. [3,4,5] . Recent investigations of the combined fin and supporting surface have shown that the presence of fins induces two-dimensional variations within the fin, e.g. [6,7,8] . Suryanarayana [7] has reported that the difference between fin assembly heat transfer rates predicted by one- and two-dimensional analyses can be as much as 80 per cent. It is therefore essential for the effective design of finned heat exchangers to consider the complete fin assembly and to employ a multi-dimensional analysis.

The two-dimensional analysis of conductive-convective heat flow through an assembly of longitudinal rectangular fins attached to a plane wall requires the solution of a Laplacian mixed boundary-value problem, e.g. [6,7,8] . This can be achieved by various numerical techniques, e.g. the finite-difference [9] , finite-element [10] and boundary integral equation [11] methods. This fin assembly problem is also susceptible to an analytical treatment [12] . The separation of variables method enables the derivation of a series solution. However, this solution is not in a closed form; the determination of the coefficients associated with the series expansion requires the solution of a system of linear algebraic equations. The generation of this algebraic representation is achieved by truncating the series and then collocating in a manner analogous with the discretization process of a numerical scheme.

The main objective of the present study is to investigate the relative performance of the finite-difference (FD), finite-element (FE), boundary integral equation (BIE) and series truncation (ST) techniques in determining the heat transfer rate through an assembly of longitudinal rectangular fins attached to a plane wall. In this investigation the general situation in which the fin and supporting surface have different thermal conductivities is considered.

2. ANALYSIS

The following analysis is based upon the classical assumptions employed in the examination of conducting-convecting finned surfaces, namely, constant thermal conductivities, uniform heat transfer coefficients and perfect wall-to-fin contact, e.g. [6,7,8] . These simplifications are introduced not only to reduce the complexity of the problem but also to minimise the number of variable parameters while still retaining the essential features of the actual physical situation.

Consider an assembly of longitudinal rectangular fins attached to a plane wall, as depicted schematically in Fig. 1. The geometrical symmetry of the fin arrangement indicates that it is only necessary to examine that section of the assembly bounded by the contour OABCDEFO, Fig. 1. Therefore, for steady-state two-dimensional heat flow, the determination of the fin assembly temperature distribution requires the simultaneous solution of

$$\nabla^2\theta_w = 0 \qquad \text{within} \qquad \Omega_w \tag{1}$$

and

$$\nabla^2\theta_f = 0 \qquad \text{within} \qquad \Omega_f \tag{2}$$

subject to the boundary conditions

$$\text{on OA} \qquad \theta_f' = -\frac{Bi_2}{\kappa}\theta_f \tag{3a}$$

$$\text{on AB} \qquad \theta_f' = -\frac{Bi_2}{\kappa}\theta_f \tag{3b}$$

$$\text{on BC} \qquad \theta_f' = 0 \tag{3c}$$

$$\text{on CO} \qquad \theta_f = \theta_w \tag{3d}$$

$$\text{and} \qquad \theta_w' = -\kappa\theta_f' \tag{3e}$$

on CD $\theta_w' = 0$ (3f)

on DE $\theta_w' = Bi_1 (1 - \theta_w)$ (3g)

on EF $\theta_w' = 0$ (3h)

on FO $\theta_w' = - Bi_2 \theta_w$ (3i)

where the prime (') denotes the derivative in the direction of the outward normal to the associated surface.

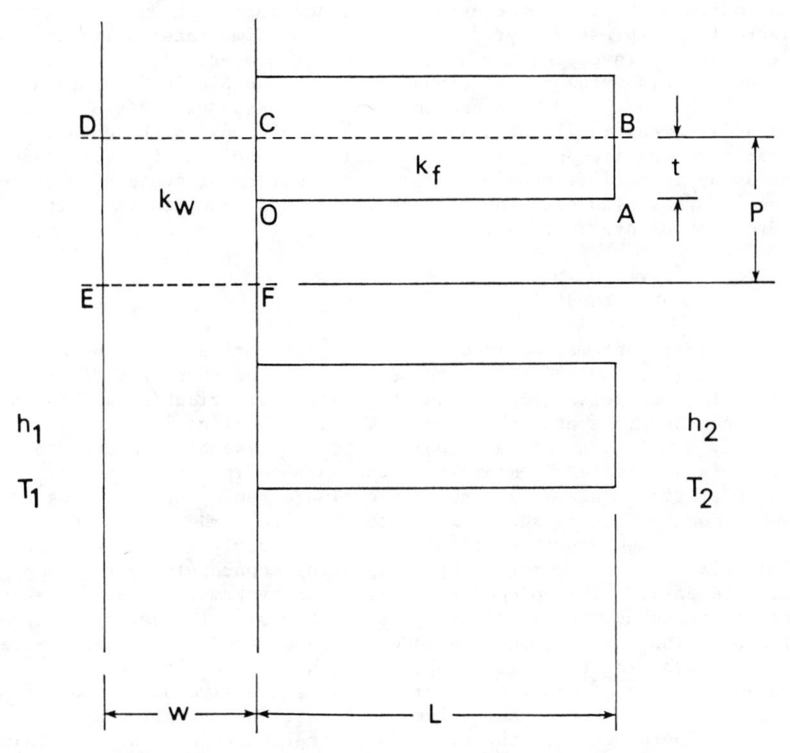

Fig. 1. Schematic representation of a fin assembly

Conditions (3c), (3f) and (3h) arise from the geometric and thermal symmetry of the fin assembly configuration and stipulate that there is no heat flux across the fictitious boundaries BC, CD and EF, respectively. Conditions (3d) and (3e) arise from the assumption of perfect wall-to-fin contact which requires that the temperature and heat flux be continuous across the contact interface, OC. The remaining boundary conditions describe the convective heat exchange from the exposed surfaces, DE and FOAB. The heat flow through the assembly is parameterised by the Biot numbers, Bi_1 and Bi_2, the ratio of the thremal conductivities κ, and the aspect ratios L/P, t/P and w/P.

3. SOLUTION METHODS

3.1 Finite Difference Method

With the finite-difference formulation the problem described by Eqs. (1), (2) and (3) is replaced by a system of linear algebraic equations in which the unknowns are the temperatures at discrete points within the fin assembly domain, [9] . This algebraic representation is generated by a relatively simple process. A rectangular mesh is super-imposed over the domain Ω and nodes are situated at the latice points of this mesh. Then, at each internal node the differential equations (1) and (2) are replaced by the appropriate five-point central difference approximations and at each boundary node the differential operators in the respective boundary condition are approximated by the appropriate three-point central difference formula [9] . Assembling these discretized expressions produces a system of simultaneous linear algebraic equations involving the unknown nodal temperatures. In this study the solution to this sytem of equations is obtained employing a Gaussian elimination technique [9] which accounts for the banded structure of the equations and thereby facilitates substantial reductions in the computational storage and time requirements. The possibility of solving the algebraic equations by an iterative technique, namely the method of successive-over-relaxation [9] has also been investigated. It was found that the iterative process does not always converge.

3.2 Finite Element Method

The finite-element method involves the reformulation of the problem defined by Eqs. (1), (2) and (3) in terms of a pair of coupled variational statements [10] one pertaining to the temperature distribution within the wall, and the other to that within the fin. The coupling is a consequence of the continuity conditions (3d) and (3e). The fin assembly temperature distribution is determined by minimising the surface integrals occurring in the variational statements. In order to evaluate these surface integrals the fin assembly domain Ω is subdivided into a finite number of triangular elements and the temperature is assumed to vary linearly within each element. The minimisation is then performed by integrating separately over each of the triangular elements. This procedure generates a system of linear algebraic equations in the unknown element corner temperatures. The relative performances of a Gaussian elimination technique and the method of successive-over-relaxation in obtaining the solution to this system of equations has been investigated. It was found that the method of successive-over-relaxation does not always give a convergent solution in that the iterative process fails to converge. Therefore, all the finite-element results presented in this study are computed employing a modified Gaussian elimination technique which takes into account the banded structure of the equations and thereby minimises the respective computational requirements.

3.3 Boundary Integral Equation Methods

The application of Green's Integral Formula [11] to the problem described by Eqs. (1), (2) and (3) gives rise to an integral equation involving two coupled contour integrals, one around $\partial\Omega_f$ and the other around $\partial\Omega_w$. The coupling arises from the interface boundary conditions (3d) and (3e). In order to obtain a solution to the integral equation, the contours $\partial\Omega_f$ and $\partial\Omega_w$ are subdivided into rectilinear segments and nodes are situated at the midpoint of each of these segments. The temperature and heat flux on each segment are approximated by piecewise-constant functions. Then, the discretized form of the integral equation is collocated at each of the boundary nodes. This generates a system of linear algebraic equations involving the unknown nodal temperatures. This system of equations is considerably smaller than that generated by an equivalent finite-difference or finite-element representation because the BIE discretization occurs only on the boundary of the fin assembly domain Ω . Consequently, even for fine discretizations, it is most appropriate to solve these equations by a direct method such as Gaussian elimination. Nevertheless, the possibility of obtaining solutions employing the method of successive-over-relaxation has also been investigated. It was found that the iterative process fails to converge irrespective of the values of the system parameters, the size of the boundary discretization and the magnitude of the relaxation parameter.

3.4 Series Truncation Method

The separation of variables technique enables the differential equations (1) and (2) to be integrated exactly and gives the solutions in terms of infinite series of hyperbolic and trignometric functions [12] . The coefficients and eigenvalues associated with these series expansions are determined from the boundary conditions (3). Enforcing the conditions (3b), (3c), (3f) and (3h) gives rise to expressions which explicitly define the eigenvalues. Enforcing the remaining boundary conditions generates a set of relations involving the unknown coefficients. However, these relations are not in a closed form. Therefore, in order to determine the coefficients it is necessary to truncate the series and then to enforce these relations approximately. This generates a system of linear algebraic equations in which the unknowns are the coefficients associated with the truncated series. The solution to this system of equations is achieved by Gaussian elimination and the corresponding temperature distribution is obtained by appropriate summation of the series.

4. DISCUSSION OF SOLUTION METHODS

From the brief descriptions presented in the preceding section it is apparent that there are basic conceptual differences between the various solution techniques. The FD formulation tackles the governing equations directly in the prescribed form, i.e. without any further mathematical analysis and requires discretization over the entire domain. The FE method reformulates the prescribed problem in terms of variational statements but nevertheless involves approximations throughout the fin assembly domain, Ω . The BIE method firstly transforms the prescribed problem into an equivalent set of integral equations by means of an analytical integration which, in effect, reduces the dimension of the problem by one. These integral equations only involve the boundary values of the temperature and consequently approximations are only introduced on the domain boundary, $\partial\Omega$. With the ST technique the governing equations are integrated exactly and approximations are only introduced in order to satisfy the boundary conditions (3d), (3e) and (3i). The ST technique is, in essence, equivalent to a numerical technique which uses very sophisticated polynomial approximations to the solution and applies these at every point within the fin assembly domain. In contrast, the FD, FE and BIE techniques use comparatively simple approximations and apply these only at discrete points within the domain.

In order to critically assess the relative performance of the solution techniques it is necessary to define some form of equivalence of the various forms of discretization. This is readily accomplished for the FD, FE and BIE methods because the application of each of these methods involves some form of subdivision of the fin assembly domain; the discretization of each of these methods is simply based upon a comparable subdivision of the domain. A rectangular grid is established over the domain Ω and the FD discretization is performed on this grid. Each of the rectangular sub-regions of the FD grid is subdivided along a diagonal, as shown in Fig. 2, and the resulting triangular elements are used for the FE discretization. The boundary elements of the FD grid are used as the boundary segments for the BIE discretization, Fig.2. Thus, the FE, FE and BIE implementations are considered to be equivalent if the respective discretizations are based upon the same mesh size.

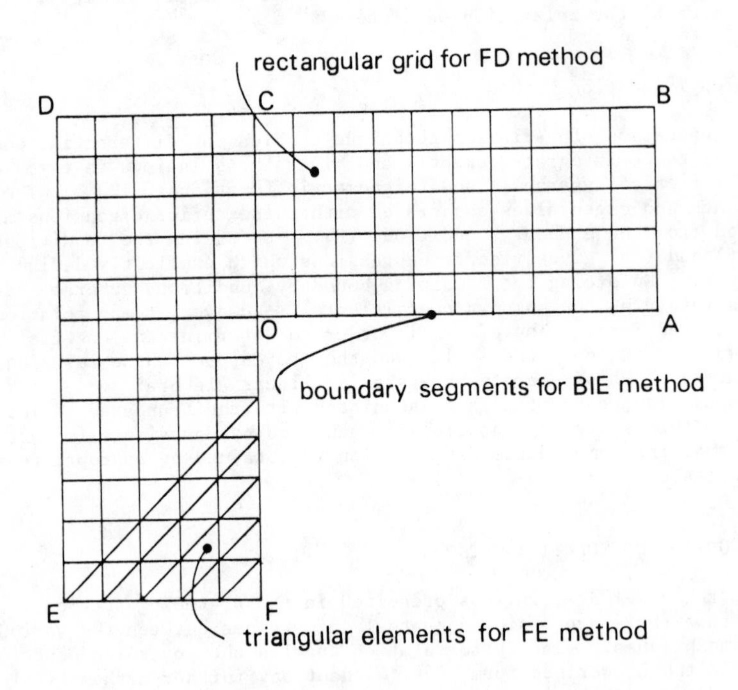

Fig.2 FD, FE and BIE discretizations of the fin assembly domain.

It is not possible to relate the ST discretization to that of the FD, FE and BIE methods because the ST solution procedure does not involve a subdivision of the fin assembly domain. However, as the algebraic representations generated by the BIE and ST methods are similarly dense, as opposed to the banded system of equations produced by the FD and FE formulations, the ST discretization shall be considered to be equivalent to that of the other techniques if the BIE and ST algebraic representations are of the same size, i.e. if the number of terms taken in the truncated series solution is equal to the number of boundary segments employed in the implementation of the BIE method.

5. HEAT EXCHANGER PERFORMANCE

The heat flow rate through the fin assembly is most conveniently expressed in the form of an augmentation factor, Aug, which is defined as the ratio of the heat transfer rate of the fin assembly to that of the unfinned wall operating under the same conditions [8] . This augmentation factor can be evaluated at either of the exposed surfaces DE and FOAB [8] , and is given by

$$\text{Aug} = \left(\frac{1}{Bi_1} + \frac{w}{p} + \frac{1}{Bi_2}\right) \int_{DE} Bi_1 \, (1 - \theta_w(q))dq \tag{4}$$

$$= \left(\frac{1}{Bi_1} + \frac{w}{p} + \frac{1}{Bi_2}\right) \left\{ \int_{FO} Bi_2 \, \theta_w(q)dq + \int_{OAB} Bi_2 \, \theta_f(q)dq \right\} . \tag{5}$$

In the context of the FD, FE and BIE solutions these integrations can be performed employing an appropriate quadrature formula. However, as these techniques only provide approximate solutions, the corresponding values for the integrations (4) and (5) need not be exactly the same, although, for the solutions to be satisfactory these should agree to within an acceptable tolerance. Therefore, in the subsequent calculations Aug_1 and Aug_2 shall denote the values of the augmentation factor corresponding to the expressions (4) and (5) respectively. A further requirement for the solutions to be satisfactory is that the corresponding augmentation factors show a convergent behaviour as the order of approximation is improved, i.e. as the mesh is refined, in the case of the FD, FE and BIE solutions, and as more terms are taken in the truncated series, in the case of the ST solutions.

With the FD and FE formulations the evaluation of the expressions (4) and (5) requires the determination of the temperature distribution throughout the domain Ω . In contrast, the BIE method yields all the necessary information for the computation of these quantities, namely the boundary distribution of θ , when the boundary integral equation representation of the problem described by Eqs. (1), (2) and (3) is solved. With the BIE formulation the fin assembly temperature distribution is simply generated from that on the boundary and need only be computed if desired.

The ST technique enables the integrations (4) and (5) to be performed analytically and has the added advantage that these may be evaluated without computing the temperature at any point within the assembly [12] .

6. RESULTS AND DISCUSSION

The solution to the problem described by Eqs. (1), (2) and (3) by any technique which involves approximations in the solution procedure invariably includes an error. The errors in the solutions predicted by the FD, FE and BIE methods are related to the associated mesh sizes [9,10,11] whilst those in the ST solutions are dependent upon the length of the truncated series [12] e.g. the central difference approximations used in FD method introduce a discretization error of the $O(H^2)$, where H is the largest of the associated mesh spacings [9] . These errors diminish as the respective discretization is refined and consequently the approximate solutions approach the exact solution. In order to check for this convergence, solutions are computed for three different levels of discretization. These are denoted by discretization A, discretization B and discretization C, and, for the FD, FE and BIE methods, correspond to the FD grids described by

Discretization	H(OA)	H(OC)	H(OX)	H(OF)
A	OA/16	OC/4	OX/4	OF/4
B	OA/32	OC/8	OX/8	OF/8
C	OA/64	OC/16	OX/16	OF/16

These particular discretizations were found to offer the most efficient use of the computational resources with respect to the accuracy of the corresponding solutions. The discretizations A, B and C correspond to a total of 125, 441 and 1649 nodes for each of the FD and FE methods, and 64, 128 and 256 boundary segments for the BIE method. The equivalent ST discretizations take 64, 128 and 256 terms in the truncated series.

Solutions have been computed for a wide range of the system parameters Bi_1, Bi_2, κ , L/P, t/P and w/P . The results for 3 particular problems are presented in Tables I, II and III. These Tables show the values of the augmentation factors, Aug_1 and Aug_2, and the respective ratios of Aug_1 to Aug_2, as predicted by the FD, FE, BIE and ST methods. These correspond to the problems defined by the system parameters,

Problem	Bi_1	Bi_2	κ	L/P	t/P	w/P
I	5×10^{-2}	10^{-2}	20.0	5.0	0.25	0.5
II	10^{-1}	10^{-2}	1.0	5.0	0.10	2.0
III	10^{-1}	10^{-2}	2.0	10.0	0.10	2.0

Table I : The FD, FE, BIE and ST solutions for problem I

METHOD	Discretization A			Discretization B			Discretization C		
	Aug_1	Aug_2	E	Aug_1	Aug_2	E	Aug_1	Aug_2	E
FD	3.389	3.188	1.063	3.285	3.185	1.032	3.233	3.183	1.016
FE	3.188	3.188	1.000	3.185	3.185	1.000	3.183	3.183	1.000
BIE	2.977	3.445	0.864	3.100	3.285	0.944	3.149	3.222	0.977
ST	3.181	3.181	1.000	3.181	3.181	1.000	3.181	3.181	1.000

The solutions to these problems illustrate various features of the FD, FE, BIE and ST solution techniques and are characteristic of the solutions observed for other values of the system parameters. In particular, for all problems considered, the solutions predicted by all four solution techniques display a convergent behaviour as the corresponding discretization is refined. However, these solutions invariably fail to achieve their respective limiting values. This slow convergence is probably caused by the presence of a boundary singularity at the re-entrant corner, O , Fig. 1 [11] . It may be possible to obtain more accurate solutions by employing modified implementations which give special treatment to the singular point and thereby facilitate solutions which converge more rapidly, e.g. [13,14,15] . However, in comparison with the standard methods, these modified implementations necessitate considerably more programming effort and involve significant changes in the data structure, e.g. [13,14,15] . A more practical method for obtaining the limiting solutions would be to employ some form of extrapolation, e.g. for problem III the limiting values of Aug_1 and Aug_2 have been computed using Richardson's formula [16] ,

$$Err(N) \propto (H(N))^{\alpha} \tag{6}$$

where $Err(N)$ is the error in the solution given by the N equation discretization, $H(N)$ is an associated mesh size and α is the order of the extrapolation; these limiting solutions are included in Table III. The excellent agreement between the extrapolated values of Aug_1 and Aug_2 emphasises the suitability of the Richardson's extrapolation method for obtaining the limiting values of the FD, FE and ST solutions, Table III. However, Richardson's extrapolation method is inappropriate for obtaining the limiting values of the BIE solutions, because these solutions include rather excessive errors.

A salient feature of all the results obtained, and clearly evident in Tables I, II and III, is the fact that the accuracy of the ST solutions is virtually independent of the system parameters; in all cases the first three significant figures in the ST solutions remain unchanged as the truncated series is extended from 64 to 256 terms, e.g. Tables I, II and III. Furthermore, although the rate of convergence of the FD and FE methods varies from problem to problem, it has been found that the change in values of Aug_1 and Aug_2 predicted by these methods, as the discretization is refined from case A to case C, is always less than 5 per cent. The rate of convergence of the BIE solutions also changes from problem to problem, but the changes in the values of Aug_1 and Aug_2, as the discretization is refined from case A to case C, are appreciably larger than those evident in the FD, FE and ST solutions. In fact, it has been found that the BIE solutions can change by over 30 per cent as the boundary discretization is refined from 64 to 256 boundary segments. These variations in the rate of convergence of the FD, FE and BIE solutions can be attributed to the fact that the accuracy of the solutions predicted by these methods is dependent upon the mesh size used for discretization, and the mesh size is, in turn, dependent upon the dimensions of the region Ω . The fin assembly dimensions for problem I are considerably smaller than those for problem III, consequently, the errors in the solutions for problem I are less than those for problem III.

The results predicted by the four solution techniques always show a convergent behaviour as the respective discretization is refined, however, only the FE and ST solutions satisfy the energy conservation criterion that Aug_1 be identically equal to Aug_2, i.e., $E = 1.0$. The accuracy with which

Table II : The FD, FE, BIE and ST solutions for problem II

METHOD	Discretization A			Discretization B			Discretization C		
	Aug_1	Aug_2	E	Aug_1	Aug_2	E	Aug_1	Aug_2	E
FD	3.338	3.253	1.026	3.282	3.241	1.013	3.253	3.233	1.006
FE	3.255	3.255	1.000	3.241	3.241	1.000	3.232	3.232	1.000
BIE	2.080	4.256	0.489	2.667	3.715	0.718	2.999	3.422	0.876
ST	3.224	3.224	1.000	3.224	3.224	1.000	3.223	3.223	1.000

Table III : The FD, FE, BIE and ST solutions for problem III

METHOD	Discretization A			Discretization B			Discretization C			Limit		
	Aug_1	Aug_2	E	Aug_1	Aug_2	E	Aug_1	Aug_2	E	Aug_1	Aug_2	E
FD	3.663	3.572	1.025	3.598	3.553	1.013	3.563	3.541	1.006	3.524	3.521	1.001
FE	3.571	3.571	1.000	3.553	3.553	1.000	3.541	3.541	1.000	3.520	3.520	1.000
BIE	2.622	4.827	0.543	3.139	4.131	0.760	3.381	3.776	0.896	3.595	3.404	1.056
ST	3.529	3.529	1.000	3.528	3.528	1.000	3.528	3.528	1.000	3.528	3.528	1.000

the FD solutions satisfy these conditions improves as the mesh is refined from discretization A to discretization C, although the condition E = 1.0 is never achieved by these solutions. However, the discretization C FD solutions are never more than 2 per cent in error of the requirement that E = 1. The accuracy with which the BIE solutions satisfy the energy conservation criterion also improves as the discretization is refined from case A to C. However, it has been found that these BIE solutions can lead to values of E which differ by over 50 per cent from the requirement that E = 1.0, e.g., see Table II.

In order to assess the relative performance of the four solution techniques, in addition to comparing the accuracy of the solutions given by these methods, it is also necessary to compare the respective computational requirements. The computational storage and time requirements of the various implementations of the four solution techniques have, therefore, been determined and are displayed in Table IV. From the data presented in Table IV it is clearly evident that for each particular level of discretization the ST method requires considerably more storage than the other methods, and, furthermore, is substantially slower, except in comparison with the discretization C implementations of the FD and FE methods. However, whereas the discretization A ST solutions are always accurate to at least 3 significant figures, the discretization C FD, FE and BIE are usually only accurate to 2 significant figures. Thus, not only is the ST method more accurate than the numerical methods, but it requires substantially less computational storage and time in order to attain this higher degree of accuracy.

Table IV : Computational requirements of the FD, FE, BIE and ST methods.

METHOD	Discretization A		Discretization B		Discretization C	
	CPU Time	Storage	CPU Time	Storage	CPU Time	Storage
FD	0.2	45	4.5	285	130.0	2095
FE	0.2	45	4.5	285	130.0	2095
BIE	0.8	45	3.2	140	15.8	530
ST	2.0	80	9.9	280	58.0	1062

CPU Time is in seconds

Storage is in Kbytes

7. CONCLUSIONS

The relative performance of the FD, FE, BIE and ST techniques in determining the heat transfer rate of an assembly of longitudinal rectangular fins attached to a plane wall has been investigated. The results indicate that the FE and ST methods are the best suited to this fin assembly problem because the solutions predicted by these methods not only display a uniform convergent behaviour as the respective discretization is refined but also always satisfy the energy conservation criterion (E = 1.0). The ST method is by far the best method for the particular fin assembly problem considered as it gives the most accurate solutions with the minimum computational storage and time requirements. However, the ST method is inapplicable for problems involving tapered or curved fins and, on the basis of the present investigation, the FE method is recommended for the solution of such problems.

ACKNOWLEDGEMENT

The financial assistance given to M. Manzoor and P.R.Stones by the Science Research Council, is gratefully acknowledged.

NOMENCLATURE

Aug	Augmentation
Bi_1	$= h_1 P/k_w$, Biot number
Bi_2	$= h_2 P/k_w$, Biot number
E	$= Aug_1/Aug_2$
h	heat transfer coefficient, W/m^2K
H(OA)	mesh spacing on OA
H(OC)	mesh spacing on OC
H(OF)	mesh spacing on OF
H(OX)	mesh spacing on OX
k	thermal conductivity, W/mK
L	fin length, m
P	half fin-pitch, m
t	half fin-base thickness, m
T	temperature distribution, K
T_1, T_2	fluid temperatures, K
w	wall thickness, m
κ	$= k_f/k_w$

θ = $(T-T_2)/(T_1-T_2)$, dimensionless temperature

Ω_f region bounded by OABCO

Ω_w region bounded by OCDEFO

Ω = $\Omega_f + \Omega_w$

$\partial\Omega_f$ contour OABCO

$\partial\Omega_w$ contour OCDEFO

$\partial\Omega$ = $\partial\Omega_f + \partial\Omega_w$

Subscripts

1 plain side

2 fin side

f fin

w wall

REFERENCES

1. Gardner K.A.. 1945. Efficiency of extended surfaces. Trans.ASME, (Vol.67, pp.621-631.

2. Mikk I. 1980. Convective fin of minimum mass. Int.J.Heat Mass Transfer, Vol.23, pp. 707-711.

3. Irey R.K. 1968. Errors in the one-dimensional fin solution. Trans.ASME. J. of Heat Transfer, Vol.90, pp.175-176.

4. Levitsky M. 1972. The criterion for the validity of the fin approximation, Int.J.Heat Mass Transfer, Vol.15, pp.1960-1963.

5. Lau W. and Tan C.W. 1973. Errors in the one-dimensional heat transfer analysis. Trans.ASME.J. of Heat Transfer, Vol.95, pp.549-551.

6. Sparrow E.M. and Lee L. 1975. Effects of fin-base temperature depression in a multifin array. Trans. ASME. J. of Heat Transfer, Vol.97, pp.463-465

7. Suryanarayana N.V. 1977. Two-dimensional effects on heat transfer rates from an array of straight fins. Trans. ASME. J. of Heat Transfer, Vol.99, pp.129-132.

8. Heggs, P.J. and Stones P.R. 1980. The effects of dimensions on the heat flow rate through extended surfaces. Trans. ASME. J. of Heat Transfer, Voo.102, pp.180-182.

9. Smith G.D. 1974. Numerical Solution of Partial Differential Equations. Oxford University Press.

10. Zienkiewicz O.C. 1971. The Finite Element Method in Engineering. McGraw Hill. London.

11. Jawson M.A. and Symm G.T. 1977. Integral Equation Methods in Potential Theory and Electrostatics. Academic Press. London.

12. Heggs P.J., Ingham .D.B. and Manzoor M. 1981. The analysis of fin assembly heat transfer by a series truncation method. Accepted for publication by Trans. ASME. J. of Heat Transfer.

13. Griffiths D.F. 1977. A numerical study of a singular elliptic boundary value problem. JIMA, Vol.19, pp.59-69.

14. Wait R. 1977. Singular isoparametric finite elements. JIMA, Vol.20 pp.133-141.

15. Symm G.T. 1973. Treatment of singularities in the solution of Laplace's equation by an integral equation method. National Physical Laboratory Report NAC 31.

16. Ralston A. 1965. A First Course in Numerical Analysis. McGraw Hill, New York.

Development of Inverse Finite Element Techniques for Evaluation of Measurements Obtained from Welding Process

J.W. MACQUEENE, R.L. AKAU, G.W. KRUTZ,
and R.J. SCHOENHALS
Purdue University
West Lafayette, Indiana 47907

ABSTRACT

This paper illustrates methodology used in determining the efficiency of an arc welding process by the inverse finite element method. In order to test the validity of the finite element method, a simple one dimensional model was first investigated. The calculated temperatures from the forward finite element scheme were compared with results obtained employing a finite difference method and also with the exact solution. These comparisons exhibited very good agreement in general. However, it was also verified that the finite element method, when used with a consistent capacitance approach, yielded maximum principle instability resulting in erroneous temperature calculations in those instances. After verification of the forward finite element approach, an inverse one dimensional finite element program was developed for determining the imposed heat flux at the surface, given the time-temperature history at an interior point. Iterating on boundary temperature rather than boundary heat flux was found to produce faster convergence and less susceptibility to numerical oscillations. Next, a two dimensional forward finite element program was developed, and the calculated results were compared with temperature measurements obtained from an experimental apparatus. The deviations between the values obtained from the finite element program and the experiment were found to be primarily due to the errors inherent in the experimental apparatus itself. A two dimensional inverse finite element program was then developed using Beck's method, which incorporates one future time step. The program successfully predicted the heat flux for two different situations (step change in surface heat flux and a ramp-type surface heat flux) based on the known time-temperature history at an interior point. Several experiments were performed employing an arc welding apparatus. Calculated efficiency values were found to be in agreement with results from a previous investigation.

1. INTRODUCTION

Welding processes are a vital part of the manufacturing industry, but despite their widespread use, little is known about the temperature changes which accompany these processes. Temperature variations which occur during welding may lead to such undesirable side effects as weld embrittlement and residual stresses. Another problem of increasing concern in recent years is energy efficiency; welding processes consume large quantities of energy, portions of which may be lost rather than being applied to the weld itself.

This research has been devoted to the development of numerical techniques for predicting temperature histories in a weld cross section and determining heat input from a welding apparatus. The procedure investigated requires solution of the inverse heat transfer problem. The more traditional forward heat transfer problem involves specification of boundary conditions and solution for interior temperature histories. On the other hand, the inverse problem involves the specification of internal temperature histories at one or more discrete interior points (as can be obtained from thermocouples) and solution for boundary conditions as well as temperature histories in the remainder of the interior.

The finite element method was chosen as the numerical technique best suited to handling the complexities and nonlinearities inherent in modeling of a welding process. These difficulties include irregular geometry, radiation, phase change and variation of thermal properties with temperature. As part of the research, a series of less complex heat transfer problems was investigated in order to develop and verify the algorithms involved, prior to modeling of the actual welding situation.

2. THEORY

The finite element method is a numerical technique for solving boundary value problems which can be applied in situations where solution by classical means may be impractical. The phenomenon of interest (stress, strain, temperature, etc.) is assumed to be piecewise continuous across each element according to a specified convention (linear, quadratic, cubic, etc.). An equilibrium type equation may be written for each element and the equations for all elements cascaded and solved simultaneously for the quantity in question. For transient problems, as encountered in certain types of heat transfer situations, the solution is an iterative one giving distributions at discrete values of time. As a result, several forward marching time stepping schemes have been developed, most notably the Euler, Crank-Nicolson, and pure implicit methods.

The derivation of the governing equations for the finite element method as applied to forward transient heat transfer is well documented in the literature. Myers[1], Segerlind [2], Zienkiewicz [3] and Huebner [4] all provide clear explanations. In essence, the finite element method transposes the governing differential equation for heat transfer in an object into a series of simultaneous equations which may be solved by standard techniques such as Gaussian elimination followed by reverse substitution. The governing differential equation for two dimensional heat conduction is

$$\rho \, c_p \frac{\partial T}{\partial t} = \frac{\partial}{\partial x} \left(k \frac{\partial T}{\partial x}\right) + \frac{\partial}{\partial y} \left(k \frac{\partial T}{\partial y}\right). \qquad [1]$$

where:

ρ - density, kg/m^3

c_p - specific heat, watt-sec/kg-K

T - temperature, K

k - thermal conductivity, watts/m-K

The equivalent finite element representation, discretized in time as well as space, is expressed by

$$([K] + \frac{2}{\Delta t}[C])\{T\}^{t+1} = (\frac{2}{\Delta t}[C] - [K])\{T\}^{t} + (\{F\}^{t+1} + \{F\}^{t}). \qquad [2]$$

where:

[K] - stiffness matrix, watts/K

[C] - capacitance matrix, watt-sec/K

Δt - time step, sec

$\{T\}^{t+1}$ - future nodal temperature vector, K

$\{T\}^{t}$ - present nodal temperature vector, K

$\{F\}^{t+1}$ - future forcing vector, watts

$\{F\}^{t}$ - present forcing vector, watts

Equation [2] is based on the Crank-Nicolson, or central difference, time stepping scheme. Further explanation of certain terms is in order. The stiffness matrix [K] characterizes the material thermal conductivity and the geometry of the model as well as temperature dependent boundary conditions such as convection and radiation. This matrix is banded and symmetric in nature. The capacitance matrix [C] characterizes the material specific heat and latent heat. In order to avoid maximum principle instability, a lumped capacitance scheme was used, resulting in a diagonal capacitance matrix. The lumped capacitance matrix for a two dimensional bilinear triangular element is

$$[C^e] = p\,\frac{c_p A}{3}\begin{vmatrix}1 & 0 & 0\\ 0 & 1 & 0\\ 0 & 0 & 1\end{vmatrix} \qquad [3]$$

where A is the cross sectional area of an element.

The type of instability refered to above is discussed by Fujii [5], Macqueene et al [6] and Macqueene [7], and is exemplified by a negative change in internal temperature in response to a positive change in boundary heat flux for a body initially at equilibrium. This behavior is typical of models employing a consistent capacitance scheme where the capacitance matrix for a two dimensional bilinear triangular element is

$$[C^e] = p\,\frac{c_p A}{12}\begin{vmatrix}2 & 1 & 1\\ 1 & 2 & 1\\ 1 & 1 & 2\end{vmatrix} \qquad [4]$$

Although maximum principle instability effects diminish after several time steps, it is important to avoid them in inverse solutions. Lastly, the forcing vector {F} represents the presence of boundary conditions, such as imposed heat flux, convection, and radiation.

Another type of instability, referred to as mean square instability, manifests itself in the form of numerical oscillations in calculated interior temperature values. The occurrence of this instability is dependent upon the time stepping scheme and the size of the chosen time step. Lemmon and Heaton [8] and Myers [9] give stability criteria for one and two dimensional finite element models, respectively. For one dimensional linear elements,

$$\frac{k \Delta t_c}{\rho c_p (\Delta x)^2} = \frac{1}{6}. \quad [5]$$

where:

Δt_c - critical time step, sec

Δx - element length, m

For two dimensional bilinear triangular elements,

$$\frac{k \Delta t_c}{\rho c_p L^2} = \frac{1}{18}. \quad [6]$$

where L is the minimum element side length. The critical time step, Δt_c is the maximum satisfactory time incriment above which oscillatory behavior will occur, and below which stable behavior will result.

Techniques employed for handling the nonlinearities of the welding process followed those recommended in the literature. Radiation, as suggested by Myers [1], was modeled as analogous to convection, with the resultant effective heat transfer coefficient being determined using the previously calculated elemental surface temperature. Variation of thermal properties with temperature was accomodated by recalculating the stiffness and capacitance matrices based on the thermal properties corresponding to the average elemental temperatures calculated at the previous time, as demonstrated by Friedman [10] and Krutz [11]. The energy associated with phase change was treated by appropriately varying the elemental specific heat when the average elemental temperature was in the melt range, as recommended by Carnahan et al [12]. Heat transfer in the weld pool was accounted for by the use of an effective thermal conductivity value for the liquid phase, as recommended by Krutz [11].

The formulation of an inverse solution was based on techniques developed by Krutz et al [13] and Beck et al [14]. The former method is an iterative one whereby, at each time, the surface heat flux is varied until the temperature calculated by means of a forward finite element program agrees with a known temperature (experimentally measured) within a small arbitrarily prescribed error. The latter method invloves minimization of the sum squared difference based on the experimental and calculated temperatures at locations where temperatures are measured, taking into consideration data at times in the future of the one being analyzed. This technique helps reduce the effect of lag time between a change at the surface and the resultant sensing at the thermocouple location.

3. ONE DIMENSIONAL MODEL

The purpose of the earlier stages of the research was to test the applicability of the finite element method to the modeling of transient heat transfer in metals, with particular emphasis on the inverse solution. Although the methods were developed with the intent of eventually analyzing heat transfer from a welding arc to a metal plate, several less complex models were used to verify the methods.

A one dimensional forward model employing linear elements provided the opportunity to develop the necessary computer algorithms while at the same time maintaining simplicity. Heat transfer in a steel rod of constant cross

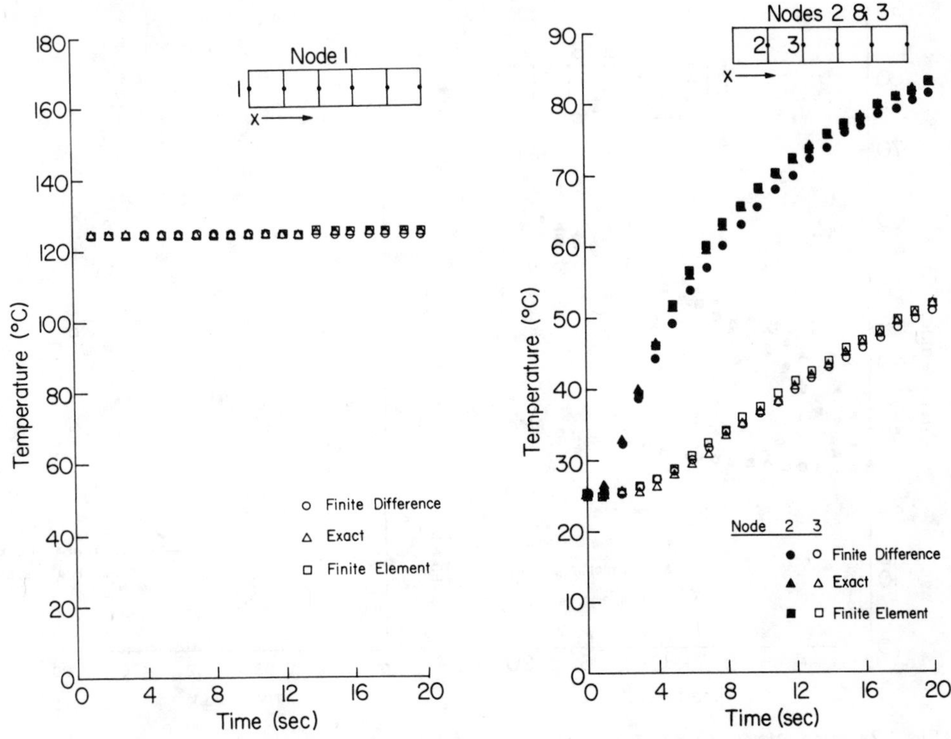

Fig. 1a. Imposed Constant Boundary Temperature Condition (125 C) Used to Test Forward Solution Techniques-Node 1.

Fig. 1b. One Dimensional Calculated Results Obtained Using Forward Techniques-Nodes 2 and 3.

section was investigated. The model consisted of six equally spaced nodes which delineated five linear elements of identical thermal properties and initial temperature. Forward solutions were obtained by exact, finite difference, and finite element methods for two different boundary conditions at one end: step change in boundary temperature and step change in boundary heat flux. All other surfaces were modeled as insulated.

The finite element results were found to compare favorably with the finite difference and exact solutions. Figures 1a and 1b show results obtained for the case of a step change in boundary temperature. Figure 1a shows the imposed step change which was the same for all three cases. Figure 1b shows the differences in the predicted temperature values at two interior points. Both the finite difference and finite element models employed a Crank-Nicolson time stepping method. Finite element solutions were obtained for lumped and consistent capacitance schemes. The lumped scheme produced results which agreed with the other solutions at all points and times. However, the consistent scheme produced results exhibiting maximum principle instability. These instabilities diminished with time and the solution approached that obtained from the lumped scheme, but the initial instability was significant. Thereafter, the lumped capacitance scheme was employed to assure the avoidance of maximum principle instability.

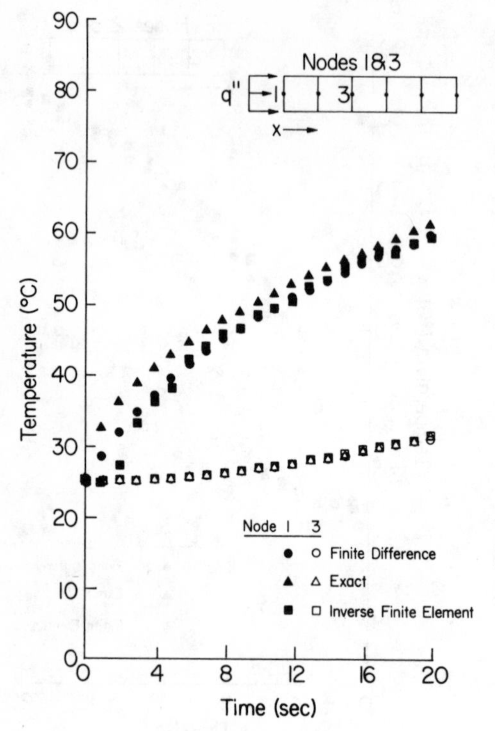

Fig. 2a. One Dimensional Calculated Results for an Imposed Constant Heat Flux of 100 kw/m^2-Nodes 1 and 3.

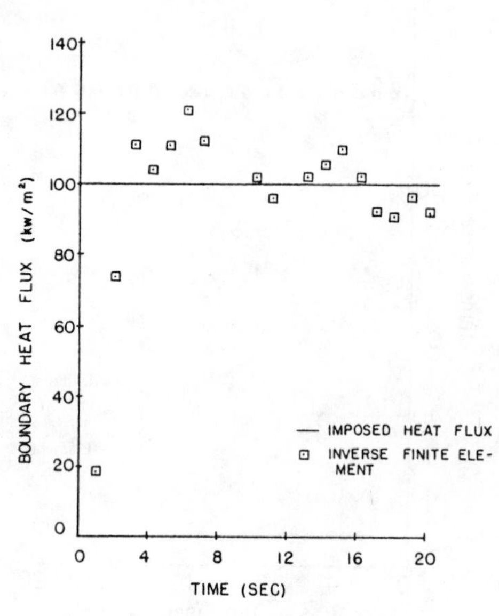

Fig. 2b. One Dimensional Finite Element Program Prediction of Boundary Heat Flux and Comparison with Imposed Boundary Heat Flux 100 kw/m^2.

Following the work on the forward finite element solution, an inverse program was written and applied to the steel rod problem previously treated. The initial techniques employed for the one dimensional inverse problem were similar to those developed by Krutz et al [13]. The methods involved a forward finite element solution for which the boundary heat flux was varied at each time until the known temperature value at a specified location (point of measurement) and the corresponding calculated temperature agreed. This program proved to be slow to converge and subject to numerical oscillation in calculating boundary heat flux and boundary temperature history.

The inverse program was modified to iterate on boundary temperature, rather than heat flux as had been done previously. Once the boundary temperature had been calculated by an inverse Crank-Nicolson scheme, the boundary heat flux was determined by substituting the temperature history into a pure implicit solution and solving for the heat flux in the forcing vector. This program was found to be faster to converge and less subject to numerical oscillation in calculating boundary heat flux (though not completely free of oscillation). The temperature history predictions for the other nodes agreed quite well with those predicted by the forward solution. Examples of the results obtained from the one dimensional inverse program are shown in Figs. 2a and 2b. In this case a boundary heat flux of 100 kw/m^2 was imposed, and the

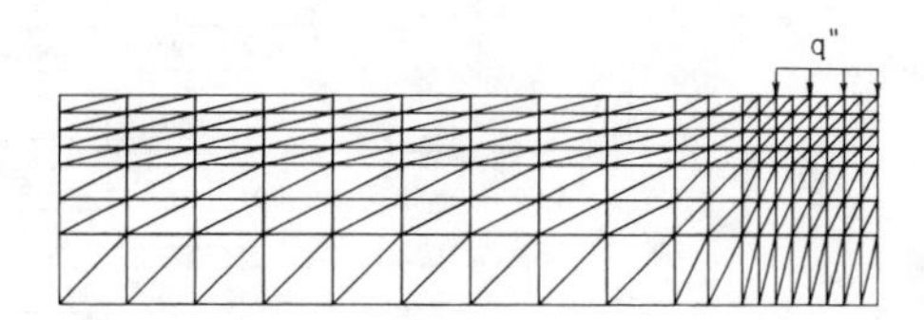

Fig. 3. Finite Element Mesh Used in Analysis of Steel Plate.

temperature histories at the various nodes were calculated utilizing forward techniques. To test the inverse program, only the temperature history calculated by the forward technique at node 2 was provided to it. With this information alone, the inverse program generated predictions of the temperatures at all the remaining nodes and also the boundary heat flux. Figure 2a compares the temperature predictions of the inverse program with those generated by the forward solution, while Fig. 2b compares the heat flux predicted by the inverse program with the imposed constant heat flux of 100 kw/m^2.

Overall, the one dimensional inverse program seemed satisfactory for predicting temperature history, but was still subject to some numerical oscillation in the heat flux predictions. This could be improved, however, by using averaging techniques to damp out the oscillation.

4. TWO DIMENSIONAL MODEL

A forward finite element program was written for solving generalized two dimensional transient heat transfer problems. Linear triangular elements were chosen for their simplicity and their adaptability to modeling of irregular domain shapes. The program has the capability of simulating a variety of boundary conditions which include convection, imposed heat flux, and specified boundary temperature. As in the one dimensional program, a Crank-Nicolson time stepping scheme was employed. The program was written in such a manner as to economize on both computer storage requirements and computational time. In particular, the algorithms for matrix reduction and reverse substitution were constructed so as to take advantage of the banded nature of the matrices.

A number of trials were made using the two dimensional forward finite element program to test the effects of time step, varied heat flux conditions, and capacitance schemes. In most of the cases studied, a 160 node, 266 element model of a steel plate subjected to a localized heat flux was employed (see Fig. 3). The plate thickness was 0.038 m, and its upper surface was subjected to a uniform heat flux over a width of 0.032 m. All the surfaces of the steel plate, except the portion subjected to heating, were considered to be insulated. Variation of the time step did not appear to significantly affect either accuracy or stability of the temperature calculations, even when the time step exceeded the critical time step specified by Myers [9] for avoiding mean square instability. It appears that Myers' critical time step is a conservative estimate and that, in some cases, this critical time step can be exceeded while still maintaining stability. As expected, the use of a consistent capacitance scheme resulted in some maximum principle instabilities at nodes immediately beneath the surface where heat flux was applied. These instabilities were small and became insignificant after several time steps.

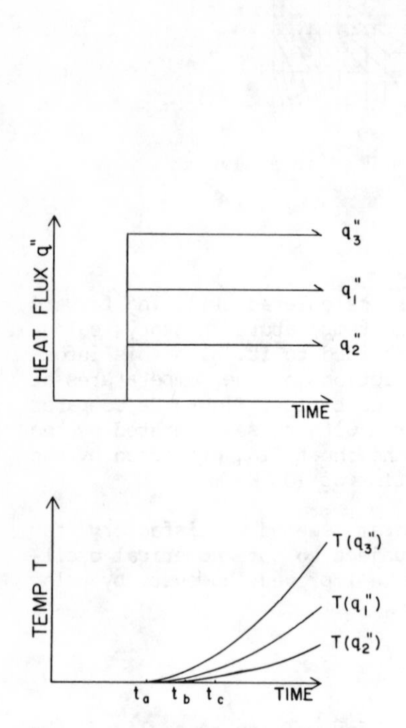

Fig. 4. Temperature Histories at an Interior Point Due to Three Different constant Surface Heat Fluxes.

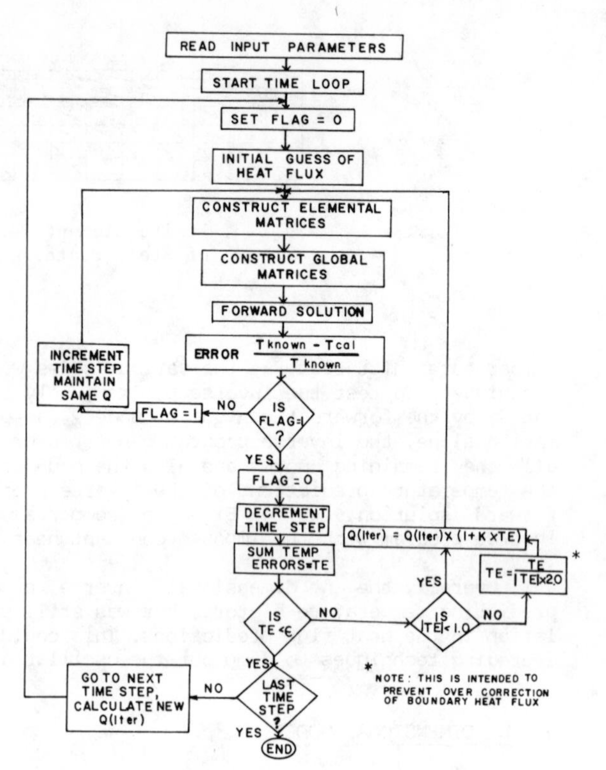

Fig. 5. Flow Chart of Two Dimensional Finite Element Program Incorporating Use of Future Temperature.

Following the development of the forward two dimensional finite element program, a two dimensional inverse program was written. The inverse program is basically a modification of the forward program, involving the addition of a program loop inside the time step loop which compares calculated and known temperatures and then changes boundary conditions accordingly. The method adopted is quite similar to the approach taken by Krutz et al [13], but took advantage of one technique suggested by Beck et al [14] for inverse analysis; this was the inclusion of the known temperature values at times in the future of the one under consideration. This has the effect of eliminating some of the time lag between the onset of a change in boundary condition and a resultant detectable response at an interior point where the temperature history is known. Graphically, this may be viewed as the response of an interior point to several different step changes in boundary heat flux as shown in Fig. 4. If one were applying inverse techniques to the temperature history $T(q''_1)$ in an attempt to determine the boundary heat flux at time t_b, it would be extremely difficult since the accurate discrimination between the time-temperature curves resulting from several possible heat fluxes is not possible at this time. The boundary heat flux could mistakenly be calculated as q''_2 or q''_3. However, if one takes into consideration the temperature history at

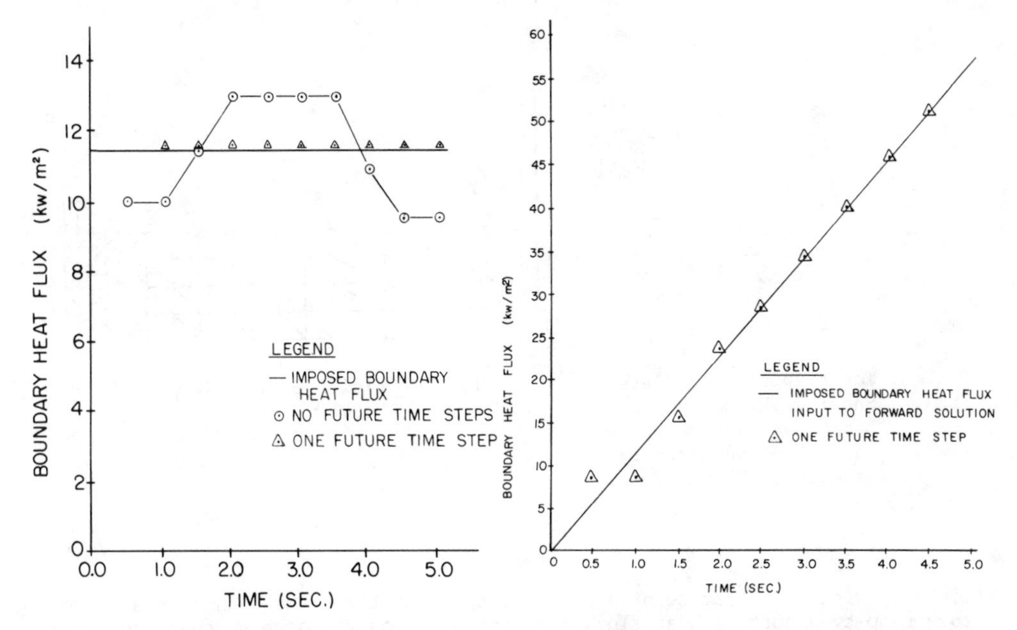

Fig. 6. Two Dimensional Inverse Program Calculated Boundary Heat Flux for a Large Steel Plate .038m Thick Subjected to a Constant Boundary Heat Flux over a Width of .032m.

Fig. 7. Two Dimensional Inverse Program Calculated Boundary Heat Flux for a Large Steel Plate .038m Thick Subjected to a Ramp-Type Heat Flux Over a Width of .032m.

time t_c as well as t_b, resolution is improved and it becomes easier to distinguish that the boundary heat flux at time t_b is indeed q''_1.

The future time step modification was added to the inverse program by the calculation of total temperature error over two consecutive time steps for a given iteration heat flux value. Although more than one future time step could conceivably be taken into consideration, the use of only one proved to be sufficient [15]. A flow chart of the two dimensional inverse program employing one future time step is shown in Fig. 5.

This inverse program was tested for two cases employing the steel plate model with good results. The first involved temperature history at a particular point generated by the forward program for a step change in boundary heat flux. The calculated heat fluxes from an inverse program taking into consideration one future time step and an inverse program using no future data are shown in Fig. 6. These were generated by suppying each of the inverse programs with only the temperature history at a single interior point centered directly beneath the applied surface heat flux. This temperature history was previously obtained from the forward program solution. In Fig. 6 the numerical oscillations associated with the inverse program using no future data can be seen as well as the rapid convergence, stability and accuracy of the solution calculated by the inverse program employing data from one future time step. The second case analyzed was that of a boundary heat flux increasing

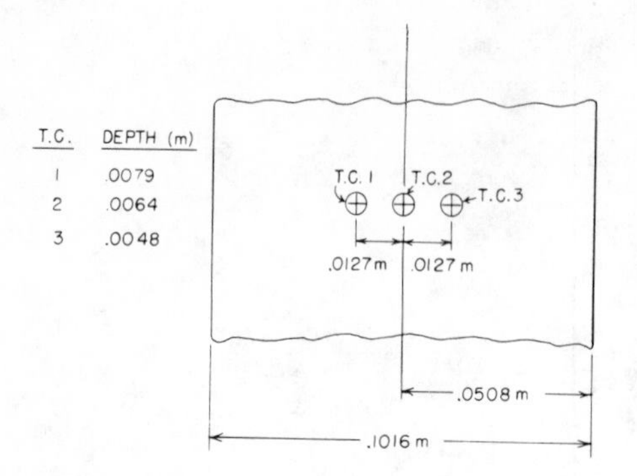

Fig. 8. Top View of Weld Plate Showing Thermocouple Locations (Thermocouple no. 2 Located Directly Beneath the Path of the Arc).

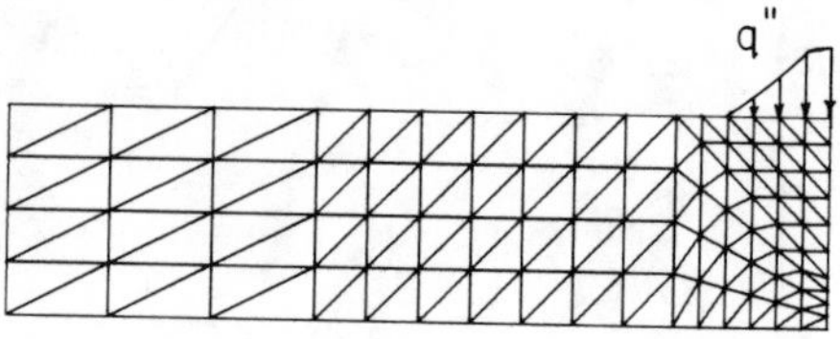

Fig. 9. Finite Element Mesh of Weld Model.

linearly with time from zero (a ramp input). Except for the change from a step to a ramp-type surface heat flux, the procedure was the same as that used for the first case described above. The heat flux obtained from the inverse program employing future data and its comparison with the imposed boundary heat flux are shown in Fig. 7. With the exception of some initial inaccuracy, the inverse program produced very satisfactory results. It is suspected that the initial inaccuracy could be reduced by tightening the error criterion.

It should be realized that the inverse technique described is not an inverse solution in the ideal mathematical sense of the term. That is, the problem is not solved by inversion of the governing differential equation or by inverting the finite element equations (inversion of a 160 by 160 matrix is highly impractical). Further, knowledge of boundary conditions is not totally lacking. The inverse technique developed is, in actuality, an iterative forward solution with what amounts to a trial and error approach for determining boundary heat flux. Some knowledge is required regarding boundary conditions, such as where the boundaries are subject to convection, where the boundaries are insulated and where boundary heat flux is imposed.

5. APPLICATION OF THE INVERSE METHOD TO A WELDING PROCESS

The two dimensional inverse finite element program was used to model the heat transfer for a tungsten inert gas welding process. The experimental apparatus incorporated a traversing mechanism which enalbed the welding arc to move at a constant velocity and arc gap. Temperatures were recorded in the interior of a steel plate with chromel-alumel thermocouples. Three thermocouple locations (Figure 8) were chosen so as to coincide with nodes of the finite element mesh for the plate (Figure 9). Due to symmetry, only half of the plate cross section was considered.

For low carbon steel, the following property values were used.

Thermal Conductivity (watts/m-K):

$$k = 77.634 - 0.0458\ T_{ave} \text{ for } T_{ave} < 1300\ K$$

$$k = 30.0 \text{ for } T_{ave} \geq 1300\ K$$

Specific Heat (watt-sec/kg-K):

$$c_p = 253.91 + 0.558\ T_{ave} \text{ for } T_{ave} < 775\ K$$

$$c_p = 685.6 \text{ for } T_{ave} \geq 775\ K$$

Density:

$$\rho = 7850\ kg/m^3$$

Latent Heat of Fusion:

$$\Delta H = 271{,}440 \text{ watt-sec/kg}$$

T_{ave} is the average element temperature,

$$T_{ave} = \frac{T_i + T_j + T_k}{3}$$

where the subscripts i, j and k denote the nodal points for a particular bilinear triangular element. Both thermal conductivity and specific heat were recalculated for each time step using the average element temperature from the previous time step.

In order to take into account latent heat affects, the method presented by Carnahan et al [12] was used whereby latent heat is treated as an addition to the capacitance matrix during phase change. For the lumped capacitance scheme, the capacitance matrix for an element undergoing phase change is

$$[C^e] = \rho\ \frac{A(c_p + \alpha \Delta H)}{3} \begin{vmatrix} 1 & 0 & 0 \\ 0 & 1 & 0 \\ 0 & 0 & 1 \end{vmatrix} \quad [7]$$

where α is a constant defined as

$$\alpha = \frac{1}{T_{liq} - T_{sol}} \quad [8]$$

and

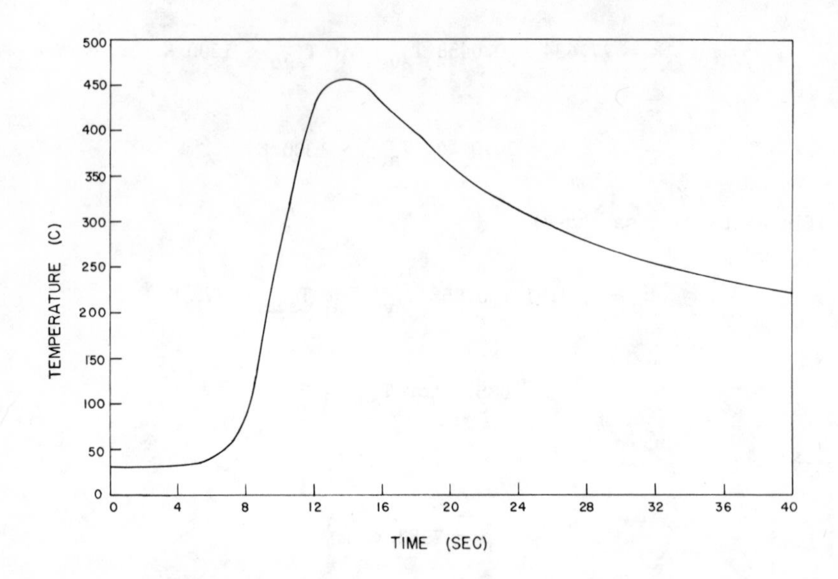

Fig. 10. Typical Response of Thermocouple no. 2 (Located Directly Beneath the Path of the Arc).

T_{sol} - solidus, temperature at which melting begins (1783 K)

T_{liq} - liquidus, temperature at which liquid begins to solidify (1797 K)

A typical thermocouple response obtained from thermocouple no. 2 (Fig. 8) is given in Fig. 10. The temperature increases as the arc approaches, reaches a maximum, and then slowly decreases after the arc moves passed the thermocouple location. Information of this type was provided to the inverse finite element program, which determined the input heat flux. In order to do this, it was necessary to make some assumptions regarding the distribution of input heat flux from the arc. According to Friedman [10] and Krutz [11], the distribution is Gaussian and may be expressed by

$$q'' = \frac{3\, q_i}{\pi\, \bar{r}^2} \exp\left[-3 \left(\frac{r}{\bar{r}}\right)^2\right]. \qquad [9]$$

where:

q'' - heat flux, watts/m^2

q_i - total heat input, watts

r - radial distance from center of arc, m

$\bar{r}$ - radius within which 95% of heat input occurs, m

For the purpose of the inverse program this equation was used with an assumed value of $\bar{r}$ while the heat input, q_i, was unknown. In general, at a particu-

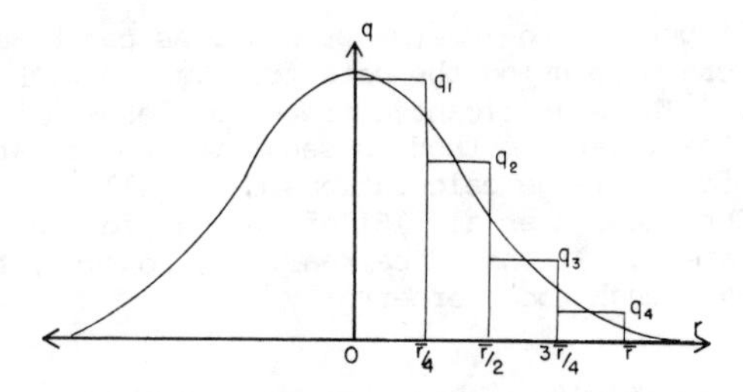

Fig. 11. Discretization of Heat Flux Distribution.

lar time during this process, the center of the traveling arc was displaced relative to the thermocouple. However, the observed temperature at this instant was considered as being equivalent to that resulting from a non-moving, weaker pseudo-arc centered directly over the thermocouple. Thus, the effective q_i value of this stationary pseudo-arc first increased with time and then decreased. A graphic representation of the heat flux distribution as discretized for the finite element model is shown in Fig. 11. Application of this distribution in the inverse program along with the measured thermocouple response (Fig. 10) led to calculated values of the total input heat transfer rate. This was compared with the measured power output of the arc welder in order to calculate an efficiency factor for the welder according to

$$\text{Efficiency} = \frac{q_i}{E \times I} \times 100\% \qquad [10]$$

where:

E - measured welder supply voltage, volts

I - measured welder supply current, ampheres

Results are presented in Table 1. In all cases the response of thermocouple

TABLE 1. Results From Welding Experiment

Test	Arc Velocity (cm/sec)	Welder Voltage (volts)	Welder Current (amps)	Welder Power (watts)	$\bar{r}$ (cm)	q_i (watts)	Efficiency (%)
A	.254	14	150	2100	.47625	802	38.2
					.635	1000	47.7
					.79375	1328	63.2
B	.254	21	260	5460	1.27	2048	37.5
					1.5875	2974	54.5
C	.254	19	200	3800	1.27	2643	69.5
					.794	1360	35.8

no. 2 was used as input to the inverse program. As can be seen in the table, three calculations were made using the data from Test A with three different assumed values of $\overline{r}$. The significant difference between the three efficiencies indicates that the inverse method is sensitive to variation of $\overline{r}$. The efficiency values for all the calculations made fall within or close to the range predicted by Christensen et al [16] of 36-46% for a D.C. TIG welder operating on mild steel. It should be realized, however, that this range is rather broad and leaves much room for error.

Because of the sensitivity of the inverse method to the parameter $\overline{r}$, it was desired to obtain confirmation of the results beyond that provided by the rough comparison of calculated efficiencies with those obtained by Christensen et al [16]. For Test B, the procedure used was the same as that for Test A. However in this case the calculated temperature histories at the locations of thermocouples no. 1 and no. 3 were compared with the experimental recorded responses of thermocouples no. 1 and no. 3. This was done for two different assumed values of $\overline{r}$. The calculated predictions obtained with $\overline{r}$ = 0.0127 m (0.5 in) were found to be more representative of the experimental data.

6. CONCLUDING REMARKS

Results obtained in this project have evolved from development of numerical techniques and the associated operation of an experimental apparatus. Both will continue to be used in further studies, and certain refinements and improvements are future goals. The potential for further application of the methods developed is sizeable.

When interpreting results, the shortcomings of the experimental apparatus should be realized. The presence of the thermocouple holes and the thermocouple themselves may have some effect on the heat transfer. Electrically induced inaccuracies, such as noise and drift, were not considered. The techniques described could be employed for analyzing results gathered from several different welding passes and formulating at least relative, if not absolute, efficiencies. The methods could certainly be utilized in an attempt to improve efficiency, though it is not known how the optimum conditions might be arrived at without further verification of the technique.

The value of $\overline{r}$, in the equation for the heat flux distribution, was shown to have a significant effect on the calculated heat input. Unfortunately, no simple means of accurately determining $\overline{r}$ has yet been fully developed. However, use of additional thermcouples as described in connection with Test B (Table 1) offers a potential path for future inprovement of the method. In some portions of the literature "photographic methods" are suggested for experimental determination of $\overline{r}$, but the discussion of these techniques is not very specific. It is also possible that some information might be gained from metallurgical analysis of weld cross sections.

ACKNOWLEDGEMENTS

This research was supported by the National Science Foundation under Grant ENG-78-26293.

REFERENCES

1. Myers, G.E. 1971. Analytical Methods in Conduction Heat Transfer. McGraw-Hill Book Company, New York.

2. Segerlind, L.J. 1976. Applied Finite Element Analysis. John Wiley and Sons, Inc., New York.

3. Zienkiewicz, O.C. 1971. The Finite Element Method in Engineering Science. (2nd Ed.), McGraw-Hill Publishing Co., Ltd., London.

4. Huebner, K.H. 1975. The Finite Element Method for Engineers. John Wiley and Sons, New York.

5. Fujii, H. 1973. Some remarks on finite element analysis of time-dependent field problems, Theory and Practice in Finite Element Structural Analysis, Ed. by Yoshiaki Yamada and Richard H. Gallagher, Tokyo, University of Tokyo Press, Tokyo seminar on Finite Element Analysis, pp. 91-106.

6. Macqueene, J.W., Akau, R.L., Krutz, G.W. and Schoenhals, R.J. 1981. Numerical methods and measurements related to welding processes, Paper written to be presented at 2nd International Conference on Numerical Methods in Thermal Problems, Venice, Italy, July.

7. Macqueene, J.W. 1981. Application of Finite Element Methods to the Inverse Heat Transfer Problem in Welding. MS Thesis, Purdue University, W. Lafayette, IN.

8. Lemmon, E.C. and Heaton, H.S. 1969. Accuracy, stability and oscillation characteristics of finite element method for solving heat conduction equation, ASME Paper No. 69-WA/HT-35.

9. Myers, G.E. 1977. Numerically-induced oscillation and stability characteristics of finite-element solutions to two-dimensional heat-conduction transients. Engineering Experiment Station Report No. 43, Madison, Wisconsin, August.

10. Friedman, E. 1975. Thermomechanical analysis of the welding process using the finite element method, ASME Paper 75-PVP-27, New York.

11. Krutz, G.W. 1976. Thermo-Metallurgical Model Predicting the Strength of Welded Joints Using the Finite Element Method. PhD Thesis, Michigan State University, E. Lansing, MI.

12. Carnahan, B., Luther, H.A. and Wilkes, J.O. 1969. Applied Numerical Methods, John Wiley and Sons, Inc., New York, pp. 465-473.

13. Krutz, G.W., Hore, P. and Schoenhals, R.J. 1978. Application of the finite element method to the inverse heat conduction problem, Numerical Heat Transfer, Vol. 1, pp. 489-498.

14. Beck, J.V., Litkouhi, B. and St. Clair, Jr., C.R. 1980. Efficient numerical solution of the nonlinear inverse heat conduction problem, ASME Paper 80-HT-3, New York.

15. Hill, R.G. and Mulholland, G.P. 1979. The accuracy and resolving power of one dimensional transient inverse heat conduction theory as applied to discrete and inaccurate measurements, International Journal of Heat Transfer, Vol. 22, pp. 1221-1229.

16. Christensen, N., Davies, V.L. and Gjermundsen, K. 1965. Distribution of temperatures in arc welding, British Welding Journal, February, pp. 54-75.

Behavior of the Finite Element Method with Coarse Discretization and a Discontinuous Boundary Condition*

E.C. LEMMON
Intermountain Technologies, Inc.
1400 Benton, P.O. Box 1604
Idaho Falls, Idaho 83401

1. INTRODUCTION

This paper discusses the behavior of a coarse discretization finite element algorithm to be applied to the type of problem where the boundary condition on one side is in the form of a two-step staircase function, where the position of level change is a function of time. For example, consider a vertical rod partially submerged in a liquid as shown

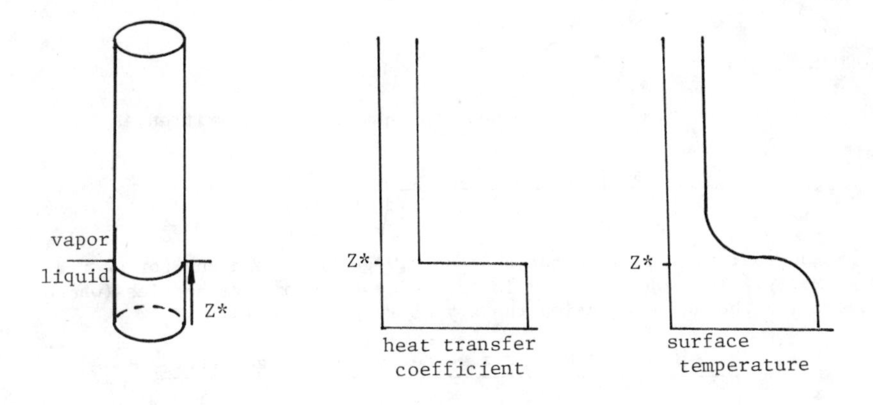

where Z* is a function of time. The convective heat transfer coefficient will be of the two-step, staircase function form. For problems of this type, detailed two-dimensional calculations will show that the temperature at the surface as a function of Z is at least a cubic. Hence, the minimum number of degrees of freedom in the Z direction will be four. The number of degrees of freedom required in the radial direction will depend on other factors such as the number of different materials used, etc.

The algorithm developed is based on an application of the Method of Weighted Residuals (MWR) using the Galerkin approach with only three regions of discretization in the vertical direction. The methodology is generally termed the Finite Element Method (FEM).

* Part of this work was performed for the Electric Power Research Institute

Comparisons will be given between the results of the FEM algorithm and the simple classical finite difference method. It will be shown that the FEM has the courtesy to inform the analyst that something may be wrong; whereas, even though the classical finite difference method results may look reasonable, they may be erroneous. The important message being sent by the FEM results is that the imposed boundary condition needs to be re-examined or that the problem, as posed, is just too difficult to solve adequately with the number of elements chosen. The paper examines both of these messages and addresses the appropriate response of the analyst. Among the responses discussed (with comparisons of results) is the replacement of the two-step boundary condition with an equivalent ramp variation and the resulting successes and problems. Also discussed are the results obtained by various lumping techniques.

The FEM is then extended to include a moving mesh algorithm, which introduces some new problems which are addressed. Comparisons are then again made between the various algorithms.

The paper then concludes that the moving mesh finite element algorithm developed has the ability to reasonably match surface temperatures and conserve energy. It is re-emphasized that the FEM will send important messages to the analyst about its ability to solve the problem unless the analyst has "cleverly" suppressed the messages, in which case the FEM will be as well-behaved as the classical finite difference method. The results may also be equally correct or erroneous.

2. FORMULATION

The standard two dimensional conduction equation[1] is written as

$$\rho c \frac{\partial T}{\partial t} = \frac{1}{x^r} \frac{\partial}{\partial x}\left(x^r k \frac{\partial T}{\partial x} \right) + \frac{1}{x^\theta} \frac{\partial}{\partial y}\left(\frac{k}{x^\theta} \frac{\partial T}{\partial y} \right) + u''' \tag{1}$$

where the superscript r is zero for a plane x,y geometry and one for an r,θ or r,z geometry. The superscript θ is zero except for r,θ geometries (where it is one). In the above equation the x,y correspondence is

	x,y geometry	r,z geometry	r,θ geometry
x	x	r	r
y	y	z	θ

The first law may be written in matrix form as

$$\rho c \overset{\circ}{T} = \frac{1}{r} \left(\lfloor \nabla \rfloor \; x^r k \; (\lfloor \nabla \rfloor^T \; T) \right) + u''' \tag{2}$$

where the del vector is

$$\Delta = [\frac{\partial}{\partial x} \;\; \frac{1}{x^\theta} \frac{\partial}{\partial y}]$$

and the parentheses around the del vector indicate what ∇ is operating on. The general boundary conditions may also be written in matrix form as

$$\lfloor n \rfloor \quad k(\lfloor \nabla \rfloor^{T} T) = q_{bin} \tag{3}$$

where $\lfloor n \rfloor$ is the standard direction cosines vector.

The MWR requires that[2]

$$\int_{vol} \left[\frac{1}{x^r} (\nabla x^r k(\nabla^T T)) W_j + u''' W_j - \rho c \overset{\circ}{T} W_j \right] dvol = 0. \tag{4}$$

Using the divergence theorem to include the boundary conditions and discretizing results in the following[3]

$$\sum_{i=1}^{m} \int_{suri} W_j q_{bin} \, dsur - \sum_{i=1}^{n} \int_{vol_i} \frac{1}{x^r} (W_j \nabla) x^r k (\nabla^T T) \, dvol_i$$
$$+ \sum_{i=1}^{n} \int_{vol_i} W_j u''' \, dvol_i - \sum_{i=1}^{n} \int_{vol} \rho c W_j \overset{\circ}{T} \, dvol_i = 0 \tag{5}$$

where n = # regions or elements
m = # exterior surfaces.

Each vol_i in the above discretization is termed an element and the above equations are then the finite element equations.

The model developed is only for orthogonal x,y; r,z or r,θ geometries. Hence, it is advantageous to discretize each body of interest into orthogonal sub-bodies.

Within each of these subregions or elements vol_i, the temperature profile is chosen to be of the form

$$T^i(x,y) = N_1 T_1 + N_2 T_2 + N_3 T_3 + N_4 T_4. \tag{6}$$

Where the local node numbering scheme is as illustrated,

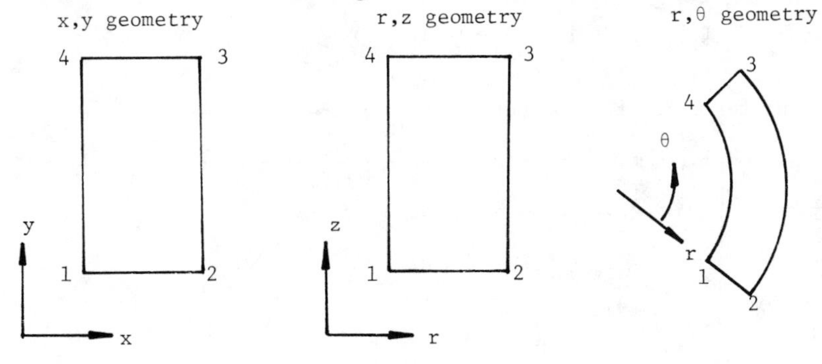

Linear shape factors (N_i) are used in the y (or z or θ) direction and in the x direction. In the r direction logrithmic shape factors are used (except of course if r_1=0, in which case a linear shape factor is used). The shape factors are as follows:

$$N_1 = (x_2-x)(y_2-y)/\Delta x\ \Delta y \quad \text{or} \quad (y_2-y)\ell n(x_2/x)/\Delta y\ \ell n\ (x_2/x_1)$$

$$N_2 = (x-x_1)(y_2-y)/\Delta x\ \Delta y \quad \text{or} \quad (y_2-y)\ell n(x/x_1)/\Delta y\ \ell n\ (x_2/x_1)$$

$$N_3 = (x-x_1)(y-y_1)/\Delta x\ \Delta y \quad \text{or} \quad (y-y_1)\ell n(x/x_1)/\Delta y\ \ell n\ (x_2/x_1)$$

$$N_4 = (x_2-x)(y-y_1)/\Delta x\ \Delta y \quad \text{or} \quad (y-y_1)\ell n(x_2/x)/\Delta y\ \ell n\ (x_2/x_1) \tag{7}$$

where the subscripts on x and y do not correspond to the respective nodal valves but to the coordinates of the bottom (y_1) and top (y_2) and inside (x_1) and outside (x_2) of the element. These shape factors were chosen to correspond to the exact solution form for one-dimensional steady-state problems.

Within the Galerkin Approach of the MWR, the weighting coefficients within an element are chosen to be the shape factors[3]. With the shape factor vector Ψ defined as

$$\lfloor \Psi \rfloor = [\ N_1 \quad N_2 \quad N_3 \quad N_4\ ] \tag{8}$$

the contribution of one element to the overall equation set is

$$-\ [K^i]\ \{T\} - [C^i]\ \{\mathring{T}\} + \lfloor q^i \rfloor \tag{9}$$

where

$$[K^i] = \int_{vol_i} \frac{1}{x^r} (\lfloor \Psi \rfloor^T \lfloor \nabla \rfloor)\ x^r k\ (\lfloor \nabla \rfloor^T \lfloor \Psi \rfloor)\ d\ vol$$

$$[C^i] = \int_{vol_i} \rho c\ \lfloor \Psi \rfloor^T \lfloor \Psi \rfloor\ dvol$$

$$[q^i] = \int_{vol_i} \lfloor \Psi \rfloor^T u'''\ dvol_i + \int_{sur_i} \lfloor \Psi \rfloor^T q_{bin}\ dsur_i$$

$$\{T\} = [T_1\ T_2\ T_3\ T_4]^T \quad \text{and} \quad \{\mathring{T}\} = \frac{\partial}{\partial t}\{T\}.$$

The resulting terms for the conductance matrix are

$$[K^i] = \frac{kvol_i}{e} \begin{bmatrix} a_1 + b_1 & -a_1 + b_3 & -a_2 - b_3 & a_2 - b_1 \\ & a_1 + b_2 & a_2 - b_2 & -a_2 - b_3 \\ & & a_1 + b_2 & -a_1 + b_3 \\ \text{symmetric} & & & a_1 + b_1 \end{bmatrix} \tag{10}$$

where $a_1 = \Delta y^2/3$ and $a_2 = \Delta y^2/6$. The other terms, e, b_1, b_2 and b_3 are dependent on the geometry. For plane x,y geometry $e = \Delta x^2 \Delta y^2$, $b_1 = b_2 = \Delta x^2/3$ and $b_3 = \Delta x^2/6$. With the shorthand convention that $L_i = \ell n\, x_i$, $L_2 = \ell n\, x_2$ and $L_{21} = \ell n\, (x_2/x_1)$ the values for r,z geometry are $e = \bar{x}\ \Delta x^2 \Delta y^2 L_{21}$,

$$b_1 = [(L_2^3 - L_1^3)/3L_{21}] - [(L_2^2 - L_1^2)L_2/L_{21}] + L_2^2,$$

$$b_2 = [(L_2^3 - L_1^3)/3L_{21}] - [(L_2^2 - L_1^2)L_1/L_{21}] + L_1^2, \text{ and}$$

$$b_3 = -[(L_2^3 - L_1^3)/3L_{21}] + [(L_2^2 - L_1^2)(L_2 + L_1)/2L_{21}] - L_1 L_2.$$

Using the same ℓn shorthand notations, the values for the r,θ geometry are

$$e = \bar{x}\ \Delta x \Delta y^2 L_{21},\quad b_1 = [(x_2^2 - x_1^2)/4L_{21}] - [x_1^2(1 + L_{21})/2],$$

$$b_2 = [(x_2^2 - x_1^2)/4L_{21}] - [x_2^2(1 - L_{21})/2], \text{ and } b_3 = [(x_2^2 + x_1^2)/4]$$

$$- [(x_2^2 - x_1^2)/4L_{21}].$$

The resulting capacitance matrix is

$$[C^i] = \frac{\rho c\ vol_i}{e} \begin{bmatrix} a_1 b_1 & a_1 b_3 & a_2 b_3 & a_2 b_1 \\ & a_1 b_2 & a_2 b_2 & a_2 b_3 \\ & & a_1 b_2 & a_1 b_3 \\ \text{symmetric} & & & a_1 b_1 \end{bmatrix} \qquad (11)$$

where $a_1 = \Delta y^3/3$ and $a_2 = \Delta y^3/6$. For the plane x,y geometry

$e = \Delta x^3 \Delta y^3$, $b_1 = b_2 = \Delta x^3/3$ and $b_3 = \Delta x^3/6$. For r,z and r,θ geometries

$$e = \bar{x}\ \Delta y^3 \Delta x L_{21}^2,\quad b_1 = [x_2^2/4] - [x_1^2(L_{21}^2 + L_{21} + 0.5)/2],$$

$$b_2 = -[x_1^2/4] + [x_2^2(L_{21}^2 - L_{21} + 0.5)/2] \text{ and}$$

$$b_3 = [x_1^2 - x_2^2 + (x_2^2 + x_1^2)L_{21}]/4.$$

For the first term in the flux vector, u''' within the element is assumed to be constant in the x direction and linear in the y direction. The resulting u''' vector is then

$$\int_{vol_i} u'''\ \Psi^T\ dvol = \frac{\Delta y}{3} \begin{bmatrix} a\ (u_1''' + \frac{u_2'''}{2}) \\ b\ (u_1''' + \frac{u_2'''}{2}) \\ b\ (u_2''' + \frac{u_1'''}{2}) \\ a\ (u_2''' + \frac{u_1'''}{2}) \end{bmatrix} \qquad (12)$$

where for the slab x,y case (and both the other cases if $x_1=0$) $a = b = \bar{x}^r \Delta x/2$. For the other two cases, $a = [(x_2^2/4) - x_1^2(L_{21} + 0.5)/2]/L_{21}$ and $b = [(x_1^2/4) + x_2^2(L_{21} - 0.5)/2]/L_{21}$.

The quantity q_{bin} in the second part of the flux vector is the sum of the convective and imposed flux terms, i.e.,

$$q_{bin} = q'' - h\,(T - T_\infty). \tag{13}$$

Hence, at $x = x_j$ ($j = 1$ or 2)

$$\int_{sur_i} \Psi^T q_{bin}\, dsur = \int_{y_1}^{y_2} x_j^r\, \Psi^T q''\, dy - \int_{y_1}^{y_2} x_j^r\, h\, \Psi^T \Psi \{T\}$$

$$+ \int_{y_1}^{y_2} x_j^r\, h\, \Psi^T \Psi\, \{T_\infty\}\, dy. \tag{14}$$

Now, in general, h and q" may be a function of y. For the applications of interest, these boundary condition quantities may be of a moving staircase (two step) type function over one face of an element. This type of boundary condition is very difficult to apply because the variation of T (and T_∞) between y_1 and y_2 is linear. The best results would be obtained if y* always coincided with a nodal point, but obviously this is not always possible. The first part of this boundary term results in the following:

$$\int_{y_1}^{y_2} x_1^r\, \Psi^T q''\, dy = \frac{x_1^r}{\Delta y} \left\{ q''_{11} \begin{bmatrix} a \\ o \\ o \\ b \end{bmatrix} + q''_{12} \begin{bmatrix} c \\ o \\ o \\ d \end{bmatrix} \right\}$$

and

$$\int_{y_1}^{y_2} x_2^r\, \Psi^T q''\, dy = \frac{x_2^r}{\Delta y} \left\{ q''_{21} \begin{bmatrix} o \\ a \\ b \\ o \end{bmatrix} + q''_{22} \begin{bmatrix} o \\ c \\ d \\ o \end{bmatrix} \right\} \tag{15}$$

where $a = y_2(y^*-y_1) - (y^{*2}-y_1^2)/2$, $b = [(y^{*2}-y_1^2)/2] - y_1(y^*-y_1)$,
$c = y_2(y_2-y^*) - y_2^2-y^{*2})/2$ and $d = [(y_2^2 - y^{*2})/2] - y_1(y_2-y^*)$

where, of course, y* may be different for the two sides. The subscripts on q''_{ij} are defined as $i = 1$ for x_1 or $i=2$ for x_2 and $j = 1$ if valve between y_1 and y* or $j = 2$ if valve between y* and y_2.

The second part of the boundary term results in the following:

$$\int_{y_1}^{y_2} x_1^r \quad h\, \Psi^T\Psi\, \{T\} =$$

$$\frac{x_1^r}{\Delta y^2}\left\{ h_{11}\begin{bmatrix} g_1 & 0 & 0 & g_2 \\ & 0 & 0 & 0 \\ & & 0 & 0 \\ \text{sym} & & & g_3 \end{bmatrix} + h_{12}\begin{bmatrix} g_4 & 0 & 0 & g_5 \\ & 0 & 0 & 0 \\ \text{sym} & & 0 & 0 \\ & & & g_6 \end{bmatrix}\right\} \begin{bmatrix} T_1 \\ T_2 \\ T_3 \\ T_4 \end{bmatrix}$$

and

$$\int_{y_1}^{y_2} x_1^r \quad h \quad \Psi^T\Psi\, \{T_\infty\} \quad dy =$$

$$\frac{x_1^r}{\Delta y^2}\left\{ h_{11}\begin{bmatrix} g_1 & 0 & 0 & g_2 \\ & 0 & 0 & 0 \\ \text{sym} & & 0 & 0 \\ & & & g_3 \end{bmatrix} + h_{12}\begin{bmatrix} g_4 & 0 & 0 & g_5 \\ & 0 & 0 & 0 \\ & & 0 & 0 \\ \text{sym} & & & g_6 \end{bmatrix}\right\} \begin{bmatrix} T_\infty\ (x_1, y_1) \\ 0 \\ 0 \\ T_\infty\ (x_1, y_2) \end{bmatrix} \tag{16}$$

where $g_1 = (y^*-y_1)[(y^*-y_1)^2/3 + \Delta y(y_2-y^*)]$, $g_2 = (y^*-y_1)[-(y^*-y_1)^2/3 - y_1(y^*+y_2) + (y_1+y_2)(y^*+y_1)/2]$, $g_3 = (y^*-y_1)(y^*-y_1)^2/3$, $g_4 = (y_2-y^*)(y_2-y^*)^2/3$, $g_5 = (y_2-y^*)[-(y_2-y^*)^2/3-y_2(y^*+y_1) + (y_1+y_2)(y_2+y^*)/2]$ and $g_6 = (y_2-y^*)[(y_2-y^*)^2/3 + \Delta y(y^*-y_1)]$.

The double subscript on h_{ij} is as previously described for q''_{ij}. The third part of the boundary term results in the following:

$$\int_{y_1}^{y_2} x_2^r \quad h \quad \Psi^T\Psi\{T\}\ dy =$$

$$\frac{x_2^r}{\Delta y^2}\left\{ h_{21}\begin{bmatrix} 0 & 0 & 0 & 0 \\ & g_1 & g_2 & 0 \\ & & g_3 & 0 \\ \text{sym} & & & 0 \end{bmatrix} + h_{22}\begin{bmatrix} 0 & 0 & 0 & 0 \\ & g_4 & g_5 & 0 \\ & & g_6 & 0 \\ \text{sym} & & & 0 \end{bmatrix}\right\} \begin{bmatrix} T_1 \\ T_2 \\ T_3 \\ T_4 \end{bmatrix}$$

and

$$\int_{y_1}^{y_2} x_2^r \; h \; \Psi^T \Psi \{T_\infty\} \; dy =$$

$$\frac{x_2^r}{\Delta y^2} \left\{ h_{21} \begin{bmatrix} 0 & 0 & 0 & 0 \\ & g_1 & g_2 & 0 \\ & & g_3 & 0 \\ sym & & & 0 \end{bmatrix} + h_{22} \begin{bmatrix} 0 & 0 & 0 & 0 \\ & g_4 & g_5 & 0 \\ & & g_6 & 0 \\ wym & & & 0 \end{bmatrix} \right\} \begin{bmatrix} 0 \\ T_\infty (x_2, y_1) \\ T_\infty (x_2, y_2) \\ 0 \end{bmatrix} \tag{17}$$

where the g's are as previously defined.

There is a special problem with the integral of $x_j^r \; h \; \Psi^T \Psi \; \{T\}$ from y_1 to y_2 term. It is that the temperature vector is included but these values are not yet determined. To circumvent this difficulty, the terms in the element contribution

$$- [K^i] \; \{T\} \; - [C^i] \; \{\overset{\circ}{T}\} \; + \; \lfloor q \rfloor \tag{18}$$

are redefined as

$$[K^i] = \int_{vol_i} \frac{1}{x^r} \; (\Psi^T \nabla) \; x^r k \; (\nabla^T \Psi) \; dvol \; + \int_{y_1}^{y_2} x_j^r \; h \; \Psi^T \Psi \; dy$$

$$[C^i] \; = \int_{vol_i} \rho c \; \Psi^T \Psi \; dvol$$

$$[q] \; = \int_{vol_i} u''' \; \Psi^T \; dvol + \int_{y_1}^{y_2} x_j^r \; \Psi^T \; q'' \; dy \; + \int_{y_1}^{y_2} x_j^r \; h \; \Psi^T \Psi \{T_\infty\} \; dy.$$

After the contributions from all of the elements are properly summed, the resulting set of equations will be in the form

$$[K] \; \{T\} \; + \; [C] \; \{\overset{\circ}{T}\} \; = \; \lfloor q \rfloor. \tag{19}$$

A standard backward difference implicit algorithm is then used to solve the set of equations.

3. SIMPLE BOUNDARY CONDITIONS

As an example of why the finite element method may be preferred over the simpler finite difference method, even if the boundary conditions are not complex, consider an r,θ section of a pipe (initially all at the same temperature) which is exposed to a uniform convective environment. This problem was solved with two different meshes. One with 25 nodes and one with 91 nodes. For the 25 node mesh, both the finite element and simple finite difference method were used;but for the 91 node mesh, only the finite difference method was used. The same time step was also used for both meshes and both methods. Only the symmetric half of the model was actually modeled. The results for four typical nodes will illustrate the point. For the node locations shown

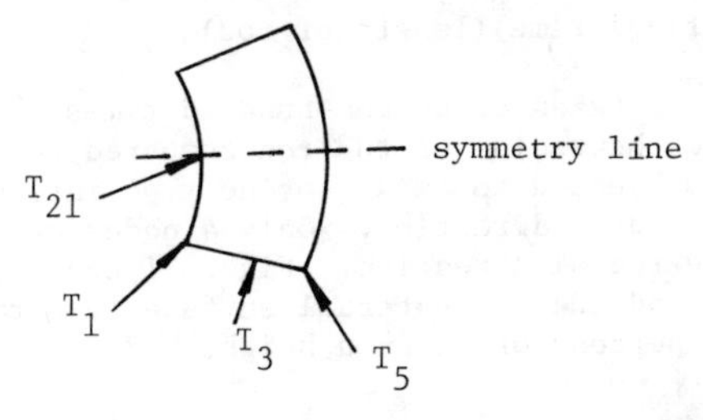

the results are as follows, where the finite difference 91 node model is used as the standard of comparison.

		Finite Element Error (%)	Finite Difference Error (%)
1st time step	$\bar{T}$	+ 0.009	+ 0.046
	T_1	- 1.28	- 5.0
	T_5	- 1.28	- 4.96
	T_3	- 0.32	- 2.69
	T_{21}	- 0.56	- 2.74
5th time step	$\bar{T}$	+ 0.061	+ 0.37
	T_1	- 2.18	- 8.02
	T_5	- 2.28	- 8.75
	T_3	- 1.41	- 5.31
	T_{21}	- 0.69	- 4.93

The error is defined as

$$\text{error} = \frac{T_i \text{ (25 node model)} - T_i \text{ (corresponding 91 node model)}}{T_\infty - T_{\text{initial}}} \times 100. \quad (20)$$

Also, $\bar{T}$ is given where $\bar{T}$ is the integrated average temperature in the pipe section. As illustrated, the finite element error is about 1/5th of the finite difference error for the same number of nodes for this example with very simple boundary conditions.

4. DIFFICULT BOUNDARY CONDITIONS

In the example that follows, results are given for a 12-node finite difference and finite element models and an 85-node finite difference model (which is used as the standard of comparison). The boundary condition for the problem is of the two-step staircase function type. For the finite difference models, the heat transfer coefficient was determined as

$$h = (\%\ \text{area wetted by liquid})h_{liquid} + (\%\ \text{area wetted by vapor})h_{vapor}. \quad (21)$$

In the problem, the liquid level varies with time as

$$z^* = (\text{time/final time})(\text{length of rod}) \quad (22)$$

and the liquid h is taken to be one hundred times the vapor h. In the problem $T_\infty < T_{initial}$ and the radius of the rod compared to the rod length is 1 to 10. The rod is also subjected to axial cosine type internal generation which increases in the radial direction. Only 4 nodes are used in the axial direction and 3 in the radial direction. Figure 1 shows the % error in $\bar{T}$ as a function of time and the rod external surface temperature at the time when z* equals twenty percent of the rod height.

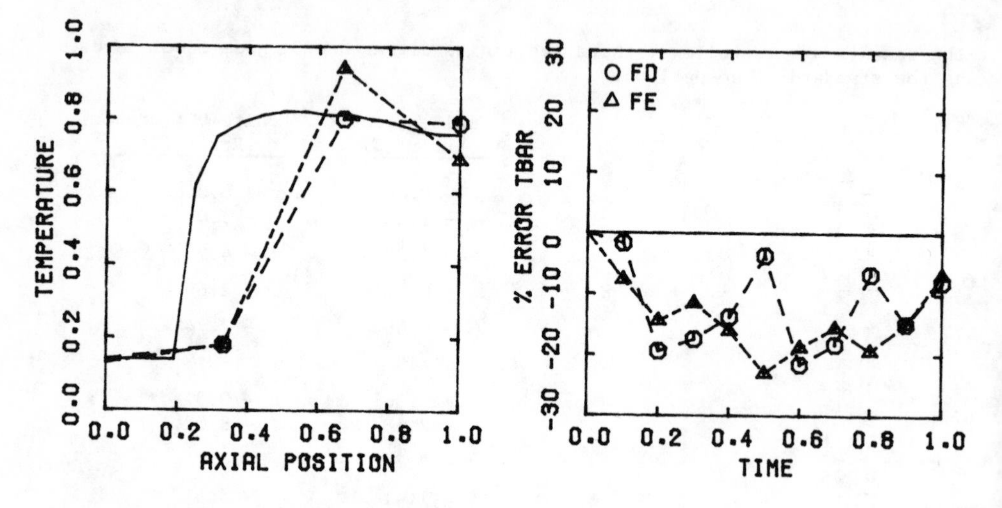

Fig. 1 Discretization effect.

As illustrated in the figure, for the discretization chosen, both the finite difference and finite element results are erroneous. Note, especially, that the finite element surface temperature prediction is in poor agreement over at least two-thirds of the distance. The exaggerated shape is sending a message that the discretization is too coarse. On the other hand, the finite difference surface temperature results are in fair agreement over about one-half of the distance.

The reason the results (between the two algorithms) are different is due mainly to the linkage differences between the two methods. These differences are illustrated for a surface node where the solid line represents a conductance link, a dashed line represents a convective link, and a dotted line represents a capacitance link.

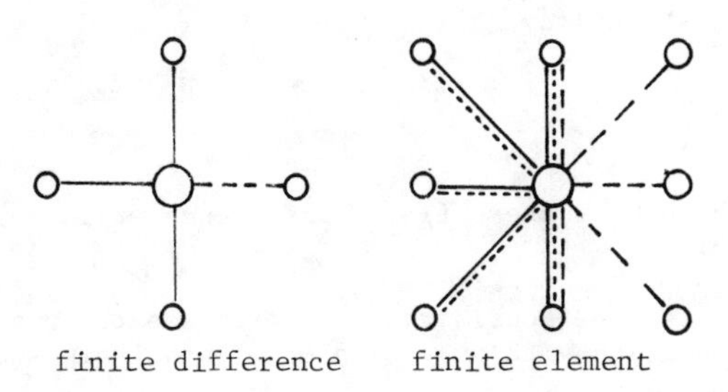

The finite element surface temperature results may be improved without changing the discretization, but the important error message may be suppressed. For example, look at the effect of changing the convective boundary term. First, consider the procedure of diagonally lumping (on a row) the boundary terms given previously in Eq. (16) and Eq. (17). The physical effect of this is that a boundary node will no longer be implicitly "convectively-linked" to adjacent surface nodes. The numerical effect of this lumping is shown in Figure 2. Although the surface profile seems to improve, the overall T error increases.

Another approach that could be used to eliminate the implicit convective linking between adjacent surface nodes is to try to make the finite element boundary term "equivalent" to the finite difference boundary term. If this is done, the g's in Eq. (16) and Eq. (17) become the following:

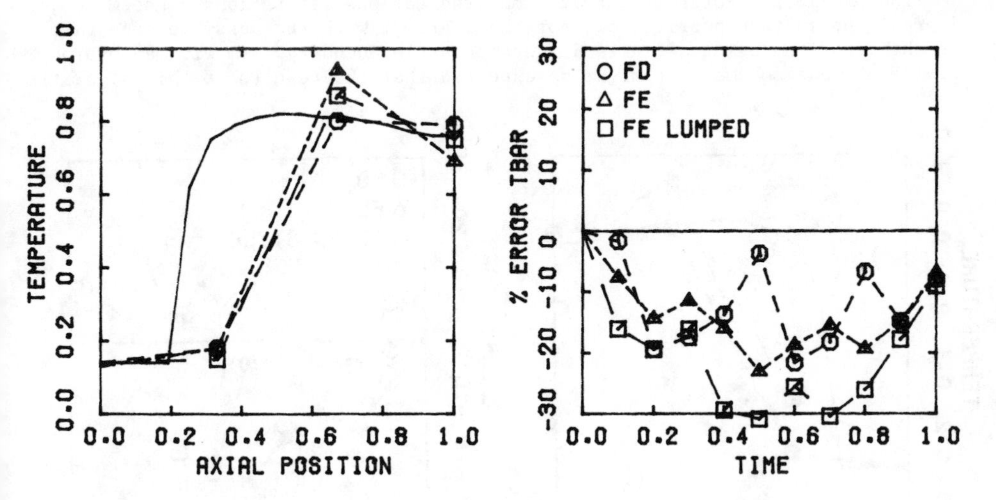

Fig. 2 Boundary term lumping effect.

g_1 = minimum $[1., 2(y^*-y_1)/\Delta y](\Delta y^3/2)$,
$g_2 = 0$,
$g_3 = 1.-g_1$,
g_6 = minimum $[1., 2(y_2-y^*)/\Delta y](\Delta y^3/2)$,
$g_5 = 0$, and
$g_4 = 1.-g_6$.

The numerical effect of the use of these finite difference style boundary terms is shown in Figure 3.

A third approach that might be considered is to replace the two-step staircase type boundary condition with an equivalent linear ramp such that

$$\left[\int_1^2 h(y^*)\ [T-T_\infty]\ dy\right] = \left[\int_1^2 h^{ramp}\ [T-T_\infty]\ dy\right] \qquad (23)$$

This, of course, will not break the convective linking between adjacent surface nodes, but it will smooth the boundary conditions to a linear form. The g's in Eq. (16) and Eq. (17) then become: $g_1 = g_6 = y^3/4$ and $g_2 = g_3 = g_4 = g_5 = \Delta y^3/12$. In Eq. (16) and Eq. (17), h is replaced with h^{ramp} chosen in accordance with Eq. (21). The real problem with this approach is that iteration is required since h_1^{ramp} and h_2^{ramp} are dependent on the unknown surface temperatures. The numerical effect of using this ramp h profile results is approximately the same effect as using the full FEM algorithm.

The previous figures illustrate that the various alterations do seem to improve the surface profile, but not the T error, with the possible exception of the algorithm using a finite difference style boundary term with an overall finite element scheme. It might be expected that the results of this algorithm

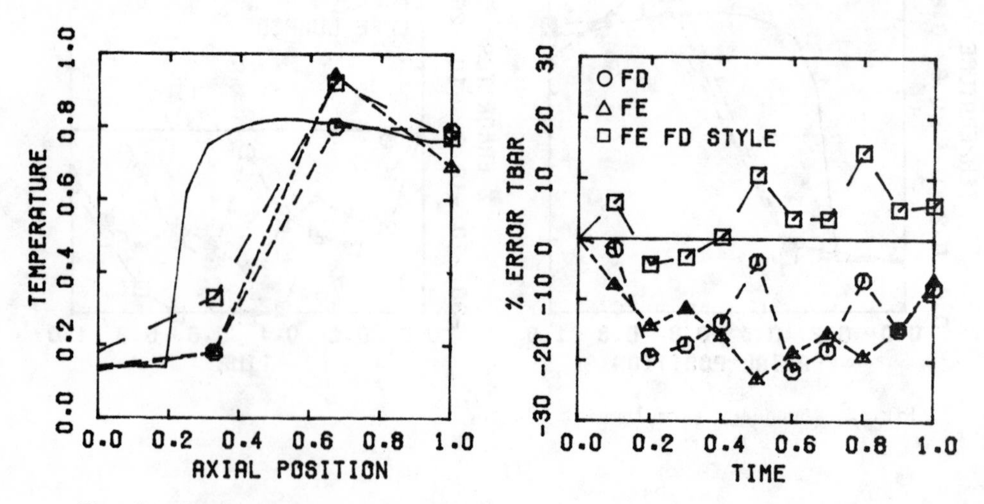

Fig. 3 Finite difference style boundary term effect.

should be much closer to the regular finite difference results than they are. The reason for the variance is due to the fact that conductance and capacitance effects are also modeled differently in the finite element and finite difference methods.

An alternate way to obtain the conductance matrix that results in a nodal conduction linkage similar to the simple finite difference approach is to use four triangular linear elements in an averaging procedure as illustrated:

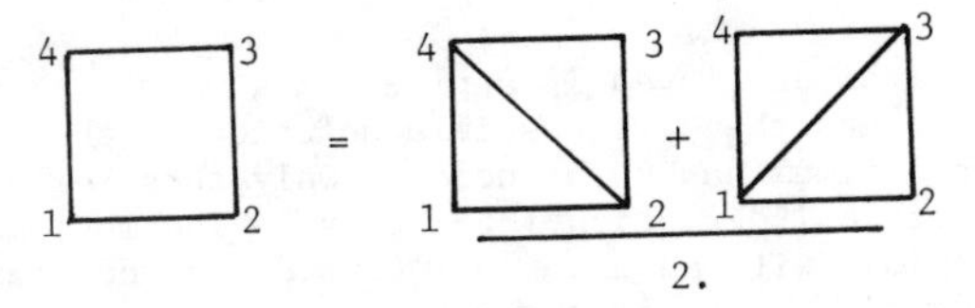

i.e., construct a rectangular element from four triangular elements. When this is done, the terms in Eq. (10) become: $e = \Delta x^2 \Delta y^2$, $a_1 = (\Delta y)^2/2$, $a_2 = 0$, $b_1 = (\Delta x)^2/2$ and $b_2 = b_3 = 0$.

Note: the linkage is now similar to the finite difference algorithm, i.e., diagonal nodes are no longer linked. (This diagonal linkage is not severed for an arbitrary quadrilateral element -- only for a rectangular element.) The numerical result of this finite difference type linkage for the particular problem of interest is a very small change.

The effect of the capacitance term on the results can be illustrated by row diagonally lumping the capacitance matrix. Note that for the regular finite element algorithm (Eq. (11)), the capacitance for a nodal equation is a function of all adjacenet nodes (including diagonal ones). Lumping removes this linkage. The numerical effect of this capacitance lumping is shown in Figure 4. Note the improvement on the surface profile along with the increase in error in the $\bar{T}$ error.

An alternate approach that is very similar to the finite difference approach is to require that $c^i_{j\ell} = 0$ if $j \neq \ell$ and $c^i_{jj} = \rho c \, vol_j$ where vol_j is the appropriate volume to be lumped to node j. The numerical effect of this approach is very similar to the previous lumping approach.

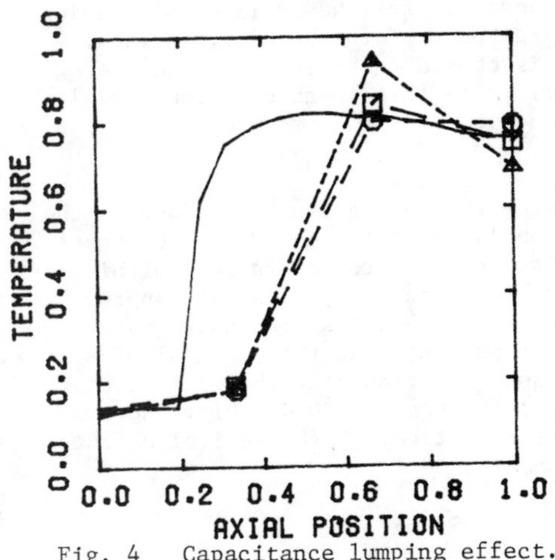

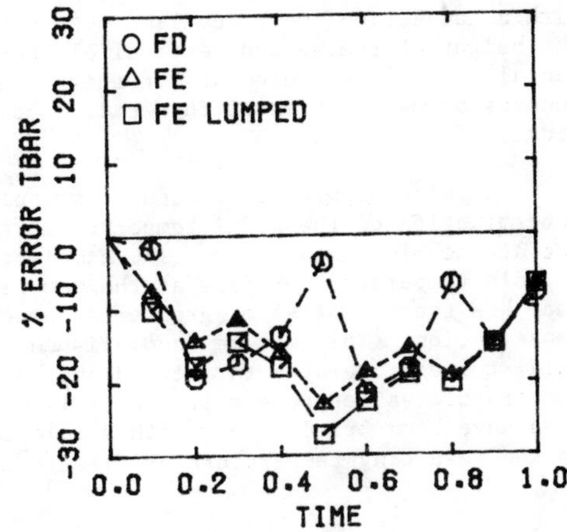

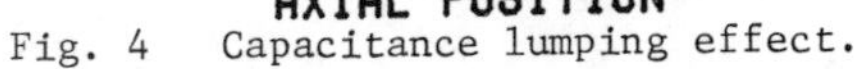

Fig. 4 Capacitance lumping effect.

From the results presented for the problem considered, it has been shown that the finite element algorithm will send a message in the form of exaggerated temperature profiles if the discretization is too coarse. This message may be unwisely suppressed by changing the boundary and capacitance formulation. For the discretization used, both the finite element and finite difference results were erroneous.

5. MOVING MESH

The finite element algorithm developed is applied in a very specialized manner using a moving mesh to get the best possible solution to the types of problems of interest with a minimum number of nodes. Only three elements (4 nodes) are used in the vertical direction (θ, z or y). The moving mesh technique used is best explained with an example. Consider a rod where the liquid level varies from one time valve to the next as shown:

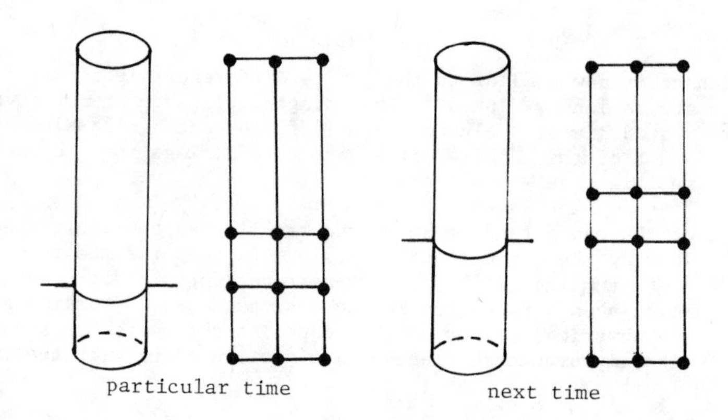

The method used would automatically form the mesh for each time as illustrated with the additional constraint that no element would have a vertical height less than the radial width. Hence, it is possible for the z* line to coincide with a convection interface line over a large part of the boundary surface. The height of the second vertical element is chosen to be equal to the average radial width of the elements at this level. Note that in this region, axial conduction may be greater than radial conduction or the surface boundary convective flux.

The major problem that occurs in applying the moving mesh technique is the determination of the nodal temperatures to be used at the new node locations but at the old time values. The simplest approach is to interpolate within the old temperature profile at the new node locations. An alternate approach that has the potential of greater accuracy is to require approximate energy conservation. This may be accomplished by requiring that the integral of axial temperature at both the old and new node locations for the last time temperature values be equal. There is more than one way to do this. Several ways have been tried, along with simple interpolation. The numerical effects on the resulting temperature profiles are small.

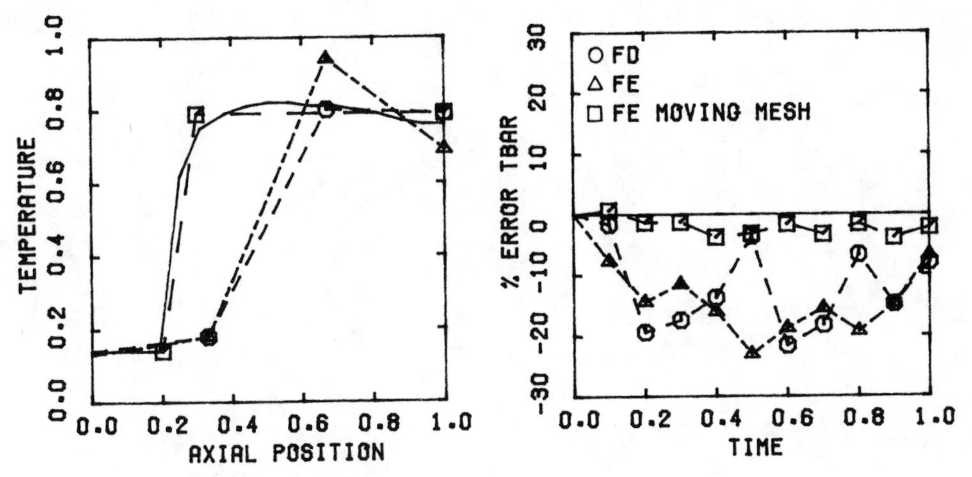

Fig. 5 Moving mesh effect.

The overall effect of using the finite element moving mesh algorithm is shown in Figure 5. The surface profile is greatly improved and the $\bar{T}$ error is significantly reduced. This illustrates that the moving mesh algorithm helps overcome the discretization problem but it may also be suppressing error messages.

6. CONCLUSIONS

For the type of problem considered with simple boundary conditions, it has been illustrated that the finite element method has the potential to give more accurate results than the simple finite difference method for the same discretization. However, for boundary conditions of the moving staircase type function, neither the finite element nor finite difference method does well unless a very fine discretization is used. The finite element method does, however, send the message in the form of exaggerated temperature profiles that something is wrong. It has also been illustrated that this error message can be suppressed by simplifying the finite element algorithm. The behavior of the FEM results from the convective and capacitance linkage. Hence, the error message may be suppressed by changing the boundary and capacitance formulation. This message suppression may not be wise.

The moving mesh finite element model algorithm used has the ability to reasonably match surface temperatures and conserve energy. The method has the potential to give better results than static mesh algorithms.

7. REFERENCES

1. Arpaci, V. S., Conduction Heat Transfer, Addison-Wesley Publishing Company, Reading, Massachusetts, 1966, pp. 44.

2. Crandall, S. H., Engineering Analysis, McGraw-Hill, New York, 1956, pp. 230-231.

3. Huebner, K. H., The Finite Element Method for Engineers, John Wiley & Sons, New York, 1975, pp. 242-253.

HIGHER-ORDER SCHEMES

"Mehrstellen" Techniques for the Numerical Solution of Unsteady Incompressible Viscous Flow in Enclosures

Y. LECOINTE, J. PIQUET, and M. VISONNEAU
E.N.S.M. — Laboratoire d'Hydrodynamique Navale, France

Abstract

This paper is devoted to the study of a new class of h^4-accurate compact discretization techniques of "Mehrstellen" type for the Navier-Stokes equations in their vorticity-stream function formulation. Two confined flow problems are considered ; they are the driven cavity problem and the case of free convection in a rectangular enclosure with heat and concentration diffusion for which the Boussinesq-Oberbeck approximation is used.

Introduction

In a companion paper [1], several difficulties connected with the efficiency of a new Navier-Stokes solver for the study of several aspects of unsteady viscous flow were discussed. In what follows, some others aspects are studied and new results are presented. Work is concerned with the Navier-Stokes equations in their vorticity-stream function formulation, discretized spatially by the "Mehrstellen" techniques ; the main features of the method are as follows. The Poisson equation is solved by an optimized A.D.I. method. The "Mehrstellen" discretization used is defer-corrected so that h^6 accuracy on ψ can be obtained. The vorticity equation is time-differenced with the help of a Beam & Warming two-step, quasi one-leg method which is Δt^2-accurate and A-stable, and which allows the splitting of the space operator so that unidimensional problems are solved by different "Mehrstellen" schemes with or without upwinding.

The first part of the paper is mainly devoted to the presentation of some properties of Mehrstellen methods for a simple linear differential equation. In the second part, the discretization of Navier-Stokes equations is considered. The third part is concerned with the driven cavity problem where the afore-mentioned h^4-accurate methods are compared to one of the most efficient h^2-accurate algorithms [2] regarded here as a reference tool. The fourth part gives some results pertaining to the free convection problem. The last part is devoted to the automatic mesh generator to be used for problems in arbitrary shaped enclosures. Some examples of computed meshes are presented.

1. "MEHRSTELLEN" METHODS FOR A SIMPLE DIFFERENTIAL EQUATION

1.1. "Mehrstellen" Methods : Construction and Errors

"Mehrstellen" methods have a long history which goes back to early works of Numerov and Collatz [3]. The methods have been extensively used for boundary layer problems by Krause et Al [4], more recently by Ciment et Al [5] and Berger et Al [6]. These techniques appear to be well suited for the modelling of diffusion-convection phenomena where two (or more) spatial operators of the following form are usually involved :

$$Lu \equiv \varepsilon u_{xx} + bu_x + cu = f. \tag{1}$$

In most applications and particularly in the context of large Reynolds number flow, ε is much smaller than b and c.

"Mehrstellen" techniques (also called Operator Compact Implicit Techniques) as applied to Eq. (1) can be written on the following form :

$$\tau_j(U_j) = \varepsilon(r_j^+ U_{j+1} + r_j^c U_j + r_j^- U_{j-1})/h^2 - (q_j^+ f_{j+1} + q_j^c f_j + q_j^- f_{j-1}) = 0 \tag{2}$$

Such schemes lead to a tridiagonal system which is solved by factorization. They are formally at most fourth-order accurate in the sense that the truncation error is :

$$\tau_j(u) = \sum_{\nu=0}^{\infty} T_j^{[\nu]} U_j^{[\nu]} = O(h^4), \quad \text{when } h \to 0 \text{ for fixed } \varepsilon.$$

The expression of $T_j^{[\nu]}$ is now classical and given in [6].

The standard "Mehrstellen" scheme is obtained by writing $T_j^{[\nu]} = 0, \nu = 0,1\ldots4$. Such conditions specify r_j^+, r_j^-, r_j^c, q_j^+, q_j^-, q_j^c (see e.g. [5][6]). By writing the weaker condition $T_j^{[\nu]} = 0$, $\nu = 0, 1, 2$; $T_j^{[3]}$ and $T_j^{[4]} = O(h^4)$, it is possible to formulate unrestricted schemes which do not exhibit a mesh Reynolds number limitation on h. Monotonicity and stability arguments introduced in [6] have been examined again and were somewhat weakened in [1]. An interesting property of these unrestricted schemes is their built in monotonicity property which is derived from the fact that they automatically switch their form from an h^4-accurate Numerov discretization (3) when $b = c = 0$,

$$\tau_j^{(N)}(U_j) \equiv \varepsilon(U_{j+1} - 2U_j + U_{j-1})/h^2 - \frac{1}{12}(f_{j+1} + 10f_j + f_{j-1}) = 0, \tag{3}$$

to a second order accurate upwind scheme when the mesh Reynolds number $R_j = hb_j/\varepsilon$ becomes large, the upwinding direction depending on the sign of b_j[1]. A particular problem arises at a boundary where a Neumann condition is used as is the case for instance in free convection problems where flux densities are often specified at the boundary. It is then necessary to use a modified scheme. For example, at the boundary in question ($x_j = 0$, $j = 0$) the following relationship ought to be used :

$$\tau_j^b(U_0) \equiv \varepsilon(r_0^c U_0 + r_0^+ U_1 + r_0^- U_0')/h^2 - (q_0^c f_0 + q_0^+ f + q_0^{++} f_2) = 0, \tag{4}$$

where U_0' is given by the boundary condition. The coefficients r_0 and q_0 are obtained by requiring that $\tau_j^b(u_0) = O(h^3)$.

The afore-mentionned schemes have been applied in [1] to the following test-problem with Dirichlet boundary conditions :

$$Lu \equiv u'' + bu' = 0. \quad (5) \qquad u(0) = U_0. \quad (6) \qquad u(1) = 0. \tag{7}$$

Now, if the Neumann condition $u'(0) = U_0'$ is imposed in place of Eq. (6), the local error can be explicitly calculated as :

$$U_j - u(x_j) = U_0' R^2 \psi(R)[\phi(x_j) + b^{-1}\Lambda(x_j)] - U_0' R^4 (e^{-b} - e^{-bx})/180 + O(R^5). \tag{8}$$

with

$$\psi(R) \equiv (10p_1 - 10p_2 - 5p_3 - 3)/72. \quad \text{iff } 4p_4 = 2p_2 + p_3 - p_1. \tag{9}$$

$$\phi(x) \equiv e^{-b}(1-e^{-bx}) - xe^{-bx}(1-e^{-b}). \tag{10}$$

$$\Lambda(x) \equiv \{e^{-bx} - xe^{-bx} - b\}\{e^{-b} - 1\} + b\{xe^{-bx} - 1\}. \tag{11}$$

p_1, p_2, p_3 and p_4 are "at hand" coefficients introduced in [6] and the optimal values of which are given in the appendix. It can be verified that the condition on p_4 which is necessary for h^4 local accuracy implies also that $\bar{r_j}$ is a second order polynomial in R_j.

1.2. Conservative "Mehrstellen" Methods

It is well known that conservative methods are in fact more stable than non-conservative ones, so a construction of conservative "Mehrstellen" methods can be useful. We shall now show that this can be done at the expense of doubling the number of tridiagonal systems to be solved. The argument can be demonstrated by reference to the following ordinary differential equation :

$$(\varepsilon u')' + (bu)' = f. \tag{12}$$

A conservative scheme requires the specification of the flux $\phi = \varepsilon u' + bu$ such that $\phi' = f$ which is discretized as :

$$f_{j+1} + 4f_j + f_{j-1} = 3(\phi_{j+1} - \phi_{j-1})/h. \tag{13}$$

A Mehrstellen method is then applied to $\phi = \varepsilon u' + bu$ in the following form :

$$M_h u \equiv \varepsilon(\overset{+}{r_j} U_{j+1} + \overset{c}{r_j} U_j + \overset{-}{r_j} U_{j-1})/h - (\overset{+}{q_j}\phi_{j+1} + \overset{c}{q_j}\phi_j + \overset{-}{q_j}\phi_{j-1}) = 0. \tag{14}$$

The coefficients $\overset{+}{r_j}$ and $\overset{+}{q_j}$ are classically determined and will be given in the appendix. Their expression shows that it is impossible to obtain $\bar{r_j} > 0$ for every value of $R_j = hb_j/\varepsilon$. For instance, the standard conservative Mehrstellen scheme can be written :

$$\varepsilon[(3+R_{j-1})U_{j+1} + 4R_jU_j + (R_{j-1}-3)U_{j-1}]/h = \phi_{j+1} + 4\phi_j + \phi_{j-1}. \tag{15}$$

to which can be associated the following pentadiagonal system if the fluxes are eliminated from Eq. (13) and Eq. (15) :

$$3\varepsilon[(3+R_{j+2})U_{j+2} + 4R_{j+1}U_{j+1} - 6U_j - 4R_{j-1}U_{j-1} + (3R_{j-2})\,U_{j-2}]/h =$$

$$f_{j+2} + 8f_{j+1} + 18f_j + 8f_{j-1} + f_{j-2}. \tag{16}$$

Thus the numerical solution is obtained by the superposition of four basic solutions q^j[10]. Two characteristics roots $q_0 = 1$ and $q_1 = (-2R+\sqrt{3(R^2+3)})/(R+3)$ approximate, for b = const., the characteristic roots of the differential problem (1). Two other roots are spurious $q_2 = -1$ and $q_3 = (-2R-\sqrt{3(R^2+3)})/(R+3)$. They lead to oscillations on the Nyquist frequency and should be eliminated by using procedures discussed in [11].

1.3. Another Filtering Procedure

A negative result which bears some analogy with Dahlquist theorems should be mentionned here. If one defines explicit, compact, accurate filters with help of coefficients of tridiagonal matrices A_i to be determined by Taylor formula, the following definition is introduced :

$$\hat{U}_i = A_1U_i + hA_2U_i' + h^2A_3U_i'' = U_i+2\sigma h^4U_i^{IV}/4!+2\theta h^6U_i^{VI}/6!+O(h^8) \tag{17}$$

where $\hat{U}_i$ is the filtered field. If one then stipulates that no phase shift is allowed and that the Nyquist frequency $2\Delta x$ is completely damped out, one finds that the whole set of coefficients in A_i can be expressed with only two parameters σ and θ. The relation (17) is equivalent to the following form :

$$\hat{U}_i = U_i[1 - f(\bar{n})]. \tag{18}$$

where $\bar{n} = \frac{2\pi k}{\lambda}$, λ being the wave length of the wave to be filtered,

$$f(\bar{n}) = Z_\sigma(\bar{n})\sigma - Z_\theta(\bar{n})\theta$$

with :

$$Z_\sigma(\bar{n}) = 9\pi^2C_1(\bar{n})/(48-5\pi^2) + C_\sigma(\bar{n}), \quad Z_\theta(\bar{n})= 2\pi C_1(\bar{n})/(48-5\pi^2) - C_\theta(\bar{n})$$

where :

$$C_1(\bar{n}) = 2(1 - \frac{\bar{n}^2}{2} - \cos\bar{n}) - \frac{3}{4}\bar{n}(\sin\bar{n} - \bar{n}) - \frac{\bar{n}^2}{12}(1 - \cos\bar{n}).$$

$$C_\theta(\bar{n})=- \frac{\bar{n}}{2}(\sin\bar{n}-\bar{n})- \frac{\bar{n}^2}{6}(1-\cos\bar{n}) \; ; \; C_\sigma(\bar{n})= \frac{5\bar{n}}{4}(\sin\bar{n}-\bar{n})+ \frac{\bar{n}^2}{4}(1 - \cos\bar{n}).$$

Now, if one assumes admissibility for the filter $0 \leq \hat{U}_i/U_i \leq 1$; then one finds that no values for σ and θ exist.

1.4. Upwind Hermitian Methods

In that follows, we mention another type of schemes which embodies upwinding while retaining high accuracy. "Mehrstellen" methods can be alternately regarded as a particular hermitian method in which all derivatives are eliminated ; thus, it could be of interest to try to upwind hermitian schemes. Hermitian schemes are based on the following type of relationship :

$$S(\alpha,\beta,\gamma,\theta) \equiv KU_i + KLU_i' + h^2MU_i'' = 0, \tag{19}$$

where K,L,M are operators defined by :

$K = 16\gamma I-8\gamma\mu-3\beta D_0$; $L=16\theta I+(3\beta-8\theta)\mu-(3\alpha-5\gamma)D_0$; $M=4\alpha I+(\alpha-\gamma)\mu+(4\theta-\beta)D_0$,

with $\mu U_i = U_{i+1} + U_{i-1}$; $D_0 U_i = U_{i+1} - U_{i-1}$,

$\alpha,\beta,\gamma,\theta$, are parameters which can be arbitrarily chosen.

A compact block implicit method is obtained by considering, besides the ordinary differential equation (1) to be solved, two formulae $S_1U_i = S_2U_i = 0$ corresponding to two sets of coefficients $\alpha,\beta,\gamma,\theta$. It is always possible to form a pentadiagonal system for the unknowns U_i (see [1] or [10]).

If $\langle A/B\rangle \equiv A_1B_2 - A_2B_1 = b_0 1 + b_1\sigma + b_2\mu + b_3D_0 + b_4D_0\mu$ with $\sigma U_i=U_{i+2}+U_{i-2}$ where the coefficients b_i are linear combinations of $\langle\alpha/\beta\rangle$, $\langle\beta/\theta\rangle$, etc... The pentadiagonal system can then be written in the operational form :

$$h^{-2}\langle K/L\rangle \,\varepsilon U_j + h^{-1}\langle M/K\rangle\,(bU)_j + \langle L/M\rangle\,[c-b')U - f]_j = 0. \tag{20}$$

which provides the discrete system equivalent to (11).

The schemes will be h^4 accurate iff $<\beta/\theta> = 0$ or $\vec{\beta} = \lambda\vec{\theta}$ where $\vec{\beta} = (\beta_1,\beta_2)$ the Hermite 6 family [12] can then be easily recovered. Upwind schemes can also be easily written down : the matrix associated to the $<L/M>$ operator must be triangular ; this condition gives :

$$-4<\alpha/\theta> + 4<\beta/\theta> + 12<\gamma/\theta> - 2<\alpha/\gamma> - 2<\beta/\gamma> = 0. \tag{21}$$

$$4<\alpha/\theta> + 4<\beta/\theta> + 4<\gamma/\theta> - 5<\alpha/\gamma> - 3<\alpha/\beta> = 0. \tag{22}$$

h^4 accuracy implies $\vec{\alpha} = \frac{26-5\lambda}{14-3\lambda}\vec{\gamma} + \mu\vec{\theta}$ with $\mu = 6-\lambda + 2(26-5\lambda)/(14-3\lambda)$ so that for $\theta_1 = \theta_2 = 1$, the three free parameters γ_1, γ_2 and λ lead to a whole family of upwind schemes.

2. DISCRETIZATION OF NAVIER-STOKES EQUATIONS

2.1. The Poisson Equation

The Poisson equation is considered in the following formulation :

$$D(\psi) \equiv A(\xi)\,\psi_{\xi\xi} + B(\xi)\,\psi_\xi + \psi_{\eta\eta} = \zeta. \tag{23}$$

This equation is solved using a Numerov η-discretization (3) combined with a Mehrstellen ξ-discretization in an optimized A.D.I. method [8]. The fourth order accurate solution which is obtained after incomplete convergence is used to calculate the truncation error E in which the derivatives are approximated with five points formulae both in the ξ and η-directions. The deferred correction procedure then comprises the iterative solution of $D(\psi) = \zeta + E$ until convergence. The LU decomposition of the tridiagonal to be solved at each iteration is performed once for all, it follows that the extra cost due to the deferred convection remains always small while sixth order accuracy is obtained. However, it has been shown in [1] that a practically sufficient improvement in accuracy can be attained with only one iteration.

2.2. Time Discretization Algorithms

An approximate factorization of the Beam & Warming [9] type is used. It is based upon the formulation of a linear two step method and is combined with a linearization of the convective operators. The result can be written as :

$$[1 - \hat{\omega}\,\Delta t\, L_y^e]\bar{W} = \phi^{n+1,n}. \quad (24) \qquad [1 - \hat{\omega}\,\Delta t\, L_x^e]W^+ = \bar{W}. \tag{25}$$

$$\zeta^{n+2} = W^+ + (1+\hat{\alpha})\,\zeta^{n+1} - \hat{\alpha}\,\zeta^n. \tag{26}$$

$$\phi^{n+1,n} = \frac{\Delta t}{1+\hat{\xi}}\,(L_x^e + L_y^e)\{1+[\hat{\xi}+\hat{\theta}(\hat{\alpha}-1)+\tfrac{1}{2}]D^-\}\zeta^{n+2} + \left[\frac{\hat{\xi}}{1+\hat{\xi}} - \hat{\alpha}\right] D^-\,\zeta^{n+1}. \tag{27}$$

where $D^- = 1-E$; $E\,\zeta^n = \zeta^{n+1}$. L_x^e and L_y^e are extrapolated spatial operators obtained with the help of $\sigma_e(E) = (1+\hat{\phi}_e)E - \hat{\phi}_e 1$ where $\hat{\phi}_e = \hat{\theta} + \hat{\phi}$ in order to ensure Δt^2-accurate linearization. More precisely, if $L_y = \sigma_e(E)\,L_x$:

$$\sigma(E)[L_x\zeta]^n - L_x^e[\sigma(E)\zeta]^n = \Delta t^2[\hat{\theta}L_x^n\zeta_{tt}^n + 2(\hat{\xi}+1/2)(\hat{\xi}+3/2)(\frac{\partial L_x}{\partial t})^n\,\zeta_t^n]+\ldots \tag{28}$$

$\hat{\omega} = \hat{\theta}/(1+\hat{\xi})$; $\hat{\alpha}$, $\hat{\xi}$ and $\hat{\theta}$ are Beam & Warming parameters of the linear two-step method which is Δt^2-accurate iff $\hat{\phi} = \hat{\xi} - \hat{\theta} + 1/2$ and A-stable iff $\hat{\xi} \leqslant 2\theta - 1$, $\hat{\xi} \geqslant -1/2$ and $-1 \leqslant \hat{\alpha} \leqslant 1$.

The relationship (25), (26) and (27) warrant the following remarks :

(i) the accuracy of this approximate factorization compares favourably with the accuracy of a standard A.D.I. method ; however, its main advantage lies in the fact that a threedimensional extension is straight forward.

(ii) the iteration on the vorticity ζ^{n+2} (unknown at the boundaries) will not need a recalculation of the velocity field which is very time consuming and appears to lead sometimes to convergence problems.

(iii) the method used for the computation of $\phi^{n+1,n}$ critically affects the accuracy. It has been shown in [1] that first and second derivatives in Eq. (27) must be computed with the help of mehrstellen formulae. The best choice leads to a gain of two decades of accuracy.

(iv) the afore mentionned A-stability conditions do not appear to be sufficient for points adjacent to the boundaries because of the following reason (which has also been outlined in [7]). If one considers the discrete Fourier transform ($I_m^2 = -1$), in the case of the square cavity $0 \leqslant x \leqslant 1$, $0 \leqslant y \leqslant 1$:

$$\xi^n_{i,j} (\text{resp. } \psi^n_{i,j}) = Z^n (\text{resp } P^n) \exp [I_m (i\theta_x + j\theta_y)]. \qquad (29)$$

$\theta_x = k_x \Delta x$, $\theta_y = k_y \theta_y$ where k_x and k_y are the wave numbers of Fourier components. Relations (29) will be valid only for interior points $0 < i < I$; $0 < j < J$. On the boundaries, a specific treatment is needed instead of (29). For example, on $j = J$:

$$\psi^n_{i,J} = 0. \quad (30) \quad \zeta^n_{i,J} = (-\frac{1}{2} Z^n + \frac{3}{\Delta y^2} P^n) \exp[I_m (i\theta x + (J-1)\theta_y] + \frac{3}{\Delta y} U_{i,J}. \quad (31)$$

if the vorticity is specified by the h^2-accurate Woods condition (32) :

$$\zeta_{i,J} = - \zeta_{i,J-1}/2 - 3(\psi_{i,J} - \psi_{i,J-1})/h^2. \qquad (32)$$

The amplification matrix can then be written under the following form (see e.g. [7]) :

$$\binom{Z^{n+1}}{P^{n+1}} = g \binom{Z^n}{P^n} + c,$$

where it is sufficient to consider only one iteration on the Poisson equation. It can be shown that :

(1) The classical study of the decoupled system corresponding to a complete interior molecule leads always to an unconditionally stable method because the linear two-step method is A-stable.

(2) The specification of the vorticity at the boundaries implies a limitation on the diffusion number $D = \Delta t/(Re\, h^2)$ while the amplification of Z^n leads to a limitation on the mesh Reynolds numbers $Re|u|h$ and $Re|v|h$. Numerical tests performed on the square cavity problem with fourth-order schemes seem to indicate that the strongest limitations come from the two mesh Reynolds numbers and that the maximum allowed time step of h^4-accurate methods is considerably smaller than the allowed time step of second order methods. This result is thought to be related to the heavy viscous damping which exists in second order methods as compared to the more selective damping of fourth-order methods.

3. THE DRIVEN CAVITY PROBLEM

3.1. Presentation

The Navier-Stokes equations have been solved in a square cavity in their non-dimensional form :

$$\Delta\psi = \zeta \; ; \; u = -\psi_y \; ; \; v = \psi_x \; ; \; \zeta = v_x - u_y . \tag{33}$$

$$\zeta_t + u\zeta_x + v\zeta_y = Re^{-1}\,\Delta\zeta . \tag{34}$$

Three alternative algorithms have been used for the vorticity equation while the Poisson equation is solved in each case with the standard h^4-accurate ADI-OCI scheme presented in 2b. The following schemes are thus considered for (34) :

- the upwind conservative h^2-accurate ADI scheme (U-C-h^2) used in [2].
- the standard "Mehrstellen" h^4-accurate scheme (CMeh-h^4).
- the OCI h^4-accurate scheme with optimal values for p_1, p_2, p_3, p_4 (UOCI-h^4.

An h^2-accurate Woods boundary condition is used for the boundary vorticity ζ_b with (U-C-h^2) while a h^4-accurate boundary condition [1] is used for (CMeh-h^4) and (UOCI-h^4). When not specified, a one time-step discretization is used. No iteration on the value of ζ_b is performed at each time step. Consequently numerical results are only Δt-accurate in the transient part.

For "Mehrstellen" type algorithms, corner points must be excluded. Derivatives on the boundaries near these points need to be computed with the help of uncentered relationship [1]. In each direction, an ordinary differential equation of the form (1) has to be integrated and an uncentered "Mehrstellen" formula is necessary ; it can be written :

$$\varepsilon(r_j^+\zeta_{j+1} + r_j^c\zeta_j + r_j^-\zeta_{j-1})/h^2 - (q_j^c f_j + q_j^- f_{j-1} + q_j^= f_{j-2}) = 0 \tag{35}$$

f_{j+1} is excluded because it comes from $\bar{W}$ defined by (24). $\bar{W}$ is unknown on x = 0 and x = 1 during the second (x-) sweep (see (25)). Here again, the coefficients r_j and q_j are computed by writing that (35) is at least h^3-accurate, while the numerical solution for the test problem (7) remains fourth-order for reasons which have already been outlined in § 1.1.

3.2. Flow Evolution

For Re = 100. In each case, the flow is started from rest, all variables are initialized to zero except the driven wall vorticity ζ_w which is specified by an h^4-accurate relation. Fig. 1 and Fig. 2 give the evolution of $\Delta\zeta \equiv \mathrm{Sup}_{i,j}|\zeta_{i,j}^{n+1} - \zeta_{i,j}^n|$ for two different time steps. For every case, the behaviour of (CMeh - h^4) is better than the behaviour of (UOCI-h^4) ; this result is linked to the known superiority, at moderate Reynolds numbers, of centered convective schemes on upwind convective schemes.

For Re = 500, it has not been possible to start from rest and without relaxation on the value of ζ_w. It proved more convenient to start h^4-accurate schemes from a quasi steady situation obtained with (U-C-h^2). Then convergence is obtained without difficulty even if the steadyness is not completely satisfactory near the driven wall. Such a result seems to indicate that Re=500 is the upper limit

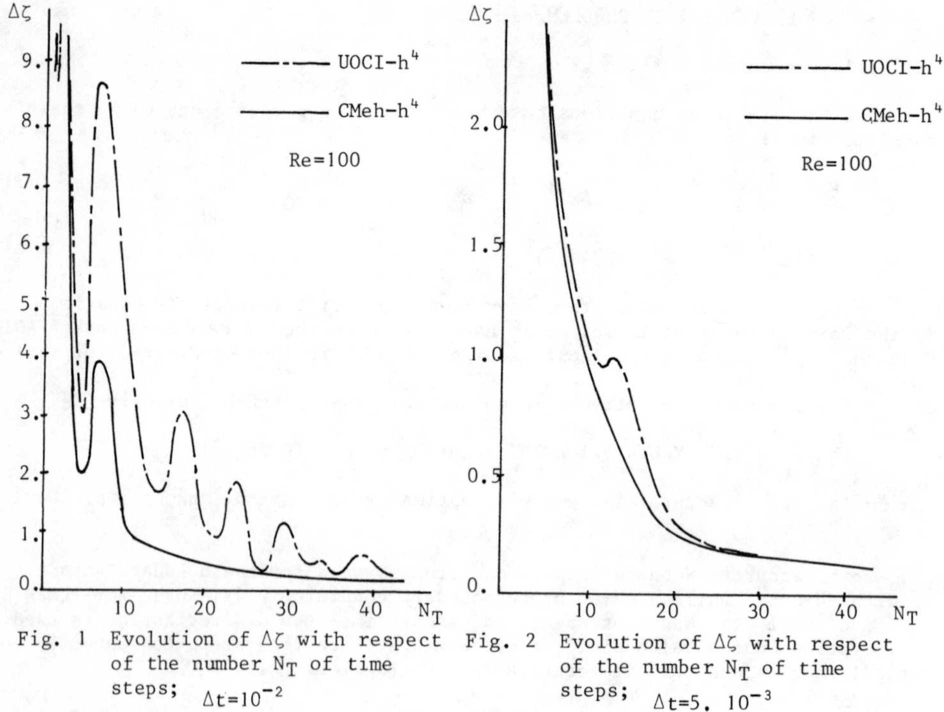

Fig. 1 Evolution of $\Delta\zeta$ with respect of the number N_T of time steps; $\Delta t=10^{-2}$

Fig. 2 Evolution of $\Delta\zeta$ with respect of the number N_T of time steps; $\Delta t=5.\ 10^{-3}$

for which a h^4-accurate non-conservative scheme can converge.

For Re = 2000, h^4-accurate schemes have not proved able to converge and the results given in the steady limit correspond to (U-C-h^2).

3.4. Steady results

Figure 3 gives a schematic sketch of the square cavity flow with adequate boundary conditions.

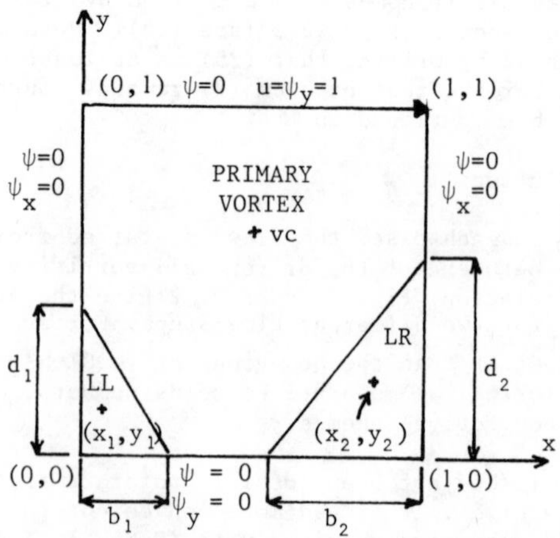

Fig. 3 Schematic sketch of square cavity flow.

The relevant parameters of the flow, such as the coordinates of and the values of ζ and ψ at the primary vortex centre are given for Re = 100 and for a 21x21 mesh in the Table (see at the end of the work). Comparison with results given in [1] shows that the left secondary vortex needs a 31x31 mesh to be obtained both with (U-C-h^2) and fourth order methods. It can be seen that the values of ψ_{vc} and ζ_{vc} are higher for a 21x21 mesh than for a 31x31 mesh. This seems to contradict the usual convergence "from below" of finite difference methods but it is in fact due only to the different convergence criterium which is used (results were given in [1] at t_{RES} = 9.1 while here t_{RES} = 16 or 24). Finally, it should be emphasized that the two h^4-accurate methods lead to practically undistinguishable results. The Table gives also results for Re = 500 and Re = 2000 and includes the sizes of each secondary vortex. The plots given in Fig. 4 confirm qualitative features which are derived from the two tables : (U-C-h^2) shows at Re = 500 for t_{RES} = 38 two imbedded right secondary vortices and no left secondary vortex (see also Fig.4b).

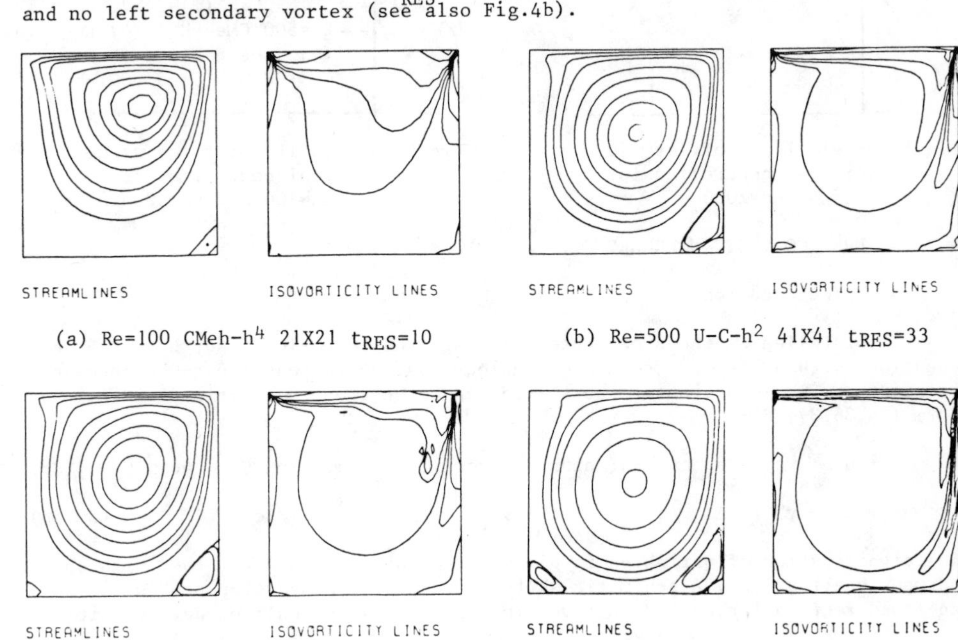

(a) Re=100 CMeh-h^4 21X21 t_{RES}=10 (b) Re=500 U-C-h^2 41X41 t_{RES}=33

(c) Re=500 CMeh-h^4 41X41 t_{RES}=.65 (d) Re=2000 U-C-h^2 41X41 t_{RES}=30

Fig.4 Plots of streamlines and isovorticity lines for several Reynolds numbers

Such a solution is taken as an initial condition for h^4 methods which very quickly lead to a more commonly accepted picture of the flow (Fig. 4c). The troublesome nature of U-C-h^2 results is due to the fact that convergence is not rigorously achieved. It appears also that the magnitude of ψ_2 for Re = 500 is of the same order as the magnitude given in [13] but at Re=400. Results given at Re=2000 show two imbedded vortices in each lower corner. No third secondary vortex seems to be present even if the streamline plots (Fig. 4d) show a void which develops near the upper part of the left wall due to the concavity changes of the streamlines. Such a result is not in agreement with an earlier inference [14] wherein a secondary vortex in the upper left corner should be generated at a critical Reynolds number between 1000 and 1500. A possible explanation of this contradiction might lie either in the chosen mesh or in the used convergence test which would not be rigorous enough. Here again, the intensities of the secondary vortices are lower than those given in [13] but higher than those given in [15]. Such a situation is quite satisfactory if one considers that results [13] could be rather overpredicted (see [16]). Fig. 5 gives the u-velocity profile along the vertical centreline at Re=2000 while Fig. 6 gives the same profile at Re = 100 and Re = 500.

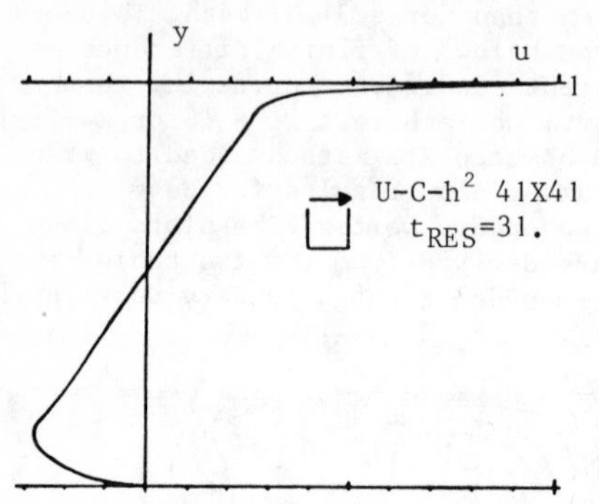

Fig.5 u-velocity profiles along vertical centreline for Re=2000

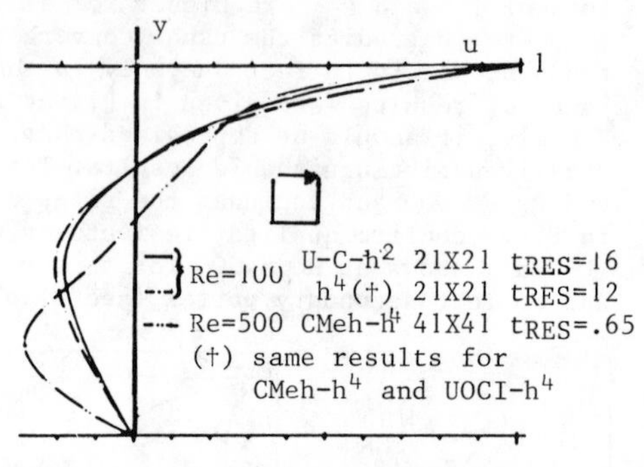

Fig.6 u-velocity profiles along vertical centreline for Re=100 and Re=500

4. FREE CONVECTION PROBLEMS

4.1. The equations

"Mehrstellen" methods have been also applied to the unsteady Navier-Stokes equations with a heat and solute diffusion equation in Boussinesq-Oberbeck approximation. The equations to be solved can be written in their non-dimensional form (34,36,37,38):

$$\zeta_t + u\zeta_x + v\zeta_y = \sigma \ \Delta\zeta + Ra(\sin\Omega \ T_y - \cos\Omega \ T_x) - Rs(\sin\Omega \ C_y + \cos\Omega \ C_x) \quad (36)$$

$$T_t + uT_x + vT_y = \Delta T \quad ; \quad C_t + uC_x + vC_y = (\Delta C + Sm \ \Delta T)/Sc \quad (37\text{-}38)$$

The signification of variables is given in the nomenclature together with suitable adimensionalizations. A schematic sketch of the free convection problem in an enclosed rectangular cavity is given in Fig. 7 with typical boundary conditions.

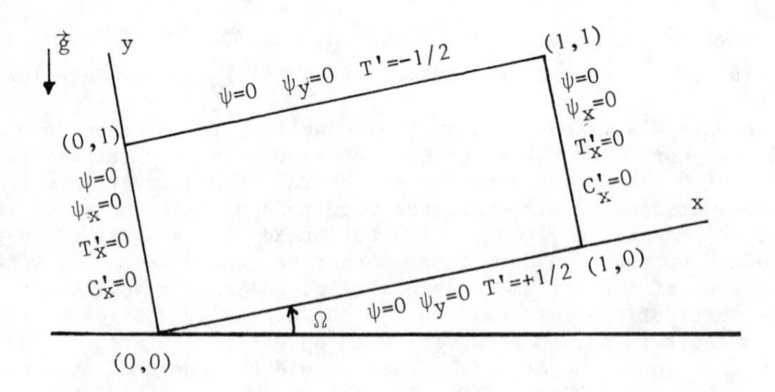

Fig.7 Schematic sketch of the free convection problem

4.2. The physics

It is now well known [17, 18] that when gradients of more than one diffusion property are important, instabilities can develop even when the net density decreases upwards. While diffusion would stabilize the flow if one single solute is present, it can act to release the potential energy of the heavy component present at the top. Such a phenomenon usually called double diffusive convection is associated with the fact that (i) molecular diffusivities of the two components are different and (ii) these components make opposite contributions to the vertical density gradient. In what follows, we consider only the diffusive case where a destabilizing temperature gradient is imposed together with a stabilizing salinity gradient. In such a case, convection movements are first localized near the hot wall and only in a thin layer which thickens until it reaches a maximum thickness. This phenomenon does not appear in a one component fluid. An important feature of such flows is the stability of very strong scalar gradients which can appear like horizontal interfaces inside the convection cell. Unrestricted OCI schemes are believed to be well suited to such a problem because of their aptitude to represent strong gradients without "wiggles".

4.3. The numerics

The first numerical experiments are presented in Fig. 8. They are related to a destabilization of the flow which follows from a small inclination (Ω = 3°) of the cavity from t = 0 to t = 0.4 after which Ω = 0.

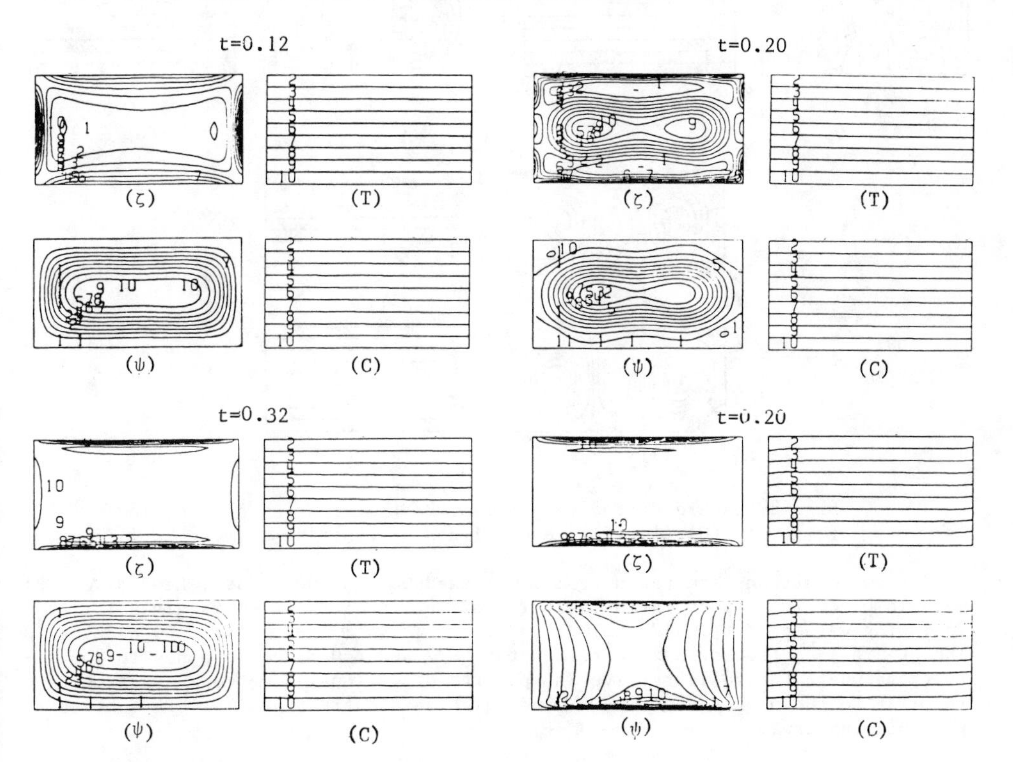

Fig.8 Double diffusive problem. Destabilization of the flow (ζ) (resp.(C),(ψ),(T)) means: lines of constant ζ (resp.C,ψ,T)

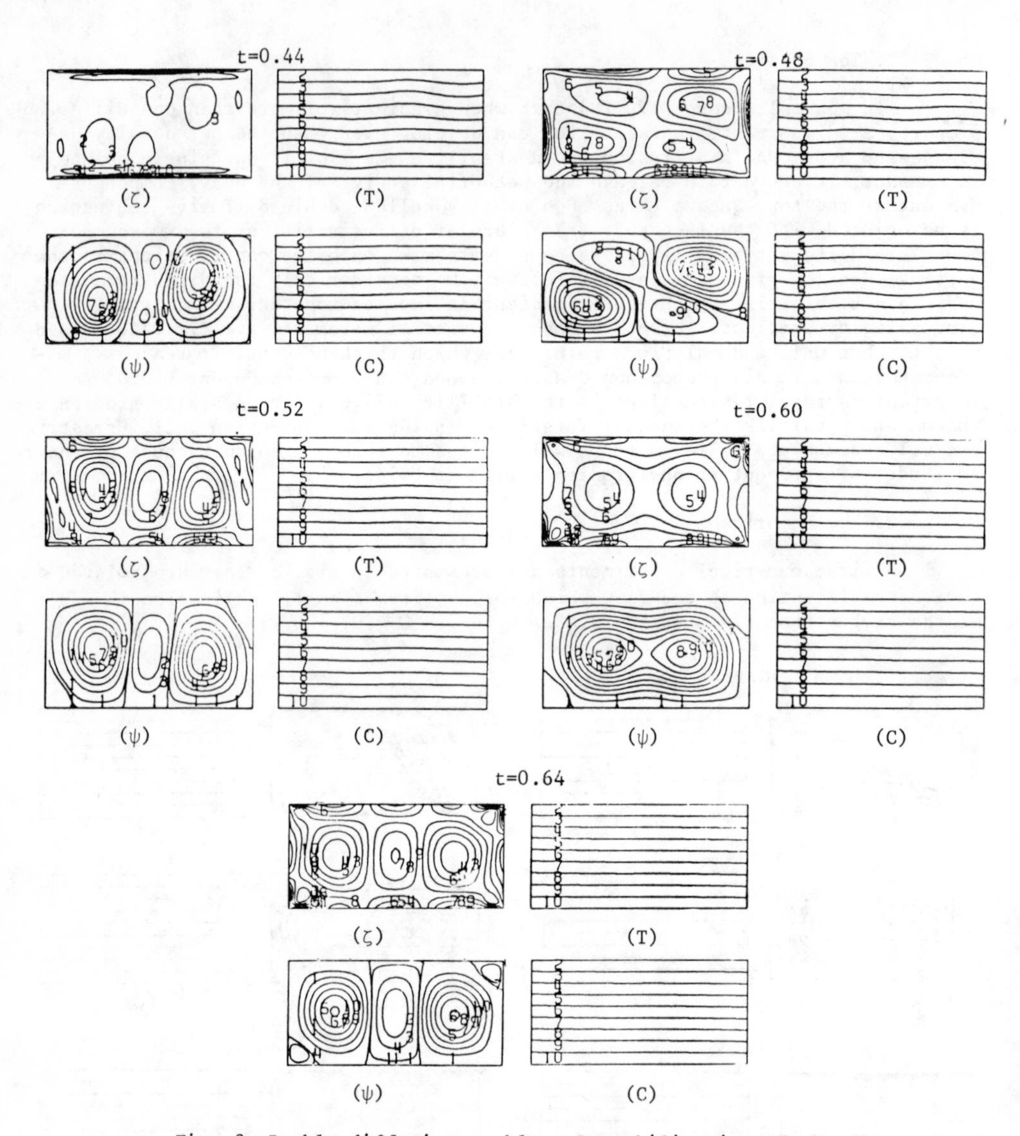

Fig. 8 Double diffusive problem. Destabilization of the flow
(ζ) (resp.(C),(ψ),(T)) means : lines of constant ζ (resp. C,ψ,T)

Flow conditions are taken from [18] : Ra=8600, Rs=10000, σ=1, Le=3.3. A 21X21 mesh is used. The aspect ratio is 2. The evolution of the flow is given for the following values of t : .12 ; .20 ; .32 ; .40 ; .44 ; .48 ; .52 ; .60 and .64. The one roll configuration occurring at t=0.12 and t=0.32 corresponds to two situations where the rolls revolve in opposite directions. Some more experiments (similar to those presented in [18] and which need a great deal of CPU time) are presently underway.

5. AUTOMATIC MESH GENERATION

5.1. Finite difference methods

The methods which have been used rest upon "TOMCAT" procedure [20] : two Laplace equations are considered : $\Delta\xi = P$; $\Delta\eta = Q$ with here $P = Q = 0$. Once the physicalboundaries of the domain have been specified, one has to solve :

$$L(x) \equiv \alpha x_{\xi\xi} - 2\ \beta x_{\xi\eta} + \gamma x_{\eta\eta} = 0. \text{ and } L(y) = 0 \text{ where :} \tag{39}$$

$$\alpha = x_\eta^2 + y_\eta^2 \ ;\ \beta = x_\xi x_\eta + y_\xi x_\eta \ ;\ \gamma = x_\xi^2 + y_\xi^2. \tag{40}$$

If the mesh is relative to a single body, Dirichlet and Neumann conditions are used alternatively on the boundaries in a manner similar to [21] in such a way that $\beta = 0$ and $\alpha = \gamma = J$, Jacobian of the transformation, when convergence is achieved. In the case where a double body is studied, the "TOMCAT" procedure does not lead to an orthogonal mesh. This is a consequence of the fact that Cauchy-Riemann equations cannot be simultaneously fulfilled on the wall ABA and on the "outer" boundary DEF. Thus iterations are necessary in order to modify the locations of mesh points on DEF (see fig. 9) in such a way that the ξ-lines become exactly orthogonal to the η-lines. Fig. 10 gives results obtained by a strict use of "TOMCAT" ; Fig. 11 gives the converged orthogonalized mesh.

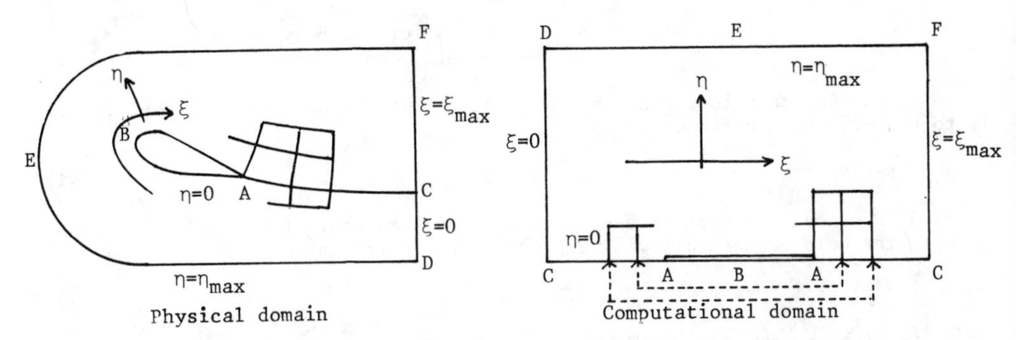

Fig. 9 Sketch of the automatic mesh generation procedure.

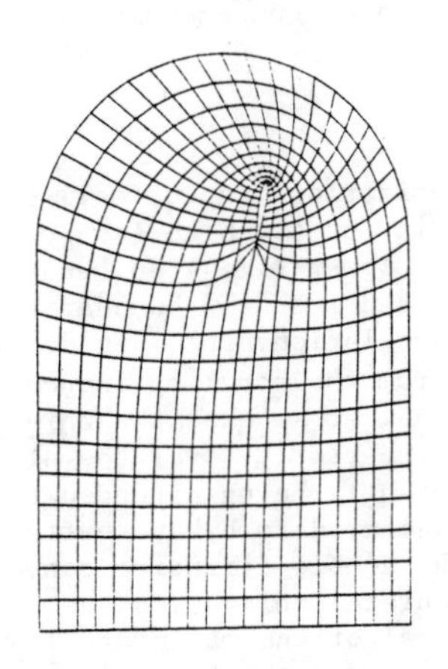

Fig.10 Mesh obtained with "TOMCAT".

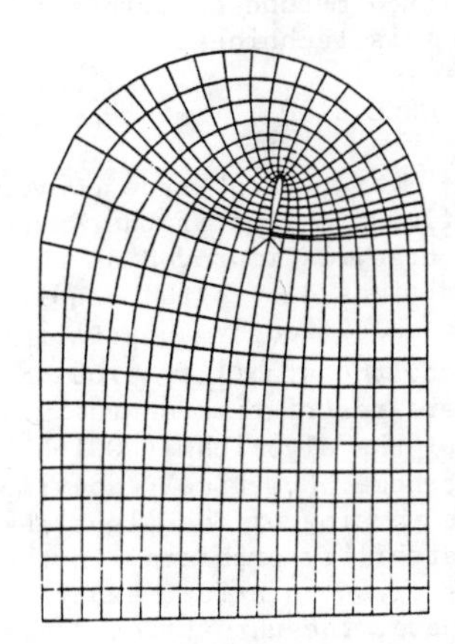

Fig.11 Mesh obtained after iterated orthogonalization procedure.

It appears that only the ξ-lines are greatly displaced by the orthogonalization procedure. The insensivity of the η-lines to this procedure results from the fact that the mesh points on DCF are defined once for all. Of course, the mesh obtained must be corrected by a coordinate attraction procedure. This is done afterwards by introducing two analytically defined transformations $\phi = \phi(\xi);\chi=\chi(\eta)$ so that the second order part of the Navier-Stokes equations written in ϕ,χ-coordinates will remain separable if it is separable in ξ, η-coordinates.

5.2. Singularity methods and conformal mapping.

This method has been used only round a body immersed in an infinite domain to be truncated. It involves three steps. (i) use of a singularity method (dipoles distribution) in order to specify $\xi = \xi_w(x,y)$ on the body $\eta = 0$. The body representation in the ξ,η-plan is given in Fig.12.

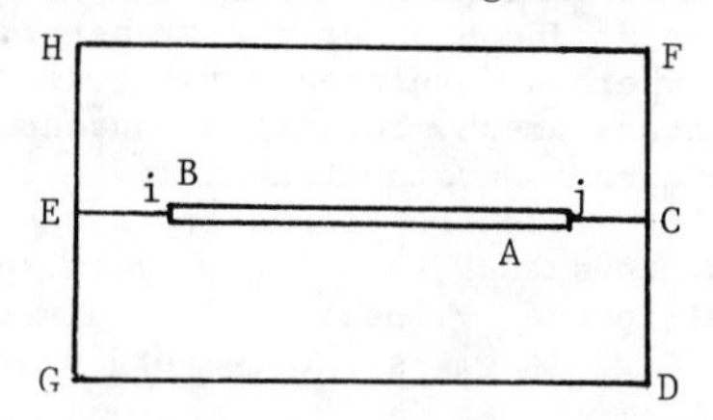

Fig. 12 Representation of the body in the computational domain.

(ii) An analytical conformal mapping allows the passage from the ξ,η -plan to the ϕ,χ -plan defined here by :

$$w - w_o = k(\Theta + \Theta^{-1}) \; ; \; \Theta = \phi + I_m\chi \; ; \; w = \xi + I_m\eta \tag{41}$$

(iii) Physical coordinates are finally given with respect to (ϕ, χ) coordinates with the help of the following expression to be truncated at the K leval :

$$z = x + I_m y = z_o + A_o\Theta + \sum_{k=1}^{\infty} A_k / \Theta^k , \tag{42}$$

A_o is given by the far field while $\{A_k\}$ $k = 1, \ldots K$ are obtained by identification with $\Theta = \Theta_w\{\xi_w(x,y)\}$. This method appears less time consuming that the finite difference method described in 5.1. Fig. 13 shows one example of a mesh generated by this technique.

6. CONCLUSION

The "Mehrstellen" type convective discretizations appear well suited for viscous flow problems if the Reynolds number is not too high ($\leqslant$ 500). Nevertheless, accuracy is improved at the expense of a lower time step because of stability conditions due to the coupling between ζ and ψ at the boundaries (where ζ has to be specified by an artificial boundary relationship). Besides the time-step limitation, the stability problem resulting from the coupling induces an even more severe restriction on the mesh Reynolds number so that the unrestricted version of the algorithm (UOCI-h^4) proves no superiority over the standard Mehrstellen scheme. Numerical experiments are presently being extended to the conservative version of the algorithm which is believed to behave better with respect to stability problems. In the case of the double diffusive convection problem, the first numerical experiments with Mehrstellen schemes seem quite encouraging. Here, the unrestricted version of the algorithm may prove its usefulness as it is able to take into account steep gradients without wiggles. Lastly, the incorporation of the previously described mesh generators in the Navier-Stokes solvers is now in progress.

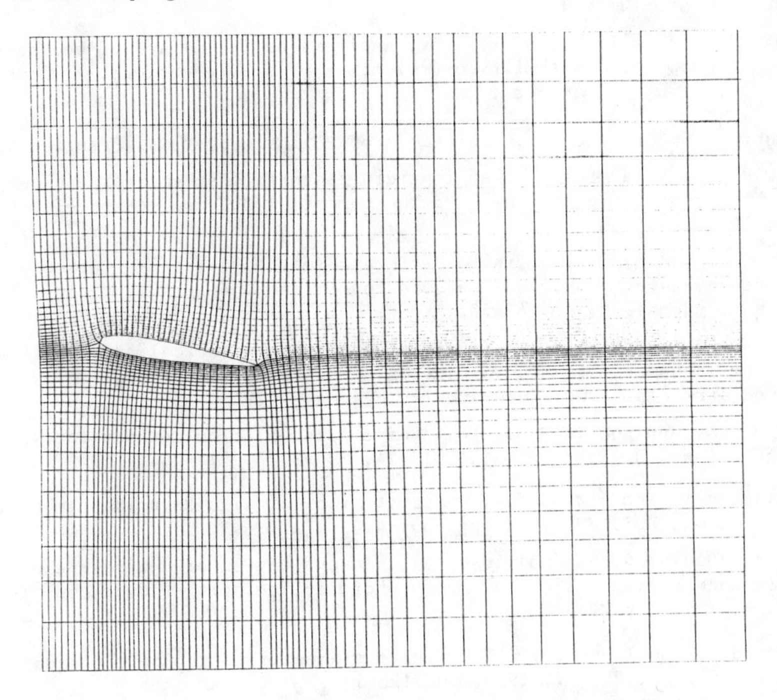

Fig. 13 Mesh generated by the procedure described in §5.2

Acknowledments

Authors are indebted to M. Bellocq for calculations relative to Part 5. The financial support of this work through DRET Contracts 79/649 and 81/075 is also gratefully acknowledged.

References

1 Lecointe Y. and Piquet J. On the numerical solution of somes types of unsteady incompressible viscous flow, Numerical Methods in Laminar and Turbulent Flow, Pineridge Press, Swansea, 1981, pp. 53-64.

2 Daube O. and Ta P. Loc.Etude numérique d'écoulements instationnaires de fluide visqueux incompressible autour de corps profilés par une méthode combinée d'ordre $O(h^2)$ et $O(h^4)$. Journ.Méca.,Vol.17, 1978, pp. 651-678.

3 Collatz L. The numerical Treatment of Differential Equations, Springer Verlag (1960).

4 Krause E., Hirschel E.H. and Kordulla W., Fourth order "Mehrstellen" integration for three dimensionnal turbulent boundary layers. Comp. & Fluids, Vol. 4, pp 77-92 (1976).

5 Ciment M., Leventhal S.H. and Weinberg B.C., The operator compact implicit method for parabolic equations. J. Comp. Phys., Vol. 28, 1978, pp.135-149.

6 Berger, A.E. ; Solomon J.M. ; Ciment M. ; Leventhal S.H. and Weinberg B.C., Generalized OCI schemes for boundary layer problems. Maths. Comp. Vol 35, 1980, pp. 695-731.

7 Bontoux P. ; Gilly B. and Roux B., Analysis of the effect of boundary conditions on numerical stability of solutions of N.S. equations. J. Comp. Phys. Vol. 36, 1980, pp. 417-425.

8 Wachpress E.G. ; Iterative Solutions of Elliptic Systems, Prentice Hall,1966

9 Beam R.M. and Warming R.F. An implicit factorized scheme for the compressible Navier-Stokes equations II : The numerical ODE connection.AIAA Paper 79-1146.

10 Peyret R. , A hermitian finite difference method for the solution of Navier-Stokes equations. Numerical Methods in Laminar and Turbulent Flow, Pentech Press, London 1978, pp. 43-53.

11 Lecointe Y. and Piquet J., Examination of some numerical and asymptotical problems connected to the resolution of unsteady Navier-Stokes equations around airfoils. Proc. Euromech 129. Varna. 1979.

12 Rubin S.G. and Khosla P.K., Polynomial interpolation methods for viscous flow calculations. J. Comp. Phys., Vol. 24, 1977, pp. 217-244.

13 Nallasamy M. and Prasad K.K. On cavity flow at high Reynolds numbers. J. Fluid Mech., Vol. 79, 1977, pp. 391-414.

14 De Vahl Davis, G. and Mallinson G.D. An evaluation of upwind and central difference approximations by a study of recirculating flow. Comp. & Fluids, Vol. 4, 1976, pp.29-43.

15 Olson M.D. and Tuann S.Y., New finite element results for the square cavity. Comp. & Fluids, Vol. 7, 1979, pp. 123-135.

16 Benjamin A.S. and Denny V.E. On the convergence of numerical solutions for 2D. flows in a cavity at large Re. J. Comp. Phys., Vol 33, 1979, pp.340-358.

17 Huppert H.E. and Turner J.S., Double diffusive convection. J. Fluid Mech., Vol. 106, 1981, pp. 299-330.

18 Turner J.S. Buoyancy Effects in Fluids, Cambridge Univ. Press, 1973, pp. 251-287.

19 Huppert H.E. and Moore D.R., Non linear double diffusive convection. J.Fluid Mech., Vol. 78, 1976, pp. 821-854.

20 Thompson J.F. ; Thames F.C. and Mastin C.W. ; Boundary-fotted curvilinear coordinates for solution of partial differential equations on fields containing any number of arbitrary two-dimensional bodies, NASA-CR-2729 ; Jul.1977.

21 Mobley C.D. and Stewart R.J. On the numerical generation of boundary-fitted orthogonal curvilinear coordinate systems. J. Comp. Phys. Vol 34, 1980, pp. 124-135.

Nomenclature

C : Mass fraction
h : Spatial step
I_m : $I_m^2 = -1$
L_x : $=Re^{-1}\partial^2/\partial x^2 - u\partial/\partial x$ (in § 3 & 4)
L_y : $=Re^{-1}\partial^2/\partial y^2 - v\partial/\partial y$ (in § 3 & 4)
ζ : Vorticity
Δt : Time step
Δ : $\partial^2/\partial x^2 + \partial^2/\partial y^2$
ψ : Stream function (except in (8), (9))

R, R_j : Mesh Reynolds number. $R_j = b_j h/\varepsilon$
Re : Reynolds number
u : Solution of the ODE (1)(in § 2)
u,v : Components of the velocity field
U : Solution of the discrete problem(2)

Subscripts and Superscripts

b : Boundary
i,j : Space discretization along x,y
n : Time discretization
RES : Consideration of results
w : Wall boundary

Nomenclature for the free convection problem (§ 4)

a : Height of the cavity
D : Mass diffusivity
C_o : $=(C_1+C_2)/2$
T_o : $=(T_1+T_2)/2$
α : Thermal expansion coefficient
β : "Mass" expansion coefficient
$\times$: Thermal diffusivity
ΔC_o : $=C_1 - C_2$
ΔT_o : $=T_1 - T_2$
σ_o : Soret coefficient

Subscripts

1 : upper boundary (usually cold wall)
2 : lower boundary (usually hot wall)

Adimensionalization of (')-quantities

$t' = \times^{-1} a^2 t$; $x', (y') = ax, (ay)$; $\psi' = \times^{-1}\psi$; $\zeta' = a^{-2}\times\zeta$; $C' = C_o + \Delta C_o . C$; $T' = T_o + \Delta T_o . T$

Adimensional numbers

$Ra = g\alpha a^3 \Delta T_o/\nu\times$	: Rayleigh number	$Sc = \nu/D$	: Schmidt number
$Rs = g\beta a^3 \Delta C_o/\nu\times$	: Solute Rayleigh number	$Sm = \sigma_o C_o(1-C_o)\Delta T_o/\Delta C_o$	: Soret number
$Le = \times/D$	: Lewis number	$\sigma = \nu/\times$	: Prandtl number

Appendix

Coefficients of (14)

$$q_j^- = 1 + g_1^- \, h/\varepsilon \qquad q_j^c = 4 + 2(g_1^+ + g_1^-)\, h/\varepsilon + g_2^c\, h^2/\varepsilon^2)$$

$$q_j^+ = 1 + g_1^+ \, h/\varepsilon$$

$$r_j^+ = 3 + [b_{j+1} + (5\, g_1^+ + g_1^-)/2] h/\varepsilon + (g_1^+ b_{j+1} + 2\, g_2^c) h^2/\varepsilon^2 + b_{j+1} g_2^c\, h^3 \varepsilon^{-3}$$

$$r_j^- = -3 + [b_{j-1} - (5\, g_1^- + g_1^+)/2]\, h/\varepsilon + g_1^-\, b_{j-1}\, h^2/\varepsilon^2$$

$$r_j^c = 2(2\, b_j - g_1^+ + g_1^-)\, h/\varepsilon + 2[(g_1^+ + g_1^-)\, b_j - g_2^c] h^2/\varepsilon^2 + g_2^c\, b_j\, h^3 \varepsilon^{-3}$$

where g_1^+, g_1^-, g_2^c are "at hand" coefficients.

Determination of coefficients of (2)

$$T_j^{[0]} \equiv \varepsilon h^{-2} [r_j^+ + r_j^- + r_j^c + h^2 \varepsilon^{-1}\, (q_j^+\, c_{j+1} + q_j^c\, c_j + q_j^-\, c_{j-1}) = 0$$

$$T_j^{[1]} \equiv \varepsilon h^{-1} \{r_j^+ - r_j^- - h\varepsilon^{-1} [q_j^+\, b_{j+1} + q_j^c\, b_j + q_j^-\, b_{j-1} - h(q_j^+\, c_{j+1} - q_j^-\, c_{j-1})]\}$$

$$T_j^{[2]} \equiv \varepsilon\ \{r_j^+ + r_j^- - 2(q_j^+ + q_j^c + q_j^-) - h\varepsilon^{-1} [2(q_j^+ b_{j+1} - q_j^- b_{j-1}) - h(q_j^+ c_{j+1} - q_j^- c_{j-1})]\}$$

$T_j^{[3]}$ & $T_j^{[4]} = O(h^4)$ lead to the following expressions for q_j^-, q_j^+, q_j^c in the unrestricted OCI scheme.

$q_j^- = 6+(p_1-3)R_j+p_2R_j^2$; $q_j^c = 60+10p_1R_j+p_2R_j^2+p_3R_j^2R_{j+1}$; $q_j^+ = 6+(p_1+3)R_j+(p_1+p_2)R_j^2+p_3R_j^3$.

Optimal values of p_i coefficients for $b_j > 0$.

Define : $\xi = R_{j+1}/R_j$ and $\eta = R_{j-1}/R_j$; then $\underline{p_1 = 3 \text{ and } p_2 = 0}$.

$\tilde{\sigma} = 1 + (\eta-\xi)/(10-\xi-\eta)$; $2\,\tilde{S} = 3\eta - \xi + 10 + 2hc_{j-1}/b_j$.

$$\Pi_1 = 3\xi + \begin{cases} 0 & \text{if } \tilde{\sigma} > 0. \\ 3\tilde{\sigma}^2(10-\xi-\eta)/8 & \text{if } \tilde{\sigma} < 0. \end{cases} \qquad \Pi_2 = 12 - 3\xi + \begin{cases} 0 & \text{if } \tilde{S} < 6. \\ (6-\tilde{S})^2/8 & \text{if } \tilde{S} > 6. \end{cases}$$

$\Pi_3 = p_3 - 3p_1$. ; then $\underline{p_3 = \max(\Pi_1, \Pi_2)}$.

$$\underline{p_4 = (1+\xi)^{-1}\Pi_3/2}.$$

				Primary				LL						LR					
Re	Method	Mesh	t_{RES}	x_{vc}	y_{vc}	ψ_{vc}	$-\zeta_{vc}$	x_1	y_1	$-\psi_1.10^6$	ζ_1	b_1	d_1	x_2	y_2	$-\psi_2.10^6$	ζ_2	b_2	d_2
100	U-C-h^2	21X21	24	.6275	.75	.9568	3.121												
100	CMeh-h^4	21X21	16	.6153	.75	.1034	3.216							.9489	.05	11.46	.0208		
100	UOCI-h^4	21X21	16	.6150	.75	.1036	3.2155							.949	.05	11.49	.0207		
100	CMeh-h^4	31X31	9.1	.616	.738	.1029	3.169	.03	.03	2	.016	.07	.07	.95	.095	15	.0215	.11	.13
500	U-C-h^2	41X41	38	.5556	.6	.1092	1.956							.8922 .9527	.125 .025	632 -250.9	.527 -1.14		
500	CMeh-h^4	41X41	.65†	.5476	.6	.1032	1.960	.0432	.025	3.5	.0175	.05	.07	.8947	.125	593.7	.500		
2000	U-C-h^2	41X41	31	.541	.55	.0819	1.433	.0722 .0332	.1 .025	223 -79.1	.3983 -.624	.18	.15	.8463 .9593	.075 .025	1882 -206	1.507 -1.28	.27	.34

† after convergence de U-C-h^2.

Table : Vortex properties in square cavity

A Fourth Order, Cost Effective and Stable Finite Difference Scheme for the Convection-Diffusion Equation

MURLI M. GUPTA
Department of Mathematics
The George Washington University
Washington, D.C. 20052

RAM P. MANOHAR and JOHN W. STEPHENSON
Department of Mathematics
University of Saskatchewan
Saskatoon S7N OWO, Canada

ABSTRACT

A Fourth Order Difference Scheme (FODS) is presented for solving the convection-diffusion equation in two dimensions. This scheme has a truncation error of order h^4, h being the mesh spacing. The new method is stable and cost effective. Results of some numerical experimentation with the new scheme are given in this paper.

1. INTRODUCTION

We consider the convection-diffusion equation

$$Lu = u_{xx} + u_{yy} + \lambda_1 u_x + \lambda_2 u_y = f(x,y), \qquad (1)$$

where λ_i are constants, usually large. This equation often appears in fluid-flow computations : Eq.(1) is the linearized form of the equations of motion that describe the transport of momentum, vorticity, energy , etc.

When Eq.(1) is solved by finite difference methods, it is commonly replaced either by a central difference approximation of second order or by an upwind difference approximation of first order. The central difference approximation yields good results for small values of λ_i . For large values of λ_i this approximation becomes unstable and inaccurate [1]. The upwind difference approximation remains stable for all values of λ_i . However, it suffers from the problem of false diffusion leading to inaccurate and misleading solutions [2]. Many researchers have been trying to devise a better approximation which is both accurate and stable.

Inspired by the local approximation techniques of [3,4], we have developed a new finite difference scheme for Eq.(1) which has a truncation error of fourth order. This approximation is stable and also cost effective.

Our scheme is somewhat similar in spirit to the hodie method [4] and the operator compact implicit (mehrstellen) methods (see for example [5]). The major difference lies in the derivation of our finite difference scheme (see appendix) where we do not preselect the mesh points of application of the forcing function f(x,y).

In this paper we give a brief description of the new scheme. We also present some numerical examples.

2. THE FOURTH ORDER DIFFERENCE SCHEME (FODS)

The finite difference approximation to Eq.(1) is obtained on a uniform grid using a nine point molecule, that consists of the central point "0" and the eight points $(x\pm h,y)$, $(x,y\pm h)$ $(x\pm h,y\pm h)$ denoted by 1-8 (see Figure 1). The values of the solution $u(x,y)$ and the right hand side function $f(x,y)$ at the nine points 0-8 are used to derive this approximation. A subscripted u_j indicates the value of $u(x,y)$ at the point "j".

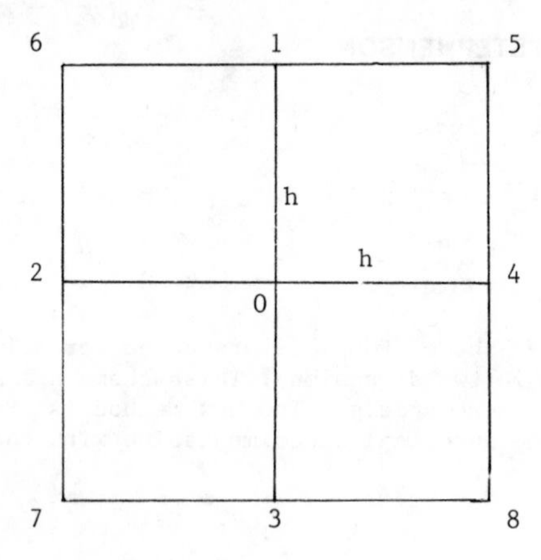

Figure 1

We use the following notation:

$$\Diamond u_0 = u_1 + u_2 + u_3 + u_4 ,$$

$$\Box u_0 = u_5 + u_6 + u_7 + u_8 ,$$

$$\alpha = \lambda_1 h/2 \; ; \; \beta = \lambda_2 h/2 .$$

Using this notation , a fourth order approximation (FODS) to Eq.(1) is given by

$$\begin{aligned} L_h u_0 \equiv\ & 4\Diamond u_0 + \Box u_0 - 20\,u_0 + \alpha\,[\,u_5 + u_8 - u_6 - u_7 + 4(\,u_4 - u_2\,)] \\ & + \beta\,[\,u_5 + u_6 - u_7 - u_8 + 4(\,u_1 - u_3\,)] + 2\,\alpha^2\,(\,u_4 + u_2 - 2u_0) \\ & + 2\,\beta^2\,(\,u_1 + u_3 - 2u_0\,) + \alpha\beta\,(\,u_5 + u_7 - u_6 - u_8\,) \\ & = 6h^2 f_0 + \tfrac{1}{2} h^4\,[\,f_{xx} + f_{yy} + \lambda_1 f_x + \lambda_2 f_y\,]_0 \,. \end{aligned} \tag{2}$$

Brief details of the derivation of Eq.(2) are given in the appendix.

We note that the finite difference approximation in Eq.(2) requires the values of the partial derivatives of the right hand side function $f(x,y)$ at the central mesh point (x,y) denoted by "0". The truncation error of this approximation is given by $h^4\psi(x,y)$, where

$$\psi(x,y) = 1/720 \, [\, 10(\Delta u + 2\lambda_1 u_x + 2\lambda_2 u_y)_{xxyy} + 6(\lambda_1 u_{xxxxx} + \lambda_2 u_{yyyyy}) + 10(\lambda_1 u_{yyy} + \lambda_2 u_{xxx})_{xy} + 5(\lambda_1^2 u_{xxxx} + \lambda_2^2 u_{yyyy}) + 20\, \lambda_1 \lambda_2 \, \Delta(u_{xy}) \,]. \tag{3}$$

The left hand side of Eq.(2) may be rewritten as :

$$L_h u_0 = u_1(4+4\beta+2\beta^2) + u_2(4-4\alpha+2\alpha^2) + u_3(4-4\beta+2\beta^2) + u_4(4+4\alpha+2\alpha^2) + u_5(1+\alpha+\beta+\alpha\beta) + u_6(1-\alpha+\beta-\alpha\beta) + u_7(1-\alpha-\beta+\alpha\beta) + u_8(1+\alpha-\beta-\alpha\beta) - u_0(20+4\alpha^2+4\beta^2). \tag{4}$$

When the partial derivatives of $f(x,y)$ are not available, the right hand side of Eq.(2) may be replaced by finite differences to obtain

$$L_h u_0 = 6h^2 f_0 + \tfrac{1}{2}h^2 \, [\, \Diamond f_0 - 4f_0 + \alpha(f_4 - f_2) + \beta(f_1 - f_3) \,]. \tag{5}$$

The approximation in Eq.(5) is also of fourth order. The truncation error is $h^4 \overline{\psi}(x,y)$ where

$$\overline{\psi}(x,y) = \psi(x,y) - 1/144 \, [\, f_{xxxx} + f_{yyyy} + 2\,\lambda_1 f_{xxx} + 2\,\lambda_2 f_{yyy} \,], \tag{6}$$

where $\psi(x,y)$ is the principal error function of Eq.(2) given in Eq.(3).

In contrast, the conventional central difference scheme (CDS) is given by

$$\Diamond u_0 - 4u_0 + \alpha(u_4 - u_2) + \beta(u_1 - u_3) = h^2 f_0 , \tag{7}$$

and the upwind difference scheme (UDS) for $\alpha>0, \beta>0$ is given by

$$\Diamond u_0 - 4u_0 + 2\alpha(u_4 - u_0) + 2\beta(u_1 - u_0) = h^2 f_0 . \tag{8}$$

3. STABILITY

When the convection- diffusion equation (1) is replaced by FODS given in Eq.(2) or (5) and an iterative procedure such as successive over-relaxation (S.O.R.) is used to obtain the numerical solution, it is important to know if the difference scheme is stable. The coefficient matrix consists of the diagonal term α_0 and the off diagonal terms $\alpha_1, \alpha_2, \ldots, \alpha_8$, where α_i are the coefficients of u_i in Eq.(4). The stability follows if the coefficient matrix is diagonally dominant, i.e., if $\sum_i |\alpha_i| \leqq |\alpha_0|$. Recently, it has been shown that the stability follows even when $\sum_i |\alpha_i| \leqq c.|\alpha_0|$ where c is a constant independent of λ_1, λ_2, and h [6]. In case of the new finite difference scheme of fourth order, this condition is satisfied with c=1.5 and the stability follows.

4. COST EFFECTIVENESS

The new finite difference scheme (FODS) is defined on the nine point molecule shown in figure 1. The resulting system of algebraic equations has a coefficient matrix with at most nine non-zero entries in each row. The bandwidth of the coefficient matrix is two more than the bandwidth of the coefficient matrices obtained with the central difference scheme (7) or the upwind difference scheme (8). If a direct solver package such as LEQT1B from I.M.S.L. is used to solve the resulting systems of algebraic equations, the cost of solution is very competitive. A typical comparison of the average CPU times on IBM 4341 is given in Table 1.

	FODS	CDS	UDS
n=10	0.66	0.50	0.48
n=20	6.61	5.81	5.60
n=30	41.64	50.25	-

Table 1 : Average CPU times (in seconds) for various schemes.

When an iterative method is used to solve these systems of algebraic equations, especially for large values of λ_i , the FODS converges for all values. It is well known that CDS fails to converge for large values of λ_i and UDS yields inaccurate solutions,even though it is convergent.

5. APPLICATIONS

We now present the results of our numerical experimentation with the fourth order difference schemes presented in this paper. We obtained the numerical solutions of the differential equation (1) for several test solutions u(x,y) with various values of λ_i . We solved Eq.(1) in a unit square with uniform mesh spacing in both coordinate directions ; $h = 1/n$, where n is the number of subdivisions in each coordinate direction.

The equations (2) and (5) were applied at each interior mesh point of the square region. The boundary values of u(x,y) were obtained from the known test solution. The coefficient matrix depended on the values of λ_1,λ_2 and was in each case non-symmetric and banded with bandwidth (2n+1). We note that the bandwidth of the coefficient matrix is (2n-1) when central or upwind difference schemes are used to solve Eq.(1).

We used a standard solver LEQT1B from I.M.S.L. to solve the matrix equations. The execution times for direct solutions are given in table 1. When we solved these matrix equations by successive over relaxation (S.O.R.), the average execution time for each iteration was 0.60 sec. with n=10, 1.35 sec. with n=20 and 5.3 sec. with n=30. It is clear that the direct solvers are faster whenever sufficient core storage is available.

In the first test, we used $u=xy^2$ which satisfies the FODS given in Eq.(2) and (5) exactly. We obtained an error of order 10^{-7} with n=5,10,20 for all combinations of λ_1,λ_2 . This error is the roundoff limit for the computer used.

The second test problem had $u = 2x(x-1)(\cos 2\pi y -1)$. The values of the maximum difference between the computed and the exact solutions are given in table 2. We also give the maximum errors obtained with the CDS solutions in the last two columns of table 2.

	FODS			CDS	
λ_1, λ_2	n=10	n=20	n=30	n=20	n=30
1,1	.2748(-3)*	.3285(-3)	.2665(-5)	.4691(-2)	.1579(-2)
10,1	.2676(-3)	.2135(-3)	.2832(-5)	.3733(-2)	.1534(-2)
10,10	.1160(-2)	.1458(-3)	.1489(-4)	.1009(-1)	.4390(-2)
100,10	.9780(-3)	.1018(-3)	.1795(-4)	.4194(-2)	.1635(-2)
100,100	.2067(-1)	.1679(-2)	.3384(-3)	.1929(-1)	.7421(-2)
500,100	.4156(-2)	.8767(-3)	.1802(-3)	.1174(-1)	.5078(-2)

* $.2748(-3) = 0.2748 \times 10^{-3}$.

Table 2: Maximum errors for problem 2

We estimated the order of convergence of the finite difference schemes from the computed data. If a difference scheme is of order h^α and e_1, e_2 are the maximum errors obtained with the mesh widths h_1, h_2 respectively, then the order of convergence is given by

$$\alpha \cong \frac{\ln(e_1/e_2)}{\ln(h_1/h_2)} .$$

The value of α for the FODS as n is increased from 20 to 30 in table 2 lies in the range (3.41, 4.25). This confirms the expectation that the FODS is indeed a fourth order method.

For the CDS the value of α ranges from 2.05 to 2.69 as expected. It is noted that the CDS solutions using n=30 are generally less accurate than the FODS solutions using n=10. The accuracy of the CDS solutions with n=20 was found to be comparable to the accuracy of the FODS solutions with n=5. The CDS solutions exhibit the typical wiggles for large values of λ_i . No such wiggles were observed with any of the FODS solutions. We also obtained the UDS solutions for the range of λ_i values and n=20,30. These solutions were found to be less accurate than the CDS solutions. The accuracy of the UDS solutions (n=20) was found to be poorer than the FODS solutions (n=5).

The third test problem had $u(x,y) = \cos 20y + \sin 20(x-y)$. The results are summarized in table 3. The fourth test problem had

$$u(x,y) = \cosh 10x/ \cosh 10 + \cosh 20y/ \cosh 20.$$

This problem has a sharp boundary layer behaviour. The results are given in table 4.

λ_1,λ_2	FODS n=20	FODS n=30	FODS n=40	CDS n=30
1,1	.9913(-2)	.1980(-2)	.6630(-3)	.1011
10,1	.1098(-1)	.2191(-2)	.7692(-3)	.9801(-1)
10,10	.1888(-1)	.3763(-2)	.1221(-2)	.1167
100,10	.7651(-1)	.1589(-1)	.5081(-2)	.1337
100,100	.3861	.1036	.3508(-1)	.1625
500,100	.2897	.1075	.4084(-1)	.3544
2000,100	.2038	.9119(-1)	.4787(-1)	.2172

Table 3 : Maximum errors for problem 3

λ_1,λ_2	FODS n=20	FODS n=30	FODS n=40	CDS n=30
1,1	.3156(-2)	.5861(-3)	.1454(-3)	.2855(-2)
10,1	.3063(-2)	.5790(-3)	.1004(-3)	.2883(-1)
10,10	.6890(-2)	.1386(-2)	.3866(-3)	.4454(-1)
100,10	.5889(-2)	.1260(-2)	.3952(-3)	.4341(-1)
100,100	.2794(-1)	.6652(-2)	.2261(-2)	.8190(-1)
500,100	.2302(-1)	.6235(-2)	.2256(-2)	.1072
1000,100	.1873(-1)	.6278(-2)	.2619(-2)	.9215(-1)
2000,100	.1581(-1)	.6357(-2)	.3116(-2)	.1888

Table 4 : Maximum errors for problem 4

In order to examine the suitability of FODS for very large values of λ_i , we computed the solutions of the above test problems for λ_i as large as 10^6. In each case we were able to obtain satisfactory solutions without detecting any spurious wiggles. The CDS solutions exhibited very strong oscillations as expected. Some of our results for very large values of λ_i are presented in table 5.

We also solved the FODS systems of algebraic equations by successive over-relaxation using a near optimal value of the relaxation parameter ω. The iterations converged for each value of λ_i used. As an example, with the second test problem, we carried out the S.O.R. iterations until convergence to 10^{-6}. The number of iterations needed for this convergence and the discretization error are given in table 6.

λ_1	λ_2	Problem 2	Problem 3	Problem 4
5000	100	.3063(-3)	.8118(-1)	.6643(-2)
10000	100	.7195(-3)	.7695(-1)	.6336(-2)
10000	1000	.1029(-2)	.1163	.9278(-2)
100000	1000	.1943(-3)	.7627(-1)	.6298(-2)
100000	10000	.3756(-3)	.1158	.9492(-2)
1000000	100000	.7383(-3)	.1157	.9546(-2)

Table 5 : Maximum errors for large λ_i (FODS, n=30)

λ_1,λ_2	Relaxation parameter ω	Number of iterations	Discretization error
1,1	1.5	38	.2266(-3)
10,1	1.38	24	.2304(-3)
10,10	1.30	23	.1190(-2)
100,1	1.20	21	.3109(-3)
500,1	1.20	69	.1085(-3)
1000,1	1.20	82	.8794(-4)

Table 6 : Data for S.O.R.,n=10 (Second Test Problem)

6. CONCLUSIONS

We have presented a fourth order finite difference approximation of the convection- diffusion equation. This approximation yields accurate solutions for large values of λ_i even when the mesh spacing is coarse.

Because of its high accuracy and stability, the fourth order scheme FODS presented here is ideally suited for the solution of the Navier- Stokes equations. This work is in progress and will be reported in the future.

There is evidence that the behaviour of finite difference schemes in one dimension is different from multi-dimensional schemes. A comprehensive report on the one- dimensional convection- diffusion equation is being published by the first author elsewhere.

REFERENCES

1. Gupta, M.M. and Manohar, R. 1980, On the use of central difference scheme for the Navier- Stokes equations, International J. Numer. Methods Engng., vol. 15,pp. 557-573.

2. Gresho,P.M. and Lee, R.L. 1981, Don't suppress the wiggles - they're telling you something,Computers and Fluids, vol. 9,pp. 223-253.

3. Chen, C.J., Naseri-Neshat, H. and Li, P. 1980, The finite analytic method, Report no. E-CJC-1-80,Energy Division,University of Iowa,Iowa City.

4. Lynch, R.E. and Rice, J.R. 1978, The hodie method and its performance for solving elliptic partial differential equations, Recent Advances in Numerical Analysis (De Boor,C. and Golub,G.H., Eds.), Academic Press,New york,pp.143-1

5. Ciment, M., Leventhal, S.H. and Weinberg, B.C. 1978, The operator compact implicit method for parabolic equations, J. Computational Phys.,vol. 28, pp. 135-166.

6. Shay, W.A. 1981, Development of a second order approximation for the Navier-Stokes equations, Computers and Fluids, vol. 9, pp. 279-288.

APPENDIX

Derivation of the Fourth Order Difference Scheme (FODS)

The convection- diffusion equation is

$$u_{xx} + u_{yy} + \lambda_1 u_x + \lambda_2 u_y = f(x,y). \quad (A.1)$$

The fourth order difference approximation is derived on a nine- point square cell of side 2h (figure 1). We assume that , locally on such a cell, the solution u(x,y) and the forcing function f(x,y) can be expressed by two- dimensional power series:

$$u(x,y) = \Sigma a_{i,j} x^i y^j \quad ; \quad f(x,y) = \Sigma c_{i,j} x^i y^j , \quad (A.2)$$

where the summation is carried out for $i+j = 0$ to ∞. On sustituting (A.2) into (A.1) we obtain the following constraints on $a_{i,j}$ and $c_{i,j}$:

$$\begin{aligned}
2 a_{2,0} + 2 a_{0,2} &= c_{0,0} - \lambda_1 a_{1,0} - \lambda_2 a_{0,1} \\
6 a_{3,0} + 2 a_{1,2} &= c_{1,0} - 2\lambda_1 a_{2,0} - \lambda_2 a_{1,1} \\
2 a_{2,1} + 6 a_{0,3} &= c_{0,1} - \lambda_1 a_{1,1} - 2 \lambda_2 a_{0,2} \\
12 a_{4,0} + 2 a_{2,2} &= c_{2,0} - 3\lambda_1 a_{3,0} - \lambda_2 a_{2,1} \\
2 a_{2,2} + 12 a_{0,4} &= c_{0,2} - \lambda_1 a_{1,2} - 3 \lambda_2 a_{0,3} \\
&\vdots
\end{aligned} \quad (A.3)$$

We note that the values of u at any of the nine nodes (fig. 1) can be expressed from (A.2), e.g.

$$u_1 \equiv u\,(0,h) = a_{0,0} + a_{0,1}h + a_{0,2}h^2 + a_{0,3}h^3 + \ldots ,$$

$$u_5 \equiv u\,(h,h) = a_{0,0} + (a_{1,0} + a_{0,1})h + (a_{2,0} + a_{1,1} + a_{0,2})h^2 + \ldots\ldots$$

Letting $\Diamond u_0 = u_1 + u_2 + u_3 + u_4$ and $\Box u_0 = u_5 + u_6 + u_7 + u_8$, we obtain from (A.2) and (A.3) :

$$4\Diamond u_0 + \Box u_0 - 20\, u_0 = 12\,(a_{2,0} + a_{0,2})h^2 + (\, 12a_{4,0} + 4\, a_{2,2} + 12\, a_{0,4})h^4 + 0\,(h^6)$$

$$= 6\, c_{0,0}h^2 + (\, c_{2,0} + c_{0,2}\,)h^4 - \lambda_1 h\,[\, 6\, a_{1,0}h + (3\, a_{3,0} + a_{1,2})h^3\,] - \lambda_2 h\,[\, 6\, a_{0,1}h + (a_{2,1} + 3\, a_{0,3})h^3] + 0\,(h^6\,)\,. \qquad (A.4)$$

It is easy to verify that,

$$6\, a_{1,0}h + (\, 3a_{3,0} + a_{1,2}\,)h^3 = \tfrac{1}{2}(\, u_5+u_8-u_6-u_7) + 2(u_4-u_2) - \tfrac{1}{2}(\, c_{1,0} - 2\,\lambda_1 a_{2,0} - \lambda_2 a_{1,1})h^3 + 0(h^5);$$

$$6\, a_{0,1}h + (\, a_{2,1} + 3a_{0,3}\,)h^3 = \tfrac{1}{2}(\, u_5+u_6-u_7-u_8) + 2(u_1-u_3) - \tfrac{1}{2}(\, c_{0,1} - \lambda_1 a_{1,1} - 2\,\lambda_2 a_{0,2})h^3 + 0(h^5).$$

Moreover,

$$u_4 + u_2 - 2u_0 = 2\, a_{2,0}h^2 + 0(h^4)\;,$$

$$u_1 + u_3 - 2u_0 = 2\, a_{0,2}h^2 + 0(h^4)\;,$$

$$u_5 + u_7 - u_6 - u_8 = 4\, a_{1,1}h^2 + 0(h^4).$$

Inserting the above into (A.4) we obtain

$$4\Diamond u_0 + \Box u_0 - 20\, u_0 + \lambda_1 h\,[\,\tfrac{1}{2}(\, u_5+u_8-u_6-u_7) + 2(u_4-u_2)] + \lambda_2 h\,[\,\tfrac{1}{2}(u_5+u_6-u_7-u_8) + 2(u_1-u_3)] + \lambda_1^2 h^2\,[\tfrac{1}{2}(u_4+u_2) - u_0] + \lambda_2^2 h^2\,[\tfrac{1}{2}(u_1+u_3) - u_0] + \lambda_1\lambda_2\, h^2/4\,[\, u_5+u_7-u_6-u_8\,]$$

$$= 6\, c_{0,0}h^2 + h^4\,(\, c_{2,0} + c_{0,2}) + \tfrac{1}{2}h^4\,(\,\lambda_1 c_{1,0} + \lambda_2 c_{0,1}\,) + 0(h^6)$$

$$= 6\, h^2\, f_0 + \tfrac{1}{2}\, h^4\,[\, f_{xx} + f_{yy} + \lambda_1\, f_x + \lambda_2\, f_y\,]_0 + 0(\, h^6\,). \qquad (A.5)$$

The fourth order difference scheme FODS given in Eq.(2) is obtained by dropping $0(\,h^6\,)$ terms on the right hand side of Eq.(A.5).

A Convectively Stable, Third-Order Accurate Finite-Difference Method for Steady Two-Dimensional Flow and Heat Transfer

B.P. LEONARD
Engineering Science
City University of New York
Staten Island, New York 10301

ABSTRACT

The QUICK 2D method is applied to a vorticity-streamfunction formulation of the Navier-Stokes equation and to the simulation of scalar (mass or thermal) transport in steady two-dimensional flow. High-convection numerical stability is achieved by using an upstream bias in the convective terms. However, because the modelled convection is third-order accurate, stabilization is achieved without sacrificing accuracy -- truncation error terms are equivalent to an added fourth-derivative in the transport equation, thus allowing accurate modelling of both convection and diffusion on practical grids. The explicit algorithm is similar to flux formulations of second-order schemes but with the addition of stabilizing upstream-wieghted normal curvature terms and a small transverse curvature term in estimating control-volume face values. Consistent modelling of gradients is equivalent to that of second-order schemes. Results are presented for laminar driven cavity flows for a range of Reynolds and Péclet numbers.

1. INTRODUCTION

The author's method of Quadratic Upstream Interpolation for Convective Kinematics (QUICK) is briefly outlined in its one-dimensional control-volume form [1]. In modelling the convection of a scalar ϕ by the QUICK method, control-volume cell face values have a truncation error proportional to $\partial^3\phi/\partial x^3$; thus, the nett CV convective flux involves a fourth-derivative truncation error term. In this sense, the QUICK convective modelling scheme is third-order accurate. In addition, because of the upstream biassing, the sign of the truncation error represents a stabilizing effect without interfering with the modelled second-derivative diffusion terms (as is the case with first-order upwinding). By contrast, it should be noted that classical second-order central differencing of convection involves a third-derivative truncation error which becomes a source of unphysical oscillations under high convection conditions. Because of the high accuracy of the QUICK method, economically practical grid sizes can be used; the inherent stability also enhances convergence properties.

The basic two-dimensional QUICK algorithm for the convection and diffusion of a scalar (e.g., temperature or vorticity component) is easily comprehended as it is based on a physically motivated integral control-volume formulation using locally two-dimensional quadratic interpolation functions for estimating CV cell face values and gradients of the transported variable. In comparison with flux formulations of central-difference methods based on local linear interpolation, the QUICK 2D algorithm is seen to add a stabilizing, upstream-weighted normal curvature term and a small transverse curvature term in estimating the CV cell face values; no extra terms are involved in evaluating normal gradients. Thus, it is a relatively straight-forward matter to "QUICKen" a second-order central-difference code which would otherwise be unmanageably wiggly under high convection conditions using practical grids.

The QUICK 2D code is particularly suited to a vorticity-streamfunction formulation of the Navier-Stokes equations using an interleaved rectangular grid such that streamfunction nodes appear at the four corners of the vorticity control-volume cells and vice versa. In this way, average convecting velocities are available at each CV face simply by differencing the corner streamfunction values. The consistent integral formulation of the Poisson equation for the streamfunction involves a slight variation of the standard "five-point" formula for the discrete Laplacian; the required average vorticity in this equation is obtained by taking the arithmetic mean of the four corner vorticity values on the streamfunction CV cell. Some care is necessary in developing consisent numerical boundary condition treatment, but this is quite straightforward.

Computations for typical steady two-dimensional test problems have been performed. For brevity, results are shown here only for the driven-lid square cavity laminar flow problem at Re = 100 and 1000, and for convective-diffusive heat transfer in a square cavity with a prescribed solenoidal velocity field and constant thermal conductivity at Pe = 50 and 1000. In the latter case, the highly accurate QUICK 2D results are compared with the unphysically wiggly second-order computation and the artificially diffusive results of the so-called "optimal upwinding" scheme [2] recommended by Patankar [3]. All computations are based on a uniform 13 × 13 square grid.

2. FORMULATION

2.1 One-Dimensional QUICK Algorithm

Figure 1 is intended to portray the modelling of convection and diffusion of a scalar ϕ by using a control-volume with faces situated half-way between node points using, in general, a nonuniform grid. In time Δt, the average incoming convective flux through the left CV face is $u_\ell \phi_\ell$ and the average diffusive flux $-\Gamma_\ell(\partial\phi/\partial x)_\ell$. Corresponding fluxes through the right CV face are similarly defined -- they are left-face fluxes of the next cell to the right.

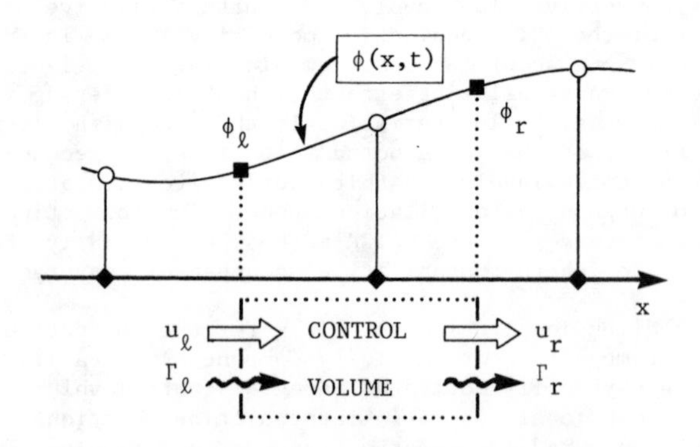

Fig. 1 One-dimensional control volume

Under steady flow conditions, $\overline{u_\ell \phi_\ell} = u_\ell \phi_\ell$ and similarly for the diffusive flux; so that if one assumes that u_ℓ and Γ_ℓ are known, it becomes necessary to model ϕ_ℓ and $(\partial\phi/\partial x)_\ell$ by suitable interpolation between node values.

In the QUICK scheme, different interpolation nodes are used for ϕ_ℓ depending on the sign of u_ℓ, as shown in Fig. 2. In either case, the interpolation involves the two nodes straddling the CV face in question together with the next upstream node. From Fig. 2 it can be seen that quadratic interpolation results in the QUICK CV left-face value and gradient being given by

$$\phi_\ell = \phi_{LIN} - \frac{1}{8}\,\text{CURV} \tag{1}$$

and

$$\left(\frac{\partial\phi}{\partial x}\right)_\ell = \frac{\phi_i - \phi_{i-1}}{\Delta x_\ell}\,, \tag{2}$$

where

$$\phi_{LIN} = \frac{1}{2}\,(\phi_i + \phi_{i-1}) \tag{3}$$

and the upstream-weighted curvature is

$$\left.\begin{aligned} \text{CURV} &= \text{CURVL} \qquad \text{if } u_\ell > 0, \\ &= \text{CURVR} \qquad \text{if } u_\ell < 0. \end{aligned}\right\} \tag{4}$$

The CURV terms are given by, for example,

$$\text{CURVR} = \Delta x_r^{\,2}\,(\text{GRADR}/\Delta x_r - \text{GRADL}/\Delta x_\ell)/\Delta x_C\,, \tag{5}$$

where

$$\text{GRADR} = \phi_{i+1} - \phi_i\,, \tag{6}$$

$$\text{GRADL} = \phi_i - \phi_{i-1}\,, \tag{7}$$

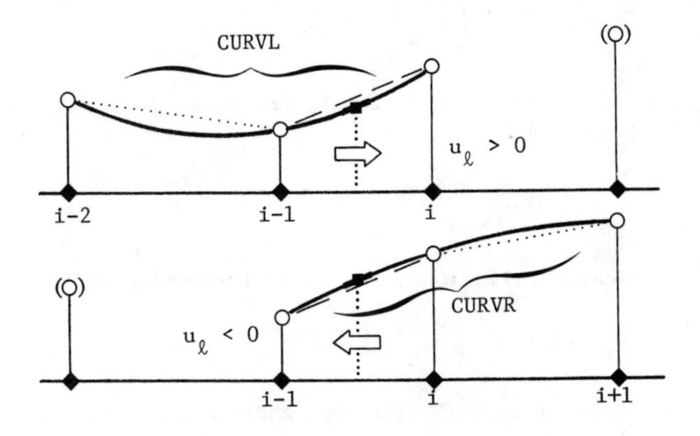

Fig. 2 Quadratic upstream interpolation

and

$$\Delta x_C = \frac{1}{2}(\Delta x_\ell + \Delta x_r); \tag{8}$$

and CURVL for node i is CURVR for node (i-1). In the case of constant grid spacing,

$$\text{CURVR} = \phi_{i+1} - 2\phi_i + \phi_{i-1} . \tag{9}$$

Note particularly from Eqs. (1) and (2) that the only difference between QUICK modelling and second-order central differencing is the appearance of the CURV term in Eq. (1). Because of a property of a parabola that the slope half-way between two points is the same as that of the chord joining the points, the QUICK gradient formula in Eq. (2) is identical to the second-order central-difference form.

By making Taylor expansions around (i-1), it is not difficult to show that

$$\phi_\ell(\text{QUICK}) = \phi_\ell(\text{EXACT}) + \frac{1}{16}\left(\frac{\partial^3\phi}{\partial x^3}\right)_i \Delta x_\ell^3 + \text{H.O.T.} \tag{10}$$

Thus, it is possible to assess the overall effect of truncation error in the governing control-volume equation. For simplicity, consider the case of pure convection at constant velocity u and with a uniform mesh spacing Δx; then a particular numerical algorithm is equivalent to an exact control-volume formulation (obtained by integrating the differential equation from $-\Delta x/2$ to $+\Delta x/2$) plus truncation error terms:

$$\frac{\partial\tilde{\phi}}{\partial t} = -\frac{u}{\Delta x}(\phi_r - \phi_\ell) + \text{T.E.}, \tag{11}$$

where $\tilde{\phi}$ is the control-volume average of ϕ.

For the QUICK algorithm, Eqs. (10), (11), and an analogous formula for ϕ_r combine to give

$$\text{T.E.} = -\frac{|u|}{16}\left(\frac{\partial^4\phi}{\partial x^4}\right)_i \Delta x^3 + \text{H.O.T.} \tag{12}$$

a high-order stabilizing term. This should be compared with second-order central differencing, for which

$$\text{T.E.} = -\frac{u}{6}\left(\frac{\partial^3\phi}{\partial x^3}\right)_i \Delta x^2 + \text{H.O.T.} \tag{13}$$

introducing unphysical oscillations, and with first-order upwinding for which

$$\text{T.E.} = +\frac{|u|}{2}\left(\frac{\partial^2\phi}{\partial x^2}\right)_i \Delta x + \text{H.O.T.} \tag{14}$$

representing artificial numerical diffusion and causing very low accuracy.

Care should be taken not to confuse the control-volume form of the convection equation, Eq. (11), with the corresponding differential equation, $\partial\phi/\partial t = - u\, \partial\phi/\partial x$. The QUICK scheme does not model this latter equation (the analogous finite-difference scheme for the differential equation is based on cubic interpolation and results in a truncation error similar to that of Eq. (12) but with a coefficient of 1/12 rather than 1/16). In the case of first and second-order discretizations, there is no difference between the truncation error in modelling the control-volume and the differential forms; however, for third-order and higher, there is.

2.2 Two-Dimensional QUICK Algorithm

In two (or three) dimensions, the exact control-volume integral formulation for the convection and diffusion of a scalar in the presence of source terms can be written

$$\iiint_V (\phi^{n+1} - \phi^n)\, dV = \int_0^{\Delta t} \left[- \oint\!\!\oint (\underset{\sim}{f}_C + \underset{\sim}{f}_D) \cdot d\underset{\sim}{A} + \iiint_V S\, dV \right] d\tau \,, \tag{15}$$

where $\underset{\sim}{f}_C$ and $\underset{\sim}{f}_D$ are convective and diffusive influx terms.

The two-dimensional QUICK algorithm is based on a locally quadratic interpolation ϕ-surface for estimating both $\underset{\sim}{f}_C$ (convecting velocity × average CV face value) and $\underset{\sim}{f}_D$ (diffusion coefficient × average normal gradient) on each control-volume face individually. The six-node grid required for quadratic interpolation is distributed so as to favor locally upstream nodes. Figure 3 shows the appropriate grid points for the left CV face when the convecting velocity components are both positive in the direction shown.

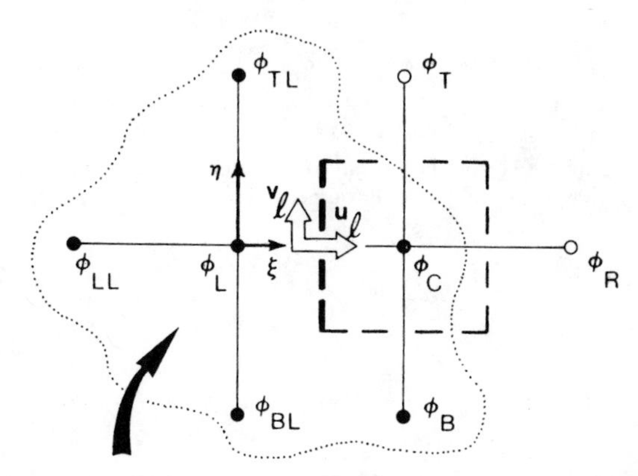

Fig. 3 Interpolation nodes for left CV face

Using the local (ξ,η) coordinate system shown, a six-point quadratic interpolation function has the form

$$\phi = C_1 + C_2\xi + C_3\xi^2 + C_4\eta + C_5\eta^2 + C_6\xi\eta , \qquad (16)$$

where of course the C's are evaluated in terms of the six node values outlined in Fig. 3.

Average CV face value. In two dimensions the average CV face value being convected across the left face is defined, quite generally, as

$$\phi_\ell = \frac{1}{\Delta y}\int_{-\Delta y/2}^{\Delta y/2} \phi(\Delta x/2,\eta)\, d\eta . \qquad (17)$$

Substituting Eq. (16) into Eq,(17) results in the basic QUICK 2D formula:

$$\phi_\ell = \phi_{LIN} - \frac{1}{8}\,\mathrm{CURVN} + \frac{1}{24}\,\mathrm{CURVT} , \qquad (17)$$

where the first term is the two-point linear interpolation, equivalent to second-order central differencing

$$\phi_{LIN} = \frac{1}{2}(\phi_L + \phi_C) , \qquad (19)$$

CURVN is the all-important stabilizing upstream-weighted second difference normal to the control-volume face, in the case shown (uniform Δx),

$$\mathrm{CURVN} = \phi_C - 2\phi_L + \phi_{LL} \qquad (u_\ell > 0), \qquad (20)$$

and the last term in Eq. (18) is a small upstream-weighted transverse curvature effect, in this case,

$$\mathrm{CURVT} = \phi_{TL} - 2\phi_L + \phi_{BL} \qquad (u_\ell > 0). \qquad (21)$$

Note that for steady flow, the sign of v_ℓ does not affect Eq. (18); nor does the value of ϕ_B (when $u_\ell > 0$). However, if u_ℓ is negative, upstream weighting results in

$$\mathrm{CURVN} = \phi_R - 2\phi_C + \phi_L \qquad (u_\ell < 0) \qquad (22)$$

and

$$\mathrm{CURVT} = \phi_T - 2\phi_C + \phi_B \qquad (u_\ell < 0). \qquad (23)$$

Average normal gradient. The corresponding average normal gradient appearing in the diffusive flux is estimated in a consistent manner. In general,

$$\left(\frac{\partial\phi}{\partial x}\right)_\ell = \frac{1}{\Delta y}\int_{-\Delta y/2}^{\Delta y/2} \frac{\partial\phi}{\partial x}(\Delta x/2,\eta)\, d\eta , \qquad (24)$$

and substitution of Eq. (16) into this equation results in

$$\left(\frac{\partial\phi}{\partial x}\right)_\ell = \frac{\phi_C - \phi_L}{\Delta x}, \tag{25}$$

which of course is identical to the second-order central-difference formula, as in the one-dimensional case. In fact, the only difference between QUICK 2D and QUICK 1D formulas is the appearance of the small CURVT term; in three dimensions, there is an analogous additional transverse curvature term in the third direction.

For two-dimensional quasi-steady flow, an update algorithm based on Eq. (15) can be written

$$\phi^{NEW}(i,j) = \phi^{OLD}(i,j) + FLUXL(i,j) - FLUXR(i,j) + FLUXB(i,j) - FLUXT(i,j) + \widetilde{S}(i,j), \tag{26}$$

using an obvious notation. However, not all these terms need be computed, since

$$FLUXR(i,j) = FLUXL(i+1,j) \tag{27}$$

and

$$FLUXT(i,j) = FLUXB(i,j+1). \tag{28}$$

At the left CV face, define the local x-component Courant number

$$CXL(i,j) = u_\ell(i,j)\,\Delta t/\Delta x, \tag{29}$$

where u_ℓ is the average convecting velocity normal to the left CV face as shown in Fig. 3. The corresponding diffusion parameter is given by

$$DXL(i,j) = \Gamma_\ell(i,j)\,\Delta t/\Delta x^2, \tag{30}$$

where Γ_ℓ is the effective diffusion coefficient at the left CV face. Similar formulas are used for the bottom CV face.

The convective and diffusive fluxes through the left face of each (i,j) cell are computed explicitly from current values as sketched in the following, using a left-to-right (increasing i) sweep:

Set: $\quad GRADL = GRADR.$ (31)

Compute: $\quad GRADR = \phi(i+1,j) - \phi(i,j).$ (32)

Set: $\quad CURVL = CURVR.$ (33)

Compute: $\quad CURVR = GRADR - GRADL - \frac{1}{3}\left[\phi(i,j+1) - 2\phi(i,j) + \phi(i,j-1)\right].$ (34)

Compute and store:

$$\begin{aligned}\text{FLUXL}(i,j) = &\ \frac{1}{2}\,\text{CXL}(i,j)\cdot[\phi(i,j) + \phi(i-1,j)] \\ &- \frac{1}{16}\Big\{\big[\text{CXL}(i,j) - |\text{CXL}(i,j)|\big]\cdot\text{CURVR} \\ &\qquad + \big[\text{CXL}(i,j) + |\text{CXL}(i,j)|\big]\cdot\text{CURVL}\Big\} \\ &- \text{DXL}(i,j)\cdot\text{GRADL}.\end{aligned} \tag{35}$$

The i-sweep is then repeated for each j value to generate the complete FLUXL array. The bottom flux array, FLUXB(i,j), is set up in a similar fashion. Then the explicit update algorithm can be written very simply as

$$\begin{aligned}\text{Set:}\quad \phi(i,j) = &\ \phi(i,j) + \text{FLUXL}(i,j) - \text{FLUXL}(i+1,j) \\ &+ \text{FLUXB}(i,j) - \text{FLUXB}(i,j+1) + \widetilde{S}(i,j).\end{aligned} \tag{36}$$

2.3 Vorticity-Streamfunction Navier-Stokes Code

The two-dimensional Navier-Stokes equations can be written in nondimensionalized form as [4]

$$\frac{\partial v_x}{\partial t} + \nabla\cdot(\underset{\sim}{v}\, v_x) = -\frac{\partial p}{\partial x} + \frac{1}{Re}\nabla^2 v_x \tag{37}$$

and

$$\frac{\partial v_y}{\partial t} + \nabla\cdot(\underset{\sim}{v}\, v_y) = -\frac{\partial p}{\partial y} + \frac{1}{Re}\nabla^2 v_y\ , \tag{38}$$

with the incompressibility constraint

$$\nabla\cdot\underset{\sim}{v} = 0. \tag{39}$$

The latter can be automatically satisfied by introducing a streamfunction ψ such that

$$\underset{\sim}{v} = \nabla\times(\psi\,\underset{\sim}{\hat{k}})\ , \tag{40}$$

where $\underset{\sim}{\hat{k}}$ is the unit vector normal to the plane of flow.

The vorticity is defined as

$$\zeta = (\nabla\times\underset{\sim}{v})_k\ ; \tag{41}$$

thus, ψ satisfies the (scalar) Poisson equation

$$\nabla^2\psi = -\zeta \tag{42}$$

The vorticity transport equation is readily found by cross-differentiating Eqs. (37) and (38), thus eliminating the pressure to give

$$\frac{\partial \zeta}{\partial t} + \nabla \cdot (\underset{\sim}{v} \zeta) = \frac{1}{Re} \nabla^2 \zeta . \tag{43}$$

In a numerical scheme, a typical time-step (or iteration loop) consists of solving Eq. (42) for ψ using "old" values for ζ on the right-hand side, then finding $\underset{\sim}{v}$ from Eq. (40), finally solving Eq. (43) for ζ.

To develop the control-volume form, Eqs. (42) and (43) must be integrated spatially over the control-volume cell, taken here to be a uniform square, $\Delta x = \Delta y = h$. Using the "ℓrtb" notation, this gives for the control-volume Poisson equation:

$$h\left[\left(\frac{\partial \psi}{\partial x}\right)_r - \left(\frac{\partial \psi}{\partial x}\right)_\ell + \left(\frac{\partial \psi}{\partial y}\right)_t - \left(\frac{\partial \psi}{\partial y}\right)_b\right]$$
$$= -\iint \zeta \, dxdy = -h^2 \tilde{\zeta} . \tag{44}$$

The normal gradient on the left CV face consistent with quadratic interpolation is

$$\left(\frac{\partial \psi}{\partial x}\right)_\ell = \frac{\psi_C - \psi_L}{\Delta x} , \tag{45}$$

and similarly for the other gradient terms. Consistent modelling of the average vorticity simply generates the arithmetic mean:

$$\tilde{\zeta} = \frac{1}{4} \sum \zeta_{corners} . \tag{46}$$

Thus the control-volume discretization for the streamfunction Poisson equation becomes

$$\psi_L + \psi_B + \psi_R + \psi_T - 4\psi_C = -\frac{h^2}{4} \sum \zeta_{corners} . \tag{47}$$

There are several convenient and accurate methods for solving this form of the discrete Poisson equation [5], so this need not be discussed further here. The variable-grid case involves the same five ψ-nodes, but with slightly different weights because of the fact that gradients must be evaluated (by quadratic interpolation) at CV face locations which are not necessarily half-way between node points. The uniform-grid streamfunction computational star is shown in Fig. 4, where hollow circles represent streamfunction nodes and black dots are vorticity nodes.

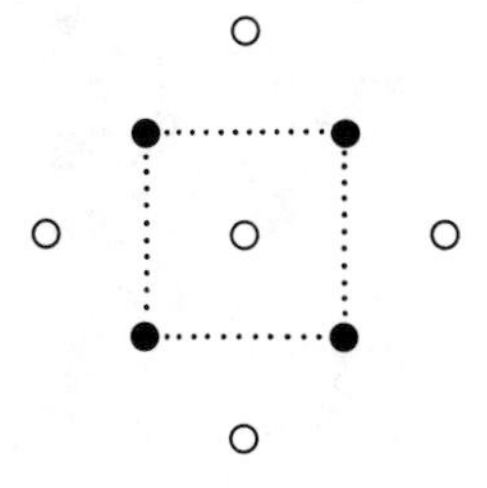

Fig. 4 Streamfunction computational star

The control-volume form of Eq. (43) using QUICK modelling for CV face values and gradients results in an equation identical to Eq. (36) (with $\tilde{S} = 0$ and ζ replacing ϕ, of course). The Courant numbers appearing in the flux terms are based on average normal velocity components computed by differencing adjacent streamfunction values. On the left face of the vorticity control-volume cell, for example,

$$CXL = (\psi_{TL} - \psi_{BL})\,\Delta t/(\Delta x \Delta y) \,. \tag{48}$$

The uniform-grid vorticity star is shown in Fig. 5.

2.4 Numerical Boundary Conditions

The physical boundary conditions at a solid boundary are:
(i) the impermeable-wall condition

$$\psi_b = \text{const} \tag{49}$$

and (ii) the no-slip condition

$$\left(\frac{\partial \psi}{\partial n}\right)_b = U \,, \tag{50}$$

where n is a normal coordinate and U a prescribed velocity. At a free surface it is possible to specify an applied shear stress, as in modelling a wind-driven lake, for example [6]. This is equivalent to specifying the boundary vorticity. There are, of course, other possibilities; e.g., at inflow boundaries, the transverse streamfunction gradient may be given in terms of a specified velocity profile. In any case, two independent conditions are needed on a closed boundary. In the case of a solid boundary, only one condition can be used on the Poisson equation (otherwise it would be over-specified), the the boundary vorticity behavior has to be adjusted in such a way that it is consistent with the other ψ condition.

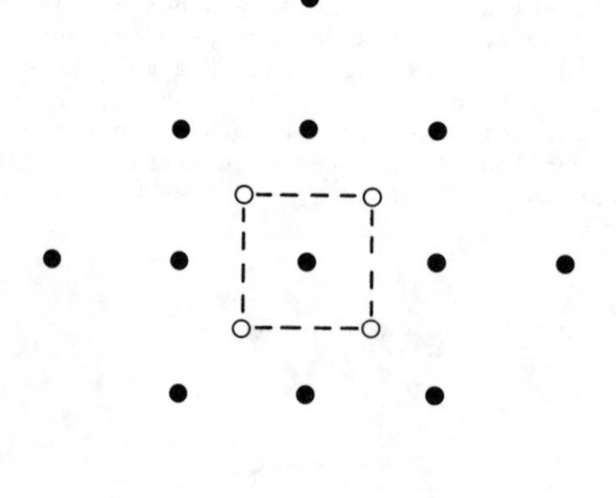

Fig. 5 Vorticity computational star

In the QUICK 2D formulation, boundary conditions are most conveniently situated at streamfunction nodes. Then solid-wall conditions can be implemented as follows, referring to Fig. 6:

(i) for each boundary streamfunction node, compute the value of ψ at an adjacent external node (in the normal direction) by cubic extrapolation using ψ values at two adjacent internal nodes, the previously computed ψ value at the boundary, and the specified normal gradient condition.

(ii) choose two external ζ values at the appropriate diagonally adjacent ζ-nodes so that, in combination with the two corresponding internal ζ-node values, the average vorticity is adjusted so that the subsequent ψ computation will generate the correct (specified) boundary ψ value.

In this way, both streamfunction conditions are satisfied to a high degree of accuracy.

Boundary vorticity information gets into the flow domain via diffusion (both physically and algorithmically) from the boundary, thus it is critical to correctly model the boundary vorticity normal gradient, $(\zeta_{ext} - \zeta_{int})/h$; and since ζ_{int} is known (from its most recently computed value), it can be seen that the consistent modelling of ζ_{ext} is fundamental to a successful simulation. In this respect, it is essential to use cubic (rather than lower-order) extrapolation for the boundary streamfunction -- thus allowing a finite ζ-gradient (proportional to the third normal derivative of ψ). Models which assume only quadratic behavior [7] are inherently inconsistent, implying $\partial\zeta/\partial n = 0$, although the computed boundary vorticity clearly does not (and cannot) have this behavior in general.

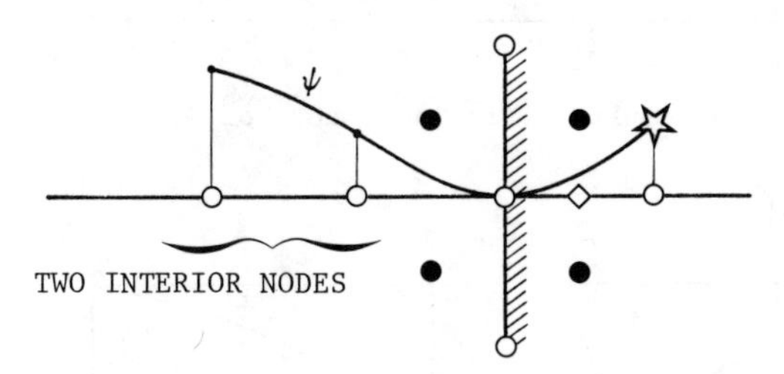

Fig. 6 Numerical boundary conditions

3. RESULTS

3.1 Laminar Flow in a Square Cavity

Figures 7 and 8 show the results of using the QUICK 2D code for computing two-dimensional steady laminar flow in a square cavity with a specified lid velocity and no-slip conditions on the walls. In this case, the Reynolds number, based on lid velocity and the length of one side, is set at Re = 100. The computation uses a uniform 13 × 13 grid. The streamline and velocity-profile results confirm those most generally accepted at this Reynolds number [4], although a possible second recirculation cell (at the lower left corner, as reported by some investigators using second-order methods) was apparently absent or too small and weak to be resolved on this grid.

At Re =1000, Figs. 9 and 10 show that the main vortex has become stronger and moved toward the geometric center, approximating solid-body rotation in that region. Two extremely weak lower recirculation cells are seen, and another is just noticeable at the top left corner. The latter grows stronger with increasing Re. Note the velocity kink in the u-profile in Fig. 10 representing the convection (without much diffusion) of the low-momentum fluid from the top-left wall region. This phenomenon also grows stronger at higher Reynolds numbers.

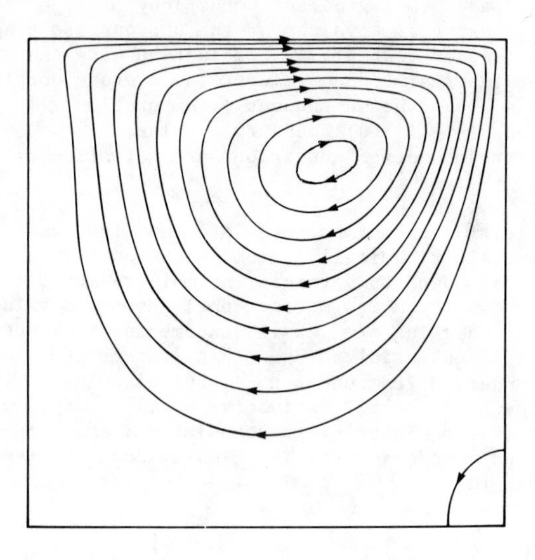

Fig. 7 Re = 100: Streamlines, in increments of 0.01; $|\psi|_{max} = 0.103$

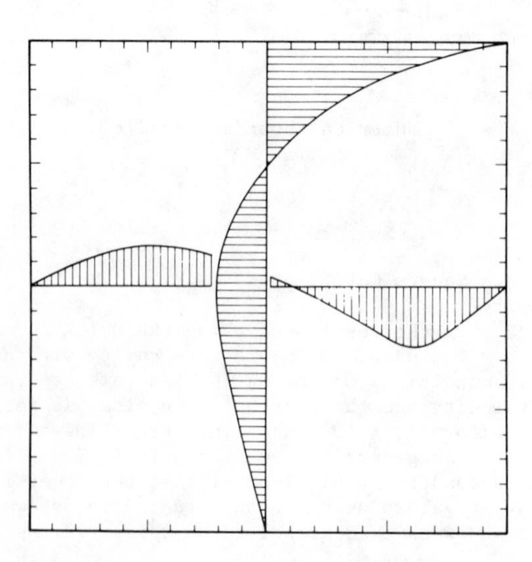

Fig. 8 Centerline velocity profiles, Re = 100

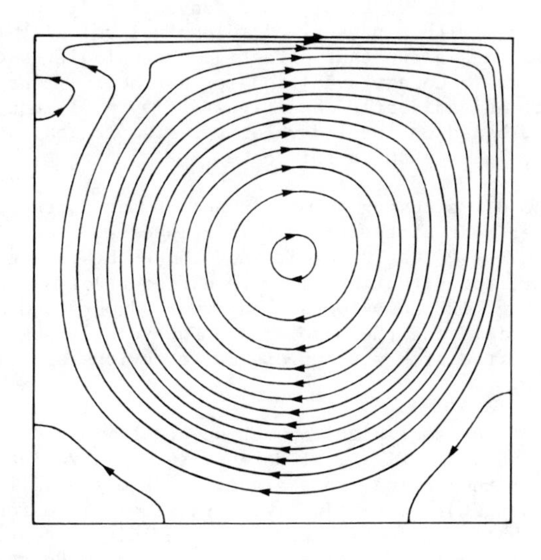

Fig. 9 Re = 1000: Streamlines, in increments of 0.01; $|\psi|_{max} = 0.131$

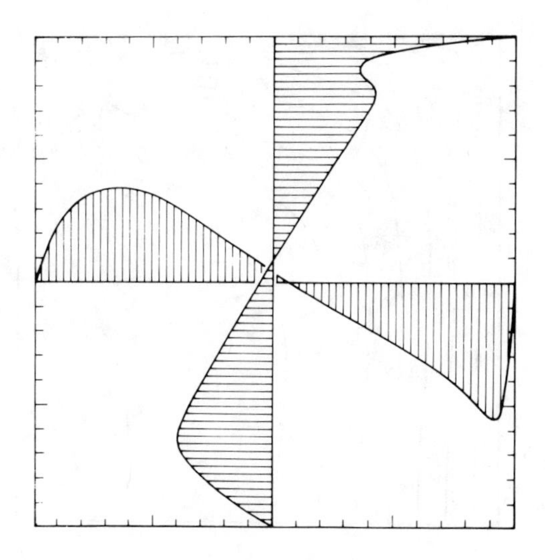

Fig. 10 Centerline velocity profiles, Re = 1000

3.2 Heat Transfer in a Driven Cavity

Figure 11 shows QUICK 2D results for convective-diffusive heat transfer in a driven cavity flow, with a prescribed solenoidal velocity field, shown by the dashed streamlines, and a constant effective thermal diffusion (conduction) coefficient. Thermal boundary conditions prescribe T = 1 at the right boundary, T = 0 at the left, and adiabatic conditions ($\partial T/\partial y = 0$) at the top and bottom. The Péclet number, based on the lid velocity, side length, and effective diffusion coefficient, is Pe = 50 in this case.

At this value of Pe, using a 13 × 13 uniform grid, the grid Péclet number is less than 1 over most of the field. In this case, there is very little difference between the QUICK 2D results and those obtained using central differencing. However, the situation is quite different at significantly larger Pe values; e.g., Fig. 12 shows the second-order computation at Pe = 1000, using the same velocity field and the same grid. Unphysical oscillations with a wavelength of twice the grid spacing are quite obvious and clearly corrupt the entire calculation.

Computation of the same high-convection problem using so-called "optimal upwinding" [2] is shown in Fig. 13. Because the grid Péclet number is larger than 5 over much of the region, this algorithm is essentially operating as pure first-order upwinding for convection (with physical diffusion terms entirely neglected) [8]. That this leads to artificially diffusive results can be seen by comparing with the QUICK 2D computation at the same Pe value shown in Fig. 14, which conservative truncation error estimates indicate to be extremely accurate.

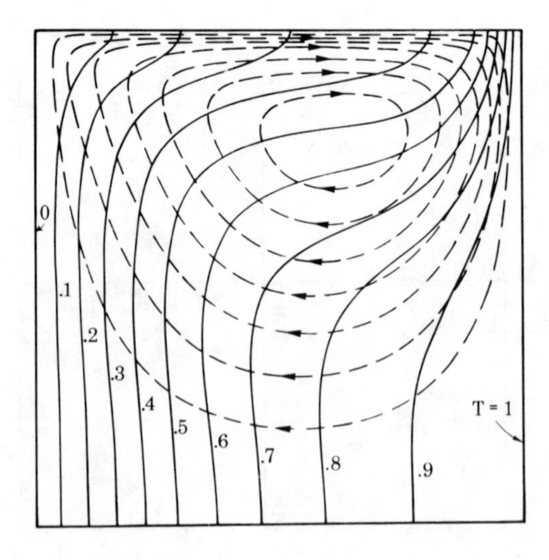

Fig. 11 Streamlines and isotherms, Pe = 50

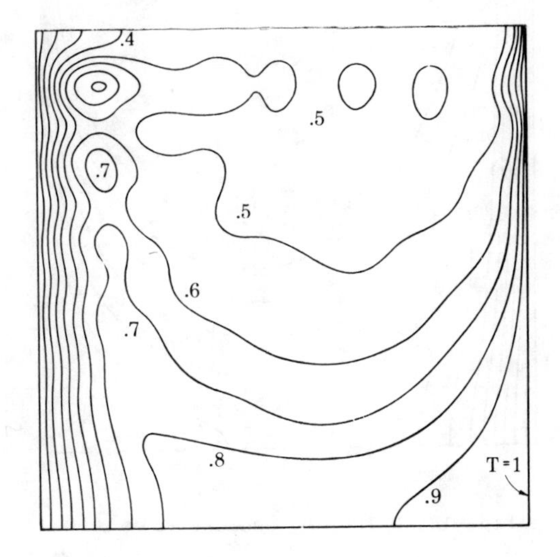

Fig. 12 Second-order central differencing, Pe = 1000

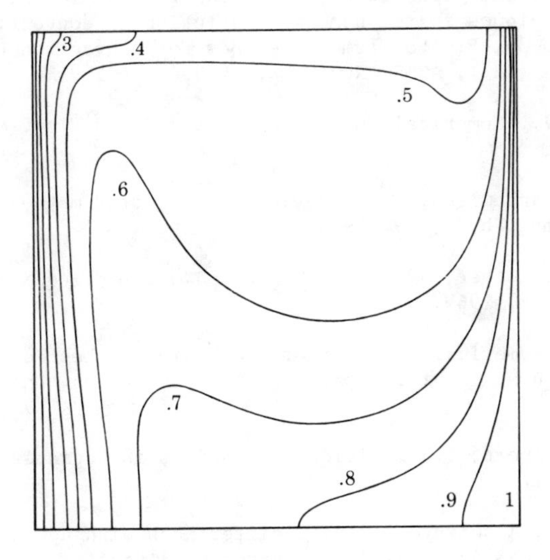

Fig. 13 "Optimal upwinding", Pe = 1000

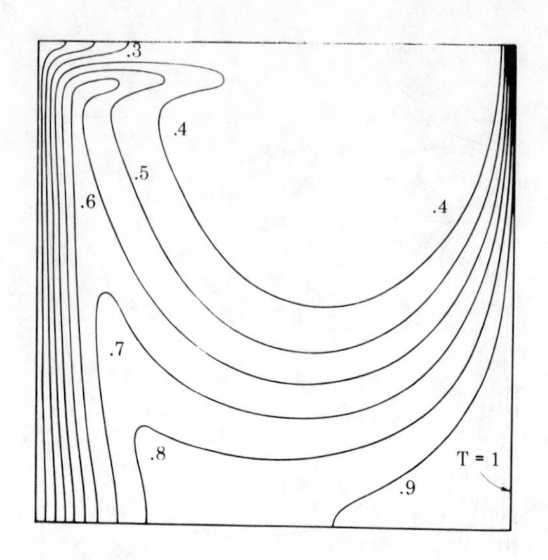

Fig. 14 QUICK 2D results, Pe = 1000

REFERENCES

1. Leonard, B.P., A stable and accurate convective modelling procedure based on quadratic upstream interpolation, Comp. Meth. Appl. Mech. & Eng., 19, 1979, pp. 59-98.

2. Heinrich, J.C. and Zienkiewicz, O.C., The finite element method and 'upwinding' techniques in the numerical solution of convection dominated flow problems, AMD-34, Finite Element Methods for Convection Dominated Flows, T.J.R. Hughes (ed.), ASME, New York, 1979, p. 105.

3. Patankar, S.V., Numerical Heat Transfer and Fluid Flow, McGraw-Hill, New York, 1980.

4. Tuann, S.-Y. and Olsen, M.D., Review of computing methods for recirculating flows, J. Comp. Phys., 29, 1978, p. 1.

5. Carnahan, B., Luther, H.A., and Wilkes, J.O., Applied Numerical Methods, Wiley, New York, 1969.

6. May, R.L., A numerical solution of the Navier-Stokes equation in a rectangular basin, Ph.D. Thesis, Department of Mathematics, University of Adelaide, 1978.

7. Thom, A. and Apelt, C.J., Field Computations in Engineering Physics, Van Nostrand, 1961.

8. Leonard, B.P., A survey of finite differences with upwinding for numerical modelling of the incompressible convective diffusion equation, Recent Advances in Numerical Methods in Fluids, 2, C. Taylor (ed.), Pentech, 1981.

FREE CONVECTION IN ENCLOSURES

A Semidirect Method for Combined Natural and Forced Convection Problems Including Solute

PATRICK J. ROACHE
Ecodynamics Research Associates, Inc.
P.O. Box 8172
Albuquerque, New Mexico 87198

ABSTRACT

A very efficient numerical method has been developed for calculating steady state combined natural and forced convection problems, including a solute. The method is an extension of a semidirect method previously developed for natural convection, and utilizes spatial marching methods to solve a linearized problem, together with a quasi-Picard iteration to solve the nonlinearity. The code has been applied to study two problems associated with salt gradient solar ponds, including the Soret effect.

1. INTRODUCTION

Semidirect methods are rapid finite-difference methods for solving steady flow problems. Fast elliptic solvers are used to solve linearized equations directly, which are then iterated to solve the nonlinearity. Previous semidirect methods are non-thermal problems used by the present author [1-9] utilized segregated (decoupled) solutions for the stream function (ψ) equation and for the linearized vorticity (ζ) equation. Even for linear problems (e.g., Re = 0) this decoupled approach requires an iterative solution due to the linear coupling of the ψ and ζ equations at no-slip boundaries. The elliptic solution is driven only by one-point iterations for wall vorticities which can converge slowly for $\Delta x \simeq \Delta y$, and which require semiempirical determination of under-relaxation factors for ζ at no-slip walls. This approach is still recommended for channel flows. The biharmonic-driver method [5] avoids this difficulty at no-slip boundaries, but does not converge at high Re.

In [10], the present author developed another semidirect method which is more suitable for combined forced- and free-convection flow problems. The method involves two innovations. First, the ψ-ζ equations (including linearized variable-coefficient advection terms) are solved by spatial marching methods [11-18] in a coupled solution, with the no-slip boundary conditions satisfied non-iteratively. The influence coefficient matrix for the marching method is twice as long compared to the decoupled equation approach, so that the storage and computer time are increased, especially for initialization. However, there is no requirement to determine iteration parameters, and the nonlinear iteration does not depend on the cell aspect ratio *per se*. The Re = 0 non-thermal problem is solved without iteration [8] as in the BID method, but high Re problems also converge, as in the decoupled equation approach, since linearized advection terms are included in the linear operator. In the second innovation, a solution for the temperature is obtained from an energy equation utilizing the Boussinesq approximation, also solved with marching methods.

Solving for T first, the linearized problem can be solved directly. For the nonlinear problem, at moderate Grashoff numbers, no under-relaxation is required, and the number of iterations was increased by only 3 or 4 compared to non-thermal problems in the worse case solved. The "Split NOS" approach [3] is still used in the nonlinear equation, so that only one initialization is required in the $\psi-\zeta$ solution for each Re. The solutions [10] were typically obtained in O(10) iterations, with the initialization requiring very roughly one half the total computer time.

In the present work, these methods are extended to the case of interest to salt gradient solar ponds, that of two diffusing species of heat and salt. A salt gradient solar pond is a solar collection and seasonal storage device which utilizes an artificially maintained salt gradient to suppress natural convection and thereby reduce heat losses. A large pool of water with an absorbing bottom collects radiant energy, so the temperature increases in a bottom convecting region. In the solar pond, a salt gradient region is maintained with the heavier salt concentration at the bottom. Thus, although the water is hotter at the bottom, which by itself would be unstable, it is also heavier at the bottom due to the salt concentration, so that stability is possible. See [19-21]. Salt gradient solar ponds belong in a class of phenomena referred to as double-diffusive because of the different diffusivities of the two components. The components may be two solutes or, in this case, heat and salt. The research done in this area has been mostly in the fields of oceanography and meteorology where the result of density gradients due to heat, salinity, and moisture content are manifested as ocean currents and changing weather. A salt gradient solar pond, like these natural phenomena, is a transient system being subjected to a periodic input of solar radiation and the continuous subsequent exchange of this heat between the fluid, its boundaries, and the ambient air. However, the present study is limited to certain aspects of the pond which can be considered steady-state, to a first approximation.

2. GOVERNING EQUATIONS

We utilize the two-dimensional Navier-Stokes equations in the vorticity form, with the Boussinesq approximation. Overbars denote dimensional quantities. Use is made of the definition of vorticity ζ,

$$\bar{\zeta} = \bar{\nabla} x \vec{\bar{v}} = \frac{\partial \bar{u}}{\partial \bar{y}} - \frac{\partial \bar{v}}{\partial \bar{x}} \tag{1}$$

and the continuity equation (again using the Boussinesq approximation)

$$\nabla \cdot \vec{v} = 0 = \frac{\partial \bar{u}}{\partial \bar{x}} + \frac{\partial \bar{v}}{\partial \bar{y}} . \tag{2}$$

The direction $\bar{\gamma}$ is normal to the gravity vector, and the vorticity equation is

$$\frac{\partial \bar{\zeta}}{\partial \bar{t}} = -\nabla \cdot (\vec{\bar{v}}\bar{\zeta}) + \nu \nabla^2 \bar{\zeta} + g \frac{\partial}{\partial \bar{\gamma}} (\alpha \nabla \bar{T} - \beta \nabla \bar{s}) \tag{3}$$

where α and β are the thermal and salinity coefficients in the linear density equation,

$$\rho = \rho_{ref}[1 - \alpha(\bar{T}-T_{ref}) + \beta(\bar{S}-S_{ref})] . \tag{4}$$

Following [11], Ch. 2, the equations are normalized for a diffusive-dominated process as follows. T_{TOP} and T_{BOT} are the temperatures at the top and bottom of the pond; similarly for salt concentrations S. $\overline{L}$ is the characteristic length of the problem, the depth of the gradient region.

$$x = \overline{x}/\overline{L},\ \gamma = \overline{\gamma}/\overline{L}$$

$$Rc = \overline{U}_C\ \overline{L}/\overline{\nu}$$

$$u = \overline{u}/\overline{U}c$$

$$\zeta = \overline{\zeta}/(\overline{U}c/\overline{L})$$

$$t = \overline{t}(\nu/\overline{L}^2$$

$$T = (\overline{T}-\overline{T}_{BOT})/(\overline{T}_{BOT}-\overline{T}_{TOP})$$

$$S = (\overline{S}-\overline{S}_{BOT})/(\overline{S}_{BOT}-\overline{S}_{TOP}) \tag{5}$$

For the characteristic velocity U_c, we choose a combination of the usual thermal and salt convective velocities (e.g., see [22]). This gives a non-singular normalization for either extreme of zero salt gradient or zero temperature gradient.

$$U_c = \sqrt{g\overline{L}\{\alpha|T_{BOT}-T_{TOP}| + \beta|S_{BOT}-S_{TOP}|\}} \tag{6}$$

Substitution yields

$$\frac{\partial\zeta}{\partial t} = -Rc\ \nabla\cdot\vec{V}\zeta + \nabla^2\zeta + \frac{G_{rt}}{Rc}\frac{\partial T}{\partial\gamma} - \frac{G_{rs}}{Rc}\frac{\partial S}{\partial\gamma} \tag{7}$$

where G_{rt} is the (usual) temperature Grashoff number, and G_{rs} is the salt Grashoff number, defined as

$$G_{rt} = g\alpha(\overline{T}_{BOT}-\overline{T}_{TOP})\overline{L}^3/\nu^2 \tag{8a}$$

$$G_{rs} = g\beta(\overline{S}_{BOT}-\overline{S}_{TOP})\overline{L}^3/\nu^2\ . \tag{8b}$$

The dimensional energy equation is

$$\rho c\left[\frac{\partial\overline{T}}{\partial\overline{t}} + \overline{\nabla}\cdot\vec{\overline{V}}\overline{T}\right] = \overline{\nabla}\cdot k\overline{\nabla}\overline{T} \tag{9}$$

where c = specific heat and k = conductivity. Normalizing as before and assuming that k is slowly varying gives

$$Pr\frac{\partial T}{\partial t} = -RcPr\nabla\cdot\vec{V}T + \nabla^2 T \tag{10}$$

where the Prandtl number is defined as

$$Pr = c\mu/k = \rho c\nu/k \tag{11}$$

The dimensional salt transport equation from Gebhart [22], strictly valid for only low concentrations, is here augmented by the Soret effect, also known as the Ludwig-Soret or thermal diffusion effect, as in Rothmeyer, [23,24].

$$\frac{\partial \bar{S}}{\partial t} = -\nabla\cdot\vec{\bar{V}}\bar{S} + \bar{\nabla}\cdot D\bar{\nabla}S + \bar{\nabla}\cdot D\hat{s}_T\bar{S}\bar{\nabla}\bar{T} \tag{12}$$

The Soret coefficient $\hat{s}_T$ is expressed as (Caldwell [24], Rothmeyer [23])

$$\hat{s}_T = \bar{s}_T \frac{m_w}{m_s+m_w} \tag{13}$$

where m_w and m_s are the mol fractions of water and salt. For the pond conditions, Rothmeyer [23], p. A-13 notes that the bracketed ratio is ~1 for salt ponds. Caldwell [25] gives the following correlation from his experiments for $\bar{s}_T$, for $12^0C \le \bar{T} \le 50^0C$. Following Rothmeyer [23], we extrapolate for $T > 50^0C$. T is in ^0C, and $\bar{s}_T$ in $1/^0C$.

$$\bar{s}_T = 10^{-3}(-1.2321 + 0.1128\bar{T} - 0.00087\,\bar{T}^2),\quad 12^0C \le \bar{T} \le 50^0C$$

$$\bar{s}_T = 10^{-3}(2.233 + 0.258(\bar{T}-50^0C)),\quad \bar{T} > 50^0C \tag{14}$$

This is apparently the best data available on the Soret affect for the pond, although only one concentration is used by Caldwell. This can only be an approximation for the pond (Rothmeyer [23]).

We define a Soret number for the pond as

$$S_p = (\bar{T}_{BOT}-\bar{T}_{TOP})\bar{s}_{Tref} \tag{15}$$

where $\bar{s}_{Tref}$ is a reference Soret coefficient calculated at some reference temperature, say $T_{ref} = \frac{1}{2}(T_{BOT}+T_{TOP})$. Defining a dimensionless Soret coefficient ratio as

$$S_T = \bar{S}_T/\bar{S}_{Tref} \tag{16}$$

and a characteristic pond salt ratio as

$$s_R = \bar{s}_{BOT}/(\bar{s}_{BOT}-\bar{s}_{TOP}) \tag{17}$$

and using other normalizing terms as before, we obtain the dimensionless salt transport equation.

$$S_c\frac{\partial S}{\partial t} = -RcSc\ \nabla\cdot\vec{V}S + \nabla^2 S + S_p\ \nabla\cdot[s_T(S+s_R)\nabla T] \tag{18}$$

where the Schmidt number is

$$S_c = D/\nu \tag{19}$$

For all calculations reported herein, we take $s_T = 1$, since the limitations of the available data preclude more precise calculations.

3. NUMERICAL METHODS

The final governing continuum equations to be solved are then the Poisson equation for stream function,

$$\nabla^2\psi = \zeta \tag{20}$$

and the vorticity equation, (7), the energy equation, (10), and the salt equation (18). These are solved by an extension of the Split NOS method presented in most detail in [3].

Conservation forms are used in rectangular coordinates. A steady state is assumed, so all $\partial/\partial t = 0$ identically. The Split NOS method of linearization is used; this is essentially a quasi-Picard iteration method which is motivated by the desire to avoid the computer time penalty associated with re-initialization of the direct linear solver. In the Split NOS linearization, the velocity at any iteration level k is split into an initial guess $\vec{V}^0$ and a perturbation $\vec{V}'$, not necessarily small.

$$\vec{V}^k = \vec{V}^0 + \vec{V}'^k \tag{21}$$

Then Eq. (7) gives

$$L_\zeta(\zeta^k) = Rc\nabla\cdot(\vec{V}'\zeta)^{k-1} + \frac{Grt}{Rc}\frac{\partial T}{\partial\gamma}^{k-1} - \frac{G_{rs}}{Rc}\frac{\partial S}{\partial\gamma} \tag{22}$$

where the linear operation L_ζ is defined by

$$L_\zeta(\zeta) = \nabla^2\zeta - Rc\nabla\cdot(\vec{V}^0\zeta) \ . \tag{23}$$

Likewise, Eq. (10) gives

$$L_T(T^k) = RcPr\nabla\cdot(\vec{V}'T)^{k-1} \tag{24}$$

where the linear operator L_T is defined by

$$L_T(T) = \nabla^2 T - RcPr\nabla\cdot(\vec{V}^0 T) \ . \tag{25}$$

Likewise, Eq. (18) gives

$$L_S(S^k) = RcSc\nabla\cdot(\vec{V}'S)^{k-1} + S_p\nabla\cdot[s_T(S+s_R)\nabla T]^{k-1} \tag{26}$$

where the linear operator L_S is defined by

$$L_S(S) = \nabla^2 S - RcSc\nabla\cdot(\vec{V}^0 S) \ . \tag{27}$$

This splitting allows L_ζ, L_T and L_S to be stationary operators, so that only one initialization of each linear solver is required for each set of parameters. In the non-trivial case of Pr = 1, we have $L_\zeta = L_T$. The resultant saving would be of interest if a decoupled equation approach were used as in [6,7] but in the present case, it is of no interest because L_ζ of Eq. (22) is solved coupled into the linear solution to the Laplacian operator of Eq. (20). Also, note that Soret terms are lagged entirely. Alternately, one could solve the temperature and salt equations simultaneously, with the linear part of the coupling included directly. This would increase stability at high Grashoff numbers, at the added expense of larger matrix solutions and added algebraic complexity in the coding. The simpler iterative method followed here did not appreciably decrease the stability for the range of parameters considered.

Initially, the governing equations were discretized by the usual $O(\Delta^2)$ centered differences in space. The no-slip condition on vorticity was implemented by way of Woods' equations (e.g., see [11]). For example, at a moving "lid" where J = JL and the wall velocity = U,

$$\zeta_{I,JL} = 3[\psi_{I,JL-1} - \psi_{I,J} + \Delta y \cdot U]/\Delta y^2 - \tfrac{1}{2}\zeta_{I,JL-1} \; . \tag{28}$$

The discretized analogues of Eqs. (20,21) are solved together, as a coupled 4th order system, with linear boundary coupling through Eq. (28). The method used for the linear solution is the marching method as described in detail in [12-14], with performance testing in [15-17]. For a grid of MxM internal points, the marching methods initialize in $O(M^3)$ operations, and give repeat solutions (for different boundary values or non-homogeneous terms) in the optimal $O(M^2)$ operations; this is the motivation for the Split NOS or quasi-Picard iteration method, in which only one initialization is required. The decision to solve the ψ and ζ equations coupled gives rise to significant penalties of time, storage, and (in some cases) round-off error; see [13] for details. However, the performance is still excellent (see below) and no semi-empirical determination of under-relaxation factors is required. This is a significant advantage to a user-oriented code in a practical engineering environment.

The actual answers obtained are the same as those obtained by any other finite difference method using the same spatial discretization (provided that we exclude those time-like methods whose solutions depends on Δt). The advantages of this method and the previously reported semidirect methods are in computer time.

For high values of the Grashoff and/or Reynolds numbers, we are not able to obtain solutions, as expected, due to cell Reynolds number effect. (See e.g. [11].) For these problems it is common practice to use upwind differencing, although it is well known that the answer obtained can only be interpreted qualitatively due to the artificial viscosity effects or "numerical diffusion" effects of the 2-point upwind difference method. Use was made of the "second upwind method" in which the inter-cell flux velocities are calculated to second-order accuracy. (Again, see e.g. [11].)

Instead of "full upwinding", the advection terms are calculated as a weighted combination of centered differences and the second upwind method, represented as

$$\text{advection terms} = (1-W)\cdot(\text{centered}) + W\cdot(\text{second upwind}) \tag{29}$$

where the weighting factor W is determined by

$$W = 1 - 1/(1+f\cdot P\Delta) \qquad (30)$$

where $P\Delta$ is the locally defined directional cell Peclet number. For the vorticity transport equation, $P\Delta = R\Delta$ where $R\Delta$ = local cell Reynolds number = Re $u\Delta x$ or Re $v\Delta y$. For the energy equation, $P\Delta = PrR\Delta$ and for the salt equation, $P\Delta = ScR\Delta$. The factor f adjusts the weighting; $f\cdot P\Delta = 0$ gives centered differences, which are adequate for low Grashoff numbers, and $f\cdot P\Delta\to\infty$ gives full upwind differences. Numerical experiments on a one-dimensional model equation indicated that $f = \frac{1}{4}$ was a good value for large $P\Delta$. This was verified by some experimentation with the full two-dimensional code, which accepts $f \equiv$ FUW as user input. We note, however, that since W changes from node to node, that this weighted upwind form (and others) is not conservative.

The implementation of weighted second upwind differencing in the semi-direct method posed some interesting complications. The difficulty is that the upwinding operator is not associative. That is, the result of upwinding on V^0 plus the upwinding on V' is not the same answer as upwinding on $V = V^0 + V'$. The upwinding operator obviously must be applied to V^0 if it is to prevent the node-to-node oscillation in large $P\Delta$ calculations. Therefore, the right hand side of the transport equations is calculated so as to give true upwinding on the total velocity V. In order to accomplish this, at each stage in the iteration process, the upwinding form of the stationary velocity V^0 is recalculated. (Storage would be prohibitive for large problems.) Then the right hand side is calculated as the difference between the upwind form on V, minus the upwind form on V^0. Although the convergence behavior is excellent, this considerably complicates the algebra of the method and adds significantly to the operation count. For example, to calculate 21 iterations in a small (11x11) grid, the upwind option increases the CPU time by a factor of $2\frac{1}{2}$ compared to using centered differences.

The code also contains an option for the second-order-accurate 3-point upwind difference forms [11]. However, these 3-point forms are known to be not as stable as the simple 2-point form. These forms cannot be applied near boundaries where there is inflow. That is, if $u > 0$, thie 3-point forms can only be applied for $I \geq 3$. A full implementation of 3-point differencing and the stationary operator including V^0 would have been very complicated indeed. Instead, we used the problem already coded for the 2-point upwind form, and applied a lagged correction between the 3-point and 2-point forms, with about a 10% penalty in CPU time. This technique was successful at moderate Grashoff numbers, but prevented iterative convergence at high Grashoff numbers, as was to be expected.

In retrospect, it would have been preferable to formulate and code only the simplest full upwind scheme (referred to as the "first upwind method" in [11]) in the direct solver. This would considerably simplify the algebra and reduce the execution time. Then the differences between the "first upwind" method and the weighted second upwind method, or preferably a more accurate quadratic upstream differencing method such as Leonard's [26], could be solved iteratively.

A similar innovation was used in regard to the boundary condition for vorticity at a no-slip wall. Probably the best and least controversial technique is that due to Israeli [27] (see also [11]) in which some finite difference form of the wall slip velocity is actually evaluated, and the iterative procedure is used to drive this value of wall slip to the correct zero value. However, this technique is essentially global (which is its theoretical advantage) which means that it cannot be included in the direct solver used for the linearized transport equations. Another second order method which is very popular and which is a local approximation is that due to Woods [11]; this form may be coded directly into the marching solution for the linearized equations. The technique adopted is then to solve the Woods equation directly with the linearized fourth order system for ξ and ζ, and then to correct this equation iteratively towards the Israeli equation within the nonlinear iterations. This technique did not lead to any noticeable increase in the number of required iterations for the salt gradient solar pond wall problem. However, it did lead to a serious degradation of iterative convergence for the heat extraction problem when applied to inflow and outflow boundaries.

Several under-relaxation factors are used in the code to enhance stability at high Grashoff numbers. None of these are dependent on the mesh spacing, nor do any require "fine tuning", which are significant advantages in any user-oriented code. The interior values of ζ and ψ are never under relaxed. The interior values of T and S are under-relaxed by the factor 1/5, which is not necessary at low Grashoff numbers. The correction from the Woods method for wall vorticity to the Israeli method is under-relaxed by the factor 1/3.

A numerical difficulty prevents accurate modeling of near vertical walls. Although the vertical wall without heating has the trivial solution of no flow, this condition is not stable in the code, possibly due to the combination of frictionless lid boundary conditions and the quasi-Picard iteration scheme. (The conservation errors due to the use of the weighted upwind scheme are not the problem, nor is the correction for the Israeli method for wall vorticity, since the problem persists with centered differences and Woods' method.) The net result is non-zero residual forcing functions even for vertical walls, $\theta_D = 90^0$. Even at the highest Rayleigh numbers used, this residual flow is fully 2 orders of magnitude smaller than the flows at $\theta_D = 85^0$, so this error is just part of the unavoidable truncation error in the solutions.

4. MODELING OF THE SALT GRADIENT SOLAR POND

The methods described are being used to study two phenomena in the salt gradient solar pond; the steady pumping of fluid along the inclined side walls, and the heat extraction problem. The detailed results of this study will be presented elsewhere. Our concern here is with the efficiency of the code developed using these methods, for which we will briefly describe the first phenomenon.

It is impossible to maintain a horizontal density stratification with zero convective flow at a no-slip wall which is inclined to the gravity vector. Wunsch [28] and Phillips [29] working independently first brought attention to this phenomenon in the oceanographic literature, and more recently Quon [30] studied the effect numerically, for the single diffusive problem. They recognized that the boundary conditions requiring no salt flux into the wall necessitate that the isopycnals be normal to the inclined wall. The result of this situation, shown in Fig. 1 for the single diffusive case, is that there is an induced flow up the wall. (For a plate inserted at an angle into a stably stratified medium, an upward flow is induced above the plate and a downward flow is induced below the plate.) The resulting motion is called diffusively-induced convection. See also Turner [30-32] and Chen [33-37] for even more interesting phenomena which occur in the transient cases. Note that this phenomenon is not an "instability" in the usual hydrodynamic sense, but is a simple non-equilibrium effect.

For modeling purposes, we represent the wall effect computationally in a region near the wall bounded by an impermeable lid, with the gradient region extending linearly into the top and bottom regions. This assumption is necessary in order to isolate the wall effects. Otherwise, at a point near the boundaries at the upper and lower end of the gradient regions, we will not have $\nabla^2 T = 0$ regardless of the wall effects, because the far-field boundary conditions from the interior of the pond are not a steady-state solution to the equations. However, the numerical method assumes that a true (ultimate) steady state already exists in the equations at the interior of the computational domain. This means that a computed pumping would result even with a vertical wall, or with wall boundary conditions corresponding to the interior region of the pond. This anamoly is avoided by applying linear gradients at the computational lid.

The boundary condition for the wall heating will obviously have a strong effect on the solutions. The calculation of the solar energy reaching the wall in the gradient region is a complex time-dependent problem. In order to calculate representative values for this study, we follow Zangrando [39], pp. 27-29, and use the form

$$f(d) = 0.73 - 0.08 \ln(d) \tag{31}$$

where d is the water depth in centimeters, and f is the fraction of impinging light remaining at depth. For a representative value of impinging solar energy, we use 100 wats/m^2. In normalized variables, this gives a heat flux on a horizontal surface at zero depth of

$$Q_{hz} = \frac{\bar{q}\,\bar{L}}{k(\bar{T}_{BOT}-\bar{T}_{TOP})} \sim 3 \; . \tag{32}$$

The flux on the inclined wall at depth is reduced by the fraction f(d) and the cosine of the wall angle, θ_D. From Zangrando [38], p. 72, p. 24, etc. we take 15 cm as representative of the depth of the top convecting region, and 1 meter as the extent of the gradient region, ZGRADR. Then

$$d[cm] = 115 - (x_w - XBJ1)*100*\sin\theta_D \tag{33}$$

The gradient boundary condition on normalized temperature is then

$$\left.\frac{\partial T}{\partial Y}\right|_w = -Q_w = +Q_{hz}*\cos\theta_D*f(d) \tag{34}$$

where $Q_{hz} \simeq 3$ for representative insolation, and $Q_{hz} \simeq 0$ for the night calculation.

The range of parameters to be studied was taken from the published data for the University of New Mexico salt gradient solar pond [38, 23-24]. For this pond, representative operating conditions gave values of the following quantities.

Prandtl No.	$P_r = 5.0$
Thermal Rayleigh No.	$Ra_t = 3.0 \times 10^{12}$
Schmidt No.	$S_c = 0.05$
Salt Raleigh No.	$Ra_H = 3.3 \times 10^9$
Pond Soret No.	$S_t = 0.15$
Characteristic Pond Salt Ratio	$S_r = 2.6$

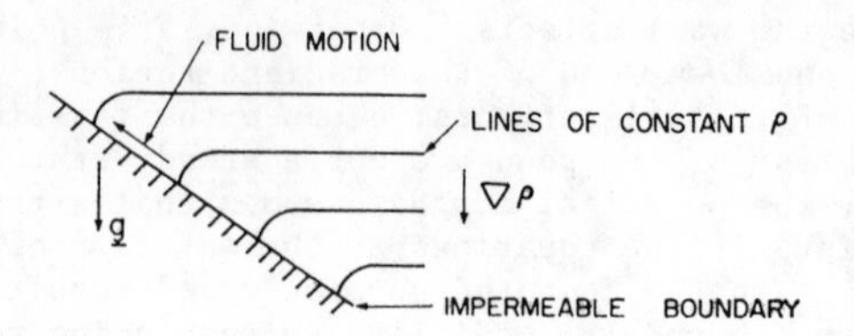

Figure 1. Motion induced by a wall in a stratified fluid. (After Quon, Ref.1.)

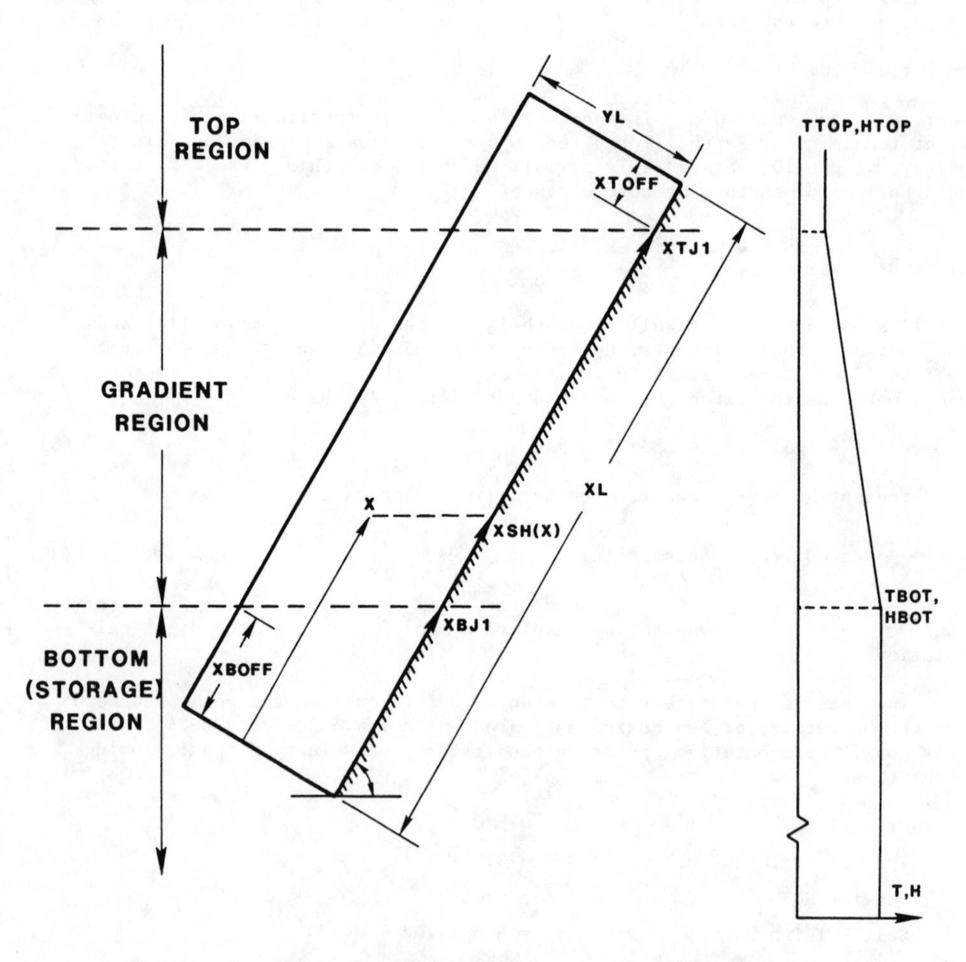

Figure 2 . Computational region for modeling the wall effect in the salt gradient solar pond.

The computational simulation of the top and bottom regions was accomplished with XTOFF = XBOFF = 0.25, and YL/XGR = 0.1. (Refer to Fig. 2.) The terms XTOFF and XBOFF determine the extent of the top and bottom "reservoir" regions, and are not expected to seriously affect the results. The term YL determines the position of the frictionless "lid" of the computational region.

5. PERFORMANCE OF THE METHODS

Timing tests for the numerical simulations are presented in Table 1. It is clear that the computer code is remarkably efficient. For a small (11x11) grid, the solution converges in 18 or 19 iterations. Even with the additional penalty involved in the weighted upwind differencing (a factor of 2½ - see above) the CPU time on a CDC 6600 is ~2½ seconds.

The CPU time/cell is a function mainly of IL (the maximum dimension in x) increasing about 20% for a 31x11 grid compared to an 11x31 grid. This asymmetry is caused by the asymmetry in the initialization of the marching method [12] and would be more pronounced if the upwinding were not used. (The manipulations involved in upwinding are all simply proportional to the number of interior points, regardless of IL or JL separately.) The one set of really large grid results in a 41x121 grid show that the number of iterations required to converge is not at all sensitive to grid size, in dramatic contrast to point- and line-iterative methods. Also, the CPU time/cell increases only about 50% for the mesh quadrupling in each direction from the 11x31 grid. (Again, this desirable insensitivity is due partly to the penalty involved in the upwinding algebra.) The CPU time of 180 seconds = 3 minutes on the CDC 6600 is remarkable for a problem of this size with four dependent variables. With a factor of five speed-up on the CDC 7600, this large problem would run in about 36 seconds, or about 15 seconds estimated without upwinding (on low Ra problems).*

Not shown in Table 1 are the errors due to the marching method, which are isolated at the upper boundary. For the 41x131 grid, the largest error is in T, and is 4.8×10^{-11}. For the other grids this error is $\leq 3.1 \times 10^{-13}$. The high accuracy is due to the large cell aspect ratio of the grid. See [12].

The efficiency of the code is not simply a result of good initial conditions, nor of a boundary-layer like behavior. The initial condition used for all these tests was zero flow. (For combined forced and free convection flows, we sometimes use the zero Reynolds number solution as an initial condition, following Gartling (see [39]). Also, the effect of the wall heating is so large that it reverses the pumping direction. The night (adiabatic wall) condition results in a flow down the wall, but the wall heating affect produces a complicated multi-cell flow with the flow in the mid-region being up the wall.

---

* This corresponds to approximately 3.1 milliseconds per cell on the CDC 7600. The same numerical methods applied to a problem without the salt equation but with the added complication of a moving boundary [10] gives convergence at low Re and Ra at NIT ~ 10 to 20, and CPU times less than 1 millisecond per cell. By comparison with a fairly efficient finite element code using a frontal solver and Newton-Raphson iteration to obtain a steady state solution, for the same number of degrees of freedom in the discretization, the present method is approximately 330x as fast.

TABLE 1. Results of the numerical simulation using a frictionless computational lid at Y = XGR/10, with f = ¼ (the upwind weighting parameter). The parameter p determines the Rayleigh numbers, with $Ra_T = 3.0 \times 10^p$ and $Ra_H = 3.3 \times 10^{p-3}$. NIT is the number of iterations required to converge to maximum $\Delta\zeta \leq 0.0001$. (NIT = U means the calculation was unstable.) All timing tests give CPU time on a CDC 6600 using a FORTRAN IV compiler with Level 2 optimization.

IL JL	θ_D	p	Q_H	NIT	ζ_{wm}	CPU (sec)	CPU/cell (msec)
11x11	75^0	10	0.	18	- 30.6	2.59	25.9
		11		18	- 97.0	2.57	25.7
		12		19	-315.	2.69	26.9
31x11		10		18	- 30.6	8.97	29.9
		11		21	- 97.6	10.1	33.7
		12		U			
11x31		10		17	-292.	7.54	25.1
		11		17	- 92.4	7.45	24.8
		12		17	-292.	7.42	24.7
41x121		10		17	- 29.1	180.	37.5
		11		17	- 91.9		
		12		17	-293.		
11x11	85^0	10		22	- 10.2	3.06	30.6
		11		27	- 32.4		
		12		22	-103.	3.05	
	70^0	10		18	- 41.5		
		11		18	-132.		
		12		17	-433.	2.48	
	34^0	10		15	-168.	2.21	
		11		U			
	70^0	12	0.	17	-433.	2.45	
			1.	19	-276.	2.71	
			2.	21	-123.	2.94	
			2.5	23	- 47.5	3.19	
			2.7	25	- 17.7*	3.40	
			3.	22	+ 26.5**	3.06	

* Multi-cell flow with ζ_w in the range -57.8 to +50.4.

** Multi-cell flow.

6. FUTURE WORK

The modeling of non-rectangular regions requires the use of sheared or body-fitted coordinates for the boundary matching along the inclined wall, and should further be done with coordinate stretching near the wall for the boundary layer resolution. The use of sheared coordinates has been accomplished [6,9] for semidirect methods using a fully segregated equation solution procedure, i.e., that in which the vorticity equation is solved as a second order system, followed by the stream function equation, etc. It is also possible to use sheared coordinates in the present solution procedure where ψ and ζ are solved coupled. The requirement will be for either a bi-tridiagonal matrix solution in the march for the coupled 9 point equation which results from standard discretization, or for a bi-bidiagonal solution for the skewed 7 point operators. (The combination of stretching in the boundary layer and shearing results in either a large storage penalty or a somewhat costly regeneration of the transformation metrics at each point, which is not unique to the semidirect methods.) Semidirect methods are particularly well-suited to the generation of body-fitted coordinates using the elliptic equation method of Thompson et al. [40]; see Roache et al. [41]. The small residuals also allow Richardson extrapolation to fourth-order accuracy, even when non-orthogonal coordinates are used (see Roache [9]). The present semidirect methods are also well suited to modeling slowly varying transient problems with large time steps.

7. SUMMARY

The semidirect methods described herein have resulted in a powerful and very efficient code for the steady flow of double diffusive problems with mixed forced and natural convections including solutes. The code gives high Rayleigh number solutions in a 11x31 grid in approximately 7½ seconds on a CDC 6600, and only 180 seconds for a 41x121 grid. This computational efficiency will allow rigorous and systematic convergence testing with two successive halvings of the mesh spacing in both directions, and allow Richardson extrapolation to fourth-order accuracy even when non-orthogonal coordinates are used.

This work was partially supported by the Solar Energy Research Institute, Golden, Colorado, under Subcontract No. AF-0-9381-1.

REFERENCES

1. Roache, P. J., Finite difference methods for the steady-state Navier-Stokes equations, Lecture Notes in Physics Series, Vol. 18, Springer-Verlag, Berlin, 1973, pp. 138-145.

2. Roache, P. J., The Split NOS and BID methods for the steady-state Navier-Stokes equations, Lecture Notes in Physics Series, Vol. 35, Springer-Verlag, Berlin, 1975, pp. 347-352.

3. Roache, P. J., The LAD, NOS, and Split NOS methods for the steady-state Navier-Stokes equations, Computers and Fluids, Vol. 3, 1978, pp. 179-195.

4. Roache, P. J., Recent developments and problem areas in computational fluid dynamics, in Lecture Notes in Mathematics Series, Vol. 461, Springer-Verlag, Berlin, 1975, pp. 195-256.

5. Roache, P. J. and Ellis, M. A., The BID method for the steady-state Navier-Stokes equations, Computers and Fluids, Vol. 3, 1975, pp. 305-320.

6. Roache, P. J., A semidirect method for internal flows in flush inlets, AIAA Paper 77-647, June 1977.

7. Roache, P. J., Semidirect calculation of steady two- and three-dimensional flows, Numerical Methods in Laminar and Turbulent Flow, Proc. First International Conference, University College, Swansea, Wales, 17-21 July 1978, Pentech Press, London, pp. 17-28.

8. Roache, P. J. and Zoltani, C. K., A preliminary investigation of the singular behavior of fluids near a sliding corner, Proc. 1979 Army Numerical Analysis and Computers Conference.

9. Roache, P. J., Scaling of high Reynolds number weakly spearated channel flows, Proc. Symposium on Numerical and Physcial Aspects of Aerodynamic Flows, California State University at Long Beach, 19-21 January 1981.

10. Roache, P. J., A semidirect method suitable for recirculating flows driven by buoyancy and shear, Proc. International Conference on Numerical Methods in Thermal Problems, 2-6 July 1979, Pineridge Press, Swansea, Wales.

11. Roache, P. J., Computational Fluid Dynamics, Hermosa Publishers, Albuquerque, New Mexico, 1976.

12. Roache, P. J., Marching methods for elliptic problems: Part 1, Vol. 1, No. 1, 1978, Numerical Heat Transfer, pp. 1-25.

13. Roache, P. J., Marching methods for elliptic problems: Part 2, Vol. 1, No. 2, 1978, Numerical Heat Transfer, pp. 163-181.

14. Roache, P. J., Marching methods for elliptic problems: Part 3, Vol. 1, No. 2, 1978, Numerical Heat Transfer, pp. 183-201.

15. Roache, P. J., GEM solutions of elliptic and mixed problems with non-separable 5- and 9-point operators, Proc. LASL Conference on Elliptic Solvers, 30 June - 2 July 1980. Santa Fe, N.M., Academic Press, M. Schultz, ed., 1981, pp. 399-403.

16. Roache, P. J., The GEM code: Direct solutions of elliptic mixed problems with non-separable 5- and 9-point operators, Proc. 1981 Army Numerical Analysis and Computers Conference, Huntsville, Alabama, 26-27 February 1981.

17. Roache, P. J., Performance of the GEM codes on non-separable 5- and 9-point operators, Numerical Heat Transfer, to appear.

18. Roache, P. J., Semidirect/Marching Methods for Discretized Partial Differential Equations, to appear.

19. Weinberger, H., The physics of the solar pond, Solar Energy, Vol. 8, No. 9, 1964, pp. 45-56.

20. Zangrando, F. and Bryant, H. C., A salt gradient solar pond, Solar Age, April 1978, pp. 21-36.

21. Tabor, H., Solar ponds, Solar Energy, Vol. 27, No. 3, 1981, pp. 181-194.

22. Gebhart, B., Heat Transfer, 2nd Edition, McGraw-Hill Inc., 1971, Ch. 8.

23. Rothmeyer, M., Saturated solar ponds - modified equations and results of a laboratory experiment, Master's Thesis, Dept. of Physics and Astronomy, Univ. of New Mexico, Albuquerque, N.M., 1979.

24. Rothmeyer, M., The Soret effect and salt-gradient solar ponds, Solar Energy, Vol. 25, No. 6, 1980, pp. 567-568.

25. Caldwell, D. R., Thermal and Fickian diffusion of sodium chloride in a solution of oceanic concentration, Deep-Sea Research, Vol. 20, 1973, pp. 1029-1039.

26. Leonard, B. P., A convectively stable, third-order accurate finite difference method for steady two-dimensional flow and heat transfer, these Proceedings.

27. Israeli, M., On the evaluation of iteration parameters for the boundary vorticity, Studies in Applied Mathematics, Vol. 51, March 1972, pp. 67-71.

28. Wunsch, C., On oceanic boundary mixing, Deep Sea Research, Vol. 17, 1970, pp. 293-301.

29. Phillips, O. M., On flows induced by diffusion in a stably stratified fluid, Deep Sea Research, Vol. 17, 1970, pp. 435-443.

30. Quon, C., Diffusely induced boundary layers in a tilted square cavity: a numerical study, J. Of Computational Physics, Vol. 22, 1976, pp. 459-485.

31. Turner, J. S., Salt fingers across a density interface, Deep Sea Research, Vol. 14, 1967, pp. 599-611.

32. Turner, J. S., Buoyancy Effects in Fluids, Cambridge at the University Press, Cambridge, U.K., 1973.

33. Turner, J. S. and Chen, C. F., Two dimensional effects in double diffusive convection, J. Fluid Mechanics, Vol. 63, Part 3, 1974, pp. 577-592.

34. Chen, C. F., Briggs, D. G., and Wirtz, R. A., Stability of thermal convection in a salinity gradient due to lateral heating, Int'l J. Heat Mass Transfer, Vol. 14, 1971, pp. 57-64.

35. Chen, C. F., Double-diffusive convection in an inclined slot, J. of Fluid Mechanics, Vol. 72, Part 4, 1975, pp. 721-729.

36. Chen, C. F., Paliwal, R. C. and Wong, S. B., Cellular convection in a density-stratified fluid: Effect of inclination of the heated wall, Proc. 1976 Heat Transfer and Fluid Mechanics Institute, J. W. Baughn and H. A. Dwyer, eds., Stanford Univ. Press, Stanford, CA., pp. 18-32.

37. Chen, C. F. and Sandford, R. D., Stability of time-dependent double-diffusive convection in an inclined slot, J. of Fluid Mechanics, Vol. 83, Part 1, 1977, pp. 83-95.

38. Chen, C. F., Time-dependent double-diffusive instability in a density-stratified fluid along a heated inclined wall, J. of Heat Transfer, Vol. 100, 1978, pp. 653-658.

39. Zangrando, F., Observation and analysis of a full-scale experimental salt gradient solar pond, Ph.D. dissertation, Dept. of Physics and Astronomy, the University of New Mexico, Albuquerque, New Mexico, 1979.

40. Gartling, D. K. and Roache, P. J., Efficiency trade-offs of steady-state methods using FEM and FDM, Numerical Methods in Laminar and Turbulent Flow, Proc. First International Conference, University College, Swansea, Wales, 17-21 July 1978, Pentech Press, London, pp. 103-112.

41. Thompson, Thames, F. C. and Mastin, C. W., Automatic numerical generation of body-fitted curvilinear coordinate system for field containing any number of arbitrary two-dimensional bodies, Journal of Computational Physics, Vol. 15, 1974, p. 299.

42. Roache, P. J., Moeny, W. M. and Filcoff, J. A., Computational solutions in body-fitted coordinates of electric fields in externally sustained discharges, Proc. 3rd IEEE International Pulsed Power Conference, Albuquerque, N.M., 1-3 June 1981.

A Thermal Convection Simulation in Three Dimensions by a Modified Finite Element Method*

C.D. UPSON, P.M. GRESHO, R.L. SANI, S.T. CHAN, and R.L. LEE
Lawrence Livermore National Laboratory
University of California
Livermore, California 94550

ABSTRACT

A novel approach to the solution of the discretized incompressible Navier-Stokes Equations is presented with emphasis on an application in three-dimensional confined thermo-convection. The technique described employs the spatial discretization inherent in the finite element method with various justifiable simplifications which make the approach similar in some aspects to a finite difference formulation. The application chosen to illustrate the advantages of this blended method is that of an incompressible fluid contained in a three-dimensional enclosure which is heated from below. The resultant convection due to this unstable situation, the multiple solutions to the Navier-Stokes equations and the method itself are described in what follows.

1. INTRODUCTION

In our effort to model the advection and dispersion of pollutants in the planetary boundary layer over complex terrain we have developed a relatively simple computer code for solving the three-dimensional Navier-Stokes equations, or variants thereof. The program, which began as an implementation of the Galerkin Finite Element Method (GFEM), now incorporates some of the insights and experiences of the finite difference community and has become an eclectic approach to simulating the motion of fluids governed by these equations. Our underlying philosophy is that of simplicity and cost-effectiveness: we use the simplest three-dimensional element, the simplest time integration technique, and in addition, simplifications of the GFEM that, we believe, are computationally justifiable.

In this paper, our computer code is applied to the simulation of a Boussinesq fluid contained in a three-dimensional rectangular box which is heated below and cooled above. The temperature difference between these two isothermal surfaces (parameterized by the Rayleigh number, Ra) determines, to a large extent, the complex spatial and temporal thermoconvection patterns. Problems of this sort have received substantial attention recently due to their relevance to natural convection in solar energy collectors, crystal growth in liquids, radioactive waste storage, and more importantly because studying systems of this sort can provide insight into the onset of phase-chaotic-induced turbulence.

---

*This work was performed under the auspices of the U. S. Department of Energy by the Lawrence Livermore National Laboratory under contract No. W-7405-Eng-48.

The numerical simulations presented were inspired by the careful experiments of Maurer and Libchaber [1]. In these experiments and others [2,3] they noted the behavior of cryogenic helium over a wide range of Ra. The flow pattern at the onset of convection was observed to be three, nearly two-dimensional roll cells with axes perpendicular to the larger horizontal dimension, as also noted in the visualization experiments of Stork and Muller [4]. When the enclosure in [1] was heated sufficiently, a bifurcation to a two-cell configuration was observed. This phenomenon is consistent with the experiments in [4] where it was noted that an even number of cells is often prefered to an odd number. In this two cell regime, Maurer and Libchaber [1] observed four modes of time-dependent convection including (1) periodic oscillatory motion, (2) bi-periodic convection where the ratio of the two dominant frequencies, f_1/f_2 is Rayleigh number dependent, (3) a frequency locking regime where the ratio of f_1 to f_2 is Ra invariant, and ultimately, (4) the onset of turbulence due to the appearance and dominance of the subharmonics of f_2, i.e. phase-chaotic behavior. Notable also in these experiments and others [5] is that the mode of convection is highly path dependent, and at times, irreproducible (i.e. the motion at a particular Ra can depend on how this Ra was reached; e.g. rapid vs. gradual heating).

Presented herein will be numerical simulations of the two flow configurations observed experimentally, the three and two-roll cell patterns. These results are, to the best of our knowledge, the first calculations of truly time-dependent three-dimensional confined Benard convection at elevated Rayleigh numbers, and they appear to agree well with experiments.

2. NUMERICAL METHOD

2.1 Continuum Equations

The governing equations for the thermal convection problem considered herein are the incompressible Navier-Stokes equations in the Boussinesq approximation, written here in a non-dimensional form,

$$\frac{\partial \underline{u}}{\partial t} + \underline{u}\cdot\nabla\underline{u} = -\nabla P + \sqrt{\frac{Pr}{Ra}}\,\nabla^2\underline{u} + \underline{k}T , \tag{1a}$$

$$\nabla\cdot\underline{u} = 0 , \tag{1b}$$

and

$$\frac{\partial T}{\partial t} + \underline{u}\cdot\nabla T = \frac{1}{\sqrt{PrRa}}\,\nabla^2 T , \tag{1c}$$

where

$$Ra = \frac{\gamma g\,\Delta T\,D^3}{\kappa\nu} \tag{2a}$$

is the Rayleigh number, and

$$Pr = \nu/\kappa \tag{2b}$$

is the Prandtl number. In the nondimensionalization, D is the characteristic length, $u_o = \sqrt{\gamma g D \Delta T}$ is the characteristic velocity, D/u_o is the characteristic time, and ρu_o^2 is the characteristic pressure. All data presented will be in this nondimensional form.

2.2 Discretized Equations

A spatially-discretized approximation to Eq. (1) is obtained via the GFEM; the resulting matrix equations (see [6] for details) are given by:

$$M\dot{U} + [K + N(U)]U + CP = f \,, \tag{3a}$$

$$C^T U = 0 \,, \tag{3b}$$

and

$$M_s\dot{T} + [K_s + N_s(U)]T = 0 \,. \tag{3c}$$

We currently use trilinear basis functions for velocity and temperature and piecewise constant basis functions for the pressure.

2.3 Non-Galerkin Modifications

Given both the substantial complexity of the full GFEM equations (particularly the mass matrix, M and the advection terms, N(U)U), as compared to those from the typical finite difference method (FDM), and especially that we wish to solve large 3D problems (> 5-10000 nodes), we have adopted several simplifying (but ostensibly "legal") shortcuts in the actual construction of the equations in (3), which we summarize here (see also [7, 8]).

Mass lumping. The first shortcut is to remove the spatial coupling between time derivatives by "lumping the mass", a simple procedure which converts M to a diagonal matrix. This technique greatly simplifies our explicit time integration scheme and the approximation has no effect on steady solutions; even for the time-varying results to be presented its effect is probably very small since our mesh is sufficiently fine (see [9]).

Reduced quadrature. A potentially more serious compromise, which permits more efficient code vectorization and reduces peripheral storage, has also been implemented in which all Galerkin integrals are evaluated using one-point quadrature rather than exact (or nearly exact) integration. One-point quadrature approximates the value of an integral over an element by evaluating the integrand at the element centroid and multiplying the result by the element volume. The various terms are affected in the following manner:

(i) The advection term, while definitely simpler than that using GFEM (see [10]), appears to be reasonably accurate. It can easily be described in words: the average velocity in an element is multiplied by the average gradient in the same element and the result is averaged (volume-weighted) over all elements (typically 8) sharing the node in question.

(ii) The gradient and divergence terms are not affected when the elements are brick-shaped as in the case of interest here - one-point quadrature is exact for C.

(iii) The diffusion matrix is singular with respect to 2 grid length waves, requiring the addition of a correction term when the simulation generates short-waves of significant amplitude (see [7] for details), which is not the case for the results presented herein.

The overall effect of these non-Galerkin modifications is to convert what was strictly an FEM code to what we believe is an effective blend of FEM and FDM; i.e. we have generated a useful FDM code via the "machinery" of the GFEM.

2.4 Time Integration

General Method. The simplest explicit time integration method is the first-order accurate forward Euler scheme, which we currently employ. Applied to the energy equation (3c), it is simply

$$T_{n+1} = T_n - \Delta t\, M_s^{-1}[K_s T_n + N_s(U_n)T_n], \tag{4}$$

where the T_n and U_n vectors are available. Application of this scheme to the momentum equation (3a) is, ostensibly, just as simple, i.e.,

$$U_{n+1} = U_n + \Delta t\, M^{-1}[f_n - KU_n - N(U_n)U_n - CP_n]; \tag{5a}$$

however, P_n is not yet available. The pressure at t_n must be first obtained by combining Eq. (3a) with a time-differentiated version of Eq. (3b), giving

$$(C^T M^{-1} C)P_n = C^T M^{-1}[f_n - KU_n - N(U)_n U_n], \tag{5b}$$

which is the consistent Poisson equation for the pressure; the matrix $C^T M^{-1} C$ is in fact a discrete approximation to the Laplacian. The velocity/pressure updates thus consist of two steps: (1) solve Eq. (5b) for P_n after evaluating the RHS at t_n, (2) update the velocity from Eq. (5a).

Since $C^T M^{-1} C$ is symmetric and invariant with time, we solve Eq. (5b) using direct, rather than iterative methods. For a given mesh and BC's, the matrix is formed, factored (into the matrix product LDL^T where L is lower triangular and D is diagonal) and stored on disk. During the time integration, each pressure update is obtained by reading the disk file and performing one forward reduction and one back substitution.

Stability Limits. The forward Euler method is known to be only conditionally stable. While the stability limits for the nonlinear system in Eq. (3) are not known a priori, the following stability limits, obtained from a von Neumann analysis of the linear advection-diffusion equation,

$$\frac{\partial T}{\partial t} + \underline{u} \cdot \nabla T = \kappa \nabla^2 T \tag{6}$$

via FDM on a uniform grid, [11] have proven quite useful:

(1) Diffusive limit:

$$\Delta t \le \frac{1/2\kappa}{1/\Delta x^2 + 1/\Delta y^2 + 1/\Delta z^2}, \tag{7a}$$

(2) Advective-Diffusive limit:

$$\Delta t \le \frac{2\kappa}{u^2 + v^2 + w^2}, \tag{7b}$$

where κ is the diffusion coefficient; in dimensionless form, κ is correspondingly replaced by $\sqrt{Pr/Ra}$ in Eq. (1a) and by $1/\sqrt{Pr Ra}$ in (1b).

Tensor Viscosity and a Relaxed Stability Limit. Unfortunately, (7b) is often quite restrictive when computing high Rayleigh number flows. By performing a Taylor-series analysis (in time) of the forward Euler time discretization of (6), it can be shown [12] that this time integration method, in effect, introduces a (negative) tensor diffusivity (or viscosity), given (in 2D) by

$$\underline{\underline{\kappa}}_N = \frac{\Delta t}{2}\begin{pmatrix} u^2 & uv \\ uv & v^2 \end{pmatrix} \tag{8}$$

into (6), such that the effective equation being modeled looks more like

$$\frac{\partial T}{\partial t} + \underline{u}\cdot\nabla T = \nabla\cdot[(\kappa \underline{\underline{I}} - \underline{\underline{\kappa}}_N)\cdot\nabla T] + O(\Delta t), \tag{9}$$

where I is the identity matrix and $O(\Delta t)$ contains terms proportional to deviatives of $\underline{u}$ which don't affect the stability of the temporal differencing. Thus, if Δt is too large, the effective diffusivity is negative and the numerical scheme becomes unstable. This effect can also be interpreted as an effective reduction in κ or an effective increase in Ra. This "artificial viscosity" is to be contrasted with the numerical dissipation inherent in for example, upwind spatial differencing and/or backward (implicit) Euler temporal differencing. The trick then, is to solve Eq. (6) only after adding the necessary "compensating diffusion" or tensor viscosity, to balance that implicitly introduced by the Euler integration scheme, a la Eq. (9); i.e., explicitly κ is replaced by $\kappa\underline{\underline{I}} + \underline{\underline{\kappa}}_N$ in the discretized equations.

While we have not yet completed the stability analysis of (6) using the FEM stencil (with or without balancing diffusion), we have been successful using results from 1D, in which (the 1D version of) Eqs. (7a) and (7b) are replaced by

$$\Delta t \leq (\kappa/u^2)\,[\sqrt{(u\Delta x/\kappa)^2 + 1} - 1]\,. \tag{10}$$

Whereas Eq.(7b) causes the Courant number ($u\Delta t/\Delta x$) to approach zero like $u\Delta t/\Delta x = 2\kappa/u\Delta x$ as the "grid Reynolds number", $u\Delta x/\kappa$ increases, the result from Eq.(10) is $u\Delta t/\Delta x \rightarrow 1$ as $u\Delta x/\kappa \rightarrow \infty$; i.e. the more reasonable Courant limit is recovered.

Subcycling. In spite of the cost-savings measures summarized above, the resulting code, when used on fairly large problems, was still rather expensive. The two remaining major contributors to the total cost of a simulation were: (1) the stability-induced time step (maximum Courant number $\leq$ 1) was, in spite of the gains afforded by adding balancing diffusion, often significantly smaller than that which would be required to obtain an accurate time integration and (2) the pressure updates, while not expensive in CPU costs (typically about 10% of the total cost of a time step), were still too expensive in I/O, i.e. reading the large disk file ($\sim$ one million words) containing the factored Laplacian matrix required several seconds.

Thus, based on the premises that Δt was "too small" based on acceptable accuracy and that the pressure and associated continuity equations do not affect the temporal stability, we devised another cost-effective strategy called subcycling, which permits less frequent updates of the pressure (relative to the stability-limited advection and diffusion processes) and a concomitant savings in computer time. Briefly the four items which constitute subcycling, shown schematically in Fig. 1, are the following (see [7] for further details):

(1) The major time steps (Δt_n, Δt_{n+1}) are based on local temporal integration accuracy and are dynamically computed via inexpensive local time truncation error estimates.

(2) The minor time steps (Δt_s), determined from stability estimates, are used to compute an approximate velocity field using a pressure gradient extrapolated from the previous major time step ($\tilde{P}_{n+1}$ in Fig. 1); i.e. the true "current pressure" and the continuity equations are ignored during subcycling.

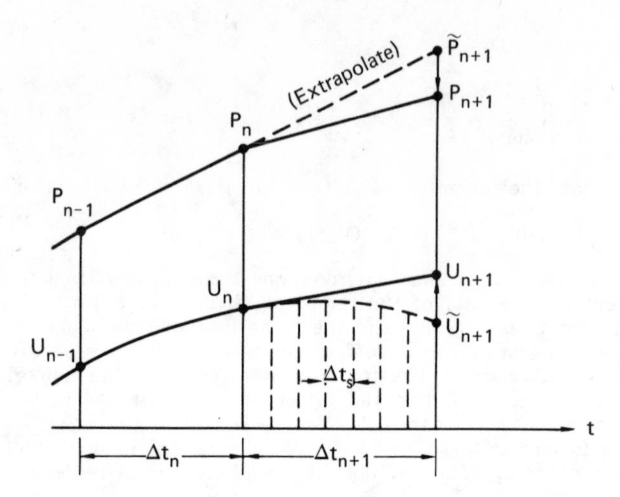

FIG. 1. Schematic representation of the pressure subcycling algorithm.

(3) At the conclusion of the sequence of minor time steps the fluid has become slightly compressible, thus at each major time step - a least squares mass adjustment procedure, which involves the same LDL^T system as that for the pressure, is employed to re-enforce satisfaction of the continuity equations (the velocity field is adjusted from $\tilde{U}_{n+1}$ to U_{n+1}).

(4) Finally, the new pressure field: P_{n+1}, compatible with the mass-consistent velocity field, is computed in the usual way.

In most of the simulations performed to date the subcycle ratio (major to minor time step) is rarely less than 5 and often as large as 10-20 or more; it has been especially effective for slowly-varying flows or those which approach a steady state, for which the stability Δt is very much smaller than that required for accuracy.

3. CONFINED RAYLEIGH-BENARD CONVECTION

3.1 Background

The computational domain used in the simulations presented is shown in Figure 2 and corresponds to the experimental enclosure used in [1]. It consists of 32 elements in the x (crossroll) direction, 16 elements in the y (vertical) direction, and eight elements in the z, or axial direction, with elements graded in the vertical to resolve the boundary layers (constant spacing was used in the two horizontal dimensions). A no-slip boundary condition for the velocity field was imposed on all surfaces except at z = 0, where a plane of symmetry is invoked. This symmetry is exhibited by the governing equations and has indeed been verified in all simulations in which the full domain (32 x 16 x 16) was employed. The temperature on the bottom surface (heated) was T = +.5, the top was cooled (T = -.5), and all sides were insulated. The aspect ratios (3.29:1.88:1.0 for the simulations herein, where the vertical dimension is the smallest), along with the two parameters already mentioned, the Rayleigh and Prandtl numbers, determine the major characteristics of the flow. For the two simulations to be presented these are kept constant at Ra = 50000, and Pr=.5 (liquid helium). Another influencing factor in some time-dependent flows is the fluid's past history. Frequently it has been observed that multiple flow configurations are possible for the same governing parameters ([5], and

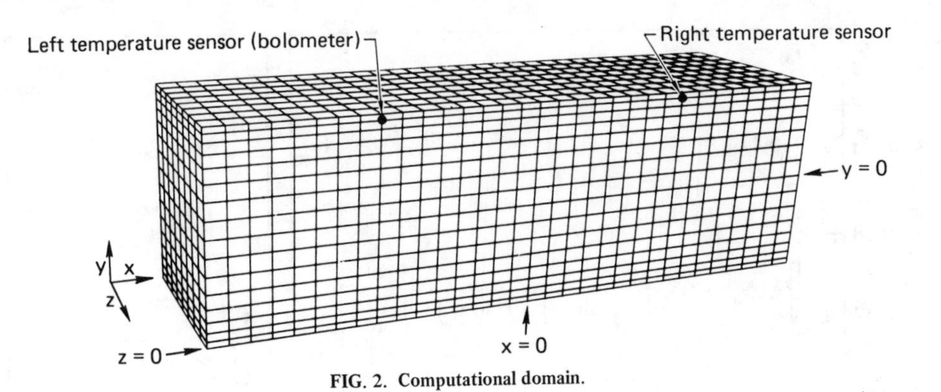

FIG. 2. Computational domain.

numerically in [13] and in this work). Thus a short digression outlining the manner in which we finally arrived at the results of this paper appears to be in order.

From the experience gained in a previous series of 2D square thermal cavity calculations [14], and in order to glean insight into the present rectangular cavity problem we first obtained a steady 2D, three cell solution at Ra = 12000. Using this solution (extended to the 3D geometry) as an initial condition, a 3D calculation was made. The resulting steady-state convective pattern, while quite similar to its 2D counterpart, exhibited a spiraling motion like that observed elsewhere [15, 16].

In hopes of observing the bifurcation to a two-cell configuration (seen in [1] at Ra = 40000) we raised the Rayleigh number to 50000, by way of a discontinuous change in the fluid properties: ν and κ (a numerically convenient method, due to the non-dimensional form of the equations). This simulation produced no bifurcation, but rather resulted in a very stable, time-periodic three-cell pattern. Repeated attempts to dislodge the third cell by perturbing the temperature field failed. Finally an ad-hoc, "two-cell" flow field was used as an initial condition; this procedure finally resulted in a clearly repetitive, oscillatory mode consisting of two roll-cells after a long transition period of about 400 time units.

3.2 The Three Roll-Cell Configuration

Temperature histories of the two nodes indicated in Fig. 2 are presented in Fig. 3a; these nodes approximate the locations of the temperature data (via bolometers) reported in [1]. The temperature of these same nodes during a typical cycle is shown, expanded in time, in the right portion of Figure 3a, partitioned into quarter-period segments: t_0 through t_4. It is clear that the fluid oscillation is periodic in time, with a period of approximately 13.7 time units. Note that the two bolometers are in phase (as observed in [1]) and that the right node senses a higher temperature than the left, due to the upwelling of hot fluid. The left node experiences colder, denser fluid in a downward motion. This can be seen more clearly in Figure 4(a-d) where the temperature field at t_0, t_1, t_2, and t_3 is shown on the z = 0 plane of symmetry. Perhaps even more informative is the velocity field, again at z = 0, portrayed in Figure 5(a-d). Here the major dynamics of the flow can be seen to be the expansion and contraction of the center cell as a function of time. In Fig. 6(a-d) are shown the horizontal temperature contours on the mid-height plane, y = 0, where the full three-dimensionality of the flow is apparent.

The fluid dynamics in this highly constrained, "excited state" can perhaps be interpreted in the following way. As the center cell decreases in radius at t_3, the near

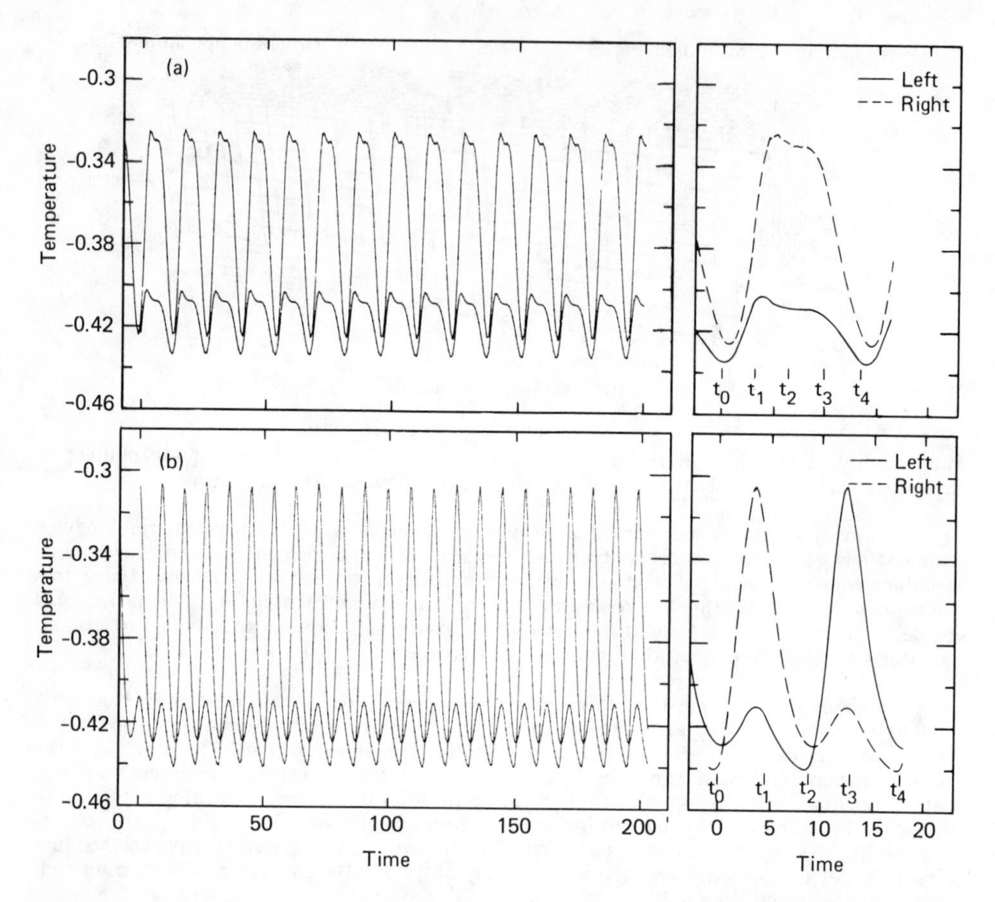

FIG. 3. Temperature oscillations of nodes indicated in Fig. 2. Right portions represent a typical cycle, partitioned into quarter cycles. (a) Three cell pattern (b) two cell pattern.

conservation of angular momentum results in an increase in rotational speed and thus increased axial velocity. At the same time the outer cells exhibit the opposite behavior due to similar causes. By the time the wave front caused by this surge in axial velocity reaches the container wall at about t_1, the center cell back at the mid-cavity (now with little axial velocity) exerts a "compressive force" on the outer cells. These cells in turn display an increased axial velocity (due to the same mechanism) resulting in a wave propagating toward the wall; thus, the cycle is completed. The motion along the axial direction resembles a sort of helix; this corkscrew-like rotation can be seen in Fig. 7 where the location of the cell vortex centers on the z = 0 plane have been plotted (the dot in the center of the figure indicates the permanent location of the center of the middle cell). It can be seen that each outer vortex center has a counter-clockwise movement while the fluid in that cell rotates in a clockwise convective pattern. While this forcing wave analogy is probably incomplete, it seems to qualitatively describe the overall fluid motion of this highly complex three-dimensional field.

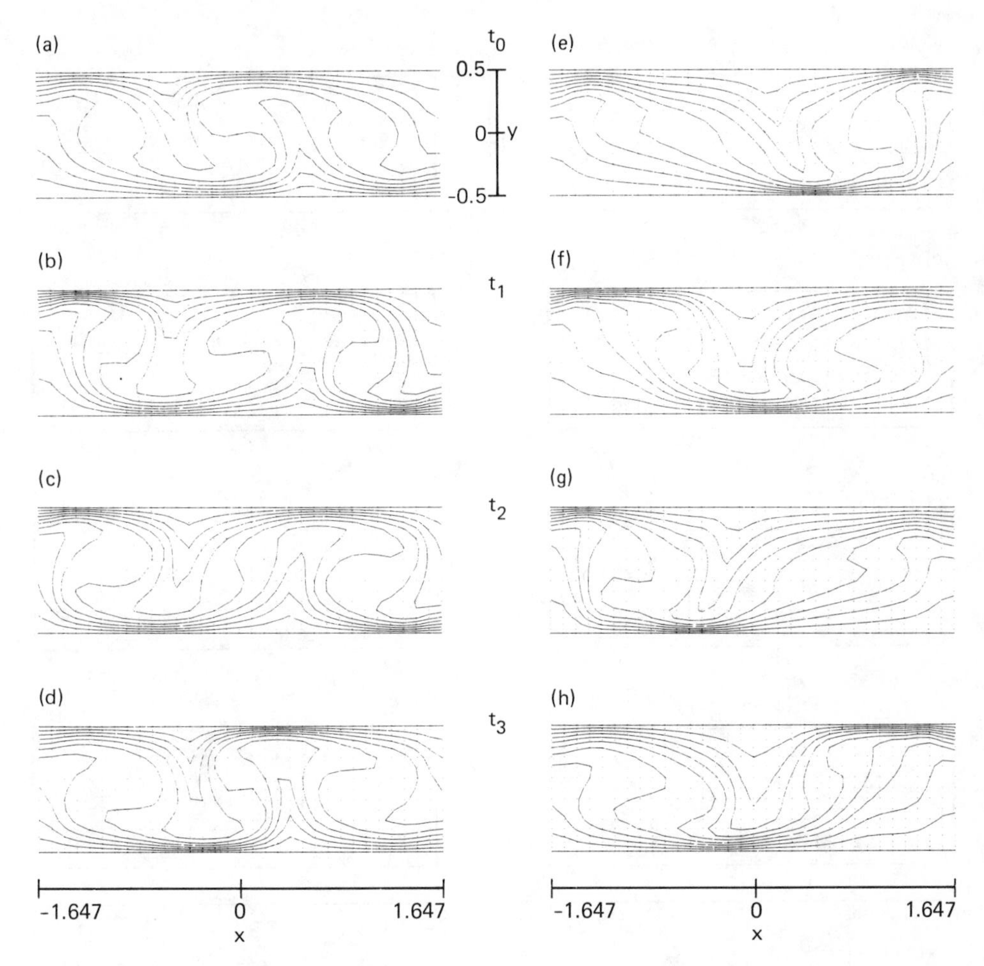

FIG. 4. Temperature contours on the Z = 0 plane. (a-d) Three cell pattern, (e-h) two cell pattern. Contour levels vary from -0.5 on the bottom surface, to +0.5 on the top, with 0.1 variation.

3.3 The Two Cell Configuration

As mentioned earlier, the two roll-cell pattern differs substantially from the previous solution. It is this flow pattern that has been investigated experimentally in some detail [1,3,5]; however, no results have been presented for Ra = 50000, thus the following comparison with experiments will be based on extrapolation of the experimental data.

From Fig. 3b it can be seen that the temperature oscillations recorded at the same two nodes differ markedly from their three cell counterparts; here the two traces are essentially identical, but opposed in phase. Also the period of the oscillation is different: 17.75 nondimensional time units (or 1.40 seconds for the experiments in [1]). Extrapolation of the results in [1] to Ra = 50000 leads to a period of approximately 1.21 seconds. Notable in Fig. 3b is the bi-periodic, or two frequency, character of the

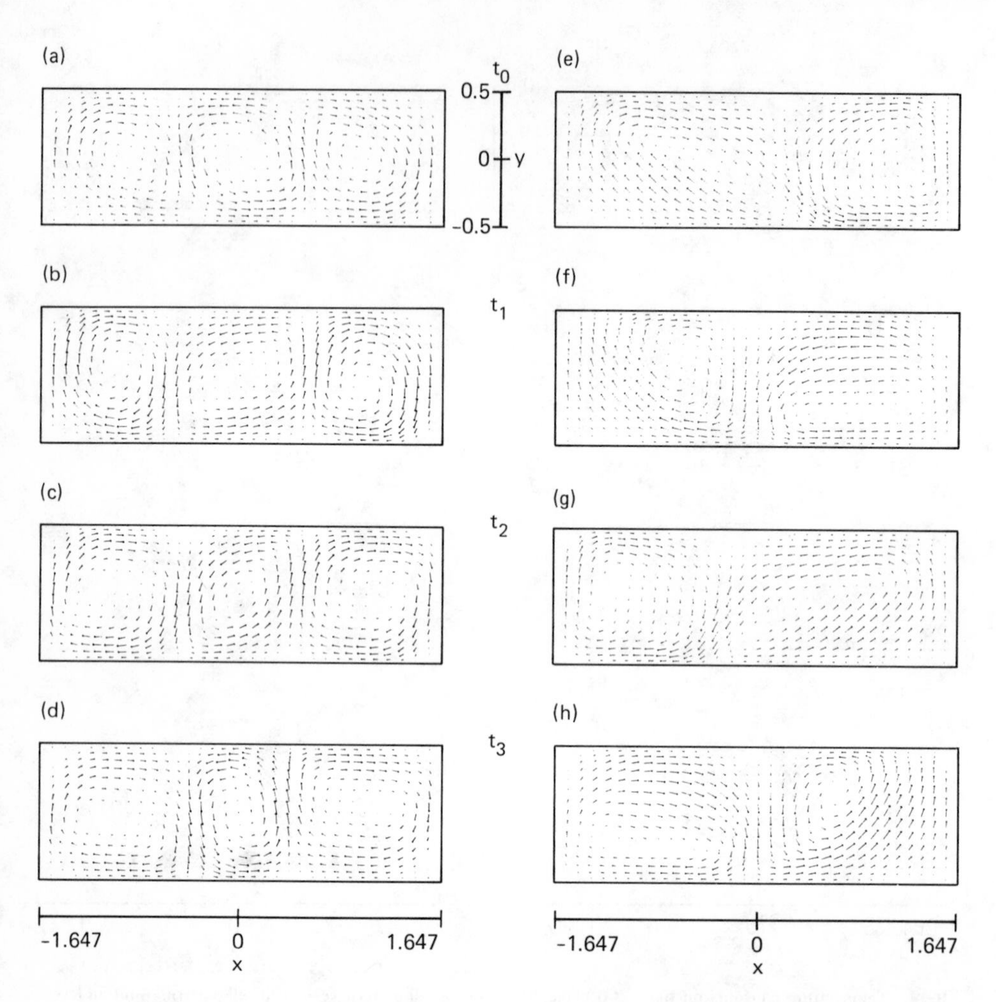

FIG. 5. U, V Velocity field on the Z = 0 plane. (a-d) Three cell pattern, (e-h) two cell pattern.

oscillation; this is indeed observed experimentally and the trace presented here bears a marked resemblance to some shown in [3] and [5]. A Fourier spectral decomposition of the temperature/time trace from the right node is shown in Fig. 8b, where the first two peaks correspond to these two major frequencies; $1/2f_1$ and f_1 respectively (or periods of 17.75 and 8.875). This differs from the three cell configuration where a nearly exponential decrease in power is seen in the multiples of the single frequency f_1 (also no sub-harmonics of f_1 can be seen in Fig. 8a). A two frequency oscillation, with $f_2 = 1/2f_1$, was also noted in [5] (under somewhat different conditions) where the power spectrum was composed of the multiples of $1/2f_1$. At yet higher Ra ($\approx$ 81000) Libchaber and Maurer [3] noticed frequency-locking where the ratio of the two frequencies became Ra invariant with $f_2 = 1/2f_1$, a simulation which we have not yet attempted.

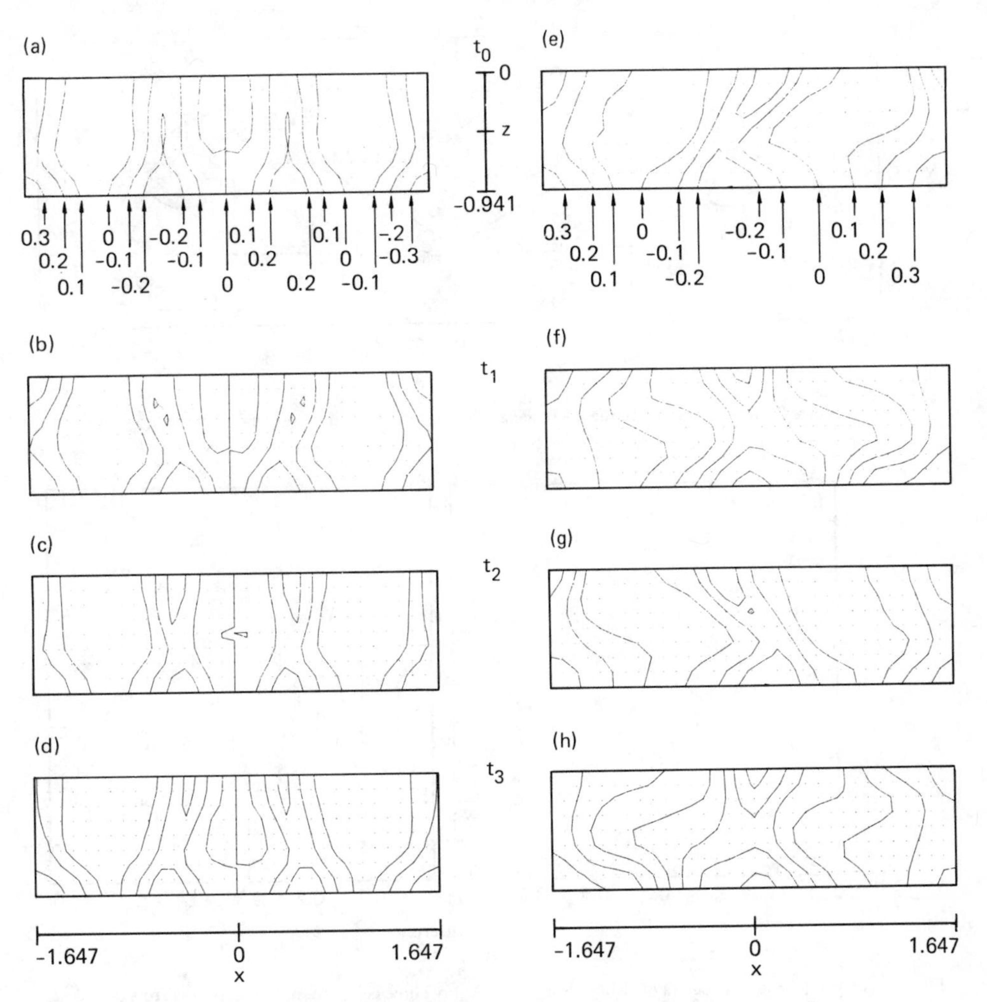

FIG. 6. Temperature contours on the y = 0 plane. (a-d) Three cell pattern, (e-h) two cell pattern.

The dynamics of the two cell configuration during a cycle (shown in Figs. 4(e-h), 5(e-h), and 6(e-h)) is seen to be almost anti-symmetric about the middle of the cycle, i.e. the flow at t_0 resembles the mirror image of that at t_2, similarly with t_1 and t_3. This behavior is expected from a bi-periodic oscillation. What is not shown in the "figure-eight" convective pattern of Fig. 5(e-h) is that the flow on a vertical plane near the container wall ($z \simeq -.7$) at t_0 resembles that at the center ($z = 0$) at t_2. Thus at t_0 the left cell is small in cross-section near the cavity faces, and larger at the center, the right cell being the opposite. Throughout the axial direction at t_1, and half a period later at t_3, the two cells are of comparable cross-section, and a clear dividing line exists between the cells. At these times on the horizontal midplane, $y = 0$, two pronounced eddies both with counter-clockwise rotation appear near $z = -.4$, as is suggested in the convoluted temperature contours of Figure 6(f,h) (with clockwise rotation at t_3). These secondary eddies are translated across the cavity in opposition, i.e. as one reaches the plane of symmetry the other vortex is simultaneously annihilated

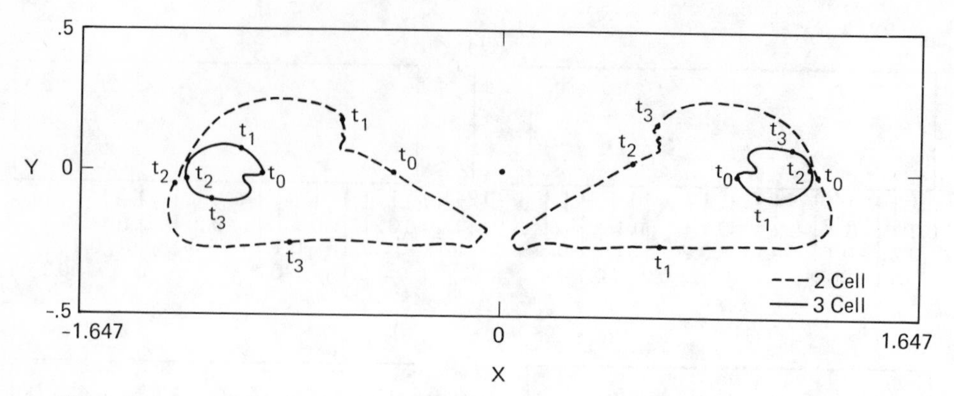

FIG. 7. Vortex center migration on the z = 0 plane. The times indicated correspond to those in Fig. 3.

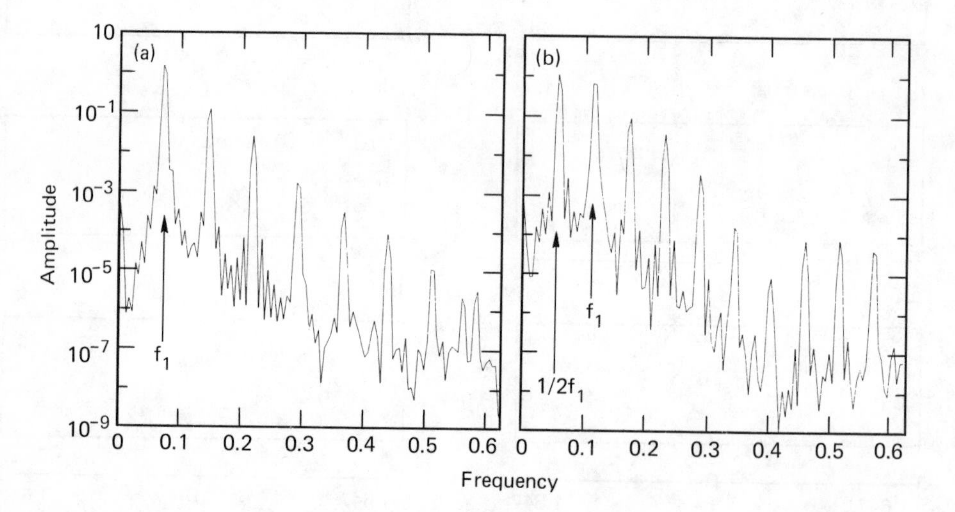

FIG. 8. Temperature power spectra of right sensor in Fig. 2. (a) Three cell pattern, f_1 corresponds to a period of 13.7 non-dimensional time units. (b) Two cell pattern $1/2f_1$ corresponds to a period of 17.75 time units.

near the opposing wall. At this time similar eddies grow in strength in complementary locations, with opposite rotation, and the flow reverses.

Overall, the flow is more energetic than the three cell pattern, as can be seen in the magnitude of the temperature oscillation in Fig. 3, and also in the migration of the two primary vortex centers on the z = 0 plane in Fig. 7. This movement is pronounced and, like the three cell configuration, the movement of the centers is opposite the rotation of the rolls themselves; however, in this case the paths are nearly mirror images of each other.

The cost of this simulation on the CRAY 1, per cycle (17.75 time units) was 2/3 minute CPU and 3 minutes I/O, using a minor step size of 0.12, which gave a subcycle ratio of 5-6.

4. CONCLUSIONS

An innovative blend of the Galerkin Finite Element Method and the Finite Difference Method has resulted in a new technique for solving the three-dimensional Navier-Stokes equations. The procedure has been summarized (see also [7]) and applied to a complex, highly three-dimensional thermally driven flow, in which two quite different solutions have been shown to exist under (nominally) the same circumstances, the initial state being the determining factor. These two flow configurations are seen to be time-dependent with the characteristics and oscillatory behavior showing at least qualitative agreement with corresponding experiments. While the basic mechanism of this oscillatory instability has been theoretically investigated by others [17], our numerical approach removes the simplifications that are required for such analyses. Here we have apparently successfully described the fluid motion and will, in a subsequent publication [18], present additional calculations permitting more direct experimental comparison, thus shedding more light on the physics of this highly non-linear flow and, perhaps, even on the transition to turbulence. (For example, we have recently obtained a 2-cell solution at Ra = 33000, for which the oscillation frequency agreed to within about 8% of the experimental value reported in [1]).

REFERENCES

1. Maurer, J., and Libchaber, A., Rayleigh-Benard experiment in liquid helium; frequency locking and the onset of turbulence, Le Journal de Physique Lettres, Vol. 40, 1979, pp. 419-423.

2. Libchaber, A., and Maurer, J., Local probe in a Rayleigh-Benard experiment in liquid helium, Le Journal de Physique Lettres, Vol. 39, 1978, pp. 369-372.

3. Libchaber, A., and Maurer, J., Une experience de Rayleigh-Benard de geometrie reduite; multipication accrochage et demultiplication de frequences, Journal de Physique, Colioque C3, Vol. 41, 1980, pp. 51-56.

4. Stork, K., and Muller, U., Convection in boxes: experiments, J. Fluid Mech., Vol. 54, 1972, pp. 599-611.

5. Gollub, J. P., and Benson, S. V., Chaotic response to periodic perturbation of a convecting fluid, Physical Review Letters, Vol. 41, 1978, pp. 948-951.

6. Gresho, P., Lee, R., Sani, R., and Stullich, T., On the time-dependent FEM solution of the incompressible Navier-Stokes equations in two and three-dimensions, in Recent Advances in Numerical Methods in Fluids, Pineridge Press, Ltd., Swansea, U.K., 1980.

7. Chan, S., Gresho, P., Lee, R. and Upson, C., Simulations of three-dimensional, time-dependent, incompressible flows by a finite element method, in Proc. AIAA 5th Computational Fluid Dynamics Conference, 1981.

8. Gresho, P., Chan, S., Lee, R. and Upson, C., Solution of the time-dependent, three-dimensional, incompressible Navier-Stokes equations via FEM, in Proc. Intern. Conference on Numer. Meth. for Laminar and Turbulent Flow, Venice, Italy, July 13-16, 1981.

9. Gresho, P., Lee, R. and Upson, C., FEM solution of the Navier-Stokes equations for vortex shedding behind a cylinder: experiments with the four-node element, Proc. Third Intern. Conference on Finite Elements in Water Resources, 1980, also to appear in Adv. Water Resources, Vol. 4, No. 4, Dec., 1981.

10. Gresho, P., and Lee, R., Don't suppress the wiggles - they're telling you something!, Comp. and Fluids, Vol. 9, 1981, pp. 223-254.

11. Hindmarsh, A., and Gresho, P., The stability of explicit Euler time-integration for certain finite difference approximations of the multi-dimensional advection-diffusion equation, Int. J. Num. Meth. Fluids, 1982 (to appear).

12. Dukowicz, J., and Ramshaw, J., Tensor viscosity method for convection in numerical fluid dynamics, J. Comp. Physics, Vol. 32, 1979, pp. 71-79.

13. Straus, J., and Schubert, G., Modes of finite amplitude three-dimensional convection in rectangular boxes of fluid-saturated porous material, J. Fluid Mech., Vol. 103, 1981, pp. 23-32.

14. Upson, C., Gresho, P., and Lee, R., Finite element simulations of thermally induced convection in an enclosed cavity, Lawrence Livermore Laboratory Report UCID-18602; also in I, Jones and C. Thompson, Numerical solutions for a comparison problem on natural convection in an enclosed cavity, Harwell Report AERE-R-9955, Oxfordshire, England, 1981.

15. Ozoe, H., Yamamoto, K., Churchill, S. W., and Sayama, H., Three-dimensional, numerical analysis of laminar natural convection in a confined fluid heated from below, J. Heat Transfer, May 1976, pp. 202-207.

16. Mallinson, G. D., and de Vahl Davis, G., Three-dimensional natural convection in a box: a numerical study, J. Fluid Mech., Vol. 83, 1977, pp. 1-31.

17. Clever, R., and Busse, F., Transition to time-dependent convection, J. Fluid Mech., Vol. 65, 1974, pp. 625-645.

18. Upson, C., and Gresho, P., in preparation, 1981.

Nomenclature

C	gradient matrix	Ra	Rayleigh number $\gamma g \Delta T D^3/\kappa\nu$
C^T	divergence matrix	t	time
D	characteristic length	t_i	time at i^{th} quarter cycle
f	global buoyancy force vector	T	temperature departure from reference; global vector of nodal temperatures
g	acceleration due to gravity	$\underline{u}$	velocity (u,v,w)
I	identity matrix	u_o	characteristic velocity $\sqrt{\gamma g D \Delta T}$
$\underline{k}$	unit vector aligned with gravity	U	global vector of nodal velocities
K	viscous matrix	γ	coefficient of thermal dilatation

K_s	thermal diffusion matrix	$\Delta x, \Delta y, \Delta z$	inter-nodal distances
M	mass matrix	Δt	time step
M_s	submatrix of M	ΔT	temperature difference between the top and bottom surfaces
N(U)	non-linear advection matrix	$\underline{\underline{\kappa}}_N$	tensor viscosity
$N_s(U)$	submatrix of N(U)	κ	thermal diffusivity
p	pressure deviation	ν	kinematic viscosity
Pr	Prandtl number ν/κ	ρ	density

Effects of Grid Distribution on the Computation of High Rayleigh Number Convection in a Differentially Heated Cavity

CHARLES QUON
Atlantic Oceanographic Laboratory
Bedford Institute of Oceanography
Dartmouth, Nova Scotia, Canada

Abstract

The problem of free convection in a differentially heated square cavity is solved numerically by FDM on nets of variable mesh size for Rayleigh numbers $A = 10^6$ and $A = 10^7$, and $\sigma = 0.71$. The results for $A = 10^6$ are compared with two sets of FEM results in detail, and with some maximum values of the velocity and temperature fields given in a recent international intercomparison study [8, 9]. The results of $A = 10^7$ are obtained from seven computations of various mesh sizes and different total number of grid points. These results are used to derive quantitative, albeit rough, mesh criterion for proper boundary layer resolution in numerical fluid dynamics.

1. Introduction

The problem of natural convection in a cavity differentially heated on the side walls was first solved by Batchelor [1] analytically for the conduction regime. Twelve years later Gill [2] published his approximate non-linear solutions for high Rayleigh number convection. In the intervening years, the experimentalists had contributed immensely towards understanding the fundamentals of the problem for a wide range of Rayleigh numbers and aspect ratios (see [3] and its references). In the last 15 years since Gill's publication, the problem has been studied numerically by many workers (see [4] and its references). The present author had extensively investigated the effects of boundary conditions and Prandtl numbers on the velocity fields and temperature distribution in a square cavity [5] and had evaluated Gill's non-linear theory against the results of computation [6].

More recently, there has been a concerted effort to compare computational results of the same problem [7] internationally. There were 36 contributions from nine different countries. The computations were carried out for Prandtl number $\sigma = 0.71$, and for Rayleigh number $A = 10^3$, 10^4, 10^5, and 10^6 by all investigators. The objective was to set up bench marks for numerical algarithms in fluid dyanmics and in heat transfer. The following variables were to be compared: the maximum velocities and positions of the velocity maxima at mid sections; the average Nusselt number on the hot wall and the positions of their maxima and minima. A report containing all these contributions, including the outlines of numerical methods in varying degrees of details [8], and a paper summarizing the main results [9] have been published. The individuals' effort has been immense, but the summary paper is disappointing. Clearly neither the report nor the summary paper as they stand contains enough information to serve as numerical bench marks. For example, a grid point maximum is not necessarily the maximum of the continuous curve fitted to the grid points. On the other hand, an interpolated maximum depends on the method of interpolation. It certainly makes no sense to compare the grid point maxima when each contributor uses different grid distribution. However, to be fair to the organizers of the comparison exercise, the participants should have provided their "best" interpolated maxima, although these were not explicitly specified.

For a highly non-linear problem such as high Rayleigh number convection in a cavity whose exact solutions we do not know, intercomparison of numerical results is invaluable, and in fact, most desirable, especially when computations are done with different numerical methods by people half a world apart. In the first half of section 5, Gartling's [8] and Winters' [8, 10] FEM results for $A = 10^6$ will be compared with my own second order FDM results [8], which was computed with 40 X 40 variable grids. The latter will be implemented with a computation on a 60 X 60 net. It is intended to establish first the similarities and differences between the results from my own algorithm and those of others, and show that some seemingly different results may in fact represent very similar solutions.

In the second half of section 5, I shall compare results of seven FD computations, carried out with different number of grid points. The grid spacings vary either in one or in both directions for $A = 10^7$, $\sigma = 0.71$. The maximum number of grid points is 60 X 60 and the minimum is 20 X 20. The objective is to see how the variation of grid distribution in either direction will affect the results, and whether or not the solutions will converge towards those obtained from the densest net. If so, we like to see whether the convergence is spatially uniform. It may also be possible to set some kind of criteria for optimal selection of grid distribution in order to obtain an acceptable solution.

Finally, a curve of Nusselt numbers vs. Rayleigh numbers on log-log scales for $10^3 \le A \le 2 \times 10^7$ will be presented. Although the computations remain numerically stable beyond $A = 2 \times 10^7$, the 2-dimensional results are probably not meaningful because physical instability may have been suppressed with the elimination of variations in the third dimension.

The numerical procedure, which is well documented in [11] for other problems will be briefly described. Selected numerical values of temperature and velocities for both $A = 10^6$ and 10^7 on 60 X 60 nets are also listed.

2. The Problem

Consider a square cavity of dimensionless measure 1 X 1 whose vertical side walls are maintained at two different constant temperatures. Impose right-handed Cartesian co-ordinates, Oxz, upon it with the origin at the center of the cavity. Then the non-dimensional governing equations are:

$$\frac{\partial \underline{V}}{\partial t} + \underline{V}.\nabla \underline{V} = -\nabla P + AT\hat{k} + \varepsilon \nabla^2 \underline{V} \qquad (1)$$

$$\frac{\partial T}{\partial t} + \underline{V}.\nabla T = \varepsilon^{-1} \nabla^2 T \qquad (2)$$

$$\nabla.\underline{V} = 0 \qquad (3)$$

with the following boundary conditions:

$$\underline{V} = 0 \quad \text{at} \quad x = \pm \frac{1}{2}, \quad z = \pm \frac{1}{2}$$

$$T = \pm \frac{1}{2} \quad \text{at} \quad x = \pm \frac{1}{2} \qquad (4a,\ b,\ c)$$

$$\frac{\partial T}{\partial z} = 0 \quad \text{at} \quad z = \pm \frac{1}{2}$$

where $\underline{V} = (u,w)$ is the velocity vector consisting of components u, w in the x and z directions respectively, and T the temperature.

$$P = \{\frac{L^2 P^*}{\rho_0 \kappa \nu} + \frac{(1+\alpha T_0) g L^3}{\kappa \nu} z^*\}$$ is the dimensionless total pressure.

Equations (1) to (3) have been non-dimensionalized with characteristic length, L, which is the height and width of the cavity, characteristic time $\tau = L^2/(\kappa\nu)^{\frac{1}{2}}$, characteristic velocity $U = L/\tau = (\kappa\nu)^{\frac{1}{2}}/L$, and characteristic pressure $P = \rho_0 \kappa\nu/L^2$. The two free dimensionless parameters are the Rayleigh number, $A = \alpha g \Delta T L^3/(\kappa\nu)$, and the Pandtl number $\sigma = \nu/\kappa = \varepsilon^2$. α, ν, κ, are respectively the coefficient of cubical expansion, kinematic viscosity and thermometric conductivity of the fluid. g is the earth's gravity in the negative z-direction, and ΔT the imposed temperature differential across the cavity. The symbolic operators are $\nabla = (\hat{i}\ \partial/\partial x + \hat{k}\ \partial/\partial z)$, and $\nabla^2 = (\partial^2/\partial x^2 + \partial^2/\partial z^2)$. There is no mathematical singularity in this problem. At large values of A, however, the problem is highly non-linear.

3. Method and Parameters of Computation

The numerical algorithm used to obtain the results discussed here was originally designed to study 2-dimensional convection in the r-z plane of a rotating annulus of fluid. The computations presented here were done with $r \to \infty$ (narrow gap approximation), and $\Omega = 0$ (no rotation). The finite difference formulation and method of solution are well documented [11]. We shall discuss only the salient points here.

(a) The Equations Solved

The equations solved are Eqs. (1) in component form and (2), and an elliptic equation for P obtained by taking the divergence of Eq. (1):

$$\frac{\partial u}{\partial t} + \frac{\partial}{\partial x}u^2 + \frac{\partial}{\partial z}uw - \varepsilon\nabla^2 u = -P_x \tag{5}$$

$$\frac{\partial w}{\partial t} + \frac{\partial}{\partial x}uw + \frac{\partial}{\partial z}w^2 - \varepsilon\nabla^2 W = -P_z + AT \tag{6}$$

$$\frac{\partial T}{\partial t} + \frac{\partial}{\partial x}uT + \frac{\partial}{\partial z}WT - \varepsilon^{-1}\nabla^2 T = 0 \tag{7}$$

$$\nabla^2 P = -\frac{\partial}{\partial t} D + A\frac{\partial T}{\partial z} + \varepsilon\nabla^2 D - \frac{\partial}{\partial x}\left(\frac{\partial u^2}{\partial x} + \frac{\partial uw}{\partial z}\right) - \frac{\partial}{\partial z}\left(\frac{\partial uw}{\partial x} + \frac{\partial w^2}{\partial z}\right) \tag{8}$$

where $D = \nabla.\underline{V}$, the FD divergence, is retained because it is non-zero, though infinitesimal. The boundary conditions are Eqs. 4(a,b,c) and the following for P in Eq. 8:

$$\frac{\partial P}{\partial x} = \varepsilon \frac{\partial^2 u}{\partial x^2} \qquad \text{at} \quad x = \pm \frac{1}{2}$$

$$\frac{\partial P}{\partial z} = \varepsilon \frac{\partial^2 w}{\partial z^2} + AT \qquad \text{at} \quad z = \pm \frac{1}{2} \tag{9a, b}$$

Co-ordinate transformation as discussed below are applied to Eqs. (5),(6),(7) and (8) and their boundary conditions in Eqs. (4) and (9). Eqs. (5), (6) and (7) are solved by ADI in each time step and (8) is solved by ADI with variable acceleration parameters [12]. Four iterations are required for Eq. (8) for each time step.

(b) Coordinate Transformation

If we transform the coordinates x and z into monotonic functions $\eta(x)$ and $\zeta(z)$, then we can rewrite Eqs. (5), (6), (7) and (8) in terms of η, ζ, and their derivatives by:

$$\frac{\partial}{\partial x} = \frac{\partial \eta}{\partial x}\frac{\partial}{\partial \eta}, \qquad \frac{\partial}{\partial x} f(x)\frac{\partial}{\partial x} = \frac{\partial \eta}{\partial x}\frac{\partial}{\partial \eta} f(\eta(x)) \frac{\partial \eta}{\partial x}\frac{\partial}{\partial \eta} \quad \ldots\ldots$$

The choice of η and ζ depends on the problem. In order to have compact grid points near the end points of x and z, we choose

$$\eta(x) = \frac{(M+1)}{2} + \frac{(M-1)}{2} \cdot \frac{\ell n\,\{(b + \tilde{x} - \frac{1}{2})/(b - \tilde{x} + \frac{1}{2})\}}{\ell n\,\{(b + \frac{1}{2})/(b - \frac{1}{2})\}} \tag{10}$$

and similarly for $\zeta(z)$. In (10), $b = 0.5/\sqrt{1-2d}$, d being the control parameter. When d approaches 0, the grid points in the x-dimension become more compact near the end points for boundary layer resolution. For simplicity, $\eta = 1, 2, \ldots M$ for $0 \leq x \leq 1$, $\tilde{x} = (x + 1/2)$. Hence $\Delta\eta = 1$ in the transform space, and $\partial\eta/\partial x$ is approximately equal to $1/\Delta x$ locally. For more details see [11, 13].

(c) Time Step Limitation of the Algorithm

Equations (5), (6), (7) and (8) form an advective diffusive system. Either advection or diffusion, or both, can limit the time step size. Since the diffusive limitation has been removed by using ADI [11], it can be shown that the time step size is limited by the CFL criterion. Given a maximum non-dimensional velocity $\sim O(10^3)$ for $A = 10^7$ with a minimum grid spacing $\sim 4 \times 10^{-3}$, one can expect $\delta t \lesssim 4 \times 10^{-6}$ for stability. However, the maximum velocity does not occur at the minimum grid spacing, we have used $\delta t = 2 \times 10^{-5}$ for $A = 10^6$ and $\delta t = 1 \times 10^{-5}$ for $A = 10^7$. We did not strive for optimal δt for a once and for all kind of computation.

5. Results of Computation

We shall investigate two sets of very high Rayleigh number results here. The first set is for $A = 10^6$, which is the highest Rayleigh number for the bench mark comparison [8]. Gartling [8] and Winters [8,

10] had tabulated numerical values along a few vertical or horizontal lines. These values will be compared with my own FD results. Most of the maximum values given in [9] for $A = 10^6$ will also be plotted for comparison. The main objective is to show why it is misleading to compare only the maxima of various fields.

The second set of results is for $A = 10^7$. This set of results consist of those from seven different computations with various grid distributions. The objective is not to try to extrapolate for the "best" results. We shall show that for this problem, and perhaps for all problems of boundary layer type, a proper distribution of grid points in the appropriate locations is at least as important as the total number of grid points used. This may help to optimize the use of computing resources. It, however, also demands a priori knowledge of the physics of the problem.

(a) $A = 10^6$, $\sigma = 0.71$. A comparison Between FD and FE Results

The finite element results are those by Gartling [8] and those by Winters [10]. Two sets of FE vs two sets of FD results provide a good comparison. While Gartling's results have been cited in [9] as one of two "best" sets of results (the other is by Upson, Gresho and Lee [8] who also used FEM and whose results will be identified later), Winters' results were not anywhere cited or commented on in [9]. As we shall see, Winters' results are comparatively "accurate". Most of the velocity maxima and the Nusselt number maxima in [9] are also plotted. The scatter in the plots will show that it is not adequate to provide only field maxima for bench mark comparison.

The variable mesh size of my own 40 X 40 grids is shown as the 6B scale in Fig. 2. The results of Exp. 6B were cited in [9] as "accurate" to 1 to 2%. As a confirmation study, a new computation on a 60 X 60 net was done with variable grids shown as the 6A scale in Fig. 2. For both Exp. 6A and 6B, the grid distributions in both x and z directions are identical. The plots have been done manually. They should be accurate enough for our discussion.

Fig. 1 plots the z-distribution of the horizontal velocity u at x = 0, the center line of the cavity. Due to the centro-symmetry of the problem, the velocity would reverse in sign if heating and cooling are reversed on the side walls. Because a characteristic velocity $U = \sqrt{\kappa\nu}/L$ has been used for my own computation, dimensionless results with a characteristic stream function $\Psi = \kappa$ or velocity $U = \kappa/L$, must be divided by $\varepsilon = \sqrt{\sigma}$ before being compared with the results presented here. In the following comparison, such conversions have been made.

Fig. 1 consists of a main curve with four sets of data: Winters, ⊗, Gartling ⌖ and Quon, 40 X 40, ○, and 60 X 60, ●. The inset is an enlargement of a small section which contains the velocity maximum of the main curve. Many of the u_{max} in [9] are plotted in the inset. The ID numbers are the original numbers in [9]. The few contributors of interest to us here are the following: de Vahl Davis, 3, whose fourth order FD results were taken as the best for comparison; Quon, 16 (the open circle); Gartling, 24; Upson, Gresho and Lee, 20; and Winters, 31. Upson et al are identified here, because theirs and Gartling's results were cited as best in [9].

The main curve in Fig. 1 shows that Exp. 6A, the fine grid FD computation designated by solid dots, has decreased the maximum velocity of

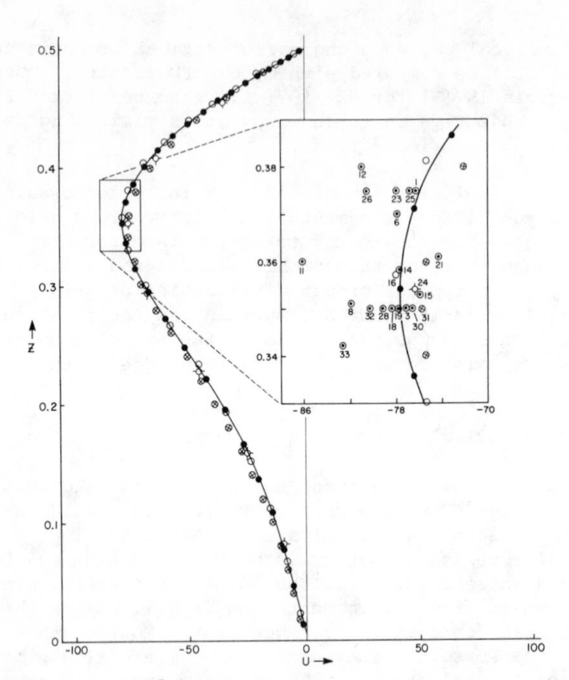

Fig. 1 $A = 10^6$. Horizontal velocity U at mid-plane in the upper half of the cavity. Symbol designation: •, Exp. 6A; o, Exp. 6B; ⊗, Winters; ⌖, Gartling.

Exp. 6B by 0.4%. The general functional shape is preserved. In comparison with the FE results, the FD values are consistently higher than the FE results between the position of the maximum and the wall ($0.3 < z < 0.5$). The difference between the u_{max} of FD and Gartling's FE computation is about 1.6%. For $0 < z < 0.3$, the FD values are consistently lower than the FE values. However, the difference between the two FE results are larger than that between Gartling's and the FD results.

The scatter in the u_{max} as shown in the inset of Fig. 1 is large. An overall comparison indicates that the most likely position for u_{max} is at $z = 0.35$. The solid curve joining the FD results does not differ much from that. The magnitude of u_{max} of a number of participants are within 2% of de Vahl Davis' value, point 3.

Fig. 2 compares the vertical velocities near the hot wall. It consists of three main graphs and an inset of the maximum vertical velocity at mid-height, $z = 0$. The three main graphs are w at $z = 0, \pm 0.4$. The curve for $z = 0$ includes Gartling's and Winters' data, while at $z = \pm 0.4$, only Winters FE data are available. Exp. 6A has slightly increased w_{max} from Exp. 6B, about 0.3%. Gartling's results coincide with those of Exp. 6A. On all levels, Winters' results are very close to the FD results with a few data points noticeably higher than the curve for $z = 0.4$ near $\tilde{x} = 0.15$. The inset again shows considerable amount of scatter. Gartling's and de Vahl Davis' w_{max} fall on the curve. Winters' and Upson et al's are slightly higher. These results

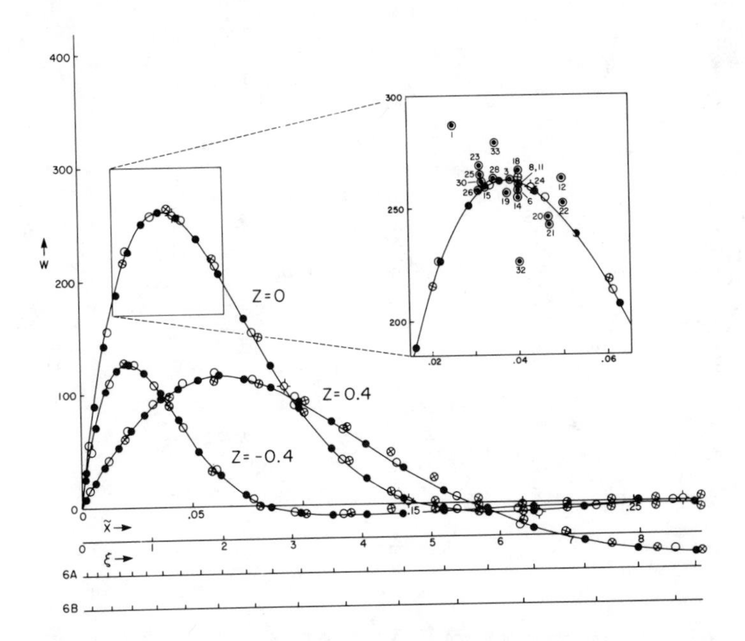

Fig. 2 $A = 10^6$. Vertical velocity near the hot wall at three levels of z. $\tilde{x}$ is the dimensionless distance from the hot wall. $\zeta = A^{\frac{1}{4}}\tilde{x}$ is the boundary layer length scale. The lower two scales 6A and 6B indicate the grid position.

and a few other points can be considered as very good results if we try to match them with the solid curve, provided that they are grid point values. If they are interpolated maxima, the results are quite different. However de Vahl Davis' is an interpolated w_{max}, and it coincides almost exactly with the curve's maximum.

Gartling's, Winters' and the temperature data of the present study fit very well to the same functional forms at selected levels in z (not shown for lack of space). It appears that the velocity fields are more sensitive to a finer net than the temperature. This is an expected response because T is a monotonic function of x while w has a large maximum within the boundary layer. Fig. 3 plots the dimensionless normal temperature gradient on the hot wall. It is equivalent to the local Nusselt number. It should be pointed out here that in the algorithm used here, the wall is sandwiched between two temperature points. Therefore the normal temperature gradients on the wall are computed from two sets of nearest neighbouring points, which have the smallest grid spacing in the whole net, equal to 7.2×10^{-3} ($\sim$1/139) for Exp. 6B and equal to 3.80×10^{-3} ($\sim$1/263) for Exp. 6A. These grid spacings correspond to those of 140 X 140 and 264 X 264 constant grids respectively. The inset contains most of the contributed Nusselt number maxima given in [9].

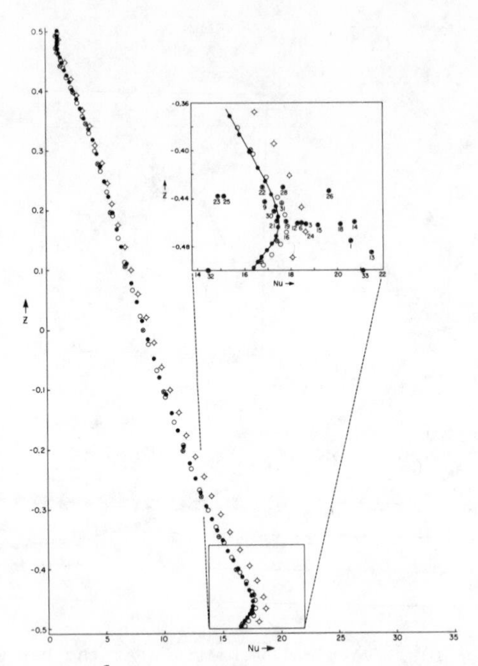

Fig. 3 A = 10^6. Local Nusselt number computed on the hot wall by Nu = $\partial\eta/\partial x\partial\eta T$, where $\partial\eta T$ is the normal temperature gradient on the wall in transformed space.

The main curve in Fig. 3 shows that the two FD and Winters' results almost coincide, while Gartling's results are approximately 7% higher at the maximum, and consistently higher than the other results in the rest of the curve. The inset in Fig. 3 shows even larger discrepancies. The difference between the two FD results is about 2% at the maximum, which is larger than the difference between Exp. 6A and Winters' result. de Vahl Davis', point 3, like Gartling's, is about 7% higher, although he has since revised his results [14] to about where point 12 is, which is about 5% higher than the results of Exp. 6A. Upson et al's values, point 30, is slightly lower than those of Exp. 6A. Their results can be very similar to the curve shown in Fig. 3 if they have given their grid point maximum. On the other hand, the results can also be very different if point 30 is an interpolated maximum. There are at least seven contributors whose Nusselt number maxima are sandwiched between Gartling's and Upson et al's results. The position of a majority of the Nusselt number maxima are very close to that of Exp. 6A.

In Table 1 we have summarized some of these results in the format of the intercomparison report. Columns 3b and 16a are additional new results. Columns 29 and 30 differ only in the way the Nusselt numbers were computed. The only difference between Upson I and Upson II is that the latter used the so-called "consistent flux method" to calculate Nu. It seems for coarse element computation, the flux method is considered to be more accurate for calculating heat transfer. We have therefore plotted Upson II in Fig. 3. Note that in Table I, Gartling and Upson I also give 6 and 4% higher average Nusselt number, Nu_o, respectively, while

Table I

Summary of Results for $A = 10^6$

ID No.	3	3a	3b	16	16a	24	29	30	31
AUTHORS	de Vahl Davis & Leong	de Vahl Davis	de Vahl Davis	Quon	Quon	Gartling	Upson, Gresho, & Lee, I	Upson, Gresho, & Lee, II	Winters
Nu_o	8.615	8.903	8.817	8.871	8.843	9.382	9.1699	8.8170	8.83
$Nu_{(max)}$	18.635	18.562	18.230	17.765	17.440	18.630	18.508	17.294	17.6
$@\tilde{z}$ =	0.039	0.045	0.0417	0.0330	0.0359	0.0322	0.043	0.045	0.056
$Nu_{(min)}$	1.065	1.002	0.989	1.011	1.009	1.007	0.9837	0.9805	0.975
$@\tilde{z}$ =	1.00	1.00	1.00	0.9963	0.9980	0.9892	0.988	1.00	1.00
$U_{(max)}$	64.960	64.93	64.63	65.69	65.42	64.368	64.593	64.593	63.9
$@\tilde{z}$ =	0.850	0.850	0.850	0.8572	0.8544	0.8540	0.850	0.850	0.85
$W_{(max)}$	221.28	221.29	219.36	219.74	220.39	218.424	220.64	220.64	222.
$@\tilde{x}$ =	0.038	0.040	0.0379	0.0330	0.0359	0.0430	0.0316	0.0316	0.039
$\|\Psi\|_{(mid)}$	16.41	16.35	16.32		16.40				
$\|\Psi\|_{(max)}$	16.840	16.772	16.750		16.81	16.851	16.707		
$@\tilde{x}$ =	0.150	0.154	0.151		0.1546	0.1459	0.172		
$@\tilde{z}$ =	0.547	0.545	0.547		0.5316	0.5820	0.5		

Remarks: The characteristic stream function and velocity for Table I are respectively κ and κ/L as in [9]. Hence the velocities must be divided by $\sqrt{\sigma}$ if to be compared with those given in other parts of this paper.

Winters, who also used FEM and presumably calculated his Nusselt number from the normal gradient at the wall, average Nusselt number within 1% of the others. Since Winters used much finer elements next to the boundaries than the others, we conjecture that Gartling and Upson et al have obtained higher local Nusselt numbers because the boundary meshes are not small enough to give sufficient resolution, at least for the computation of the normal temperature gradient at the wall. We shall confirm this conjecture in subsection (b). On the other hand, judging by the other field quantities, including the temperature fields, FEM can do at least as well as FDM with a comparable number of degrees of freedom.

The important conclusion we have drawn from these comparisons is that bench mark comparisons must not include only the maxima; we must compare the functional forms of the solutions. We have also observed that Winters' results [8, 10] are as "accurate" as the best of results quoted in [9].

(b) $A = 10^7$, $\sigma = 0.71$. An Investigation of the Effects of Grid Distribution

In the last section, the two FD solutions, though very similar, show a marked trend that a finer net yields slightly reduced amplitude in many of the fields. In this section, we shall investigate seven sets of results obtained from seven separate computations for $A = 10^7$. The motivation for choosing such a high Rayleigh number is twofold: (i) to extend an approximate curve for Nusselt numbers vs Rayleigh numbers beyond $A = 10^6$ by a decade. Up to $A = 10^5$, the log-log plot for Nu vs A can be considered linear for all practical purposes. Deviation from linearity seems to appear at $A \sim 3 \times 10^5$. (ii) At $A = 10^7$, the whole system is extremely non-linear.

The boundary layer thickness being $O(A^{-\frac{1}{4}})$, approximately equal to 1.8×10^{-2} which makes the boundary layer resolution a primary computational challenge. The seven separate computations vary not only in the number of grid points, but also in the manner of variation in either or both directions. The experiments are designated from A to G. Table II summarizes the manner of grid variations. Besides the intercomparison of these seven sets of results, we are also able to compare them with some of Gartling's results for $A = 10^7$, $\diamond$, and Upson et al's maxima, $\odot$.

Fig. 4a shows the horizontal velocity in the upper half of the cavity at mid plane, $x = 0$. The solid curve joins the points of Exp. 7A. These results are very revealing. Let's first compare Upson et al's and Gartling's results with the FD results. Upson et al's maximum is very close to the solid curve. Again without knowing the functional form of Upson et al's solutions, it is very difficult to make a proper assessment of the comparison. Gartling's results and the solid curve are reasonably close. Their deviations from the solid curve have characteristics similar to a number of the FD results, we shall discuss them together.

We can divide Fig. 4a into three segments: (1) $0.4 < z < 0.5$, (2) $0.25 < z < 0.4$, and (3) $0 < z < 0.25$. Segment (1) can be considered as the horizontal boundary layer, where the dynamics is local and hence the accuracy depends on how well the solutions are resolved locally. Hence Exp. 7B, 7C and 7G which have better local grid resolutions than the others should also be expected to do better. Exp. 7F which has more grid points overall than all others except Exp. 7A and 7B, and Exp. 7D, which has the same number of grid points as Exp. 7C, do considerably worse. Let's recall that Exp. 7D has almost constant grids in the z-direction while Exp. 7F has them almost constant in both directions. Exp. 7E, which has only 20 variable grid points, has done almost as well as Exp. 7F whose grid points are double in number but almost at constant intervals. It is very clear that how well the solutions do in this area strongly depends on the local resolution of the boundary layers.

Segment 3 is in the interior. Exp. 7A and 7B and Gartling's results agree reasonably well. Exp. 7D, which does pretty badly in segment 1, is doing almost as well as Exp. 7C. One is tempted to conclude again that the local resolution is the determining factor. However, Exp. 7F, whose grid resolution in the interior is better than that of Exp. 7B, gives rather poor results. A more interesting observation is the following. We note that Exp. 7G which does rather well in segment 1 gives the worst results in segment 3. Exp. 7E which does poorly in segment 1, also does poorly in segment 3. However, the results of Exp. 7E are comparable if not better than Exp. 7F. Comparing Exp. 7E and 7G, we note that Exp. 7G has better overall resolution between $z = 0$ and 0.5, and give much better results in segment 1 than Exp. 7E. Yet the former's results are much worse than the latter's in the interior, segment 3. The results in segment 2, which are the transitional results between segment 1 and segment 3 are very mixed. All results, including Gartling's, compare least well here.

Fig. 4b plots vertical distribution of temperature at the center line, $x = 0$. It is even more obvious here that Exp. 7F and 7G

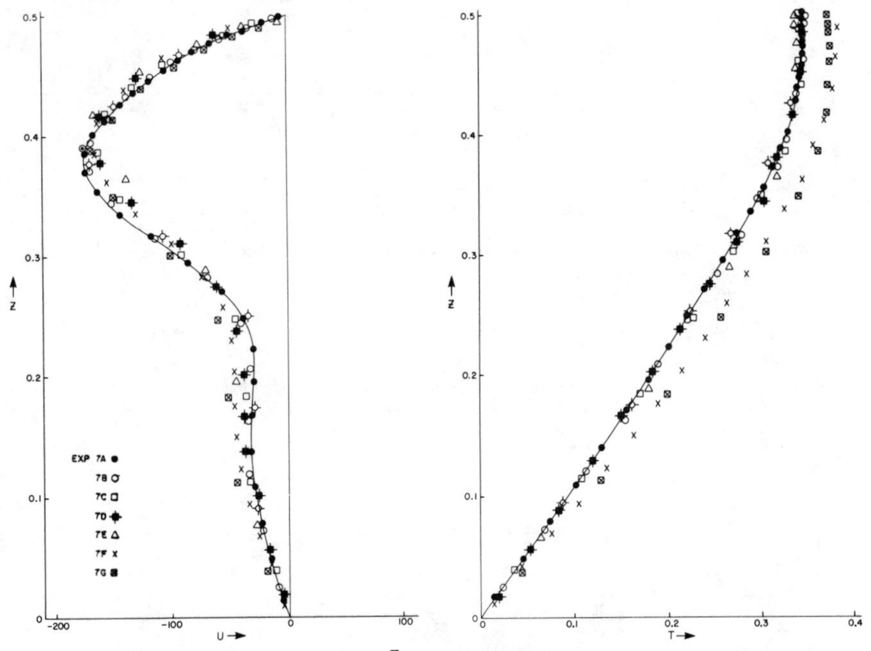

Fig. 4 (a) $A = 10^7$. Composite plot of the horizontal velocity U at mid-plane in the upper half of the cavity.
(b) Vertical distribution of temperature at mid-plane in the upper half of the cavity.

yield the worst temperature distribution, although they have better vertical resolutions than some of the other experiments.

Taking the results of Exp. 7A as the best of FD results presented here we see that: (1) a good vertical resolution alone does not guarantee an overall good agreement in either the flow or the temperature distribution in the interior. (2) dynamically, the horizontal boundary layer is viscous and non-thermally-driven, therefore, it depends strongly on the vertical spatial resolution, but does not depend on the vertical distribution of temperature. (3) The temperature near the horizontal boundaries is a result of forced convection. Therefore if the velocity field is not well resolved, the temperature field cannot be correct. This is demonstrated by the results on Fig. 4b. The question concerning the "accuracy" of the interior velocity cannot be answered until we have studied the results of the vertical boundary layer.

Before comparing the results of the vertical boundary layer, let's note that for high Rayleigh number convection, the vertical boundary layer thickness is $\ell \sim (A^{-\frac{1}{4}})$. For $A = 10^7$, $\ell \sim 1.8 \times 10^{-2}$, which is about 1/55 the total width of the cavity.

Fig. 5a and 5b are plots of the vertical velocity near the hot wall

Table II

Manner of Grid Variations

Exp. No.	7A	7B	7C	7D	7E	7F	7G	6A	6B
Net Size	60 X 60	40 X 40	30 X 30	30 X 30	20 X 20	40 X 40	30 X 30	60 X 60	40 X 40
Control Parameter in X, d_1=	0.06	0.06	0.03	0.03	0.02	0.45	0.45	0.06	0.08
Min. interior Grid size in x	0.00402	0.00632	0.00534	0.00534	0.00674	0.02466	0.03353	0.00402	0.00777
Control Parameter in z, d_2=	0.06	0.06	0.03	0.45	0.02	0.45	0.03	0.06	0.08
Min. interior Grid Size in z	0.00402	0.00632	0.00534	0.03353	0.00674	0.02466	0.00534	0.00402	0.00777
No. of interior Grid points Within $\tilde{x}$=.05	8	5	4	4	4	2	1	8	5
No. of interior Grid points within $\tilde{z}$=.05	8	5	4	1	4	2	4	8	5
Symbols	●	○	□	✦	△	x	⊠	●	○
Remarks	Fine Grids in x,z	Fine Grids in x,z	Fine Grids in x,z	Fine Grids in x Coarse Grids in z	Fine Grids in x,z	Coarse Grids in x,z	Coarse Grids in x Fine Grids in z	Fine Grids in x,z	Fine Grids in x,z

at three levels of z, z = 0 in Fig. 5a and $z = \pm 0.4$ in Fig. 5b. There are six different scales for the abscissa (Exp. 7C and 7D have a common horizontal scale). $\tilde{x}$ is the non-dimensional distance from the hot wall and $\zeta = \tilde{x} A^{\frac{1}{4}}$ is the boundary layer scale. The lower six scales indicate the grid points of various experiments.

At z = 0 in Fig. 5a, we have the wmax from Upson et al's, ⊙ , and four w points from Gartling's, ✧ . The latter fall fairly close on the solid curve, while Upson et al's maximum is approximately 4% higher than the grid point maximum given in Fig. 5a. Of the FD solutions, Exp. 7F and 7G fare worse than the others. It is not at all surprising that they do, if we examine their spatial resolutions. Between the maximum of the curve and the boundary, there is only one grid point. Exp. 7E, which has only 20 X 20 variable grids, is doing surprisingly well, except for its third data point from the boundary. It is slightly over 1% higher than the grid maximum of Exp. 7A, although displaced by a non-dimensional distance of 0.003 to the interior. The numerical values sound very small, but that particular data point is very conspicuously out of place in Fig. 5a. Exp. 7C and 7D have the same number, and exactly the same horizontal distribution of grid points, although the vertical distribution is very different (see Fig. 4). In spite of these differences, the spatial variations of W are almost exactly the same for both cases, and in fact, very similar to those of Exp. 7A and 7B. When data on the other two levels at $z = \pm 0.4$, as given in Fig. 5b, are examined, all other experiments show marked deviations from Exp. 7A and 7B, whose data points still form a coherent set. At all levels, one can draw one single curve to represent the two sets of data for Exp. 7A and

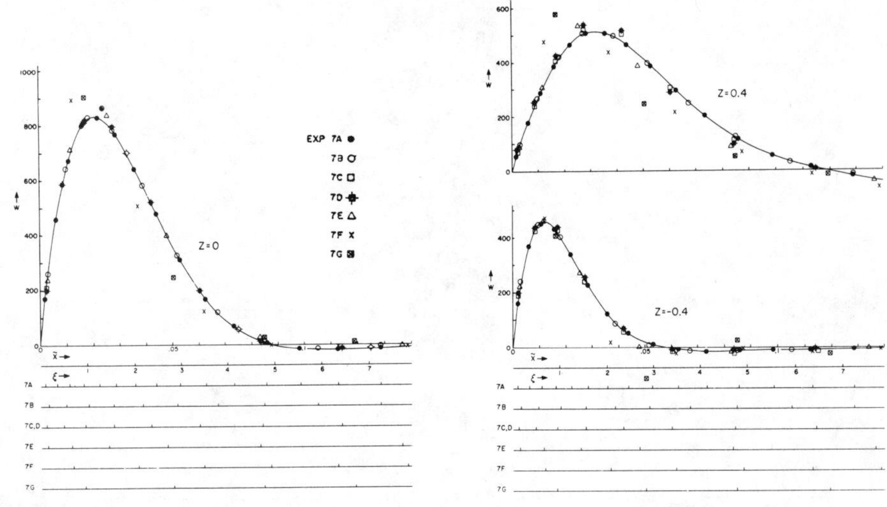

Fig. 5 (a) $A = 10^7$. Vertical velocity at mid-height, z = 0. Gartling's results are represented by ◇, and Upson et al's w_{max} by ⊙. $\tilde{x}$ is the dimensionless distance from the hot wall and $\zeta = A^{\frac{1}{4}} \tilde{x}$ is the boundary layer length scale. The lower six scales indicate the grid positions of the seven FDM experiments.
(b) Vertical velocity at $z = \pm 0.4$ near the hot wall.

7B.

Figs. 6a and 6b display the spatial variations of temperature at three levels of z. At z = 0 in Fig. 6a, all except Exp. 7F and 7G form a single coherent set of points. Again, Gartling's three points fall right on the curve. On the other two levels shown in Fig. 6b, all experiments again show some, and Exp. 7F and 7G show substantial amount of scatter from the results of Exp. 7A and 7B.

It seems clear now that unless the vertical boundary layer flows are adequately resolved, one cannot expect a good overall agreement. We shall return to the discussion of resolution of boundary layers later.

Fig. 7 shows an intercomparison of local Nusselt numbers on the hot wall for $A = 10^7$, which includes Gartling's results between $z = \pm 0.5$ and Upson et al's maximum in the inset. Exp. 7F and 7G, which have very poor horizontal grid resolution, show the least agreement with all the other experiments. As for $A = 10^6$, Gartling's results for $A = 10^7$ compare consistently higher than those for the FD computations, which, except Exp. 7F and 7G, yield a fairly coherent set of points.

The inset shows the detailed variation of the local Nusselt numbers for a selected few cases. Exp. 7C does even better than Exp. 7B when compared with Exp. 7A. Athough Exp. 7B, has more grid points than

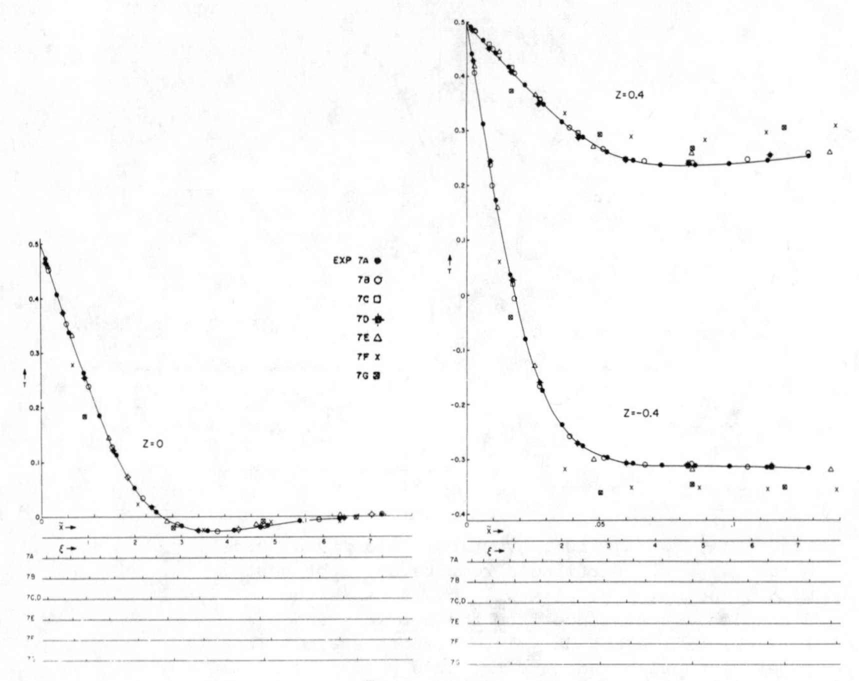

Fig. 6 (a) $A = 10^7$. Horizontal distribution of temperature at mid-height, z = 0.
(b) $A = 10^7$. Horizontal distribution of temperature at $z = \pm 0.4$. See caption of Fig. 5 for explanation.

Exp. 7C, and yields overall better agreement than the latter, it has slightly less dense grid distribution than Exp. 7C in the boundary layer regions. It appears that increasing the grid density in the corner region reduces the Nusselt number maximum. By inference then, Upson et al's results ought to be considered most accurate. (We should also point out that Upson et al had extra dense elements in the four corner regions [8]). However, we must defer this judgment until we can make a comparison of the spatial variation of various solutions. The caution is supported by the results of Exp. 7G shown in Fig. 7. It has the lowest Nusselt number maximum, but has the worst overall agreement with the rest of the experiments.

In Fig. 8 we present the stream function and contour temperature maps of Exp. 7A. These will help focus our attention on potential problematic areas. The vertical boundary layers are well recognized features whose vertical velocity and temperature fields vary very rapidly normal to the wall. Hence they require good spatial resolution in the orizontal directions. The largest temperature gradient is found in the corner at the base of the hot wall (lower right in the right diagram), and at the diagonally opposite corner, while the largest vorticity is found at mid-height. It is obvious that in order to provide good resolutions to boundary layers near both sides of the vertical walls, dense grids are required in the boundary layer regions through the total height of the cavity.

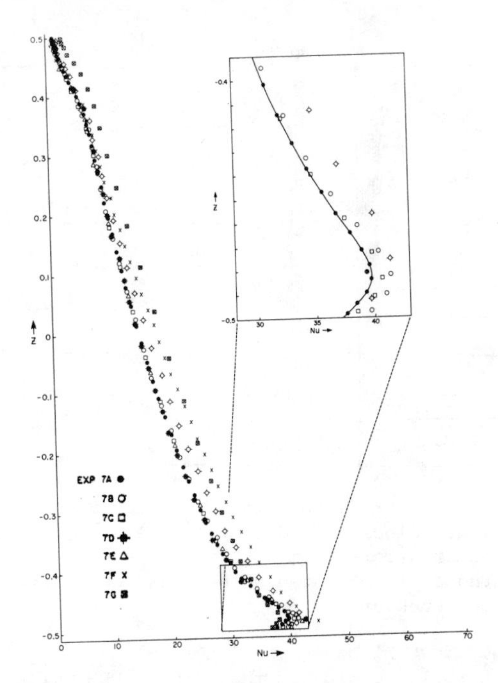

Fig. 7. $A = 10^7$. Local Nusselt number computed on the hot wall. The inset contains Upson et al's Nu_{max} ⊙ , Gartling's distribution, ⯁ , Exp. 7A, ● , Exp. 7B, o, and Exp. 7C, □.

Less well understood regions are the upper right and lower left corner regions where the vertical gradient of the horizontal velocities are very strong. Back flows are also prominent there. It is important that both velocity components be well resolved in these areas which are the source of mass transport in the horizontal boundary layers. Otherwise the horizontal velocity downstream cannot be expected to be adequately represented.

Although there is no horizontal thermal boundary layer near the top and bottom of the cavity, convection of temperature is by and large forced by the horizontal velocities. Unless the velocity is adequately represented, the thermal field will also be likely in error.

A practical question we like to answer is "what is adequate resolution?" These results show that for FD computations, we must have three or four grid points between the velocity maximum and the boundary at mid height, where the velocity gradient is steepest, and a similar vertical grid spacing near the horizontal boundaries. For $A = 10^7$, the vertical velocity maxima is approximately situated at $x \simeq 1.2A^{-1/4} \sim 2.1 \times 10^{-2}$ as shown in Fig. 5a. A net of 120 X 120 constant grid would provide three interior grid points between the wall and w_{max}, such as Exp. 7B has. The density of five grid points between the wall and w_{max}, such as Exp. 7A provides, would require a net of 215 X 215 grids at constant intervals. Therefore, it is not difficult to see the advantage of variable grids for

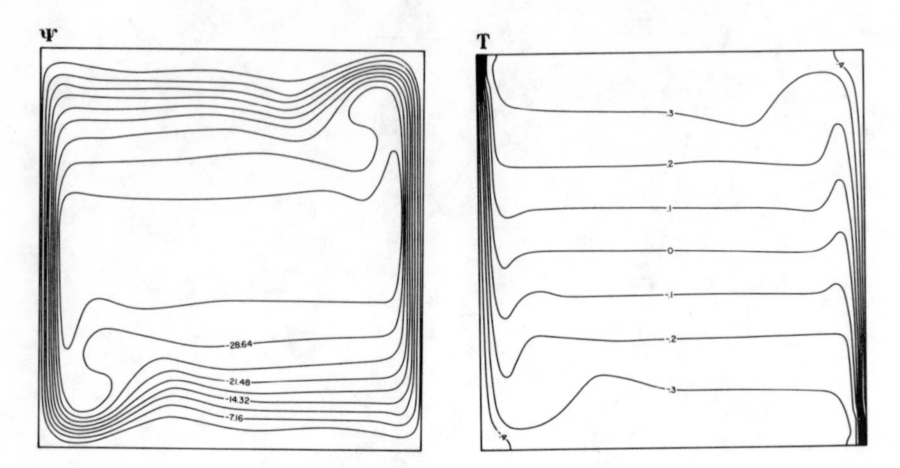

Fig. 8 $A = 10^7$. Stream function, Ψ, integrated from the vertical velocity, and temperature, T. Note that the characteristic stream function is $\sqrt{\kappa\nu}$. The cavity is heated on the right hand boundary and cooled on the left hand boundary.

boundary layer problems. de Vahl Davis and Jones [9] have conveyed some misleading impression in their conclusion that "those FDM which have used a non-uniform mesh have not, on the whole, performed better than those which used only a uniform mesh." The conclusion is misleading because: (1) six out of eight FDM they mentioned used non-uniform grids ranging from 16 X 16 to 29 X 29 for $A = 10^6$. My own, 40 X 40 (Exp. 6B), was the densest and the 8th was 35 X 35, while de Vahl Davis used 61 X 61, and later 81 X 81 nets of constant grids for $A = 10^6$. Among those who used uniform grids, about 80% used 40 X 40 or higher, near 50% used 50 X 50 or higher, and the highest one was 82 X 82. Therefore they compare much coarser variable grids with dense constant grids. (2) Variable grids alone do not guarantee accurate results, as the study of Exp. 7 has shown. One must take advantage of variable grids to provide adequate resolution in areas with the steepest gradient in the variables. The ability to place dense grids where they are most needed is the strength of variable grid algorithms. It is not clear to what extent these other studies mentioned above have made full use of this advantage. (3) In order to compare the performance of variable grid and constant grid formulation, one must use exactly the same finite differencing on the same equations (e.g. 2nd order central finite difference for the primitive equations, or 4th order cental difference for the Ψ, ζ equations, etc.), because the approximations themselves may introduce sufficient variation to mask, even if only partially, the improvement due to variable grids. Exp. 7B and 7F, or Exp. 7C, 7D and 7G, provide such comparisons. The advantages of variable grids are obvious.

Fig. 9 summarizes my own computed Nusselt numbers for a square cavity with $\sigma = 0.71$. The points for $A = 4 \times 10^6$ was computed from 40 X 40 and $A = 2 \times 10^7$ from 60 X 60 variable grids whose results have not been included for discussion here. The deviation from linearity at

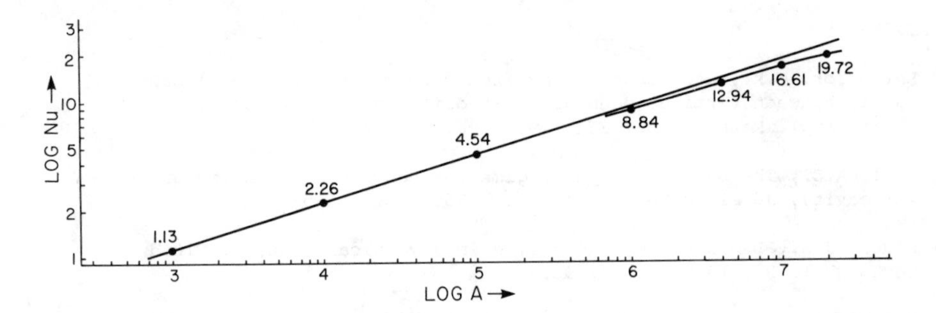

Fig. 9 Log-Log plot of Nusselt number, Nu, vs Rayleigh number, A.

$A > 10^5$ is believed to be real. Though the average Nusselt number is an important quantity that gives an indication as to the non-linearity of the system, it is an integrated quantity and is rather an insensitive one for the purpose of comparison. The same comment should apply to the stream function maximum which is an integrated quantity from the velocity components.

6. Conclusion

From the discussion presented in this paper, we conclude that in order to make a meaningful comparison between two or more sets of computational results, comparing field maxima is not enough. One must compare the functional forms of all fields, preferably along a few line segments. Therefore for bench mark comparison, we must provide the original grid point results and their corresponding grid positions, at least for three levels at $x, z = 0, \pm 0.4$. For problems possessing centro-symmetry like the one under discussion, agreement on the center line does not necessarily reflect the same degree of agreement in the other regions as Figs. 5 and 6 show. The comparison for $A = 10^6$ here is far from conclusive. Perhaps it would be useful for the FEM workers to further refine their boundary element to see how their results change. It is my belief that the fine grid results presented here for both $A = 10^6$ and $A = 10^7$ are among the best finite difference results. This statement needs confirmation from the FEM workers and other FDM workers.

It is beyond doubt that, for both FDM and FEM, variable grid spacings and elements provide versatility and economy for boundary layer type of computation. We have shown that one must provide at least three or four interior grid points between the maximum of the rapidly varying vertical velocity and the wall, and similar vertical resolution near the horizontal boundaries. It was demonstrated that for $A = 10^7$, fields interact non-linearly and globally, one must have adequate spatial resolution in all regions to ensure reasonable answers.

ACKNOWLEDGEMENTS

The author wishes to thank Dr. Patrick J. Roache for an enlightening discussion on the problem.

REFERENCES

1 Batchelor, G.k., Heat transfer by free convection across a closed cavity between vertical boundaries at different temperatures, Quart. Appl. Maths., Vol. XII, 1954, pp. 209-233.

2 Gill, A.E., The boundary-layer regime for convection in a rectangular cavity, J. Fluid Mech., Vol. 26, 1966, pp. 515-536.

3 Elder, J.W., Laminar free convection in a vertical slot, J. Fluid Mech., Vol. 23, 1965, pp. 77-98.

4 Mallinson, G.D. and de Vahl Davis, G., Three-dimensional natural convection in a box: a numerical study, J. Fluid Mech., Vol. 83, 1977, pp. 1-31.

5 Quon, C., High Rayleigh number convection in an enclosure - a numerical study, Phys. Fluids, Vol. 15, 1972, pp. 12-19.

6 Quon, C., Free convection in an enclosure revisited, J. Heat Trans., Vol. 99, 1977, pp. 340-342.

7 de Vahl Davis, G., Jones, I.P., and Roache, P.J., Natural convection in an enclosed cavity: a comparison problem, J. Fluid Mech., Vol. 95, 1979, inside back cover, pt4.

8 Jones, I.P. and Thomson, C.P. (Eds.), Numerical Solutions for a Comparison Problem on Natural Convection in an Enclosed Cavity, AERE-R-9955, HMSO, 1981.

9 de Vahl Davis, G., and Jones, I.P., Natural convection in a square cavity - a comparison exercise. Proc. 2nd Inter. Conf. Numerical Methods in Thermal Problems, Venice, 1981 (in press).

10 Winters, K.H., A numerical study of natural convection in a square cavity, AERE-R-9747, HMSO, 1980.

11 Quon, C., A mixed spectral and finite difference model to study baroclinic annulus waves, J. Comp. Phys., Vol. 20, 1976, pp. 442-479.

12 Varga, R. S., Matrix Iterative Analysis, Prentice-Hall Inc., Englewood Cliffs, New Jersey, 1962, pp. 209-249.

13 Roberts, G.O., Computational meshes for boundary layer problems, Proc. of the 2nd Inter. Conf. on Numerical Methods in Fluid Dynamics, (M. Holt, Ed.), Spring-verlag, Berlin/Heidelberg/New York, 1971, pp. 171-177.

14 de Vahl Davis, G., Natural convection of air in a square cavity - an accurate numerical solution. Report 1981/FMT/1, The University of New South Wales, Australia.

APPENDIX

IN THE FOLLOWING TABLES, $\tilde{X}$=X+0.5, AND $\tilde{Z}$=Z+0.5. THEY RESPECTIVELY MEASURE THE DIMENSIONLESS DISTANCE FROM THE COLD WALL AND THE BOTTOM BOUNDARY OF THE CAVITY. THE CHARACTERISTIC VELOCITY FOR U AND W IS $\sqrt{\kappa\nu}$ /L.

A=1.0E6 $\tilde{Z}$	NU($\tilde{Z}$)	A=1.0E6 $\tilde{Z}$	NU($\tilde{Z}$)
.1002E+01	.1009E+01	.4842E+00	.8661E+01
.9980E+00	.1009E+01	.4527E+00	.9148E+01
.9938E+00	.1011E+01	.4215E+00	.9649E+01
.9891E+00	.1020E+01	.3908E+00	.1015E+02
.9838E+00	.1038E+01	.3609E+00	.1066E+02
.9779E+00	.1070E+01	.3319E+00	.1116E+02
.9713E+00	.1122E+01	.3039E+00	.1166E+02
.9641E+00	.1199E+01	.2772E+00	.1215E+02
.9560E+00	.1309E+01	.2517E+00	.1264E+02
.9471E+00	.1454E+01	.2276E+00	.1312E+02
.9372E+00	.1637E+01	.2050E+00	.1358E+02
.9264E+00	.1855E+01	.1838E+00	.1404E+02
.9144E+00	.2102E+01	.1640E+00	.1449E+02
.9013E+00	.2375E+01	.1456E+00	.1494E+02
.8870E+00	.2669E+01	.1286E+00	.1537E+02
.8714E+00	.2982E+01	.1130E+00	.1579E+02
.8544E+00	.3310E+01	.9869E-01	.1619E+02
.8360E+00	.3650E+01	.8559E-01	.1656E+02
.8162E+00	.3997E+01	.7364E-01	.1689E+02
.7950E+00	.4344E+01	.6277E-01	.1715E+02
.7724E+00	.4688E+01	.5291E-01	.1734E+02
.7483E+00	.5027E+01	.4399E-01	.1743E+02
.7228E+00	.5366E+01	.3592E-01	.1744E+02
.6961E+00	.5710E+01	.2865E-01	.1735E+02
.6681E+00	.6067E+01	.2211E-01	.1718E+02
.6391E+00	.6445E+01	.1622E-01	.1696E+02
.6092E+00	.6845E+01	.1094E-01	.1673E+02
.5785E+00	.7270E+01	.6198E-02	.1653E+02
.5473E+00	.7716E+01	.1953E-02	.1641E+02
.5158E+00	.8182E+01	-.1847E-02	.1641E+02

A=1.0E7 $\tilde{Z}$	NU($\tilde{Z}$)	A=1.0E7 $\tilde{Z}$	NU($\tilde{Z}$)
.1002E+01	.1349E+01	.4842E+00	.1548E+02
.9980E+00	.1349E+01	.4527E+00	.1635E+02
.9938E+00	.1360E+01	.4215E+00	.1728E+02
.9891E+00	.1399E+01	.3908E+00	.1820E+02
.9838E+00	.1490E+01	.3609E+00	.1916E+02
.9779E+00	.1650E+01	.3319E+00	.2011E+02
.9713E+00	.1889E+01	.3039E+00	.2108E+02
.9641E+00	.2201E+01	.2772E+00	.2205E+02
.9560E+00	.2572E+01	.2517E+00	.2302E+02
.9471E+00	.2990E+01	.2276E+00	.2397E+02
.9372E+00	.3452E+01	.2050E+00	.2493E+02
.9264E+00	.3961E+01	.1838E+00	.2588E+02
.9144E+00	.4515E+01	.1640E+00	.2683E+02
.9013E+00	.5100E+01	.1456E+00	.2780E+02
.8870E+00	.5688E+01	.1286E+00	.2878E+02
.8714E+00	.6246E+01	.1130E+00	.2979E+02
.8544E+00	.6753E+01	.9869E-01	.3083E+02
.8360E+00	.7209E+01	.8559E-01	.3193E+02
.8162E+00	.7634E+01	.7364E-01	.3309E+02
.7950E+00	.8057E+01	.6277E-01	.3431E+02
.7724E+00	.8508E+01	.5291E-01	.3556E+02
.7483E+00	.9004E+01	.4399E-01	.3680E+02
.7228E+00	.9553E+01	.3592E-01	.3797E+02
.6961E+00	.1015E+02	.2865E-01	.3893E+02
.6681E+00	.1080E+02	.2211E-01	.3955E+02
.6391E+00	.1149E+02	.1622E-01	.3964E+02
.6092E+00	.1222E+02	.1094E-01	.3929E+02
.5785E+00	.1298E+02	.6198E-02	.3846E+02
.5473E+00	.1379E+02	.1953E-02	.3762E+02
.5158E+00	.1462E+02	-.1847E-02	.3762E+02

A=1.0E6

$\tilde{Z}$	$U(-.4,\tilde{Z})$	$U(0,\tilde{Z})$	$U(.4,\tilde{Z})$
.4842E+00	-.1618E+01	.1729E+01	.4985E+01
.4527E+00	.1545E+01	.5349E+01	.8497E+01
.4215E+00	.4396E+01	.9440E+01	.1213E+02
.3908E+00	.6792E+01	.1428E+02	.1590E+02
.3609E+00	.8629E+01	.2006E+02	.1983E+02
.3319E+00	.9969E+01	.2685E+02	.2397E+02
.3039E+00	.1117E+02	.3457E+02	.2831E+02
.2772E+00	.1292E+02	.4295E+02	.3284E+02
.2517E+00	.1613E+02	.5156E+02	.3749E+02
.2276E+00	.2165E+02	.5986E+02	.4216E+02
.2050E+00	.2995E+02	.6721E+02	.4675E+02
.1838E+00	.4085E+02	.7293E+02	.5113E+02
.1640E+00	.5351E+02	.7650E+02	.5521E+02
.1456E+00	.6663E+02	.7764E+02	.5889E+02
.1286E+00	.7887E+02	.7640E+02	.6208E+02
.1130E+00	.8916E+02	.7312E+02	.6470E+02
.9869E-01	.9691E+02	.6827E+02	.6666E+02
.8559E-01	.1021E+03	.6241E+02	.6784E+02
.7364E-01	.1050E+03	.5600E+02	.6813E+02
.6277E-01	.1059E+03	.4940E+02	.6739E+02
.5291E-01	.1050E+03	.4285E+02	.6549E+02
.4399E-01	.1023E+03	.3651E+02	.6233E+02
.3592E-01	.9723E+02	.3047E+02	.5780E+02
.2865E-01	.8951E+02	.2478E+02	.5190E+02
.2211E-01	.7884E+02	.1946E+02	.4464E+02
.1622E-01	.6524E+02	.1450E+02	.3616E+02
.1094E-01	.4899E+02	.9910E+01	.2664E+02
.6198E-02	.3055E+02	.5674E+01	.1633E+02
.1953E-02	.1051E+02	.1782E+01	.5514E+01
0.	0.	0.	0.

A=1.0E6

$\tilde{X}$	$U(\tilde{X},-.4)$	$U(\tilde{X},0)$	$U(\tilde{X},.4)$
.5000E+00	.6872E+02	-.2170E-06	-.6872E+02
.4684E+00	.7148E+02	.4110E+00	-.6751E+02
.4370E+00	.7614E+02	.8272E+00	-.6742E+02
.4061E+00	.8284E+02	.1254E+01	-.6802E+02
.3757E+00	.9130E+02	.1687E+01	-.6897E+02
.3463E+00	1008E+03	.2102E+01	-.7002E+02
.3178E+00	.1102E+03	.2428E+01	-.7101E+02
.2904E+00	.1182E+03	.2534E+01	-.7184E+02
.2643E+00	.1239E+03	.2253E+01	-.7249E+02
.2395E+00	.1272E+03	.1444E+01	-.7295E+02
.2161E+00	.1283E+03	.8468E-01	-.7321E+02
.1942E+00	.1278E+03	-.1661E+01	-.7325E+02
.1737E+00	.1258E+03	-.3447E+01	-.7304E+02
.1546E+00	.1223E+03	-.4847E+01	-.7251E+02
.1370E+00	.1172E+03	-.5495E+01	-.7156E+02
.1207E+00	.1100E+03	-.5210E+01	-.7007E+02
.1057E+00	.1008E+03	-.4045E+01	-.6782E+02
.9199E-01	.8975E+02	-.2257E+01	-.6460E+02
.7947E-01	.7736E+02	-.2310E+00	-.6015E+02
.6807E-01	.6436E+02	.1634E+01	-.5434E+02
.5772E-01	.5154E+02	.3023E+01	-.4721E+02
.4834E-01	.3959E+02	.3774E+01	-.3910E+02
.3985E-01	.2905E+02	.3885E+01	-.3060E+02
.3219E-01	.2021E+02	.3484E+01	-.2240E+02
.2529E-01	.1316E+02	.2764E+01	-.1512E+02
.1908E-01	.7843E+01	.1925E+01	-.9203E+01
.1351E-01	.4085E+01	.1137E+01	-.4831E+01
.8502E-02	.1674E+01	.5163E+00	-.1972E+01
.4017E-02	.3837E+00	.1295E+00	-.4436E+00
0.	0.	0.	0.

A=1.0E6

$\tilde{Z}$	$W(-.4,\tilde{Z})$	$W(0,\tilde{Z})$	$W(.4,\tilde{Z})$
.5000E+00	-.8160E+02	-.3422E-07	.8160E+02
.4684E+00	-.8536E+02	-.4105E+00	.7742E+02
.4370E+00	-.8864E+02	-.8948E+00	.7292E+02
.4061E+00	-.9147E+02	-.1448E+01	.6817E+02
.3757E+00	-.9398E+02	-.1946E+01	.6324E+02
.3463E+00	-.9643E+02	-.2178E+01	.5814E+02
.3178E+00	-.9916E+02	-.1935E+01	.5285E+02
.2904E+00	-.1025E+03	-.1116E+01	.4731E+02
.2643E+00	-.1064E+03	.1943E+00	.4150E+02
.2395E+00	-.1107E+03	.1743E+01	.3542E+02
.2161E+00	-.1147E+03	.3190E+01	.2911E+02
.1942E+00	-.1175E+03	.4230E+01	.2271E+02
.1737E+00	-.1184E+03	.4685E+01	.1639E+02
.1546E+00	-.1167E+03	.4546E+01	.1035E+02
.1370E+00	-.1122E+03	.3938E+01	.4809E+01
.1207E+00	-.1049E+03	.3061E+01	-.4917E-01
.1057E+00	-.9548E+02	.2116E+01	-.4066E+01
.9199E-01	-.8446E+02	.1257E+01	-.7132E+01
.7947E-01	-.7261E+02	.5724E+00	-.9197E+01
.6807E-01	-.6057E+02	.9207E-01	-.1027E+02
.5772E-01	-.4891E+02	-.1981E+00	-.1044E+02
.4834E-01	-.3808E+02	-.3350E+00	-.9828E+01
.3985E-01	-.2840E+02	-.3627E+00	-.8621E+01
.3219E-01	-.2010E+02	-.3228E+00	-.7030E+01
.2529E-01	-.1331E+02	-.2493E+00	-.5275E+01
.1908E-01	-.8046E+01	-.1675E+00	-.3563E+01
.1351E-01	-.4238E+01	-.9393E-01	-.2072E+01
.8502E-02	-.1748E+01	-.3860E-01	-.9347E+00
.4017E-02	-.3988E+00	-.6604E-02	-.2331E+00
0.	0.	0.	0.

A=1.0E6

$\tilde{X}$	$W(\tilde{X},-.4)$	$W(\tilde{X},0)$	$W(\tilde{X},.4)$
.4842E+00	.3618E+01	-.7632E-01	.1012E+00
.4527E+00	.8705E+01	-.2385E+00	.2573E+01
.4215E+00	.1515E+02	-.4286E+00	.3992E+01
.3908E+00	.2270E+02	-.6547E+00	.4593E+01
.3609E+00	.3070E+02	-.8821E+00	.4626E+01
.3319E+00	.3803E+02	-.9875E+00	.4331E+01
.3039E+00	.4319E+02	-.7331E+00	.3915E+01
.2772E+00	.4474E+02	.1804E+00	.3546E+01
.2517E+00	.4173E+02	.1942E+01	.3349E+01
.2276E+00	.3400E+02	.4358E+01	.3411E+01
.2050E+00	.2195E+02	.6590E+01	.3787E+01
.1838E+00	.6221E+01	.7063E+01	.4494E+01
.1640E+00	-.1243E+02	.3636E+01	.5489E+01
.1456E+00	-.3307E+02	-.5967E+01	.6610E+01
.1286E+00	-.5439E+02	-.2359E+02	.7482E+01
.1130E+00	-.7480E+02	-.5007E+02	.7380E+01
.9869E-01	-.9252E+02	-.8476E+02	.5136E+01
.8559E-01	-.1060E+03	-.1253E+03	-.7798E+00
.7364E-01	-.1140E+03	-.1676E+03	-.1186E+02
.6277E-01	-.1164E+03	-.2069E+03	-.2889E+02
.5291E-01	-.1133E+03	-.2381E+03	-.5118E+02
.4399E-01	-.1057E+03	-.2571E+03	-.7627E+02
.3592E-01	-.9480E+02	-.2616E+03	-.1001E+03
.2865E-01	-.8160E+02	-.2508E+03	-.1182E+03
.2211E-01	-.6709E+02	-.2259E+03	-.1261E+03
.1622E-01	-.5198E+02	-.1889E+03	-.1212E+03
.1094E-01	-.3675E+02	-.1423E+03	-.1024E+03
.6198E-02	-.2173E+02	-.8863E+02	-.7018E+02
.1953E-02	-.7084E+01	-.3041E+02	-.2640E+02
0.	0.	0.	0.

A=1.0E6

$\tilde{Z}$	$T(-.4,\tilde{Z})$	$T(0,\tilde{Z})$	$T(.4,\tilde{Z})$
.4842E+00	.8343E-02	-.1424E-01	-.3296E-01
.4527E+00	-.1596E-01	-.4275E-01	-.5754E-01
.4215E+00	-.3966E-01	-.7137E-01	-.8188E-01
.3908E+00	-.6246E-01	-.1002E+00	-.1055E+00
.3609E+00	-.8408E-01	-.1293E+00	-.1282E+00
.3319E+00	-.1043E+00	-.1583E+00	-.1495E+00
.3039E+00	-.1228E+00	-.1867E+00	-.1694E+00
.2772E+00	-.1398E+00	-.2134E+00	-.1875E+00
.2517E+00	-.1555E+00	-.2372E+00	-.2038E+00
.2276E+00	-.1704E+00	-.2574E+00	-.2183E+00
.2050E+00	-.1854E+00	-.2740E+00	-.2311E+00
.1838E+00	-.2011E+00	-.2872E+00	-.2422E+00
.1640E+00	-.2183E+00	-.2977E+00	-.2518E+00
.1456E+00	-.2372E+00	-.3061E+00	-.2599E+00
.1286E+00	-.2576E+00	-.3126E+00	-.2666E+00
.1130E+00	-.2790E+00	-.3176E+00	-.2721E+00
.9869E-01	-.3008E+00	-.3214E+00	-.2764E+00
.8559E-01	-.3223E+00	-.3242E+00	-.2795E+00
.7364E-01	-.3426E+00	-.3262E+00	-.2816E+00
.6277E-01	-.3611E+00	-.3276E+00	-.2826E+00
.5291E-01	-.3770E+00	-.3285E+00	-.2827E+00
.4399E-01	-.3898E+00	-.3291E+00	-.2820E+00
.3592E-01	-.3995E+00	-.3295E+00	-.2806E+00
.2865E-01	-.4064E+00	-.3297E+00	-.2788E+00
.2211E-01	-.4108E+00	-.3298E+00	-.2768E+00
.1622E-01	-.4135E+00	-.3299E+00	-.2749E+00
.1094E-01	-.4148E+00	-.3299E+00	-.2733E+00
.6198E-02	-.4154E+00	-.3299E+00	-.2721E+00
.1953E-02	-.4156E+00	-.3299E+00	-.2715E+00
0.	-.4156E+00	-.3299E+00	-.2715E+00

A=1.0E6

$\tilde{X}$	$T(\tilde{X},-.4)$	$T(\tilde{X},0)$	$T(\tilde{X},.4)$
.4842E+00	-.3221E+00	.2272E-03	.3201E+00
.4527E+00	-.3235E+00	.6527E-03	.3178E+00
.4215E+00	-.3243E+00	.9855E-03	.3152E+00
.3908E+00	-.3240E+00	.1145E-02	.3126E+00
.3609E+00	-.3224E+00	.1035E-02	.3100E+00
.3319E+00	-.3192E+00	.5738E-03	.3075E+00
.3039E+00	-.3141E+00	-.2335E-03	.3052E+00
.2772E+00	-.3071E+00	-.1186E-02	.3031E+00
.2517E+00	-.2988E+00	-.1808E-02	.3011E+00
.2276E+00	-.2900E+00	-.1373E-02	.2992E+00
.2050E+00	-.2818E+00	.8849E-03	.2974E+00
.1838E+00	-.2754E+00	.5414E-02	.2956E+00
.1640E+00	-.2720E+00	.1194E-01	.2938E+00
.1456E+00	-.2725E+00	.1920E-01	.2915E+00
.1286E+00	-.2774E+00	.2494E-01	.2884E+00
.1130E+00	-.2867E+00	.2623E-01	.2835E+00
.9869E-01	-.3001E+00	.2009E-01	.2752E+00
.8559E-01	-.3168E+00	.4150E-02	.2613E+00
.7364E-01	-.3359E+00	-.2267E-01	.2387E+00
.6277E-01	-.3561E+00	.5991E-01	.2044E+00
.5291E-01	-.3764E+00	-.1056E+00	.1562E+00
.4399E-01	-.3961E+00	-.1570E+00	.9345E-01
.3592E-01	-.4145E+00	-.2110E+00	.1789E-01
.2865E-01	-.4316E+00	-.2648E+00	-.6661E-01
.2211E-01	-.4472E+00	-.3164E+00	-.1550E+00
.1622E-01	-.4612E+00	-.3645E+00	-.2423E+00
.1094E-01	-.4739E+00	-.4085E+00	-.3250E+00
.6198E-02	-.4852E+00	-.4483E+00	-.4008E+00
.1953E-02	-.4954E+00	-.4840E+00	-.4693E+00
0.	-.5000E+00	-.5000E+00	-.5000E+00

A=1.0E7

$\tilde{Z}$	$U(-.4,\tilde{Z})$	$U(0,\tilde{Z})$	$U(.4,\tilde{Z})$
.4842E+00	-.5545E+01	.5066E+01	.1243E+02
.4527E+00	.1528E+01	.1498E+02	.1915E+02
.4215E+00	.8568E+01	.2375E+02	.2561E+02
.3908E+00	.1506E+02	.3011E+02	.3168E+02
.3609E+00	.2077E+02	.3293E+02	.3727E+02
.3319E+00	.2607E+02	.3226E+02	.4253E+02
.3039E+00	.3098E+02	.3025E+02	.4787E+02
.2772E+00	.3380E+02	.3096E+02	.5386E+02
.2517E+00	.3155E+02	.3903E+02	.6113E+02
.2276E+00	.2250E+02	.5735E+02	.7009E+02
.2050E+00	.8325E+01	.8484E+02	.8080E+02
.1838E+00	-.6119E+01	.1161E+03	.9286E+02
.1640E+00	-.1521E+02	.1442E+03	.1055E+03
.1456E+00	-.1400E+02	.1638E+03	.1178E+03
.1286E+00	.1889E+01	.1732E+03	.1289E+03
.1130E+00	.3589E+02	.1734E+03	.1380E+03
.9869E-01	.8891E+02	.1669E+03	.1446E+03
.8559E-01	.1575E+03	.1563E+03	.1484E+03
.7364E-01	.2339E+03	.1440E+03	.1491E+03
.6277E-01	.3082E+03	.1311E+03	.1466E+03
.5291E-01	.3715E+03	.1184E+03	.1409E+03
.4399E-01	.4184E+03	.1058E+03	.1323E+03
.3592E-01	.4465E+03	.9307E+02	.1207E+03
.2865E-01	.4548E+03	.7997E+02	.1066E+03
.2211E-01	.4398E+03	.6632E+02	.9011E+02
.1622E-01	.3958E+03	.5210E+02	.7177E+02
.1094E-01	.3182E+03	.3740E+02	.5202E+02
.6198E-02	.2086E+03	.2243E+02	.3137E+02
.1953E-02	.7455E+02	.7414E+01	.1039E+02
0.	0.	0.	0.

A=1.0E7

$\tilde{X}$	$U(\tilde{X},-.4)$	$U(\tilde{X},0)$	$U(\tilde{X},.4)$
.5000E+00	.1675E+03	-.4364E-01	-.1675E+03
.4684E+00	.1642E+03	-.2445E+00	-.1686E+03
.4370E+00	.1595E+03	-.4527E+00	-.1679E+03
.4061E+00	.1559E+03	-.6773E+00	-.1663E+03
.3757E+00	.1569E+03	-.9263E+00	-.1643E+03
.3463E+00	.1660E+03	-.1206E+01	-.1624E+03
.3178E+00	.1835E+03	-.1524E+01	-.1607E+03
.2904E+00	.2054E+03	-.1897E+01	-.1593E+03
.2643E+00	.2220E+03	-.2326E+01	-.1582E+03
.2395E+00	.2228E+03	-.2749E+01	-.1572E+03
.2161E+00	.2030E+03	-.3016E+01	-.1563E+03
.1942E+00	.1694E+03	-.2986E+01	-.1553E+03
.1737E+00	.1346E+03	-.2729E+01	-.1543E+03
.1546E+00	.1060E+03	-.2661E+01	-.1529E+03
.1370E+00	.8654E+02	-.3392E+01	-.1511E+03
.1207E+00	.7782E+02	-.5275E+01	-.1488E+03
.1057E+00	.7977E+02	-.7965E+01	-.1457E+03
.9199E-01	.9011E+02	-.1043E+02	-.1417E+03
.7947E-01	.1043E+03	-.1145E+02	-.1367E+03
.6807E-01	.1170E+03	-.1030E+02	-.1304E+03
.5772E-01	.1232E+03	-.7040E+01	-.1223E+03
.4834E-01	.1207E+03	-.2524E+01	-.1115E+03
.3985E-01	.1098E+03	.1991E+01	-.9705E+02
.3219E-01	.9222E+02	.5315E+01	-.7893E+02
.2529E-01	.7086E+02	.6753E+01	-.5844E+02
.1908E-01	.4870E+02	.6307E+01	-.3813E+02
.1351E-01	.2860E+02	.4571E+01	-.2086E+02
.8502E-02	.1296E+02	.2421E+01	-.8603E+01
.4017E-02	.3252E+01	.6970E+00	-.1893E+01
0.	0.	0.	0.

A=1.0E7

$\tilde{Z}$	$W(-.4,\tilde{Z})$	$W(0,\tilde{Z})$	$W(.4,\tilde{Z})$
.5000E+00	.1480E+02	-.4663E-02	-.1480E+02
.4684E+00	.2120E+02	.1983E+00	-.9842E+01
.4370E+00	.2932E+02	.3577E+00	-.6121E+01
.4061E+00	.3928E+02	.5173E+00	-.3483E+01
.3757E+00	.5079E+02	.8274E+00	-.1587E+01
.3463E+00	.6314E+02	.1459E+01	.5253E-01
.3178E+00	.7534E+02	.2437E+01	.1899E+01
.2904E+00	.8550E+02	.3456E+01	.4187E+01
.2643E+00	.9041E+02	.3766E+01	.6756E+01
.2395E+00	.8664E+02	.2342E+01	.9078E+01
.2161E+00	.7282E+02	-.1564E+01	.1046E+02
.1942E+00	.5108E+02	-.7800E+01	.1032E+02
.1737E+00	.2590E+02	-.1521E+02	.8466E+01
.1546E+00	.1420E+01	-.2227E+02	.5078E+01
.1370E+00	-.2003E+02	-.2773E+02	.6536E+00
.1207E+00	-.3766E+02	-.3096E+02	-.4171E+01
.1057E+00	-.5126E+02	-.3188E+02	-.8764E+01
.9199E-01	-.6052E+02	-.3075E+02	-.1260E+02
.7947E-01	-.6492E+02	-.2808E+02	-.1530E+02
.6807E-01	-.6412E+02	-.2439E+02	-.1670E+02
.5772E-01	-.5832E+02	-.2021E+02	-.1677E+02
.4834E-01	-.4835E+02	-.1597E+02	-.1567E+02
.3985E-01	-.3556E+02	-.1200E+02	-.1366E+02
.3219E-01	-.2177E+02	-.8513E+01	-.1106E+02
.2529E-01	-.9255E+01	-.5633E+01	-.8228E+01
.1908E-01	-.3036E+00	-.3393E+01	-.5498E+01
.1351E-01	.3792E+01	-.1772E+01	-.3149E+01
.8502E-02	.3595E+01	-.7142E+00	-.1386E+01
.4017E-02	.1395E+01	-.1468E+00	-.3247E+00
0.	0.	0.	0.

A=1.0E7

$\tilde{X}$	$W(\tilde{X},-.4)$	$W(\tilde{X},0)$	$W(\tilde{X},.4)$
.4842E+00	-.3614E+02	-.5850E-01	.2667E+02
.4527E+00	-.4006E+02	-.1605E+00	.1569E+02
.4215E+00	-.3474E+02	-.2463E+00	.6079E+01
.3908E+00	-.1854E+02	-.3087E+00	-.8185E+00
.3609E+00	.8365E+01	-.3449E+00	-.4859E+01
.3319E+00	.4528E+02	-.3490E+00	-.6541E+01
.3039E+00	.9004E+02	-.3038E+00	-.6569E+01
.2772E+00	.1356E+03	-.1975E+00	-.5593E+01
.2517E+00	.1683E+03	-.8702E-01	-.4094E+01
.2276E+00	.1738E+03	-.1438E+00	-.2374E+01
.2050E+00	.1501E+03	-.5111E+00	-.5831E+00
.1838E+00	.1124E+03	-.8861E+00	.1230E+01
.1640E+00	.7618E+02	-.1297E+00	.3069E+01
.1456E+00	.4480E+02	.3384E+01	.4951E+01
.1286E+00	.1598E+02	.1010E+02	.6872E+01
.1130E+00	-.1595E+02	.1674E+02	.8778E+01
.9869E-01	-.5904E+02	.1461E+02	.1051E+02
.8559E-01	-.1204E+03	-.9229E+01	.1163E+02
.7364E-01	-.2019E+03	-.6790E+02	.1090E+02
.6277E-01	-.2969E+03	-.1693E+03	.5051E+01
.5291E-01	-.3904E+03	-.3112E+03	-.1271E+02
.4399E-01	-.4650E+03	-.4783E+03	-.5262E+02
.3592E-01	-.5062E+03	-.6428E+03	-.1239E+03
.2865E-01	-.5062E+03	-.7705E+03	-.2257E+03
.2211E-01	-.4650E+03	-.8294E+03	-.3398E+03
.1622E-01	-.3892E+03	-.7984E+03	-.4299E+03
.1094E-01	-.2896E+03	-.6717E+03	-.4515E+03
.6198E-02	-.1771E+03	-.4573E+03	-.3676E+03
.1953E-02	-.5953E+02	-.1707E+03	-.1613E+03
0.	0.	0.	0.

A=1.0E7

$\tilde{Z}$	$T(-.4,\tilde{Z})$	$T(0,\tilde{Z})$	$T(.4,\tilde{Z})$
.4842E+00	-.5871E-02	-.1473E-01	-.2244E-01
.4527E+00	-.3406E-01	-.4469E-01	-.5066E-01
.4215E+00	-.6181E-01	-.7404E-01	-.7860E-01
.3908E+00	-.8861E-01	-.1024E+00	-.1061E+00
.3609E+00	-.1137E+00	-.1295E+00	-.1332E+00
.3319E+00	-.1365E+00	-.1552E+00	-.1595E+00
.3039E+00	-.1570E+00	-.1792E+00	-.1847E+00
.2772E+00	-.1755E+00	-.2013E+00	-.2082E+00
.2517E+00	-.1922E+00	-.2217E+00	-.2293E+00
.2276E+00	-.2070E+00	-.2404E+00	-.2477E+00
.2050E+00	-.2189E+00	-.2580E+00	-.2632E+00
.1838E+00	-.2275E+00	-.2745E+00	-.2761E+00
.1640E+00	-.2329E+00	-.2895E+00	-.2866E+00
.1456E+00	-.2355E+00	-.3025E+00	-.2954E+00
.1286E+00	-.2366E+00	-.3131E+00	-.3025E+00
.1130E+00	-.2378E+00	-.3216E+00	-.3083E+00
.9869E-01	-.2411E+00	-.3281E+00	-.3131E+00
.8559E-01	-.2481E+00	-.3331E+00	-.3168E+00
.7364E-01	-.2599E+00	-.3368E+00	-.3198E+00
.6277E-01	-.2766E+00	-.3395E+00	-.3221E+00
.5291E-01	-.2970E+00	-.3414E+00	-.3238E+00
.4399E-01	-.3192E+00	-.3426E+00	-.3249E+00
.3592E-01	-.3409E+00	-.3435E+00	-.3257E+00
.2865E-01	-.3601E+00	-.3440E+00	-.3261E+00
.2211E-01	-.3752E+00	-.3443E+00	-.3263E+00
.1622E-01	-.3857E+00	-.3444E+00	-.3263E+00
.1094E-01	-.3920E+00	-.3445E+00	-.3262E+00
.6198E-02	-.3951E+00	-.3445E+00	-.3261E+00
.1953E-02	-.3959E+00	-.3445E+00	-.3260E+00
0.	-.3959E+00	-.3445E+00	-.3260E+00

A=1.0E7

$\tilde{X}$	$T(\tilde{X},-.4)$	$T(\tilde{X},0)$	$T(\tilde{X},.4)$
.4842E+00	-.3294E+00	.3141E-03	.3257E+00
.4527E+00	-.3338E+00	.2497E-03	.3231E+00
.4215E+00	-.3381E+00	.1783E-03	.3215E+00
.3908E+00	-.3414E+00	.9969E-04	.3205E+00
.3609E+00	-.3433E+00	.1707E-04	.3200E+00
.3319E+00	-.3431E+00	-.6506E-04	.3196E+00
.3039E+00	-.3403E+00	-.1386E-03	.3192E+00
.2772E+00	-.3338E+00	-.1849E-03	.3188E+00
.2517E+00	-.3231E+00	-.1783E-03	.3183E+00
.2276E+00	-.3089E+00	-.1210E-03	.3177E+00
.2050E+00	-.2937E+00	-.9634E-04	.3170E+00
.1838E+00	-.2802E+00	-.2599E-03	.3163E+00
.1640E+00	-.2692E+00	-.6708E-03	.3155E+00
.1456E+00	-.2602E+00	-.9894E-03	.3147E+00
.1286E+00	-.2524E+00	-.2768E-03	.3139E+00
.1130E+00	-.2456E+00	.2747E-02	.3131E+00
.9869E-01	-.2403E+00	.8842E-02	.3122E+00
.8559E-01	-.2376E+00	.1716E-01	.3110E+00
.7364E-01	-.2392E+00	.2463E-01	.3090E+00
.6277E-01	-.2472E+00	.2626E-01	.3047E+00
.5291E-01	-.2631E+00	.1634E-01	.2951E+00
.4399E-01	-.2869E+00	-.9743E-02	.2750E+00
.3592E-01	-.3168E+00	-.5383E-01	.2371E+00
.2865E-01	-.3501E+00	-.1141E+00	.1740E+00
.2211E-01	-.3836E+00	-.1856E+00	.8148E-01
.1622E-01	-.4150E+00	-.2618E+00	-.3792E-01
.1094E-01	-.4432E+00	-.3371E+00	-.1738E+00
.6198E-02	-.4682E+00	-.4075E+00	-.3120E+00
.1953E-02	-.4902E+00	-.4714E+00	-.4416E+00
0.	-.5000E+00	-.5000E+00	-.5000E+00

Finite Element Calculation of Buoyancy-Driven Convection near a Melt/Solid Phase Boundary

CHIECHUN J. CHANG and ROBERT A. BROWN
Department of Chemical Engineering
Massachusetts Institute of Technology
Cambridge, Massachusetts 02139

ABSTRACT

Two iterative schemes based on the mixed finite element method are developed for analyzing steady natural convection in a melt adjacent to its solid phase. The simplest method decouples the calculation of the field variables and the shape of the melt/solid interface into two interlocked iterations that are performed successively. The second method uses Newton's iteration to solve simultaneously for both types of unknowns and has a quadratic convergence rate. Results for a model problem of melt and solid in a cylindrical ampoule show the Newton algorithm to be a factor of three more efficient.

1. INTRODUCTION

Convection driven by buoyancy affects heat and mass transfer in solidification processes important in engineering and scientific applications ranging from the bulk processing of metals, semiconductors, and polymers to the microscopic growth of cellular and dendritic structures in solids. Precise knowledge of the shape of the melt/solid interface is a prerequisite for modelling and understanding many of these systems. For example, the compositional uniformity of multicomponent semiconductor crystals grown from the melt is a sensitive function of the shape of the phase boundary and the pattern of the fluid flow near the interface [1].

The calculation of natural convection near a melt/solid phase boundary is a formidable free-boundary problem composed of conservation equations written in terms of the field variables, velocity and pressure in the melt and temperature in both phases. These equations are coupled to the location of the melt/solid interface through conditions at the phase boundary. For the single component melt studied here the two interfacial conditions are for the equilibrium melting temperature and the balance of heat fluxes across the phase boundary.

The convective terms in the conservation equations and the coupling between the temperature field and the location of the melt/solid interface introduce nonlinearities into the equation set. Numerical schemes for solution traditionally iterate between the calculation of the field variables for a particular interface shape and a procedure for updating the location of the interface. In the first part of the calculation one of the interfacial boundary conditions must be relaxed. This condition, either for the melting point isotherm or for the balance of heat flux across the phase boundary, is used to calculate a new location of the interface. The nonlinear convective terms in the conservation laws force the calculations for the field variables to be iterative, even for a given shape of the phase boundary.

In this paper we present two formulations based on the Galerkin finite element method for efficient and accurate solution of this free-boundary problem. The finite element method seems well suited to the solution of steady-state solidification problems [2-4]. Both the curved meshes needed for accurate approximations to melt/solid interface shapes and the common heat flux boundary conditions are easily incorporated. These advantages make the finite element method superior to techniques for finite difference solution of steady solidification problems with natural convection [5-6].

Within the framework of Galerkin finite element methods, several choices in the formulation of solidification problems are crucial. Among these are (i) the choice of the scheme for approximating the shape of the melt/solid interface, (ii) the boundary condition distinguished for determining interface shape at each iteration, and (iii) the iterative scheme used for solving the coupled set of nonlinear algebraic equations for the coefficients representing the field variables and the interface shape. Several combinations for <u>distinguished</u> boundary conditions and iterative schemes have been investigated by Ettouney and Brown [4] for steady solidification problems without natural convection; the results of this study formed the starting point for our research. First, it was shown in [4] that iterative schemes using the isotherm condition to determine phase boundary shape are more accurate than methods based on the balance of heat flux. The two iterative schemes presented here update the interface location using the isotherm condition.

Second, Ettouney and Brown [4] have demonstrated the computational advantages of applying Newton's method for simultaneous calculation of the interface shape and field variables over previously used schemes that iterate successively between these two types of unknowns. When the field equations are nonlinear Newton's method used less computation time than schemes based on successive iterations between calculation of the interface and field variables. This increase in computational efficiency was due to the well known [7] quadratic asymptotic rate of convergence of Newton's iteration compared to the linear convergence rate of the successive approximation scheme. The two formulations of the finite element method presented in Section 3 differ in the iterative scheme implemented for solving the free-boundary problem; the first is based on successive approximations and the second on Newton's method. Our comparison of the computational efficiency of these formulations reinforces the conclusions of [4]. The only previous finite element scheme to account for the role of natural convection in setting the shape of the phase boundary [8] integrated the time-dependent equations until a steady-state solution was reached; this is a successive approximation scheme with each time step accounting for an iteration.

Using Newton's method allows implementation of continuation methods [9-10] for generating approximations to solutions and of numerical techniques [11-12] for detecting and tracking multiple steady state solutions; the value of the latter schemes in analyzing the complex solution structures in problems of natural convection is just becoming evident [13]. To implement the Newton process requires calculation of the sensitivity, expressed by derivatives in the Jacobian matrix, of the field equations on the location of the melt/solid interface. This differentiation is most conveniently accomplished by mapping each integral over the flow domain to a new domain with shape that is independent of the melt/solid interface location. Ettouney and Brown [4] did this by solving the entire free-boundary problem in transformed coordinates, whereas Saito and Scriven [14-15] implemented Newton's method for free-surface viscous flows by mapping each integral over an element to a square element using the isoparametric transformation [16] and performing the differentiation there. As laid out in Section 3, these two methods are equivalent and we use the formulation based on **isoparametric** mapping.

The two iterative schemes are compared for the problem of melt and solid in a cylindrical ampoule that is positioned vertically in a linear temperature field. This configuration is a model of the convection and heat transfer in directional solidification.

2. MODEL PROBLEM

A linear temperature profile is imposed along the sidewall of a vertical cylindrical ampoule that is filled with liquid. The temperature of the sidewall is highest T_H at the bottom and lowest T_C at the top of the ampoule. The melting temperature T_m of the liquid is assumed to be between these two temperatures. The upper and lower faces of the ampoule are taken to be insulated. Liquid above the melting point isotherm is solidified and the remaining melt is set into motion driven by buoyancy forces in both the radial and axial directions.

The height of the melt/solid interface above the bottom of the ampoule is taken as a single-valued function of the radial coordinate, i.e. z=h(r), as shown in Fig. 1. In terms of this representation, the unit normal $\underset{\sim}{N}$ and tangent vectors $\underset{\sim}{t}$ along the phase boundary are

$$\underset{\sim}{N} = \frac{\underset{\sim}{e}_z - h_r \underset{\sim}{e}_r}{\sqrt{1+h_r^2}} \quad , \quad \underset{\sim}{t} = \frac{\underset{\sim}{e}_r + h_r \underset{\sim}{e}_z}{\sqrt{1+h_r^2}} \quad , \tag{1}$$

where $h_r \equiv dh/dr$ and $\underset{\sim}{e}_r$ and $\underset{\sim}{e}_z$ are members of the set $(\underset{\sim}{e}_r, \underset{\sim}{e}_z, \underset{\sim}{e}_\theta)$ of unit vectors in the cylindrical polar coordinate system.

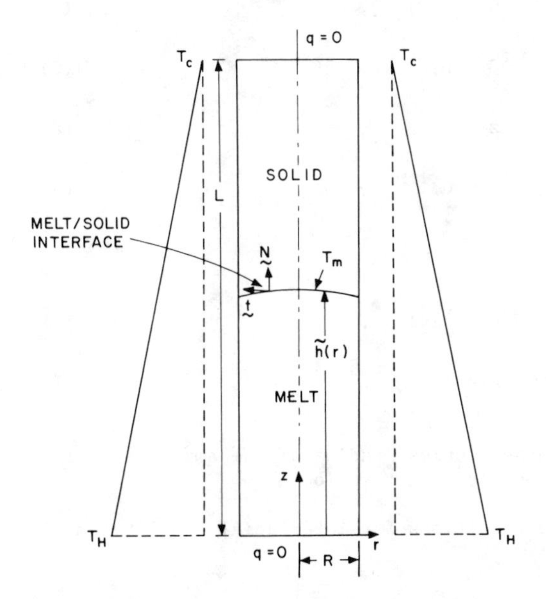

Fig. 1. Model two-phase systems consisting of melt and solid in a vertical cylindrical ampoule with a linear temperature field imposed along the sidewall of the ampoule. The bottom and top of the ampoule are insulated.

The temperature, pressure and velocity fields are taken to be axisymmetric and buoyancy-driven convection is modelled by the Boussinesq equations [17]. The equations are put in dimensionless form by scaling lengths with the height of the cylinder L, velocity $\underset{\sim}{v}_{\ell}$ with α_{ℓ}/L, pressure p with $\rho\alpha_{\ell}^2/L^2$, and melt θ_{ℓ} and solid θ_s temperatures as $(T_{\ell}-T_m)/(T_H-T_C)$ and $(T_s-T_m)/(T_H-T_C)$, respectively. The dimensionless mass, momentum and energy balances in the melt $\mathcal{D}_{\ell}$ are

$$\nabla \cdot \underset{\sim}{v}_{\ell} = 0 \quad , \tag{2}$$

$$\underset{\sim}{v}_{\ell} \cdot \nabla \underset{\sim}{v}_{\ell} = -\nabla p + Pr\nabla^2 \underset{\sim}{v}_{\ell} + RaPr\theta_{\ell}\underset{\sim}{e}_z \quad , \tag{3}$$

$$\underset{\sim}{v}_{\ell} \cdot \nabla\theta_{\ell} = \nabla^2\theta_{\ell} \quad , \tag{4}$$

where $\nabla \equiv \underset{\sim}{e}_r \partial/\partial r + \underset{\sim}{e}_z \partial/\partial z$ is the gradient operator in cylindrical coordinates. The Prandtl and Rayleigh numbers are defined as $Pr=\nu/\alpha_{\ell}$ and $Ra \equiv \beta g(T_H-T_C)L^3/\alpha_{\ell}\nu$ where ν is the kinematic viscosity of the melt, β is the coefficient of thermal expansion, and g is the acceleration of gravity. The energy balance in the solid $\mathcal{D}_s$ is simply

$$\nabla^2\theta_s = 0 \quad . \tag{5}$$

In dimensionless form, the boundary conditions on temperature and velocity along the walls of the ampoule are, in the melt,

$$\theta_{\ell} = 1 - z \quad , \quad r = R \quad , \quad 0 \le z \le h(R) \quad , \tag{6}$$

$$v_r = v_z = 0 \quad , \quad r = R \quad , \quad 0 \le z \le h(R) \quad , \tag{7}$$

$$\underset{\sim}{e}_z \cdot \nabla\theta_{\ell} = 0 \quad , \quad 0 \le r \le R \quad , \quad z = 0 \quad , \tag{8}$$

$$v_r = v_z = 0 \quad , \quad 0 \le r \le R \quad , \quad z = 0 \quad , \tag{9}$$

and, in the solid,

$$\theta_s = 1 - z \quad , \quad r = R \quad , \quad h(R) \le z \le 1 \quad , \tag{10}$$

$$\underset{\sim}{e}_z \cdot \nabla\theta_s = 0 \quad , \quad 0 \le r \le R \quad , \quad z = 1 \quad . \tag{11}$$

In equations (6-11) $R \equiv \tilde{R}/L$ is the dimensionless radius of the ampoule and is equal to the reciprocal of the ampoule's aspect ratio.

At the phase boundary $\partial\mathcal{D}_I$ the conditions for interfacial equilibrium of temperature

$$\theta_s = \theta_{\ell} = \theta_m \equiv (T_m - T_C)/T_H - T_C) \quad , \tag{12}$$

and the interfacial energy balance,

$$\underset{\sim}{N} \cdot \nabla\theta_s = K\underset{\sim}{N} \cdot \nabla\theta_\ell \quad , \tag{13}$$

must be satisfied, where $K=k_\ell/k_s$ is the ratio of thermal conductivities in the two phases. Equations (12-13) are three conditions on temperature at the melt/-solid interface. Two of these are needed as boundary conditions for the two energy balances (4-5) and the third is distinguished for calculating the shape of the phase boundary h(r). We follow Ettouney and Brown [4] and solve for continuous temperature fields that satisfy the flux condition (13). The melt/-solid interface is located by the condition for the equilibrium melting point (12).

3. FINITE ELEMENT FORMULATION

The free-boundary problem (2-13) is reduced to a finite-dimensional set of residual equations by representing velocities, pressure, temperature, and the shape of the melt/solid interface in expansions of finite element basis functions. For an approximate shape of the phase boundary both melt and solid regions are subdivided into quadrilateral elements as shown in Fig. 2. The finite-element approximation for the field variables follows previous work for natural convection in confined geometries [18-21] and uses mixed interpolation for velocity, pressure and temperature.

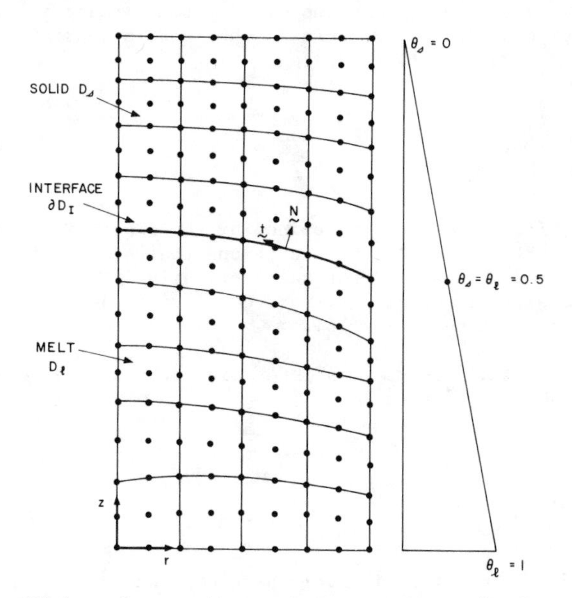

Fig. 2. Finite element discretization of melt $\mathcal{D}_\ell$ and solid $\mathcal{D}_s$ into quadrilateral elements. The melt/solid interface $\partial\mathcal{D}_I$ is a surface in the mesh.

For implementation of Newton's method it is necessary to relate analytically the location of each node in the mesh to the shape of the phase boundary. We do this by interpolating linearly N_r^E radial elements and N_z^E axial elements into each phase. The vertex nodes in this mesh are located at the coordinates (r_i,z_i) given by

$$\text{melt,}\quad r_i=(i-1)R/N_r^E \quad , \quad z_i=(i-1)h(r_i)/N_z^E \quad ; \tag{14}$$

$$\text{solid,}\quad r_i=(i-1)R/N_r^E \quad , \quad z_i=h(r_i)+(i-1-N_z^E)(1-h(r_i))/N_z^E \tag{15}$$

Equations (14-15) are the simplest relationships for interpolating the mesh; mesh grading toward any boundary can be incorporated by changing these expressions.

On the discretization defined by (14-15) the velocities in the melt and the temperature in both phases are approximated by expansions of biquadratic polynomials $\{\Phi^i(r,z)\}$ given by

$$\begin{pmatrix} v_x \\ v_y \end{pmatrix} = \sum_{i=1}^{N_\ell} \begin{pmatrix} u_i \\ v_i \end{pmatrix} \Phi^i(r,z) \quad , \tag{16}$$

$$\theta_\ell = \sum_{i=1}^{N_\ell} \theta_i^{(\ell)} \Phi^i(r,z) \quad , \quad \theta_s = \sum_{i=1}^{N_s} \theta_i^{(s)} \Phi^{(i)}(r,z) \quad , \tag{17}$$

where N_ℓ and N_s are the total numbers of biquadratic basis functions in melt and solid. The mid-side and centroid nodes for the biquadratic element are interpolated between the vertex nodes. The pressure in the melt is approximated by an expansion of bilinear polynomials $\{\psi^i(r,z)\}$ as

$$p(r,z) = \sum_{i=1}^{M} p_i \psi^i(r,z) \quad , \tag{18}$$

where M is the number of bilinear functions defined by the discretization in the melt. The expansions (16-18) each give representations that are continuous throughout the melt and solid phases and that have derivatives that are only discontinuous across interelement boundaries; more details of these bases are found in texts on finite element analysis [16].

The shape of the melt/solid interface is interpolated by a N_I-dimensional set of Hermite cubic polynomials $\Gamma^i(r)$ as

$$h(r) = \sum_{i=1}^{N_I} \beta_i \Gamma^i(r) \quad , \tag{19}$$

so that the derivative of the interface is everywhere continuous. The number of Hermite elements along the phase boundary is set to correspond to the number of radial elements in the discretization of melt and solid.

The weak forms of the field equations are formed by applying Galerkin's method to equations (2-4) in the usual way for natural convection [18], i.e.

$$\int_{\mathcal{D}_\ell} \psi^i \nabla \cdot \underset{\sim}{v}_\ell dA = 0 \quad , \quad i = 1,\ldots M \quad , \tag{20}$$

$$\int_{\mathcal{D}_\ell} \Phi^i (\underset{\sim}{v}_\ell \cdot \nabla \underset{\sim}{v}_\ell + \nabla p - Pr \nabla^2 \underset{\sim}{v}_\ell - PrRa\theta_\ell \underset{\sim}{e}_z) dA = 0 \quad , \quad i = 1,\ldots N_\ell \quad , \tag{21}$$

$$\int_{\mathcal{D}_\ell} \Phi^i (\underset{\sim}{v}_\ell \cdot \nabla \theta_\ell - \nabla^2 \theta_\ell) dA = 0 \quad , \quad i = 1,\ldots N_\ell \quad , \tag{22}$$

$$\int_{\mathcal{D}_s} \Phi^i (\nabla^2 \theta_s) dA = 0 \quad , \quad i = 1,\ldots N_s \quad , \tag{23}$$

The final form of the equation set is reached by applying the divergence theorem to (21-23), by incorporating the boundary conditions on temperature and velocity along the ampoule wall along with the interfacial energy balance (13), and by forcing the temperature to be continuous across the phase boundary. The entire set of algebraic equations can be represented as

$$\underline{R}(\underline{\alpha},\underline{\beta};Ra,Pr) = \underline{0} \quad , \tag{24}$$

where α is the vector of unknown coefficients associated with the field variables, $\underline{\alpha}^T = (\underline{u}^T,\underline{v}^T,\underline{p}^T,\underline{\theta}^{(\ell)T},\underline{\theta}^{(s)T})$, and $\underline{\beta}$ is the vector of coefficients in the expansion (19) for the melt/solid interface h(r). Each equation in (24) depends on the shape of the interface through the limits of the integrals. The shape is calculated so that a discretized version of the isotherm condition (12) is satisfied. In the isotherm formulation the calculation of the interface shape $\{\beta_i\}$ and the field variables $\{\alpha_i\}$ are decoupled into separate iterations and performed sequentially. The Isotherm-Newton schemes couples together these two iterations.

3.1 Isotherm Formulation

For an approximate interface shape, written in terms of the coefficients $\{\beta_i^{(k)}\}$, the integrals in eqs. (20-23) are defined over known regions and are computed using Gaussian integration. Then (24) is reduced to a set of nonlinear algebraic equations for the coefficients $\{\alpha_i\}$ of the field variables. This reduced set of residual equations,

$$\hat{\underline{R}}(\underline{\alpha}) = \underline{R}(\underline{\alpha},\underline{\beta}^{(k)};Ra,Pr) = \underline{0} \quad , \tag{25}$$

is solved by Newton's method, where successive approximations are calculated as

$$\underline{\alpha}^{(i+1)} - \underline{\alpha}^{(i)} \equiv \underline{\delta}^{(i)} \equiv \underline{\underline{J}}^{-1}(\underline{\alpha}^{(i)})\hat{\underline{R}}(\underline{\alpha}^{(i)}) \quad , \tag{26}$$

where the elements in the Jacobian matrix $\underline{\underline{J}}(\underline{\alpha}^{(i)})$ are expressed analytically as functions of the coefficients $\underline{\alpha}^{(i)}$. The correction vector is computed by solving a linear equation set using the frontal method of Gaussian elimination developed by Hood [21].

Field variables calculated as a solution of the residual equations (25) are a solution of the free-boundary problem only if the computed temperature field satisfies the isotherm condition (12). The melting point isotherm is interpolated from the finite element expansion (17) as

$$\theta_M = \sum_{i=1}^{N_\ell} \theta_i^{(\ell)} \phi^i(r,h(r)) \quad , \tag{27}$$

where $h(r) = \sum_{i=1}^{N_\ell} \beta_i^{(k+1)} \Gamma^i(r)$ is the updated location of the interface. This new interface shape is used to calculate the field variables; the Isotherm iteration scheme is shown schematically in Fig. 3. The computation is terminated when the coefficients of interface shape $\{\beta_i^{(k+1)}\}$ do not vary to within one part in 10^8 between two successive iterations. Although the Newton iterations (26) for the field variables converge quadratically, i.e. the error in the estimate $\underline{\alpha}^{(i)}$ is squared at each step, the overall rate of convergence of the algorithm is governed by the interpolation procedure for updating the interface shape. The updating of the interface amounts to successive substitutions and hence the overall convergence of the scheme is only linear. The rates of convergence of the separate parts of the Isotherm iteration are shown in Fig. 4 for the calculation Pr=100, $Ra=1.1x10^6$, R=0.25, and $\theta_m=0.5$. Within each phase, the finite element mesh had four elements in the radial and eight elements in the axial directions. The field variables and interface shape for $Ra=1.0x10^6$ were used as the first approximations $(\underline{\alpha}^{(0)},\underline{\beta}^{(0)})$. The change of the coefficients for the field variables and for melt/solid interface shape are both measured in the infinity norm which is defined for a vector $\underline{v}$ as $\|\underline{v}\|_\infty \equiv \max_i |v_i|$. The quadratic and linear convergence rates of the iterations for the field variables with a particular interface shape and for the overall iteration for the interface shape are clearly seen.

3.2 Isotherm-Newton Method

In the Isotherm-Newton formulation the residual equations for the field variables (24) are coupled with a set of residual equations for satisfying the isotherm condition (12) and solved simultaneously by Newton's method. The weighted-residual equations for satisfying the melting point constraint are formed by applying Galerkin's method to equation (12) evaluated along the melt/-solid interface $\partial\mathcal{D}_I$

$$R_i^{(I)}(\underline{\alpha},\underline{\beta}) = \int_{\partial\mathcal{D}_I} \Gamma^i(r)(\theta(r,h(r))-\theta_m)d\ell \quad , \tag{28}$$

where the differential unit of arc-length along the interface is $d\ell \equiv \sqrt{1+h_r^2}\,dr$. The complete set of equations is now

$$\underline{R}(\underline{\alpha},\underline{\beta}) = \begin{bmatrix} \underline{R}^{(F)}(\underline{\alpha},\underline{\beta};Ra,Pr) \\ \underline{R}^{(I)}(\underline{\alpha},\underline{\beta}) \end{bmatrix} = \underline{0} \quad . \tag{29}$$

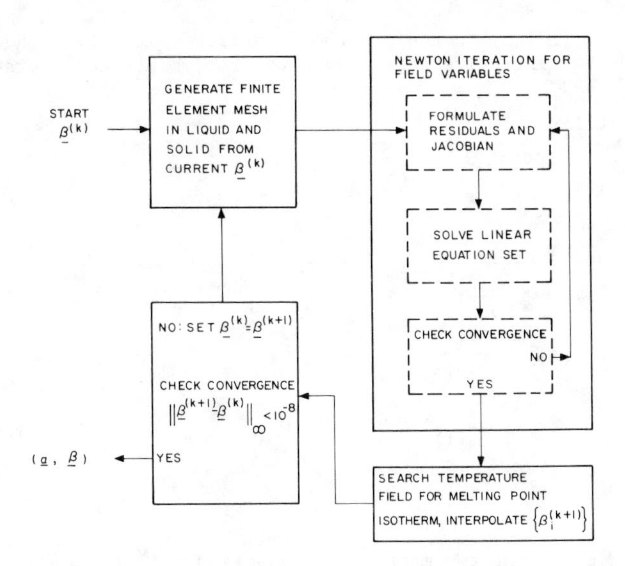

Fig. 3. Flowsheet for Isotherm algorithm.

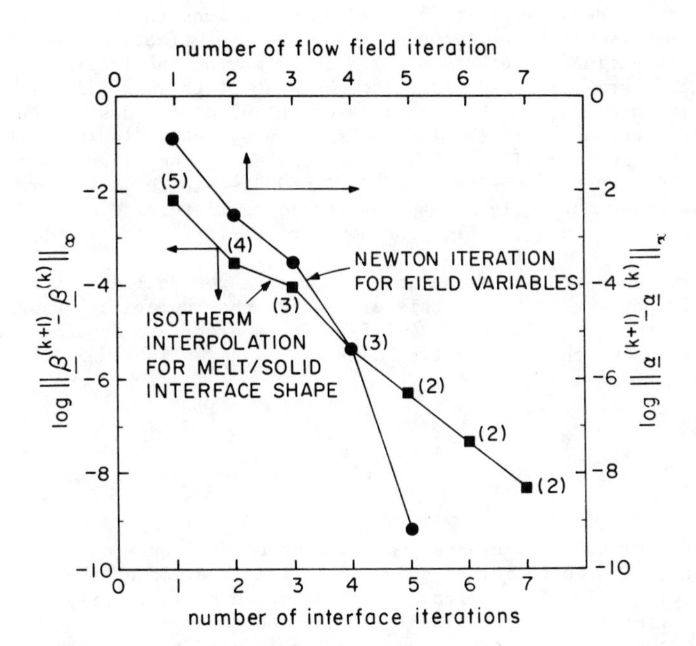

Fig. 4. Convergence of the nested iterations in the Isotherm scheme as a function of iteration number for each iteration loop. The number of iterations for the field variables necessary for each update of the melt/solid interface is shown in parenthesis and the convergence of the Newton's iteration for the field variables is for the first interface iteration.

Solution of equations (29) by Newton's method requires calculating the full Jacobian matrix of the discretized free-boundary problem at each iteration, i.e.

$$\underline{\underline{J}} = \begin{bmatrix} \hat{\underline{\underline{J}}}^{(F)} & \tilde{\underline{\underline{J}}}^{(F)} \\ \hat{\underline{\underline{J}}}^{(I)} & \tilde{\underline{\underline{J}}}^{(I)} \end{bmatrix} \tag{30}$$

where each of the sub-matrices has components

$$\hat{J}_{ij}^{(F)} \equiv \frac{\partial R_i^{(F)}}{\partial \alpha_j} \quad , \quad \hat{J}_{ij}^{(I)} \equiv \frac{\partial R_i^{(I)}}{\partial \alpha_j} \quad ,$$
$$\tilde{J}_{ij}^{(F)} \equiv \frac{\partial R_i^{(F)}}{\partial \beta_j} \quad , \quad \tilde{J}_{ij}^{(I)} \equiv \frac{\partial R_i^{(I)}}{\partial \beta_j} \quad . \tag{31}$$

The coefficients in the first two matrices in equation (31) involve the sensitivity of residual equations to changes in the coefficients of the field variables and are evaluated by differentiating the residual equations. The last two matrices measure the sensitivity of residual equations to changes in the location of the melt/solid interface and so include the effects of the changes in the shape of the finite elements brought on by moving the interface. The evaluation of these terms is more complicated because of the coupling of the finite element basis functions to the locations of the element nodes and because of the shape of the interface sets the limits of the area integrals in equations (20-23). Saito and Scriven [14-15] have shown that both complications are handled effectively by computing the terms of $\tilde{\underline{\underline{J}}}^{(F)}$ and $\tilde{\underline{\underline{J}}}^{(I)}$ in the transformed coordinates that arise naturally by mapping each quadrilateral element in (r,z) into a square element $\mathcal{D}_u$ in (ξ,η) with the boundaries $-1\leq\xi\leq 1$ and $-1\leq\eta\leq 1$.

Normally, each area and line integral in the residual equations (20-23, 28) are mapped isoparametrically to this element so that numerical quadrature can be easily performed (see [16], pp. 124-171). The appropriate mappings are simply written in terms of the biquadratic basis functions evaluated in transformed coordinates $\{\Phi^i(\xi,\eta)\}$ as

$$r = \sum_{k=1}^{9} r_k \Phi^k(\xi,\eta) \quad , \quad z = \sum_{k=1}^{9} z_k \Phi^k(\xi,\eta) \quad , \tag{32}$$

where the (r_k,z_k) $k=1,\ldots 9$ are the coordinates of the nodes around the boundary of the element. These coordinates depend on the location of the phase boundary through equations (14-15), whereas the transformed basis functions $\{\Phi^k(\xi,\eta)\}$ are independent of $h(r)$ and hence of $\{\beta_j\}$. Then the dependence of each integral written in transformed coordinates on the location of the phase boundary is explicit in terms of the nodal coordinates and the sensitivity coefficients $\{\tilde{J}_{ij}^{(I)},\tilde{J}_{ij}^{(F)}\}$ are calculated analytically; more details are found in [15] and [22]. The elemental mappings (32) serve the same purpose as the coordinate transformation for the full problem employed in [4]. Both methods convert the free-boundary problem to an equivalent problem that is nonlinear in $h(r)$ but that is defined on a fixed domain.

As shown on the flowsheet (Fig. 5), the field variables and interface shape are updated from a first approximation $(\underline{\alpha}^{(0)},\underline{\beta}^{(0)})$ by solving the linear equation set

$$\underline{\underline{J}}(\underline{\alpha}^{(k)},\underline{\beta}^{(k)})\underline{\delta}^{(k+1)} = -\underline{R}(\underline{\alpha}^{(k)},\underline{\beta}^{(k)}) \quad , \tag{33}$$

by Gaussian elimination, again using the frontal method. The new approximations $(\underline{\alpha}^{(k+1)},\underline{\beta}^{(k+1)})$ are

$$\begin{bmatrix} \underline{\alpha}^{(k+1)} \\ \\ \underline{\beta}^{(k+1)} \end{bmatrix} = \underline{\delta}^{(k+1)} + \begin{bmatrix} \underline{\alpha}^{(k)} \\ \\ \underline{\beta}^{(k)} \end{bmatrix} \quad . \tag{34}$$

The iterations are stopped when $\|\underline{\delta}^{(k+1)}\|_{\infty}$ is less than one part in 10^8 of the maximum element of $(\underline{\alpha}^{(k+1)},\underline{\beta}^{(k+1)})$.

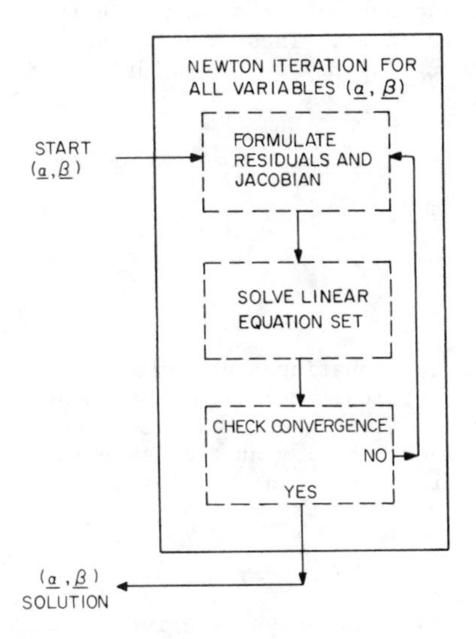

Fig. 5. Flowsheet for Isotherm-Newton algorithm.

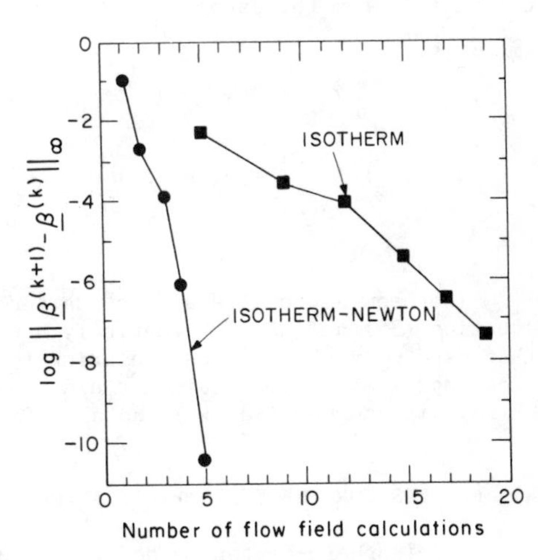

Fig. 6. Comparison of convergence rates with number of flow field calculations for Isotherm and Isotherm-Newton algorithms.

The quadratic rate of convergence of the Isotherm-Newton method, as measured by changes in the location of the phase boundary, is demonstrated in Fig. 6 for the same test case used with the Isotherm algorithm in Fig. 3. The change in interface location for the Isotherm method is also plotted on Fig. 6 as a function of the number of flow field calculations. One iteration of the Isotherm-Newton method required 1.2 times the computer time of a single calculation of the field variables (equation (26)) in the Isotherm routine. Therefore, the efficiency of the two algorithms can be compared directly on the basis of Fig. 6, since the interpolation of the phase boundary equation (27) requires negligible execution time. The Isotherm-Newton algorithm used three times less computer time than the Isotherm method. We use the Isotherm-Newton technique in all calculations reported in Section 4.

3.3 Continuation of Solution in Rayleigh Number

Sequences of solutions to equation (29) were generated by incrementally changing the Rayleigh number while fixing the Prandtl number and aspect ratio (1/R) of the ampoule. From a set of field variables ($\underline{\alpha}_c$) and interface shape ($\underline{\beta}_o$) that satisfy equation (29) for $Ra=\overset{o}{Ra}$ a first approximation ($\underline{\alpha}^{(o)},\underline{\beta}^{(o)}$) for the Rayleigh number $Ra=\overset{o}{Ra}+\Delta Ra$, where ΔRa is small, was constructed by analytic continuation [9-10] as

$$\begin{bmatrix} \underline{\alpha}^{(o)}(Ra+\Delta Ra) \\ \\ \underline{\beta}^{(o)}(Ra+\Delta Ra) \end{bmatrix} = \begin{bmatrix} \underline{\alpha}_o \\ \\ \underline{\beta}_o \end{bmatrix} + \begin{bmatrix} \underline{\alpha}_{Ra} \\ \\ \underline{\beta}_{Ra} \end{bmatrix} \Delta Ra \quad , \tag{35}$$

where the vectors $\underline{\alpha}_{Ra}\equiv(\partial\underline{\alpha}/\partial Ra)_{\overset{o}{Ra}}$ and $\underline{\beta}_{Ra}\equiv(\partial\underline{\beta}/\partial Ra)_{\overset{o}{Ra}}$ describe the change in the finite element solution vector with a small change in Ra. These vectors are calculated from the Jacobian matrix evaluated about $(\underline{\alpha}_o,\underline{\beta}_o)$ as the solutions of the linear equation sets

$$\underline{\underline{J}}(\underline{\alpha}_o,\underline{\beta}_o)\begin{bmatrix} \underline{\alpha}_{Ra} \\ \\ \underline{\beta}_{Ra} \end{bmatrix} = -(\partial\underline{R}/\partial Ra)_{\overset{o}{Ra}} \quad . \tag{36}$$

Isotherm-Newton iterations started with the continuation approximation equation (35) and $\Delta Ra \approx 10^4$ routinely converged in one less iteration than those that used only the previous solution $(\underline{\alpha}_o,\underline{\beta}_o)$ as the first guess. The continuation approximation (35) did not aid convergence when the flow at the new value of Rayleigh number ($\overset{o}{Ra}+\Delta Ra$) had a different cellular form than the flow at $\overset{o}{Ra}$.

4. RESULTS FOR THE CYLINDRICAL AMPOULE

The Isotherm-Newton method was used to calculate the buoyancy-driven flows and the shape of the melt/solid interface for an ampoule with an aspect ratio ($L/\tilde{R}$) of four, i.e. R=0.25, for K=1, and $\theta_M=0.5$. The streamfunction for each flow was calculated by solving the linear equation

$$\frac{1}{r}\frac{\partial^2\psi}{\partial r^2} - \frac{1}{r^2}\frac{\partial\psi}{\partial r} + \frac{1}{r}\frac{\partial^2\psi}{\partial z^2} = \frac{\partial v_r}{\partial z} - \frac{\partial v_z}{\partial r} \quad , \tag{37}$$

by the Galerkin finite element method with $\psi(r,z)$ represented in a biquadratic basis. Streamlines are plotted as contours of $\psi(r,z)$. Calculations were performed on both the Honeywell 6180 computer at the Massachusetts Institute of Technology and on the Control Data Cyber 203 at Langley Air Force Base. Execution times reported here are for calculations using the Honeywell system.

Sequences of calculations were performed with different finite element meshes in order to determine the effects of element size on the accuracy of the results. Since no exact solution is known for any set of parameters, the accuracy of the calculations can only be inferred by the effect of mesh refinement of the solution. Fig. 7 shows streamlines for the case Pr=0.01 and $Ra=10^5$ with six regularly spaced meshes. Each grid has in each phase twice as many elements in the axial direction as in the radial direction; then all elements in each mesh have similar shape. Surprisingly, even the extremely coarse (2x4) mesh gave a qualitatively accurate flow field for this moderately high Rayleigh number.

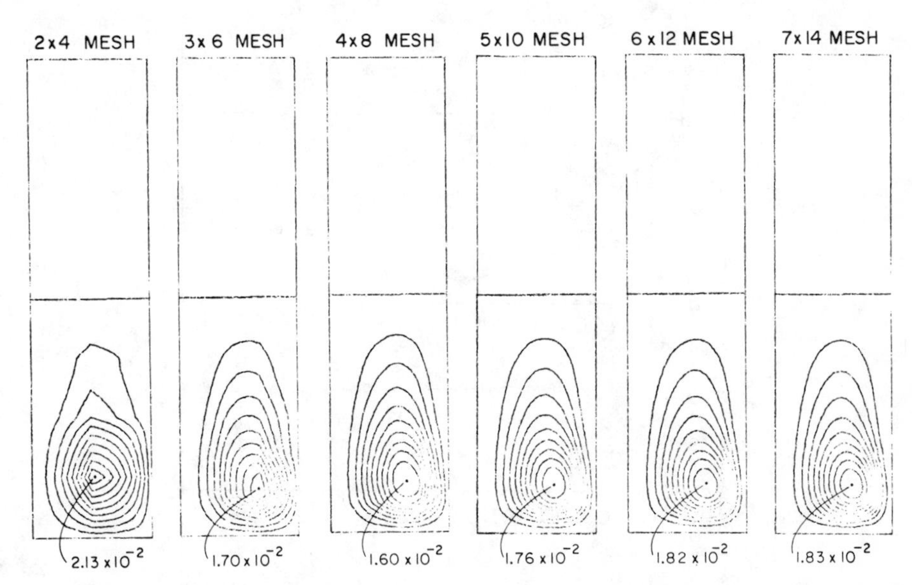

Fig. 7. Effect of finite element mesh on streamlines in the melt for Pr=0.01 and $Ra=10^5$. The meshes have N_r^E radial elements and N_z^E axial elements in each phase; the mesh used for each calculation is designated on the figure by $(N_r^E \times N_z^E)$.

The flow at $Ra=10^5$ was composed of a single axisymmetric cell with fluid moving outward along the base of the ampoule, up the sidewall and downward at the centerline. The flow was driven by a combination of the unstable axial temperature profile and the radial temperature gradients caused by the mismatch of thermal boundary conditions at the bottom of the ampoule.

The results for the six meshes are compared quantitatively in Fig. 8. The relative closure of the heat balance in the melt was calculated as

$$\Delta Q \equiv \left| \frac{Q^I - Q^M}{Q^M} \right| , \tag{38}$$

where Q^I and Q^M were the total heat fluxes that pass through the melt/solid interface and the sidewall of the cylinder, respectively;

$$Q^I \equiv \int_0^R \underset{\sim}{N} \cdot \nabla T d\ell \quad , \quad Q^M \equiv \int_0^{h(o)} \frac{\partial T}{\partial r} R dz \quad . \tag{39}$$

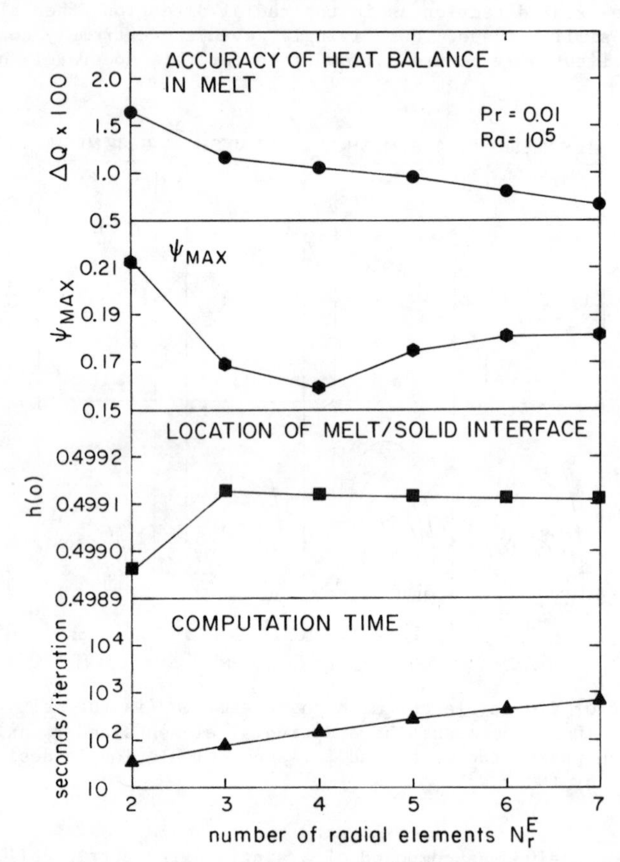

Fig. 8. Effect of finite element mesh on the accuracy of the calculations for Pr=0.01 and Ra=10^5 as measured by the overall heat balance (eq. (38)), the maximum value of ψ, and the location of the interface at the center of the ampoule h(o). Meshes with N_r^E radial elements and $2N_r^E$ axial elements in each phase were used. The execution time per iteration of the Isotherm-Newton method is also shown.

For a 4x8 mesh in the melt the overall heat balance closed to within one percent, an acceptable figure. The maximum value of the streamfunction ψ_{max} and the location of the phase boundary h(0) both converged to constant values as the mesh was refined to have six radial elements. For coarse meshes, the execution time increased logrithmically with the number of radial elements.

The calculations presented for melts with low Prandtl number were the most difficult. Results for Pr=100 and Ra=10^5 are shown in Fig. 9 for the same sequence of meshes discussed above. Both ψ_{max} and h(o) reached constant values for a mesh with only four radical elements. However, convective heat transfer

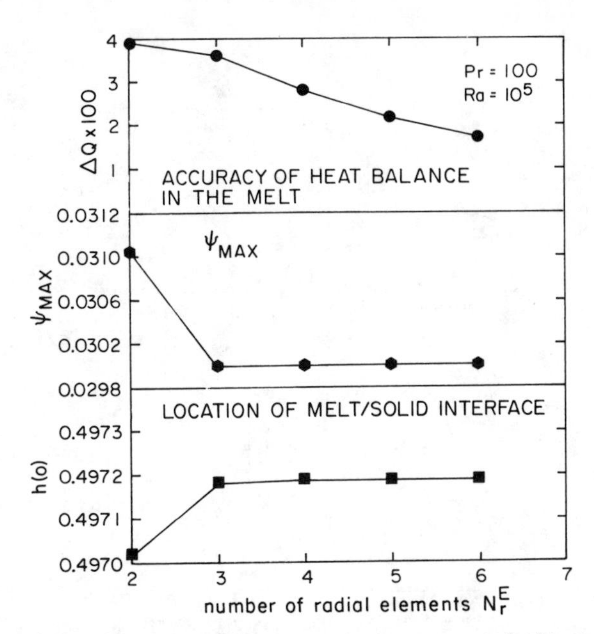

Fig. 9. Effect of finite element mesh on the accuracy of the calculations for Pr=100 and Ra=10^5.

was significant for these high Prandtl number liquids and approximation error in the flow and temperature fields adversely affected the closure of the heat balance. The changes in Q with mesh refinement indicated rearrangement of the temperature field. Profiles at axial velocity and temperature for z=0.25 are shown in Fig. 10 for Rayleigh numbers of 10^5 and 10^6 for Prandtl numbers of 0.01 and 100. For Pr=100, convection of hot melt up the sidewall caused the temperature in the liquid adjacent to the sidewall to be hotter than the wall at the same axial position.

The streamlines and isotherms for a melt with Pr=1 are shown in Fig. 11 for Rayleigh numbers of (a) 10^4, (b) 10^5, and (c) 10^6. In cases (a) and (b) the temperature fields in melt and solid correspond closely to the field for pure conduction (Ra=0). The flow fields for these two cases were also similar; at the higher Rayleigh number the cell had filled more of the melt and intensified along the sidewall. At a Rayleigh number near 10^6 the flow separated from the sidewall and a toroidal vortex with clockwise flow was formed in the upper corner. The onset of the secondary vortex also marked appreciable changes in the thermal field. Near the center of the ampoule low temperature isotherms were convected downward and out along the bottom of the ampoule. The secondary cell carried cold fluid downward along the top of the sidewall; in this region the temperature profile at a set axial position was highest in the flow, not at the wall.

Rearrangement of the flow and temperature fields can cause significant changes in the shape of the melt/solid interface as shown in Fig. 12 for Pr=1. As expected from the thermal fields, the interface shape remained flat, corresponding to pure conduction, up to Ra=10^4. The convective heat transfer at

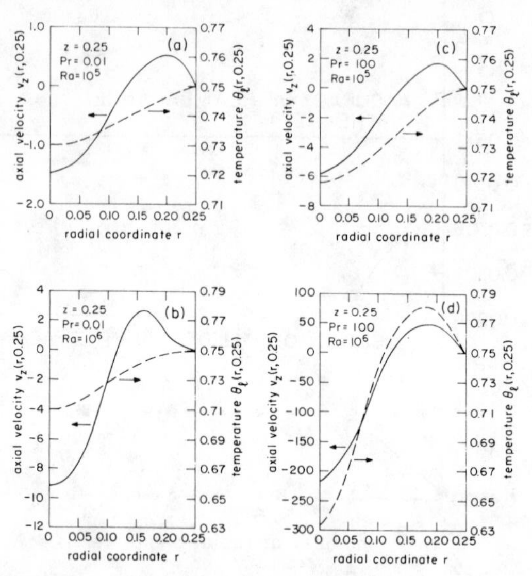

Fig. 10. Profiles of axial velocity and temperature for z=0.25 and (a) Pr=0.01, Ra=10^5, (b) Pr=0.01, Ra=10^6, (c) Pr=100, Ra=10^5, and (d) Pr=100, Ra=10^6.

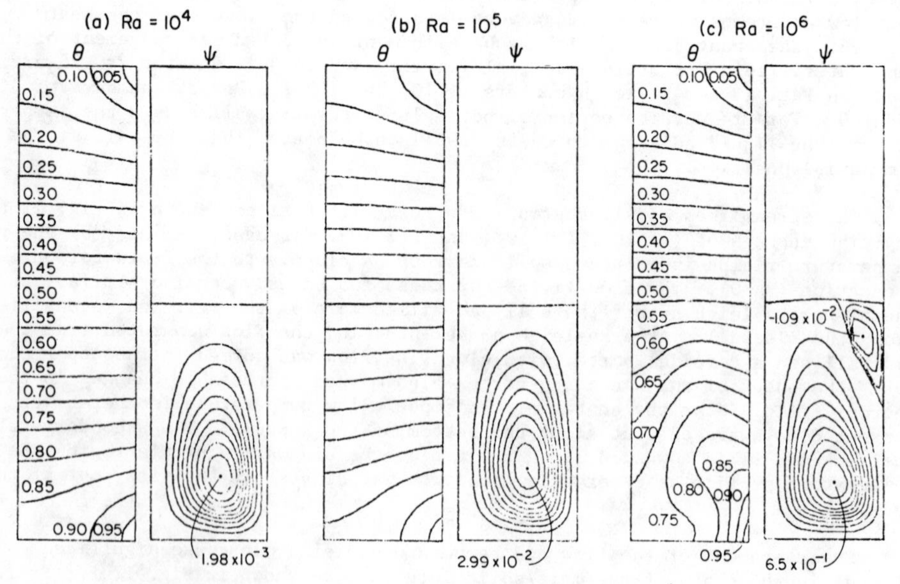

Fig. 11. Streamlines and isotherms for Pr=1 and (a) Ra=10^4, (b) Ra=10^5, and (c) Ra=10^6.

$Ra=10^5$ carried the interface slightly lower into the melt along the center-line where cold melt was dropping. The shape of the phase boundary inverted at $Ra=10^6$ because of the effect of the secondary vortex on heat transfer near the interface. Hot melt carried upward by this cell caused a maximum in interface height about midway across the radius of the ampoule.

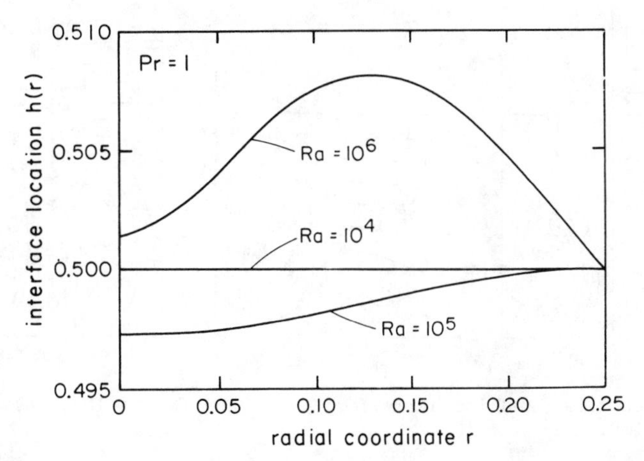

Fig. 12. Effect of Rayleigh number on the shape of the melt/solid interface for Pr=1.

Increasing the Prandtl number to 100 had little effect on the flow patterns in the melt as shown by the streamlines in Fig. 13. Again, a secondary toroidal cell was found at $Ra=10^6$ where the higher Prandtl number liquid had isotherms that were significantly more deformed than for Pr=1. The melt/solid interface shown in Fig. 14 reflected the changes in the temperature field in the melt; the maximum in h(r) present for Pr=1 was magnified at Pr=100.

As expected, the temperature field for the low Prandtl number melt (Pr=0.01) changed little, even at $Ra=10^6$. This is shown in Fig. 15 for Pr=0.01 and Rayleigh numbers between 10^4 and 10^6. The flow along the bottom and sidewall of the ampoule intensified with increasing Ra and separated into an extremely weak secondary vortex past $Ra=1x10^6$. The separation point on the sidewall was lower than for Pr=1 because of the development of higher velocity gradients in the low Prandtl number melt. Because of the extremely good conduction at Pr=0.01 the shape of the melt/solid interface changed little even at $Ra=10^6$; see Fig. 14.

Calculations at Rayleigh numbers greater than $Ra=10^6$ were difficult for all three values of Pr. The problem was most acute for Pr=0.01 where the flow field calculation became extremely sensitive to the size and location of the mesh. This is demonstrated in Fig. 16 for calculations with (Pr=0.01, $Ra=2.x10^6$) and three different regularly-spaced meshes. Calculations with (5x10) elements in each phase predicted a secondary vortex that was a factor of two more intense than the one predicted by the finer (7x14) mesh. Evidently the extra elements near the sidewall in the second mesh were needed to approximate the high velocity gradients there and the complex structure near the separation point.

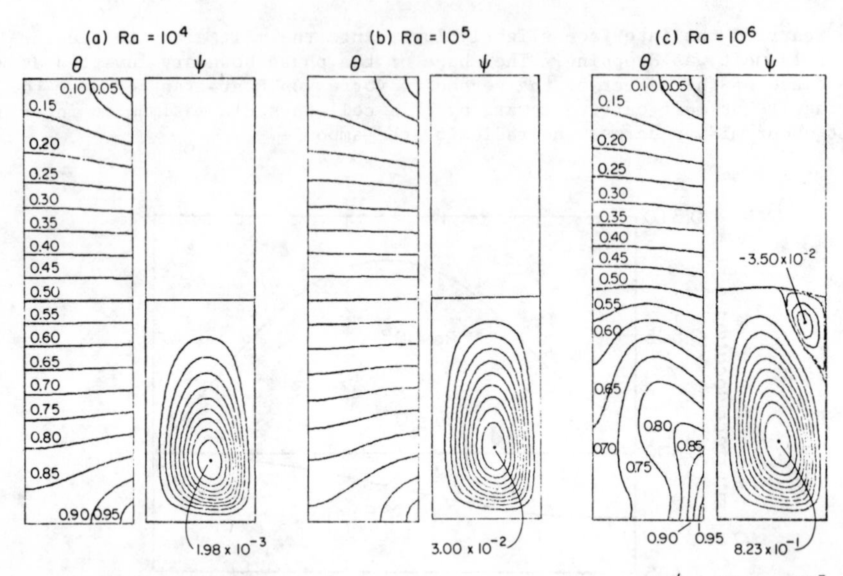

Fig. 13. Streamlines and isotherms for Pr=100 and (a) Ra=10^4, (b) Ra=10^5, and Ra=10^6.

5. CONCLUSIONS

Models of solidification processes that account for natural convection in the melt can only be studied thoroughly when efficient numerical methods are employed for their solution. The simplest iterative schemes, like the Isotherm algorithm presented here, decouple the calculation of the field variables $\underline{\alpha}$ and the shape of the melt/solid interface $\underline{\beta}$ into two interlocked iterations that are performed successively for the two sets of variables where each iteration uses the current approximation for the other set of unknowns and the overall iteration converges only linearly to the correct interface shape. Newton's method solves simultaneously for the interface shape and the field variables and gives quadratic convergence with little increase in the complexity of the programming. The savings in computer time is substantial; a factor of three for the cases tested here.

Newton's iteration initiated with a continuation approximation is a powerful solution scheme and for small steps in Ra is guaranteed to converge [23] as long as the solution in unique. The maximum stepsize in Ra for convergence of the Isotherm-Newton iteration became prohibitively small much above Ra=10^6 for all three Prandtl numbers. The Isotherm algorithm failed at nearly the same value of Ra as the Isotherm-Newton routine; for an approximate interface shape the Newton iteration for the field variables alone did not converge. Other calculations for steady natural convection in cavities have also failed at high values of Rayleigh (or Grashof) number [13,20,24]. Although the precise cause of the difficulty is still unclear, recent calculations [24] have found time-periodic flows for values of Ra where no steady flows could be calculated. Perhaps unsteady oscillating flows have branched from the steady flow and the steady solution has ceased to exist altogether at high values of Ra. This conjecture can only be tested by calculating the bifurcation points in families of cellular flows and by tracking the evolution of these families in Ra. The flow fields for steady natural convection are very complex, for even in simple

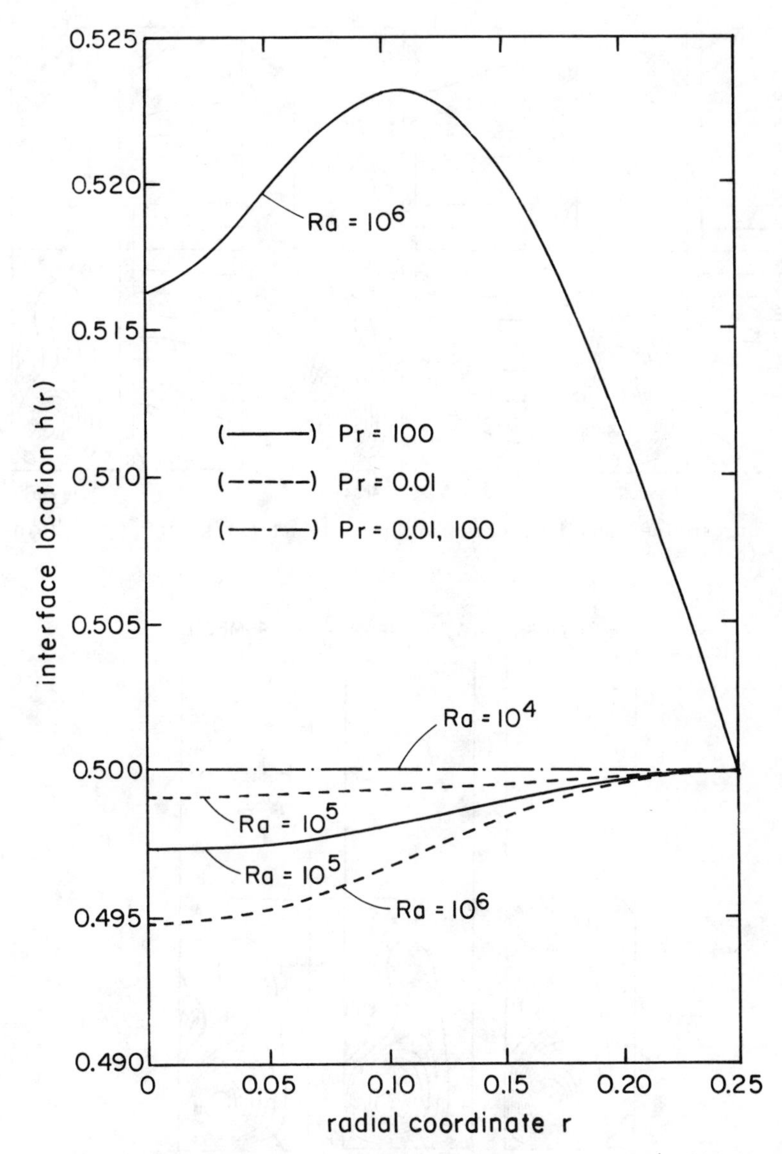

Fig. 14. Effect of Rayleigh number on the shape of the melt/solid interface for Prandtl numbers of 0.01 (---) and 100 (——). The curve (—— – —) denotes that the phase boundaries for Pr=0.01 and Pr=100 are indistinguishable.

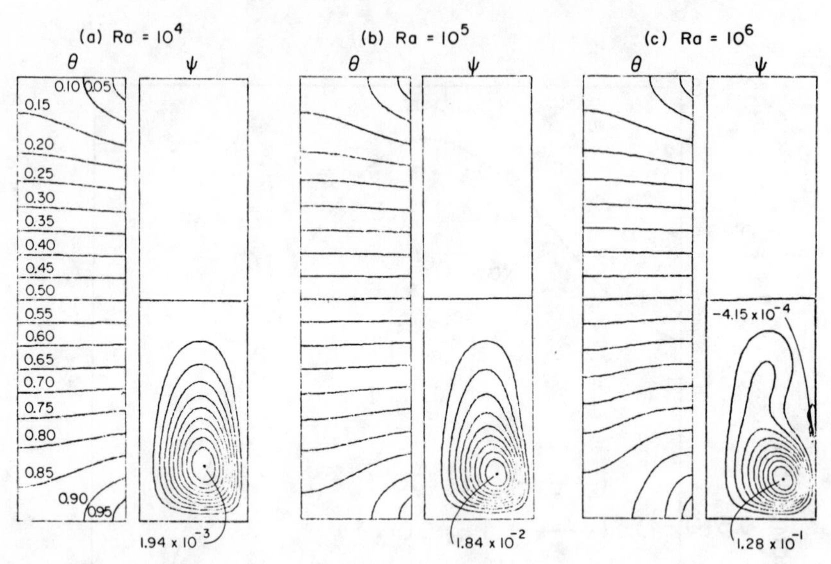

Fig. 15. Streamlines and isotherms for Pr=0.01 and (a) Ra=10^4, (b) Ra=10^5, and (c) Ra=10^6.

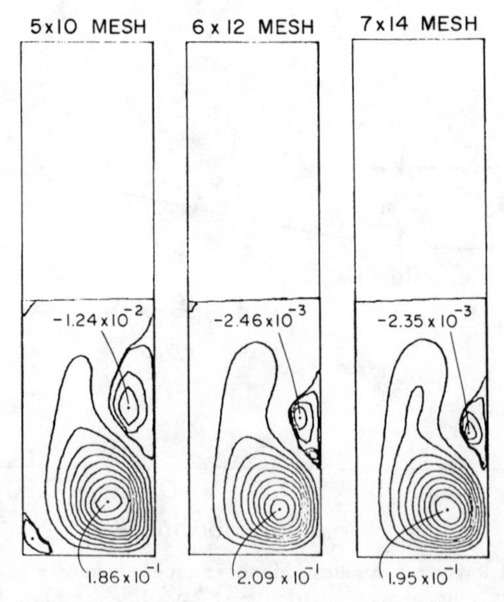

Fig. 16. Effect of finite element mesh on streamlines in the melt for Pr=0.01 and Ra=2x10^6. The meshes have N_r^E radial elements and N_z^E axial elements in each phase; the mesh used for each calculation is designated on the figure by (N_r^E x N_z^E).

geometries with liquids heated from below, multiple flows are known [25,26]. Recent results [13] for a single liquid in a closed vertical cylinder heated from below show the structure of these cellular flows and the existence of maximum Rayleigh numbers for steady and stable axisymmetric flows. The Jacobian matrix of the Isotherm-Newton routine is the basis for such calculations of multiple steady flows; results for the two-phase system described here will be presented later.

ACKNOWLEDGEMENTS

The authors are grateful to H.M. Ettouney and to H.L. Saito for stimulating discussions concerning finite element solution of free-boundary problems. This research was supported by the Materials Processing in Space Program of the U.S. National Aeronautics and Space Administration.

REFERENCES

1. Chang, C.J. and Brown, R.A. 1981. Radial segregation induced by natural convection and melt/solid interface curvature in Bridgman solidification. J. Crystal Growth, submitted.

2. Bonnerot, R. and Jamet, P. 1977. Numerical computation of the free boundary for the two-dimensional Stefan problem by space-time finite elements. J. Comp. Physics, Vol. 25, pp. 163-181.

3. Fix, G.J. 1978. Numerical methods for alloy solidification problems. In Moving Boundary Problems, ed. by D.G. Wilson, A.D. Solomon, and P.T. Boggs, Academic Press, New York.

4. Ettouney, H.M. and Brown, R.A. 1981. Finite element methods for steady solidification problems. J. Comp. Physics, submitted.

5. Kroeger, P.G. and Ostrach, S. 1974. The solution of a two-dimensional freezing problem including convection effects in the liquid region. Int. J. Heat. Mass Transfer, Vol. 17, pp. 1191-1207.

6. Tien, L.-C. 1968. Freezing of a convective liquid in a crystal growth tube. Ph.D. thesis, University of Michigan.

7. Ortega, J.M. and Rheinboldt, W.E.. 1970. Iterative Solution of Nonlinear Equations in Several Variables, Academic Press, New York.

8. Valle, A. 1979. The finite element method and the Stefan problem. Ph.D. thesis, University of Michigan.

9. Kubicek, M. 1976. Dependence of solution of nonlinear equations in a parameter, ACM Trans. Math. Software, Vol. 2, pp. 98-107.

10. Brown, R.A., Scriven, L.E., and Silliman, W.J. 1980. Computer-aided analysis in nonlinear problems in transport phenomena. In New Approaches in Nonlinear Dynamics, ed. by P. Holes, SIAM, Philadelphia.

11. Keller, H.B. 1977. Numerical solution of bifurcation and nonlinear eigenvalue problems. In Applications of Bifurcation Theory, ed. by P.H. Rabinowitz, Academic Press, New York.

12. Ungar, L.H. and Brown, R.A. 1981. The dependence of the shape and stability of captive rotating drops on multiple parameters, Philos. Trans. R. Soc. Lond., submitted.

13. Yamaguchi, Y., Chang, C.J. and Brown, R.A. 1981. Steady axisymmetric convection in a vertical cylinder heated from below. To be submitted.

14. Saito, H.L. and Scriven, L.E. 1981. Study of coating flow by the finite element method, J. Comp. Physics, Vol. 42, pp. 53-76.

15. Saito, H.L. and Scriven, L.E. 1981. Newton's method for free boundary problems by finite element analysis, Int. J. Numerical Methods in Fluids, Vol. 1, in press.

16. Bathe, K.J. and Wilson, E.L. 1976. Numerical Methods in Finite Element Analysis, Prentice-Hall, Englewood Cliffs.

17. Turner, J.S. 1973. Buoyancy Effects in Fluids, Cambridge University Press, London.

18. Zienkiewicz, O.C., Gallagher, R.H. and Hood, P. 1976. Newtonian and non-Newtonian viscous incompressible flow. Temperature-induced flows. Finite element solutions. In J.R. Whiteman (ed.), The Mathematics of Finite Elements and Applications 2, Academic Press, London.

19. Huyakorn, P., Taylor, C., Lee, R. and Gresho, P. 1978. A comparison of various mixed-interploation finite elements in the velocity pressure formulation of the Navier-Stokes equations, Computers and Fluids, Vol. 6, pp. 25-35.

20. Taylor, C. and Ijam, A.Z. 1979. A finite element numerical solution of natural convection in enclosed cavities, Comp. Meths. Appl. Mech. Engng., Vol. 19, pp. 429-446.

21. Hood, P. 1976. Frontal solution program for unsymmetric matrices, Int. J. Num. Meth. in Engng., Vol. 10, pp. 379-399.

22. Chang, C.J. 1982. Natural convection in melt crystal growth, Ph.D. thesis Massachusetts Institute of Technology.

23. Rheinboldt, W.C. 1980. Solution fields of nonlinear equations and continuation methods, SIAM J. Numer. Anal., Vol. 17, pp. 221-237.

24. Crochet, M.J. 1980. Numerical investigations of temperature oscillations in crystal growth melts. Bell Laboratory Report.

25. Liang, S.F., Vidal, A. and Acrivos, A. 1969. Buoyancy-driven convection in cylindrical geometries, J. Fluid Mech., Vol. 36, pp. 239-256.

26. Charlson, G.S. and Sani, R.L. 1970. Thermoconvective instability in a bounded cylindrical fluid layer, Int. J. Heat Mass Transfer, Vol. 13, pp. 1479-1496.

Simulation of Free Convection in Multiple Fluid Layers in an Enclosure by Finite Differences

R.W. KNIGHT and M.E. PALMER, III
Department of Mechanical Engineering
University of Maryland
College Park, Maryland 20742

ABSTRACT

Numerical simulation of the free convective heat transfer in a rectangular enclosure containing two dissimilar fluids is performed based upon a finite difference discretization. The Boussinesq approximation is assumed and the system of governing equations cast into stream function - vorticity - temperature variables. The interface is assumed to be horizontal and interface boundary conditions are derived. Results are presented in terms of global Nusselt and Grashof numbers, for fluid properties corresponding to air and water, and were found to be qualitatively similar to those for a single fluid. Recirculating regions were observed in the denser fluid (water).

1. INTRODUCTION

The convective heat transfer in an enclosure filled with several different fluids is of engineering interest. The presence of small water layers in multiple glass windows, for example, may lead to severe impairment of insulation capability. Conversely, loss of cooling fluid in a heat exchanger (which results in a pocket of air) will reduce heat transfer. In the Hall process for aluminum smelting, a layer of molten aluminum lies beneath one of cryolite. Convective heat transfer takes place in this system in the presence of electromagnetic driving forces.

Heat transfer in saturated fluids is also of interest. In this case, liquid and vapor phases of a single component fluid both participate in the heat transfer phenomena. The safety of rail tank cars carrying liquefied gases and exposed to external heat sources, such as fire or solar, is an important case.

Much research effort has been directed at the problem of free convection in an enclosure filled with a single Boussinesq fluid [1,2,3]. The use of finite difference (FD) techniques has proven successful in these studies. Examination of free convection in multiple fluid layers is limited. Simonovskii [4] treated the problem of two immiscible fluids heated from below, while Bourde and Simonovskii [5] used a finite element analysis to estimate the stability characteristics of the same problem.

In this work, the steady state convective heat transfer across a two-dimensional rectangular enclosure containing two immiscible Boussinesq fluids (approximating air and water) is simulated using finite difference techniques.

Results are presented for global heat transfer as well as fluid flow patterns and temperature profiles.

2. PROBLEM FORMULATION

Consider a two-dimensional, rectangular enclosure of height L_y and width L_x filled with two immiscible fluids as shown in Fig. 1. The fluids are assumed to have constant properties, excluding bouyancy, which is assumed to vary linearly with temperature; i.e. the Boussinesq approximation is utilized. The lower fluid, of depth h (fluid 1), is assumed to be much denser than the top fluid (fluid 2). This assumption implies that the interface between the fluids remains essentially horizontal and does not deform significantly [5].

The upper and lower walls of the cavity are insulated, while the vertical walls are isothermal; the right wall at temperature T_h and the left at T_c, where $T_h > T_c$.

With the assumptions stated above, the governing continuum equations for a steady state condition may be expressed using local fluid properties in the following nondimensional form

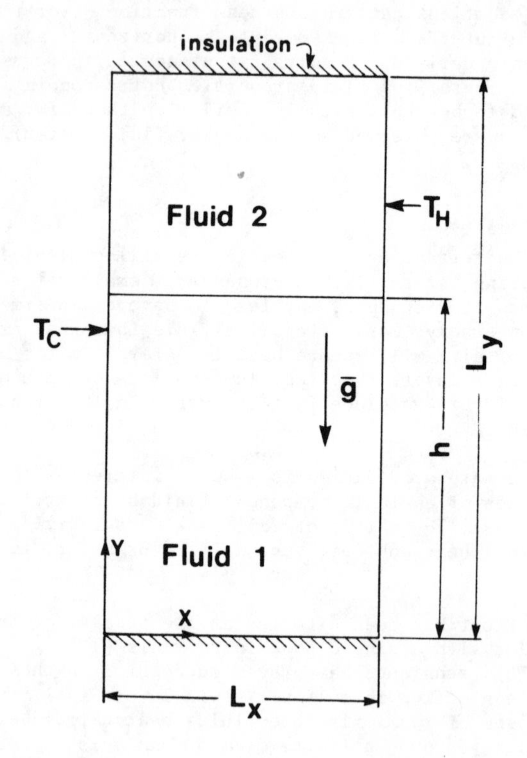

Fig. 1 Schematic of rectangular enclosure.

$$\nabla^2\phi_i = -\omega_i \tag{2.1a}$$

$$\nabla^2\omega_i = (u_i\omega_i)_x+(v_i\omega_i)_y-Gr_i(\theta_i)_x \tag{2.1b}$$

$$\nabla^2\theta_i = Pr_i\{(u_i\theta_i)_x+(v_i\theta_i)_y\} \tag{2.1c}$$

where

$$u_i = (\phi_i)_y \ , \quad v_i = -(\phi_i)_x \tag{2.1d}$$

and the subscript i differentiates the fluids. Throughout, the notation $(\upsilon)_x = \partial\upsilon/\partial x$, etc. is used.

The nondimensional boundary conditions to be satisfied along the walls are;

no slip along all walls

$$\phi_i = 0 \qquad x = 0,1;\ y = 0,L_y/L_x \tag{2.2a}$$

$$(\phi_i)_n = 0 \qquad \text{where } (\ )_n \text{ indicates normal derivative} \tag{2.2b}$$

known temperature on vertical boundaries

$$\theta_i = 0 \qquad x = 0 \tag{2.2c}$$

$$\theta_i = 0 \qquad x = 1 \tag{2.2d}$$

and insulation on horizontal walls

$$(\theta_i)_y = 0 \qquad y = 0,L_y/L_x. \tag{2.2e}$$

At the interface between the fluids ($y = h/L_x$) the physical boundary conditions which must be satisfied are;

no slip

$$U_1 = U_2 \tag{2.3a}$$

no penetration

$$V_1 = V_2 = 0 \tag{2.3b}$$

continuity of shear stress

$$\mu_1(U_1)_Y = \mu_2(U_2)_Y \tag{2.3c}$$

continuity of temperature

$$T_1 = T_2 \tag{2.3d}$$

continuity of heat flux

$$k_1(T_1)_Y = k_2(T_2)_Y \tag{2.3e}$$

and continuity of pressure

$$P_1 = P_2. \tag{2.3f}$$

Examination of conditions (2.3a-f) and the governing equations (2.1a-d) reveals one extraneous interfacial boundary condition. This is due to the a priori assumption of the interface location. In reality, the continuity of pressure determines the exact shape of the interface. A horizontal interface, however, is consistent with the Boussinesq approximation and the assumption that $\rho_1 >> \rho_2$ and may be used to replace the pressure condition, Eq. (2.3f) [5].

Conditions (2.3a & b) may be expressed in terms of stream functions, while the shear stress condition, Eq. (2.3c) may be rewritten, using Eq. (2.3b) in terms of vorticities (for a horizontal interface). The resulting interfacial boundary conditions, in nondimensional form, are;

$$\phi_1 = 0 \tag{2.4a}$$

$$\phi_2 = 0 \tag{2.4b}$$

$$\theta_1 = \theta_2 \tag{2.4c}$$

$$(\phi_2)_y = \alpha(\phi_1)_y \tag{2.4d}$$

$$\omega_2 = \beta\omega_1 \tag{2.4e}$$

and

$$(\theta_2)_y = \gamma(\theta_1)_y. \tag{2.4f}$$

Equations (2.1) along with the boundary conditions Eqs. (2.2) and Eqs. (2.3) completely describe the continuum problem.

3. DISCRETIZATION

3.1 Governing Equations

The governing equations, Eqs. (2.1), were discretized using the procedure of Raithby and Torrance [6]. This allowed easy adaptation from a Central Differencing Scheme (CDS) to an Upwind Differencing Scheme (UDS). This was necessary to ensure stability of the resulting FD equations for a wide range of forseable fluid properties and flow conditions. Although not included here, an exponential differencing scheme is viewed as a viable alternative by the authors.

Using the mesh system and notation shown in Fig. 2, the discretized form of the advection-diffusion equation (at internal nodes)

$$(u\upsilon)_x+(v\upsilon)_y = \frac{1}{R}\nabla^2\upsilon +S \tag{3.1}$$

where $u = (\phi)_y$, $v = -(\phi)_x$, is

$$A\upsilon_{i-1,j}+B\upsilon_{i+1,j}+C\upsilon_{i,j-1}+D\upsilon_{i,j+1}+E = F\upsilon_{i,j} \tag{3.2}$$

where

$$A = \frac{1}{R\Delta x_{i-1}\delta x_i} + \frac{1}{2}\,\frac{(u_{i-1/2,j}+\langle u_{i-1/2,j}\rangle)}{\delta x_i} \tag{3.3a}$$

$$B = \frac{1}{R\Delta x_i \delta x_i} + \frac{1}{2}\frac{(\langle u_{i+1/2,j}\rangle - u_{i+1/2,j})}{\delta x_i} \tag{3.3b}$$

$$C = \frac{1}{R\Delta y_{j-1}\delta y_j} + \frac{1}{2}\frac{(v_{i,j-1/2} + \langle v_{i,j-1/2}\rangle)}{\delta y_j} \tag{3.3c}$$

$$D = \frac{1}{R\Delta y_j \delta y_j} + \frac{1}{2}\frac{(\langle v_{i,j+1/2}\rangle - v_{i,j+1/2})}{\delta y_j} \tag{3.3d}$$

$$E = S_{i,j} \tag{3.3e}$$

$$F = A + B + C + D \tag{3.3f}$$

$$u_{i+1/2,j} = \frac{(\phi_{i+1,j+1} + \phi_{i,j+1} - \phi_{i+1,j-1} - \phi_{i,j-1})}{4\delta y_j} \tag{3.3g}$$

$$v_{i,j+1/2} = \frac{(\phi_{i-1,j+1} + \phi_{i-1,j} - \phi_{i+1,j+1} - \phi_{i+1,j})}{4\delta x_i} \tag{3.3h}$$

and

$$\langle \upsilon \rangle = \begin{cases} |\upsilon| & \text{for UDS} \\ 0 & \text{for CDS.} \end{cases} \tag{3.3i}$$

This nodal equation was derived by an approximate integration of the governing continuum equation over a control volume bounded by the control surface indicated by the dotted lines in Fig. 2. The $u_{i+1/2,j}$ and $v_{i,j+1/2}$ represent velocities on the control surface. Equations (3.3g,h) are necessary to ensure that the FD equations are conservative. For the source term in Eq. (2.1b) the following approximation is used

$$S_{i,j} = Gr\,\frac{\theta_{i+1,j} - \theta_{i-1,j}}{2\delta x_i} \tag{3.4}$$

3.2 Boundary Conditions

Equations (3.3) must be supplemented by discretized equations for the continuum boundary conditions. Dirichlet boundary conditions (Eqs. (2.2a, c & d), (2.4a-c & e)) are treated in the usual manner, i.e., setting the nodal value of the variable equal to the specified continuum value. The Neumann boundary conditions (Eqs. (2.2b & d), (2.4d & f)), however, require a special formulation if the conservative property of the scheme is to be retained. Since a specific formulation of Neumann boundary conditions compatible with the scheme of Raithby and Torrance was not found by the authors, such a formulation will be presented here.

Consider a node on an impermeable horizontal boundary with a Neumann condition, υ_y, for the variable υ, specified there as shown in Fig. 3. In order to conserve mass entering the control volume shown, the velocities $u_{i+1/2,j}$ must be defined as

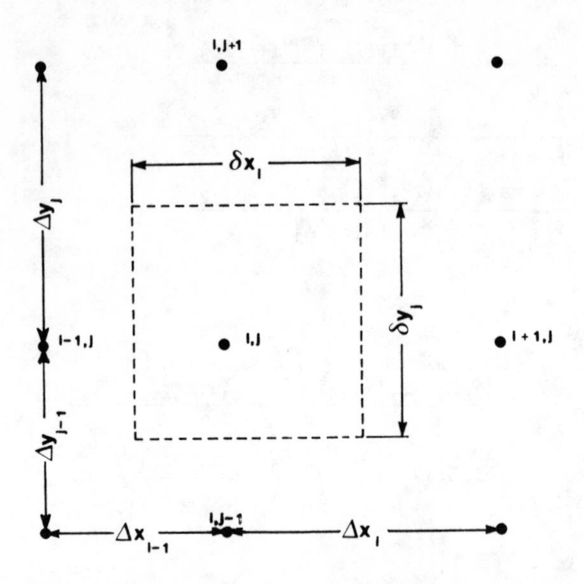

Fig. 2 Schematic and definitions of interior node point.

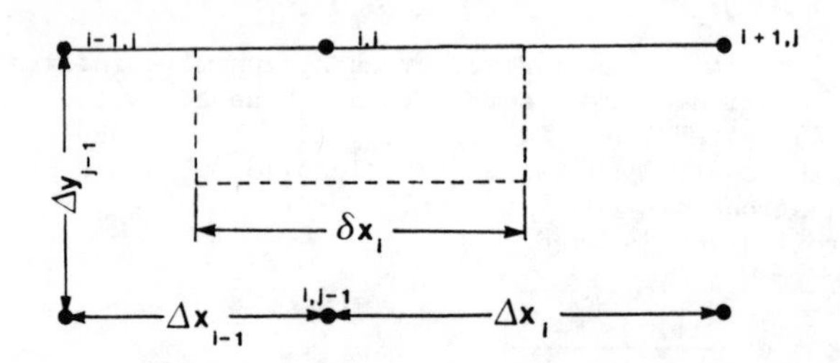

Fig. 3 Schematic and definitions of boundary node point.

$$u_{i+1/2,j} = \frac{\phi_{i+1,j}+\phi_{i,j}-\phi_{i+1,j-1}-\phi_{i,j-1}}{2\Delta y_{j-1}} . \tag{3.5}$$

This definition, along with that for $v_{i,j+1/2}$ given in Eq. (3.3h), is necessary to maintain a conservative discretization scheme.

The continuum advection-diffusion equation (Eq. (3.1)) may be integrated over the boundary control volume shown in Fig. 3 to yield an equation of the form

$$A\upsilon_{i-1,j}+B\upsilon_{i+1,j}+C'\upsilon_{i,j-1}+D'(\upsilon)_y\big|_{i,j}+E = F'\upsilon_{i,j} \tag{3.6}$$

where A, B and E are given by Eqs. (3.3a, b & e) and

$$C' = \frac{2}{R\Delta y_{j-1}^{2}} + \frac{(v_{i,j-1/2}+<v_{i,j-1/2}>)}{\Delta y_{j-1}} \tag{3.7a}$$

$$D' = \frac{2}{R\Delta y_{j-1}} \tag{3.7b}$$

$$F' = A + B + C'. \tag{3.7c}$$

Similar equations may be derived for boundaries oriented in other directions.

These equations may be used in three ways. The first is as stated above; a discrete equation representing a Neumann boundary condition which maintains the conservative aspect of the FD scheme. The second use of this equation is the reverse. If nodal values of υ are known, then Eq. (3.6) may be solved to yield an approximation to the normal derivative of υ on the boundary.

Furthermore, Eq. (3.6) has an interesting feature with regard to the boundary conditions employed for vorticities. Usual boundary conditions on the two-dimensional stream function - vorticity equations at a fixed wall are homogeneous Dirichlet and Neumann conditions on the stream function, but none on vorticity. Ad hoc formulations are usually applied to transform the Neumann conditions on stream function into a useable boundary condition for vorticity [1,2]. Roache [7] gives a typical discussion of this. If Eq. (3.6) is used for the stream function equation (Eq. (2.1a)) as a Neumann condition <u>and</u> the homogeneous Dirichlet stream function condition is applied simultaneously, it appears that one obtains two equations for the nodal value of stream function and none for vorticity. However, the nodal value of the boundary vorticity enters Eq. (3.6) as a source term. If, instead of considering the solutions of the stream function and vorticity equations seperately (and requiring one boundary condition for each), the simultaneous solution of both equations is considered, it is seen that no "imbalance" of boundary conditions occurs. Interpreting the boundary equations in this manner is, from the authors' point of view, more satisfying than the ad hoc approaches noted above, even though the resulting FD equations are identical. It may be noted that an application of the above technique can be used to remove the need of using a Taylor series expansion to obtain vorticity boundary conditions in finite element formulations, as is sometimes done.

4. SOLUTION PROCEDURE

Since iterative procedures for the solution of FD equations in one fluid (similar to those in section 3) are well known [2,7], the equations for fluid 1 and fluid 2 were solved independently.

The interface boundary conditions applied to fluid 1 were the continuity of shear (Eq. (2.4e)), continuity of heat flux (Eq. (2.4f)) and impermeability (Eq. (2.4a)). For fluid 2, the no slip (Eq. (2.4d)), continuous temperature (Eq. (2.4 c)) and impermeability (Eq. (2.4b)) conditions were applied.

Initial estimates for the unknown nodal values in each fluid and variable were assumed. The nodal variables in fluid 2 were updated using the current fluid 1 values in the interfacial boundary conditions for fluid 2. The update process consisted of a simple modification of the technique described by Han [2]. Two complete Gauss-Siedel iterations were performed on the temperature equation, followed by two under-relaxation sweeps for vorticity, using an under-relaxation factor of .5, and two Gauss-Siedel iterations for stream function. The velocity field in fluid 2 was then recomputed. For one fluid, this update process would be performed until convergence was achieved. Here, however, the boundary conditions at the interface involve incorrect values of fluid 1 variables and iterating until convergence occured would be inefficient. Empirically, three iterations was found to yield fastest ultimate convergence. This update procedure is herein reffered to as the fluid 2 loop.

Values of the nodal variables for fluid 1 were then updated using the new fluid 2 values in the fluid 1 interface conditions. The fluid 1 loop was analogous to the fluid 2 loop.

The fluid loops were applied alternately in a system loop until suitable convergence criteria were met. It was found that relative changes in vorticity between system loops was a sufficient measure of convergence of other variables as well as global Nusselt numbers. The exact criterion used here was that the maximum relative change in vorticity be less than some small positive number, e.g. 10^{-3} for the results presented here.

5. RESULTS

The solution of the two-fluid free convection problem is dependent on the following parameters: L_y/L_x, h/L_y, α, β, γ, Gr_1, Gr_2, Pr_1 and Pr_2. Since this study was concerned with the solution technique rather than the details of a parametric study, the aspect ratio of the rectangle and the physical properties of the two fluids were held constant for all cases considered. A rectangle whose height was twice its width was used for all cases, and the properties assumed for the upper and lower fluids were those of air and water, respectively, at 20° C and atmospheric pressure. These assumptions fix α, β, γ, Pr_1, Pr_2 and Gr_1/Gr_2. Three fill levels were examined, 25%, 50% and 75%, for a range of Grashof numbers in the lower fluid of $10^2 \leq Gr_1 \leq 10^4$.

A careful examination of the 50% full, $Gr_1 = 10^4$ case was first performed. The solution was obtained for various grid sizes, ranging from 11x11 nodes in each fluid to 41x41 nodes in each fluid. It was seen that the nature of the flow fields and temperature distribution obtained was similar for all grid sizes. In all other cases, 21x21 nodes per fluid was the finest grid used. For programming simplicity and computational efficiency, square grids were used in all cases. An option was available to choose CDS or UDS method for either fluid independently. For a given fill level and Gr_1, the following plan was followed. The solution was first sought using CDS in both fluids. If that diverged, UDS was tried in fluid 2 while using CDS in fluid 1. Upon failure of that method, UDS was used in both fluids. This last scheme never failed to converge for any of the cases tried. It was found that CDS could be used in both fluids at all fill levels when $10^2 \leq Gr_1 \leq 5x10^2$, the mixed plan was sufficient when Gr_1 was 10^3, and UDS was needed in both fluids for $Gr_1 \geq 2X10^3$.

Some typical stream function and temperature fields are shown in Figs. 4-7. The line defined by a change from dark to light indicates a constant function value along that line. It should be noted that the plotted stream functions are based on local fluid properties.

Fig. 4 shows a low Gr_1 flow for the 50% full case. It can be seen in Fig. 4a that a recirculating vortex, where recirculating is defined as being in the opposite direction to that expected based on the thermal driving force, occurs in fluid 1. This tendency was observed for all cases studied here and corresponds to the results presented by Bourde and Simonovskii [5]. Fig. 4b demonstrates that the temperature distribution is still very close to the conduction solution.

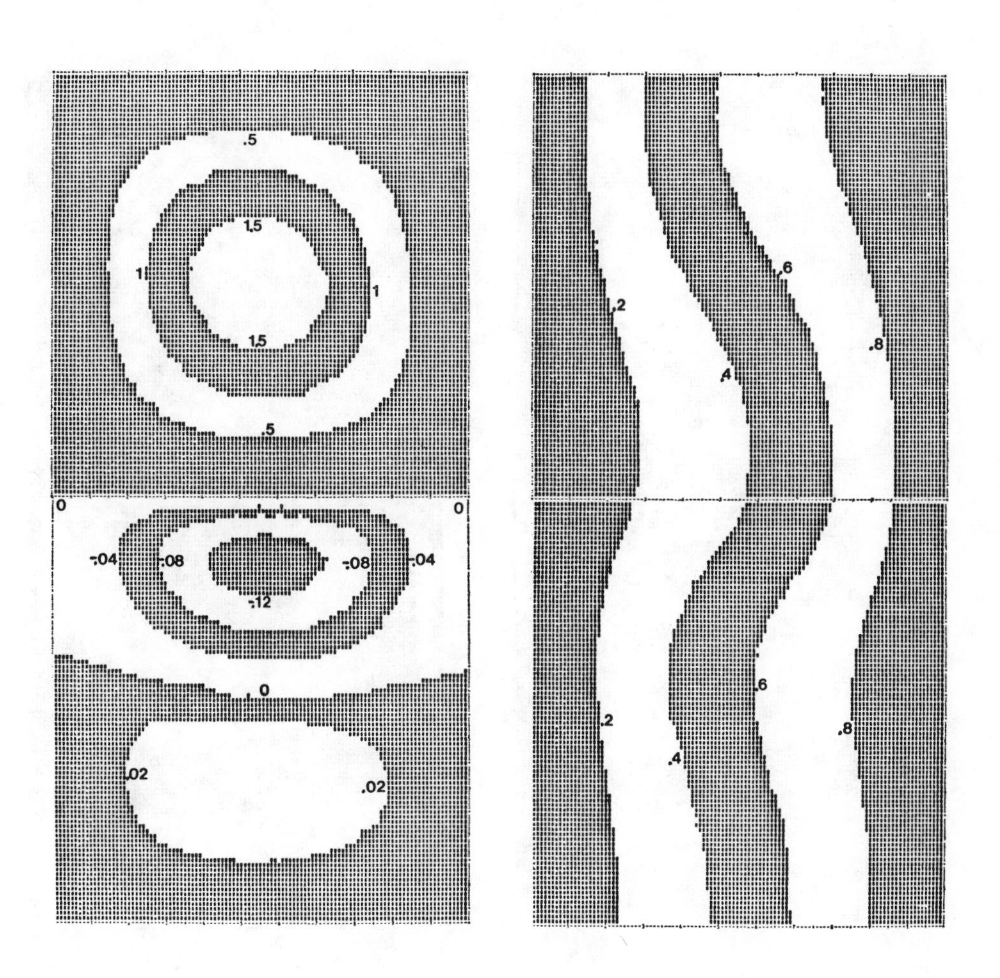

a. Stream Function

b. Temperature

Fig. 4 Contours of stream function and temperature for 50% full cavity, $Gr_1 = 100$.

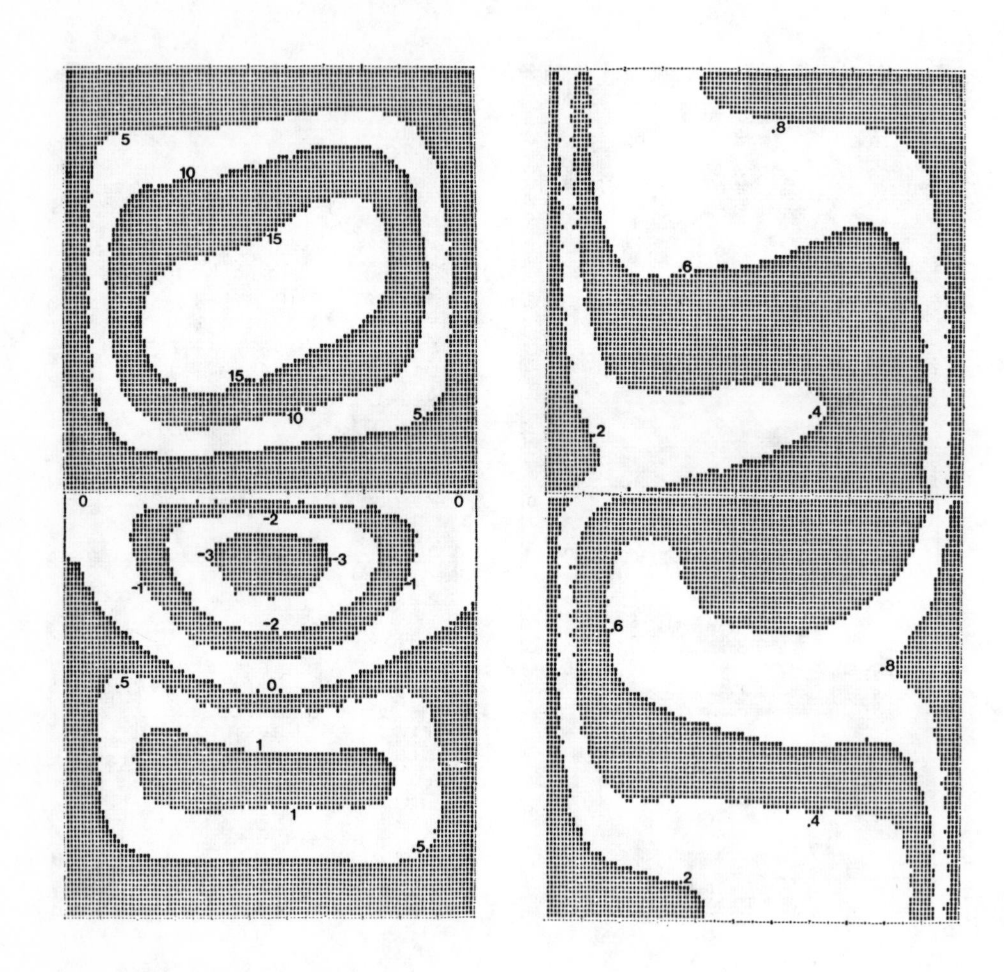

a. Stream function

b. Temperature

Fig. 5 Contours of stream function and temperature for 50% full cavity, $Gr_1 = 10000$.

At the higher Grashof number used to generate the results shown in Fig. 5, the recirculating vortex is still present in the lower fluid, water. Fig. 5b now shows how far the temperature distribution has varied from the conduction solution.

Figs. 6 and 7 show the results obtained with the highest Gr_1 used and fill levels of 25% and 75% respectively. The 25% full case shows three vorticies in the lower fluid with the largest being the a recirculating vortex. In Fig. 7a it can be seen that the vortex in the air is shifted to the left due to interaction with the water.

For all cases, the heat transfer across the fluids is of interest. The Nusselt number, Nu, was calculated based on the physical properties of fluid 1. The cases were run for three different grid sizes and the technique proposed by Churchill, Chao and Ozoe [8] was used to extrapolate the Nusselt numbers found to zero grid size. For the results calculated using CDS in both fluids, Nu was found to converge in grid size to an order of approximately two. When the mixed scheme was used, convergence was about of order 1.5; UDS gave convergence of order between 1.1 and 1.3.

The resulting extrapolated Nusselt numbers are plotted in Fig. 8. As expexted, the heat flux across the cavity increased with both fill level and Grashof number. In general, Nu is seen to be proportional to the log of the Grashof number in fluid 1.

6. CONCLUSIONS AND RECOMMENDATIONS

Prehaps the most intriguing aspect of the results was the presence of the recirculating vortex in the water. Owing to the great density difference between the two substances, the authors initially expected the air to be driven to recirculation by the water. Upon closer examination of the problem, it is seen that, for a given geometry and temperature difference, the Grashof number for air is fifteen times that for water. This is primarily due to the coefficient of thermal expansion of air being very large compared to that of water. This yields a much larger driving force in air as compared to water for a given geometry and temperature difference.

As was expected, the heat flux in the cavity was found to be strongly dependent on the level of fill. There was seen to be a large decrease in heat flux with loss of water and, conversely, a great increase in heat flux with rising water level.

The general dependence of heat flux is similar to that found in free convection in a cavity filled with a single fluid. The Nusselt number proportionality to the log of the Grashof number is as observed by many authors in the one fluid case [1,2,3].

It is hoped that this work can be expanded in several ways. An extensive parametric study in geometry and fluid properties can be performed with the existing scheme. The current technique can be readily adapted to include nonuniform grids, allowing better resolution in the fluid and thermal boundary layers. Modifications can be made to allow calculation of transient solutions. Supplementary to all of the above mentioned improvements and modifications, the search will, of course, continue for more rapid and efficient equation solvers for given elliptic equations.

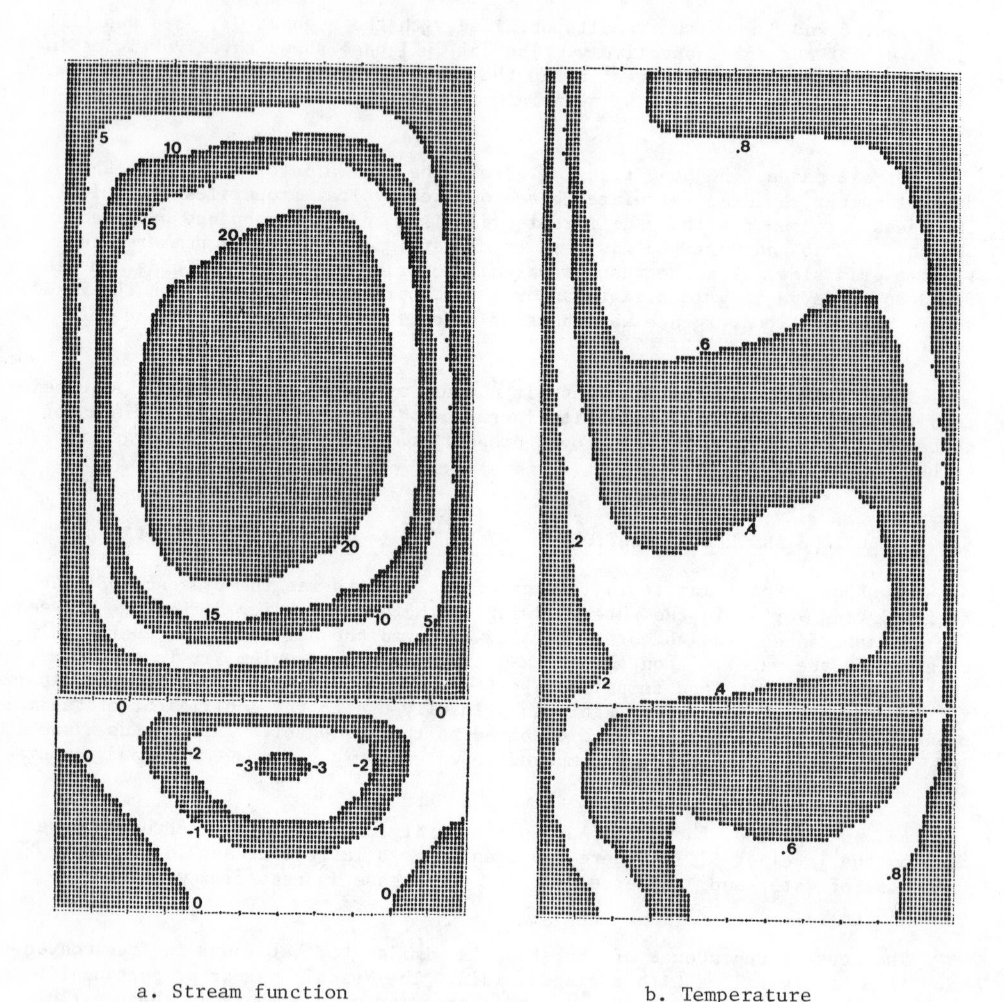

a. Stream function

b. Temperature

Fig. 6 Contours of stream function and temperature for 25% full cavity, Gr_1 = 10000.

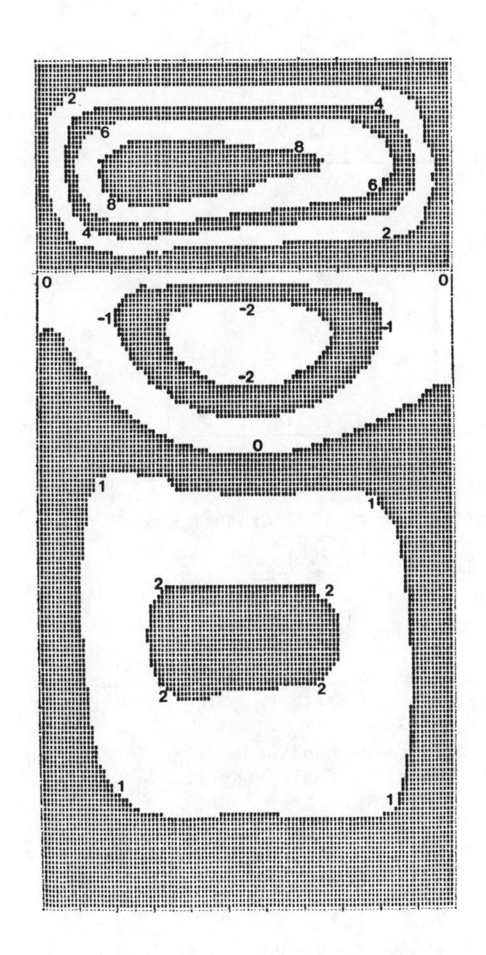

a. Stream function

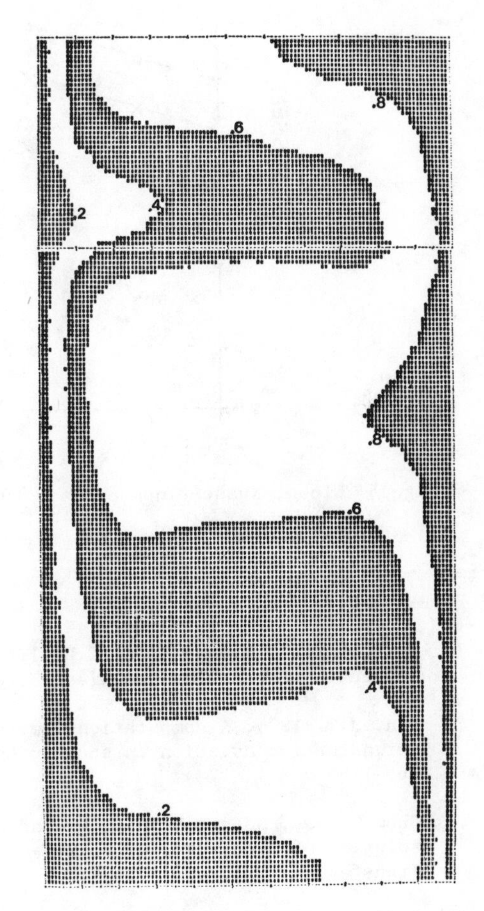

b. Temperature

Fig. 7 Contours of stream function and temperature for 75% full cavity, $Gr_1 = 10000$.

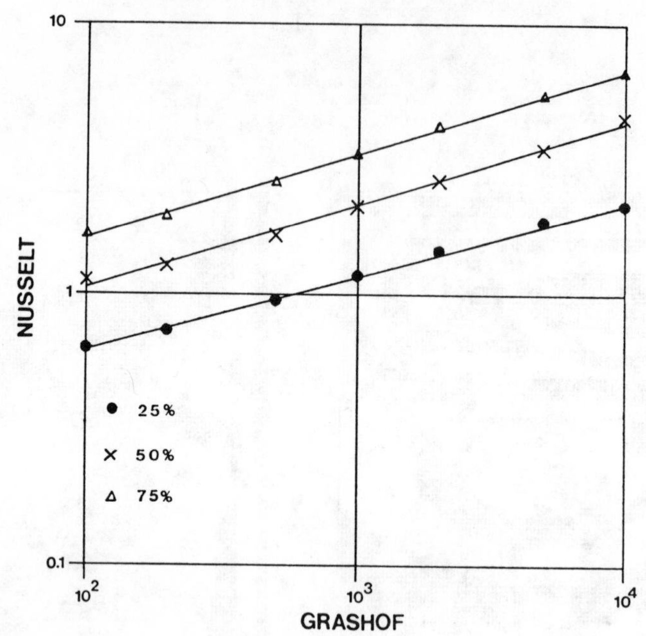

Fig. 8 Global Nusselt number as a function of fluid 1 Grashof number for various fill levels.

REFERENCES

1. Shiralkar., G.S. and Tien, C.L. 1981. A numerical study of laminar natural convection in shallow cavities. J. of Heat Transfer, Vol. 103, pp. 226-231.

2. Han, J.T. 1979. A computational method to solve nonlinear elliptic equations for natural convection in enclosures. Numerical Heat Transfer, Vol. 2, pp. 165-175.

3. Chen, C.-J., Naseri-Neshat, H. and Ho, K.-S. 1981. Finite analytic numerical solution of heat transfer in two-dimensional cavity flow. Numerical Heat Transfer, Vol. 4, pp. 179-197.

4. Simonovskii, I.B. 1979. Numerical investigation of convection in a system of two immiscible fluids heated from below. Convection Flows and Hydrodynamic Stability, Sverdlovsk.

5. Bourde, G.I. and Simonovskii, I.B. 1979. Determination of the equilibrium boundaries of a two-layer system convective stability. Applied Mathematics and Mechanics, Vol. 43, pp. 1091-1097.

6. Raithby, G.D. and Torrance, K.E. 1974. Upstream-weighted differencing schemes and their application to elliptic problems involving fluid flow. Computers and Fluids, Vol. 2, pp. 191-206.

7. Roache, P.J. 1976. Computational Fluid Dynamics, Hermosa.

8. Curchill, S.W., Chao, P. and Ozoe, H. 1981. Extrapolation of finite-difference

calculations of laminar natural convection in enclosures to zero grid size. Numerical Heat Transfer, Vol. 4, pp. 39-51.

NOMENCLATURE

A,B,C,D,E,F,C',D',F'	defined in Eqs. (3-1,2,3)
C_p	constant pressure specific heat
g	local acceleration of gravity
Gr	Grashof number $\beta' g(T_h - T_c)L_x^3/\nu^2$
h	fluid 1 height
k	thermal conductivity
L_x	width of cavity
L_y	height of cavity
Nu	Nusselt number $qL_y/(k_1(T_h - T_c))$
P	pressure
Pr	Prandtl number ν/α'
q	heat flux across cavity
R	generalized Reynolds number
S	generalized source
T	temperature
u	x direction nondimensional velocity UL_x/ν
v	y direction nondimensional velocity VL_x/ν
U	x direction dimensional velocity
V	y direction dimensional velocity
x	nondimensional horizontal coordinate X/L_x
y	nondimensional vertical coordinate Y/L_x
X	dimensional horizontal coordinate
Y	dimensional vertical coordinate
α	ν_1/ν_2
α'	thermal diffusivity $k/\rho C_p$
β	$\rho_1\nu_1/(\rho_2\nu_2)$
β'	coefficient of thermal expansion
γ	k_1/k_2
δ, Δ	defined in text
∇^2	$(\ )_{xx} + (\ )_{yy}$
μ	viscosity
ϕ	nondimensional stream function
ρ	density
θ	nondimensional temperature $(T-T_c)/(T_h-T_c)$
ν	kinematic viscosity μ/ρ
ω	nondimensional vorticity

subscripts

c	cold
h	hot
i	fluid number
i,j	nodal location
x,y	defined in text

Errata: The authors have learned that the ratio of Grashof numbers given and used in the calculations was the inverse of that for air and water. Because of this, the results shown do not correspond to an air-water system. The numerical scheme and solution technique, however, remain viable.

STREAMWISE-DIFFUSION FLOWS

Numerical Analysis of Singular Perturbation Problems

R.B. KELLOGG*
University of Maryland
College Park, Maryland

HOUDE HAN
Department of Mathematics
Beijing University
Beijing, China

1. INTRODUCTION

We consider singular perturbation problems, as exemplified by the initial-boundary value problem

$$u_t = \varepsilon \Delta u - \underset{\sim}{p}(x,t)\cdot\underline{\nabla}u - q(x,t)u + f(x,t),\ x \in \Omega \subset R^n,\ t > 0 \tag{1.1a}$$

$$u(x,t) = g(x,t),\ x \in \Gamma = \partial\Omega,\ t > 0 \tag{1.1b}$$

$$u(x,0) = u_o(x),\ x \in \Omega \tag{1.1c}$$

or the steady state version of this problem

$$-\varepsilon\Delta u + \underset{\sim}{p}(x)\cdot\underline{\nabla}u + q(x)u = f(x),\ x \in \Omega \tag{1.2a}$$

$$u(x) = g(x),\ x \in \Gamma . \tag{1.2b}$$

In these equations, and in the rest of the paper, we use a subscript notation for derivatives, $u_t = \partial u/\partial t$, etc. The symbol $\underline{\nabla}u$ denotes the gradient vector, with components $\partial u/\partial x_i$, $1 \leq i \leq n$, and $\Delta u = \Sigma\partial^2 u/\partial x_i^2$ denotes the Laplacian of u.

We are concerned with the numerical solution of these problems for small $\varepsilon > 0$. As is well known, problems of this character arise in the modelling of convective dominated flow of heat, or the modelling of the diffusion of species, in a moving medium. Equations of a somewhat similar, although more complicated character, are used to study the spread of vorticity in fluid flow. Therefore, a good insight into the numerical solution of the model problems, Eq. (1.1) or Eq. (1.2) may lead to improved methods for solving the more complicated problems that occur in nature. In addition, Eq. (1.1) and Eq. (1.2) contain substantial mathematical difficulties, and therefore seem worthy of attention.

In this paper, we shall give some of the properties of solutions of Eq. (1.1) and Eq. (1.2), and indicate the difficulties that insue for the development and analysis of numerical schemes. We shall also discuss some of the numerical analysis that has been done on these problems.

2. BOUNDARY AND INTERIOR LAYERS

---

*Supported in part by NIH Grant R01 AM 20373.

To understand the difficulties that arise in the numerical solution of Eqs. (1.1) or (1.2) for small $\varepsilon > 0$, we start with a discussion of some properties of solutions of these equations. (For some information on these boundary value problems, see Eckhaus and de Jaeger [1].) For reasonable domains Ω, coefficient functions $\underline{p}(x)$ and $q(x) > 0$, and data $f(x,t)$, $g(x,t)$, $u_o(x)$, there is a unique solution to the parabolic problem, Eq. (1.1) or the elliptic problem, Eq. (1.2). Since we are interested in these problems for small $\varepsilon > 0$, it is of interest to describe what happens to the solution u as $\varepsilon \to 0$. We will show that, for small ε, the solution u_ε experiences rapid changes, and hence has large derivatives, in certain regions of the domain Ω. These rapid changes are difficult to approximate numerically, and are therefore a source of difficulty associated with the numerical solution of convective dominated flow problems. The rapid changes in the solution are associated with the physical phenomena of boundary layers, stagnant points, internal layers, and moving fronts.

Consider the geometry of the domain Ω and the flow field $\underline{p}(x)$. We divide the boundary Γ of Ω into three parts, as indicated in Figure 1, the inflow part, Γ_-, the outflow part, Γ_+ and the characteristic part, Γ_c.

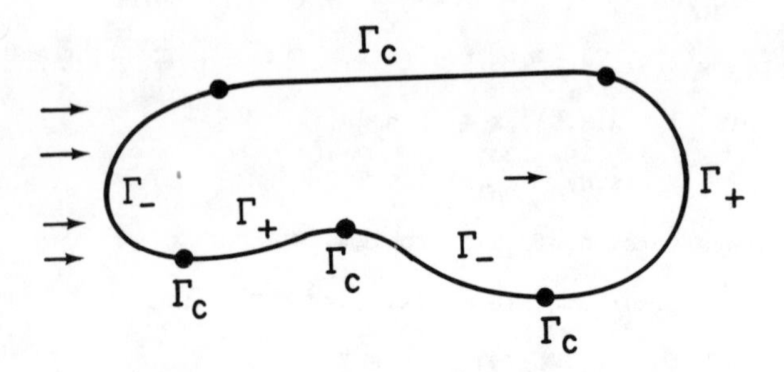

Figure 1.

It turns out that as $\varepsilon \to 0$, $u \to v$, where v satisfies the following reduced initial-boundary value problem in the transient case

$$v_t = -\underline{p}(x,t)\cdot\underline{\nabla}v - q(x,t)v + f(x,t)\ ,\ x \in \Omega,\ t > 0 \tag{2.1a}$$

$$v(x,t) = g(x,t)\ ,\ x \in \Gamma_-\ ,\ t > 0 \tag{2.1b}$$

$$v(x,0) = u_o(x)\ ,\ x \in \Omega\ . \tag{2.1c}$$

In the steady state case, v satisfies the problem

$$\underline{p}(x)\cdot\underline{\nabla}v + q(x)v = f(x),\ x \in \Omega\ , \tag{2.2a}$$

$$v(x) = g(x)\ ,\ x \in \Gamma_-\ . \tag{2.2b}$$

The nature of the convergence $u \to v$ can be made more explicit. In particular, one has

$$\int_0^T \int_\Omega |u - v|^2 dx\, dt \to 0$$

and one can make sharper convergence statements in various subregions of the domain.

Upon comparing Eq. (1.1) and Eq. (2.1), or Eq. (1.2) and Eq. (2.2), we see that the portion of the boundary condition Eq. ((1.1b) or Eq. (1.2b)) that is imposed on the boundary $\Gamma_+ \cup \Gamma_c$ has been "lost" in the reduced problem. The limiting function v is uniquely determined from the data of the reduced problem and very likely does not equal g on $\Gamma_+ \cup \Gamma_c$. Since $u = g$ on $\Gamma_+ \cup \Gamma_c$ and $u \to v$ one may infer that for small ε, u has a rapid change, and hence a large first derivative, near $\Gamma_+ \cup \Gamma_c$. In other words, u has a "boundary layer" on $\Gamma_+ \cup \Gamma_c$.

For an example of this, we consider the problem

$$-\varepsilon u''(x) - u'(x) + u(x) = 1 , \quad 0 < x < 1 ,$$

$$u(0) = u(1) = 0 .$$

The solution of this problem is given by

$$u(x) = -\frac{1 - e^{t_2}}{e^{t_1} - e^{t_2}} e^{t_1 x} + \frac{1 - e^{t_1}}{e^{t_1} - e^{t_2}} e^{t_2 x} + 1 ,$$

where

$$t_1 = 2/[1+\sqrt{1+4\varepsilon}] ,$$

$$t_2 = -[1+\sqrt{1+4\varepsilon}]/2\varepsilon .$$

We see that as $\varepsilon \to 0$, $t_1 \to 1$, $t_2 \approx -1/\varepsilon \to -\infty$. Hence, as $\varepsilon \to 0$, $u(x) \to 1-e^{-(1-x)}$ if $x > 0$. For x near 0 and ε small, we note that $\exp(t_2 x) \approx \exp(-x/\varepsilon)$ falls sharply from a value of 1, at $x = 0$, to a value near 0, for $x > 0$. Thus, for ε small, $u(x)$ changes rapidly from $u(0) = 0$ to $u(x) \approx 1-e^{-(1-x)}$, for $x > 0$. The change occurs in an interval of width roughly ε, and represents the "boundary layer" in the solution at $x = 0$.

A study of the reduced problems, Eqns. (2.1) and (2.2), reveals other phenomena of rapid change in the solution that will adversely affect the accuracy of an approximate solution. We now mention three of these phenomena.

Suppose there are stagnant points in the flow field $\underset{\sim}{p}(x)$. Examples of these are shown in Figures 2 and 3. Figure 2 provides a flow field $\underset{\sim}{p}(x)$ with one stagnant point, at x^*. In this case, x^* is a "sink", or, "attractive point" for the flow, and $\Gamma = \Gamma_-$, so there is no boundary layer. From the nature of the hyperbolic problem Equation (2.2), we see that in the steady state case, $v(x^*)$ is over determined, since many characteristics meet at x^*. It turns out that v is, nevertheless, continuous at x^*, and the value at x^* satisfies $q(x^*)v(x^*) = f(x^*)$. However, the solution $u(x)$ has, for small ε, large derivatives at x^*. These large derivatives will produce errors in the numerical solution near x^*. In contrast, Figure 3 provides a flow field with one stagnant point, which is a "source", or, "repulsive point" for the flow. In this case, $\Gamma = \Gamma_+$ so all of Γ is a boundary layer. It turns out that the solution v of Eq. (2.2) is uniquely determined by the requirement that it is continuous at x^*. Also, u and its derivatives remain uniformly bounded near x^* as $\varepsilon \to 0$.

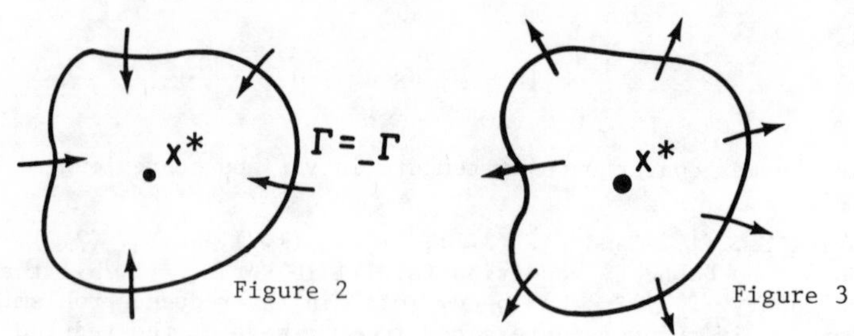

Figure 2 Figure 3

For an example of a stagnant point, we consider the boundary value problem

$$-\varepsilon u'' + \alpha x u' + u = 1 \ , \ -1 < x < 1 \ ,$$

$$u(+1) = u(-1) = 0 \ .$$

If $\alpha > 0$, $x = 0$ is a source, and if $\alpha < 0$, $x = 0$ is a sink. The reduced problems in the two cases are therefore

$$\alpha > 0: \quad \alpha x v' + v = 1 \ , \quad -1 < x < 1$$

$$\alpha < 0: \quad \alpha x v' + v = 1 \ , \ -1 < x < 1 \ , \ v(\pm 1) = 0.$$

Note that if $\alpha < 0$, the reduced problem includes the specification of boundary conditions at $x = \pm 1$. In the case $\alpha > 0$, no specification of boundary conditions is allowed. The solution of the reduced problems are:

$$\alpha > 0: \quad v(x) = 1 \ ,$$

$$\alpha < 0: \quad v(x) = 1 - |x|^{\beta} \qquad \beta = 1/|\alpha| \ .$$

Note that if $\alpha < 0$, $v(x)$ has large derivatives near $x = 0$. The solution u also has large derivatives near $x = 0$. If $\alpha > 0$, v is very smooth. In this case, the solution u has boundary layers near $x = \pm 1$.

It may happen that "internal layers" develop in the flow. An illustration of this is given in Figure 4. From the hyperbolic nature of the reduced problems, Eqns. (2.1) or (2.2), we see that these problems divide into two subproblems, imposed in the two regions Ω_1 and Ω_2 . In Ω_1 , v is determined completely by the data f, g, and the values of h on the arc $\widehat{cd}$. In Ω_2 , v is determined completely by the data f, g, and the values of h on the arc ae. Thus, v is, in general, discontinuous on the line $\widehat{ab}$. Since, for $\varepsilon > 0$, u_ε is continuous in Ω , u_ε has large derivatives near the line ab. We say that u_ε has an "internal layer" along this line.

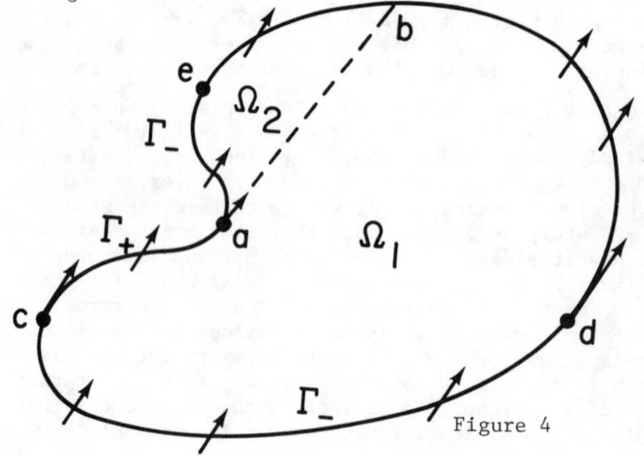

Figure 4

Another example of an interesting phenomenon in the solution of Eq. (1.1) is given by the "moving front" problem. (See Figure 5.) Let us consider Eq. (1.1) in the case of one space variable, and let $\Omega = R^1$. Suppose the initial data is, for example,

$$g(x) = \begin{cases} 0, & x < 0 \\ 1, & x > 0 \end{cases}$$

From the hyperbolic nature of the reduced problem, Eq. (2.1), we see that $v(x,t)$ has a jump discontinuity along a curve given by the equation

$$d\underline{x}/dt = \underline{p}(x,t) \tag{2.3}$$

Since, for $\varepsilon > 0$, u_ε is continuous in $\Omega x R^1_+$, u_ε has large derivatives near the curve given by Eq. (2.3). This problem models, for example, the convection and diffusion of a slug of solute placed in a moving stream of water at time $t = 0$. The curve, Eq. (2.3), is, approximately, the "moving front."

The rapid changes in u near boundary layers, internal layers, stagnant points and moving fronts are difficult to capture in a numerical solution. In the case of a nonlinear problem, shock waves would be added to this list of phenomena.

3. LOSS OF STABILITY

It is desired to obtain numerical schemes for singular perturbation problems that represent such phenomena as boundary layers, stagnant points, internal layers, and moving fronts. The difficulty in solving Eq. (1.1) or Eq. (1.2) with small ε comes in two aspects. First, from the presence of boundary or interior layers, one may infer that there are regions of sharp transition, in which u is changing rapidly. As we have remarked, it is difficult to approximate such rapidly changing functions. This difficulty may be illustrated by considering the function $u(x) = \exp(-x/\varepsilon)$ on $[0,h]$, and the linear interpolant $u_h(x) = 1-h^{-1}x(1 - \exp(-h/\varepsilon))$ to this function. The function u is of a type that frequently occurs in boundary layers. It is easily seen (see Figure 6) that the maximum of $|u(x)-u_h(x)|$ is attained at

$$x^* = \varepsilon \ \ln \frac{h}{\varepsilon(1 - \exp(-h/\varepsilon))}$$

One can verify that as $\varepsilon \to 0$, $u(x^*) \to 1$. Hence the error bound $|u(x)-u_h(x)| \leq 1$ is the best that can be asserted for $0 < \varepsilon < 1$. This suggests

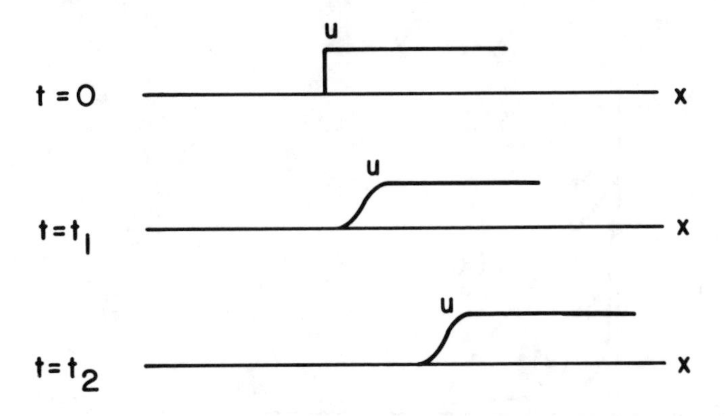

Figure 5

that in a finite difference or finite element solution of a singular perturbation problem that includes boundary layers, mesh steps of size $h << \varepsilon$ will be required in the boundary layer region. Some ways of avoiding this have been discussed in the literature, and will be mentioned in the next section.

The problem caused by sharp transitions in the solution are reflected in both the finite element and the finite difference error analysis. In the finite element case, the result of an error analysis is to bound the error in the finite element solution in terms of the best approximation of the solution by an element of the finite element subspace. The example above illustrates the difficulty in bounding this approximation error. In the finite difference case, the error analysis bounds the error in terms of the truncation error, which in turn depends on higher derivatives of the solution. As we have seen, the derivatives of the solution become large in regions of sharp transition, such as boundary layers, neighborhoods of sinks, etc. Since further study of approximation theory relates the error in approximating a function with its higher derivatives, we may say that this source of difficulty of singular perturbation problems is, for both the finite element and the finite difference methods, large or infinite higher derivatives of the solution u.

It is possible that the solution of a singular perturbation problem is smooth for all $\varepsilon > 0$. As an example of this, consider the problem

$$-\varepsilon u'' - u' + u = 1 \ , \quad 0 < x < 1$$
$$u(0) = 1 \ , \ u'(1) = 0 \ .$$

The solution of this problem is $u(x) \equiv 1$, and hence contains no boundary layers. There, are, nevertheless, difficulties with the numerical solution. These difficulties are related to a loss of stability, which will now be described.

The loss of stability is related to the change in character of Eq. (1.2) as $\varepsilon \to 0$ from an elliptic to a hyperbolic problem. To understand this, we derive the usual energy estimate for solutions of Eq. (1.2). Suppose, for convenience, that $g = 0$, multiply both sides of Eq. (1.2a) by u, and integrate over the domain Ω. Using the identity

$$u(\underline{p}\cdot\underline{\nabla}u) = \tfrac{1}{2}\underline{\nabla}(u^2\underline{p}) - \tfrac{1}{2}u^2\underline{\nabla}\ \underline{p}$$

and Green's theorem, and supposing for convenience that

$$q - \tfrac{1}{2}\underline{\nabla}\cdot\underline{p} > 0 \text{ in } \Omega \tag{3.1}$$

we arrive at the inequality

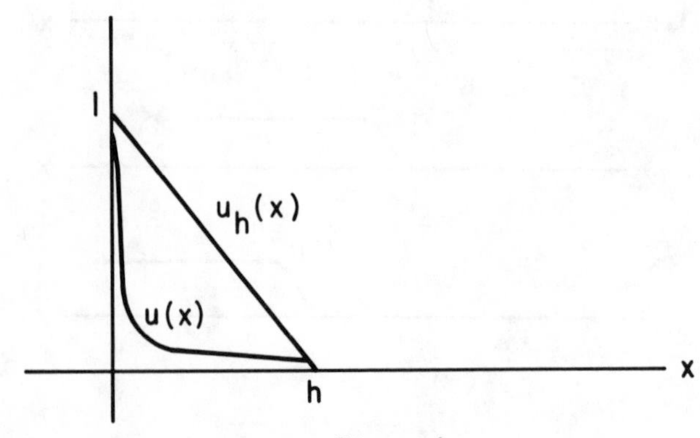

Figure 6

$$\varepsilon\int_\Omega |\nabla u|^2\,dx + \int_\Omega |u|^2 dx \le \int_\Omega |f|^2 dx \tag{3.2}$$

where $c > 0$ depends on a lower bound for $q-\frac{1}{2}\underline{\nabla}\cdot\underline{p}$, but is independent of ε. Inequalities of this character are essential in the analysis of the error in finite element and finite difference methods. However, we see that for ε small, say $\varepsilon \approx h$ = the grid spacing, the force of the inequality is lost. Note that the inequality (3.2) expresses the boundedness of the solution operator, with the energy, or, H^1 norm, on the left side, and the L_2 norm on the right side. The stability is "lost" for small ε because the constants in the inequality depend on ε. If the flow is incompressible, $\underline{\nabla}\cdot\underline{p} = 0$ and (3.1) becomes $q > 0$ which is not usually the case. If a backwards implicit time discretization is used in the convection-diffusion equation, one is led to a semi-discrete problem of the form (1.2) with $q = 1/\Delta t$.

We can deduce from Ineq. (3.2) the inequality

$$\int_\Omega |u|^2 dx \le c\int_\Omega |f|^2 dx \tag{3.3}$$

which is valid uniformly for $\varepsilon > 0$, but which is weaker than Ineq. (3.2) in the strength of the norm of u that is being estimated. In a similar way, by using the maximum principle, we may deduce for the solution u of Eq. (1.2) the estimate

$$\max\{|u(x)|:\ x \in \Omega\} \le c\,\max\{|f(x)|:\ x \in \Omega\} \tag{3.4}$$

where $c > 0$ does not depend on ε. Uniform inequalities of the form Ineq. (3.3) or Ineq. (3.4), which are uniformly valid for all ε near 0, but which have weaker norms on the left side than the usual elliptic inequalities, play an important role in the analysis of numerical methods for singular perturbation problems.

We remark in passing that our derivation of Ineq. (3.2) and Ineq. (3.3), which are important for the analysis of finite element methods, has assumed Inequality (3.1). It would be useful to obtain Ineq. (3.2) or Ineq. (3.3) without this assumption.

The contrasting behaviors of the central and upwind difference approximations for diffusion-convection problems are well known. It is interesting to note how this behavior is reflected in the stability properties of these two schemes. Consider as a model problem the two point boundary value problem

$$-\varepsilon u'' + pu' + qu = f$$

$$u(0) = u(1) = 0 .$$

p, q are positive constants.

With a uniform mesh $h = 1/N$ and mesh points $x_i = ih$, $0 \le i \le N$, we consider the central difference scheme

$$(L_{CD}u_h)_i \equiv -(\varepsilon/h^2)(u_{h,i+1} - 2u_{h,i} + u_{h,i-1}) + (p/2h)(u_{i+1} - u_i) + qu_i , \quad 1 \le i \le N-1$$

$$u_{h,0} = u_{h,N} = 0 , \tag{3.5}$$

or, the upwind difference scheme

$$(L_{UD}u_h)_i \equiv -(\varepsilon/h^2)(u_{h,i+1} - 2u_{h,i} + u_{h,i-1}) + (p/h)(u_{h,i} - u_{h,i-1}) + qu_i ,$$

$$1 \leq i \leq N-1 \;,$$

$$u_{h,0} = u_{h,N} = 0 \;. \tag{3.6}$$

It is easily seen that the solution u_h^{UD} of (3.6) satisfies, for some $c > 0$ independent of ε and h,

$$\max\{|u_{h,i}|: \; 0 \leq i \leq N\} \leq c \max\{|f_i|: \; 1 \leq i < N\} \tag{3.7}$$

which is a discrete analog of the inequality (3.4). On the other hand, one can show that, if the inequality

$$\frac{ph}{\varepsilon} < \tfrac{1}{2} \tag{3.8}$$

does not hold, the solution u_h^{CD} of (3.5) does not satisfy Ineq. (3.7). The central difference scheme loses even the weak stability property enjoyed by the solution of the continuous problem. This is related to the well-known oscillations in the solution u_h^{CD} that are present when Ineq. (3.8) holds. The left side of Ineq. (3.8) is often called a "cell Reynolds number" or "cell Peclet number". If the cell Reynolds number is $< \frac{1}{2}$, that is, (3.8) does hold, it can be shown that Ineq. (3.7) holds for the solution of (3.5).

The stability of the upwinded difference operator L_h^{UD}, or the stability of the difference operator L_h^{CD} in case the cell Reynolds number is $< \frac{1}{2}$, is related to the fact that the matrices corresponding to these operators have negative off diagonal entries and are diagonally dominant. The theory of M matrices plays an important role in the analysis of these difference schemes. It is interesting to note that, in the case of a nonlinear version of Eq. (1.2), a condition on the cell Reynolds number, or alternately a suitable upwinding, is related to the unique solvability of the corresponding nonlinear system of difference equations [2]. In this case, the theory of M functions plays a role. Unfortunately, these ideas do not seem to apply to finite element approximations to Eq. (1.2), and their applicability to other singular perturbation problems, such as the Navier-Stokes equations for large Reynolds number, is not clear.

4. NUMERICAL ANALYSIS

By numerical analysis, as applied to Eq. (1.1) or Eq. (1.2), we mean the development and error analysis of numerical schemes for the solution of these problems. Because of the difficulties of the subject, research in this area has concentrated almost entirely on the one dimensional case. Therefore, to indicate the nature of mathematical work in this area, we shall consider the problem

$$-\varepsilon u'' + p(x)u' + q(x)u = f(x) \;, \; 0 < x < 1 \;, \tag{4.1a}$$

$$u(0) = u(1) = 0 \tag{4.1b}$$

and we shall discuss some numerical work on this problem. We note that although Eq. (4.1) is often used as a model of Eq. (1.2), the one dimensional problem is considerably simpler to analyze, and in particular, there are no interior layers in Eq. (4.1). Nevertheless, the motive for studying Eq. (4.1) is not to develop schemes for the solution of this problem, but to develop insight into more complicated problems.

If $p(x)$ does not vanish in $[0,1]$, well-known stretching transformations provide an asymptotic expansion of u in terms of "inner solutions", that represent the boundary layer, and "outer solutions", that represent u in the interior of $(0,1)$. If p vanishes at isolated points, these expansions have to be supplemented by "connection formulas", that represent the solution across the stagnant point. These ideas have been used by Miranker and his co-workers to develop numerical methods for the solution of Eq. (4.1) [3,4]. In [3], for example, a scheme is developed to solve numerically the differential equations that define the first several inner and outer functions in the asymptotic expansion of u. The scheme involves the solution of a difference equation in the boundary layer, and another difference equation in the entire interval. The two difference equations are linked through the known asymptotic properties of the solution u. The method has the feature that it becomes more accurate with smaller ε. In [4] these ideas are extended to problems with stagnant points. Although no error estimates are given, many interesting numerical examples are presented to illustrate the power of the method.

One approach to resolving the behavior of the solution u near boundary layers and stagnant points is to use a refined mesh near the points of greatest change of u. An adaptive scheme for doing this is being developed by Kreiss and his co-workers [5]. By "adaptive", it is meant that a discretized form of the problem (4.1) is first solved on a coarse, uniform mesh. A criterion is developed to determine, from the approximate solution, locations where more or fewer mesh points are needed. The computational mesh is then altered and the discrete problem is resolved. The process is iterated until a satisfactory solution is obtained. In [5] the method is briefly described and numerical results are presented.

Finite element methods have been applied to fluid dynamics problems, and in particular to problems of the forms of Eqns. (1.1) and (1.2). In developing finite element methods for Eq. (1.2) and $g = 0$, say, one first writes the problem in the weak formulation

$$B(u,w) = \int_\Omega fw \, dx \,, \tag{4.2}$$

where the bilinear form B is defined by

$$B(u,w) = \int_\Omega \{\varepsilon \underline{\nabla} u \cdot \underline{\nabla} w + w\underline{p} \cdot \underline{\nabla} u + quw\} dx \,.$$

The solution u is uniquely characterized by the requirement that (4.2) holds for all reasonable functions w which are defined in Ω and which vanish on Γ. Let S_1 and S_2 denote two finite dimensional subspaces of functions which are defined on Ω and which vanish on Γ. The subspaces S_1 and S_2 should have the same dimension. The approximate solution $\tilde{u}$ of Eq. (1.2), using the subspaces S_1 and S_2, is defined by the requirements that $\tilde{u} \in S_1$ and that

$$B(\tilde{u},w) = \int_\Omega fw \, dx \,, \quad w \in S_2 \,.$$

In this general formulation, the method is sometimes known as the "Petrov-Galerkin" method. If $S_1 = S_2$, one has the Galerkin method. In the latter case, if Ineq. (3.1) holds, it is easy to derive the error estimate

$$||u-\tilde{u}||_{1,\varepsilon} \leq c \inf\{||u-w||_1 : w \in S_1\} \,, \tag{4.3}$$

where $c > 0$ depends only on the coefficients $\underline{p}(x)$ and $q(x)$, and where the norms are defined by

$$||z||^2_{1,\varepsilon} = \int_\Omega \{\varepsilon|\underline{\nabla}z|^2 + z^2\}\, dx ,$$

$$||z||^2_1 = \int_\Omega \{|\underline{\nabla}z|^2 + z^2\}dx .$$

Inequality (4.3) illustrates both the difficulties of large derivatives and loss of stability that have been mentioned above. On the one hand, when u has boundary layers, etc., the quantity on the right side of Ineq. (4.3) is not small. On the other hand, even if u is smooth, the norm on the left side of Ineq. (4.3) includes ε , so the error is, in effect, measured in a weaker norm due to the loss of stability.

In using finite elements, the formulation is often modified to build in effects such as upwinding, streamwise diffusion constants, reduced integration schemes, etc. (See, for example, [6,7].) Error analysis of these methods have not been given, and remain a challenge to the numerical analyst. Even in the case of the one dimensional problem, eq. (4.1), the only error analysis of finite element methods that take account of small ε are in the case of p not vanishing (no stagnant point). A as an example of this work, we cite the paper of de Groen and Hemker [8]. In this paper, the Petrov-Galerkin method is considered for Eq. (4.1) for a variety of subspaces S_1 and S_2 . These include collections of piecewise polynomial functions, or piecewise exponential functions, defined with respect to a given set of mesh intervals. Error estimates are made for the approximate solutions, and comparisons with numerical experiments are given.

In [9], the Eq. (4.1) is considered with $p \equiv 1$, $q \equiv 0$. Attention is focused on the loss of stability, and its implications for the finite element analysis. An inf-sup condition for the bilinear form associated with the finite element is proved which is uniform in ε . This inf-sup condition does not use the usual energy spaces but rather certain other spaces specially constructed for the problem at hand. As an example of the results obtained, we mention the error estimate

$$\left[\int_0^1 |u - \tilde{u}|^2 dx + \sum (h_j + h_{j-1})|u(x_j) - \tilde{u}\,(x_j)|^2\right]^{1/2}$$

$$\leq c \max \int_{x_{j-1}}^{x_j} [|f|+|f'|]dx + \sup \left\{\left[\int_0^1 |u-w|^2 dx + \sum (h_j+h_{j-1})(u(x_j)-w(w_j))^2\right]^{1/2}\right\}$$

where the mesh is given by

$$0 = x_0 <\ldots< x_N = 1 ,$$

$$h_j = x_j - x_{j-1} , \; 1 \leq j \leq N .$$

This inequality expresses the error in the solution in terms of a "best approximation" of the solution by any function $w \in S_1$. Using the known regularity properties of the solution one could use this inequality to pick a distribution of mesh points x_i to give a good approximation and error estimate.

A number of authors have suggested special "exponential" difference schemes for the numerical solution of (4.1) [10,11]. These difference schemes have been analyzed in a variety of situations, and the work is continuing. Most of this work has been in the case of no stagnant points, $p(x) \neq 0$ in $[0,1]$. We cite in particular the papers [12,13]. In [12] there is analyzed the Allen-Southwell-Il'in scheme, given on a uniform mesh by

$$(Lu_h^{AS})_i \equiv -(\varepsilon\gamma_i/h^2)(u_{i+1} - 2u_i + u_{i-1}) + (p_i/2h)(u_{i+1} - u_{i-1}) + q_i u_i = f_i \ , \quad (4.4)$$

$$0 < i < N \ ,$$

$$u_{h0} = u_{hN} = 0 \ ,$$

where

$$\gamma_i = (p_i h/2\varepsilon)\coth(p_i h/2\varepsilon) \ . \quad (4.5)$$

The motivation for the factor γ_i in this equation is as follows. If $p \equiv$ constant, $q \equiv 0$, the two homogeneous solutions of Eq. (4.1) are $u(x) \equiv 1$ and $u(x) = \exp(px/\varepsilon)$. In this case, the homogeneous solutions of Eq. (4.4) are $u_i \equiv 1$ and $u_i = \exp(pih/\varepsilon)$, if and only if γ_i is given by Eq. (4.5). Since, as we have seen, the exponential solution is a basic ingredient of the boundary layer, the difference equation (4.4) gives good accuracy for small ε, even in the boundary layer. On the other hand, the matrix arising from Eq. (4.4) turns out to be diagonally dominant and to have negative off diagonal entries for all $\varepsilon > 0$. The factor γ_i introduces an upwinding that switches from a centered scheme, at $p = 0$, to a fully upwinded scheme, at $\varepsilon = 0$. The difference scheme Eq. (4.4) preserves both accuracy and stability, uniformly in ε. These features make this scheme and its more complicated variants very attractive for the numerical solution of singular perturbation problems.

In [12] there is essentially, proved the error estimate

$$|u(x_i) - U_{h,i}^{AS}| \le \frac{ch^2}{h+\varepsilon} \ ,$$

where $c > 0$ and is independent of $\varepsilon \in (0,\varepsilon_o]$, and where u_h^{AS} is the solution of (4.4). (See [12], Theorem 4.4. The final term in the inequality in this paper can easily be deleted, as was pointed out by A. Berger.) In [13], a similar, but more accurate difference scheme was analyzed. The scheme is due to el-Mistiakawy and Werle [14]. In the case $q \equiv 0$ the error estimate

$$|u(x_i) - u_{h,i}| \le ch^2 \ , \ c > 0 \text{ independent of } \varepsilon \in (0,\varepsilon_o]$$

is obtained. The book [15] contain related results of exponential schemes for singular perturbation problems.

Recently, [16] some results on the el-Mistiakawy-Werle scheme have been obtained in the case that stagnant points are allowed. It is shown that there is a uniform error estimate of the form

$$\max|u(x)-u_h(x)| \le ch^\beta \ , \ c > 0 \ \text{ independent of } \varepsilon \in (0,\varepsilon_o] \quad (42)$$

on a uniform mesh of size h. Here $u_h(x)$ is an interpolant, obtained from the difference solution, the constant β is defined by

$$\beta = \min\{1, -q(x^*)/p'(x^*) \ , \text{ where } p(x^*) = 0 \ , \ p'(x^*) < 0\}.$$

If, for some x^*, $p(x^*) = 0$ and $q(x^*) = -p'(x^*)$, the result (42) is modified. In addition, [16] contains bounds for derivation of the solution near the stagnant point that are of potential usefulness for the error analysis of other methods for solving these problems.

There has been virtually no analysis done on exponential difference schemes for the higher dimensional problems (1.1) or (1.2). (For a preliminary report on some research, see [17].) However, these schemes have been tried on some two dimensional problems. The references [18,19] give some interesting numerical work on this, especially related to flow separation at high Reynolds numbers.

5. CONCLUSIONS

Some problems and progress in the numerical analysis of singular perturbation problems that are related to numerical heat transfer have been reviewed It is hoped that work in this area will continue and will have an impact on methods used by practitioners in numerical heat transfer.

REFERENCES

1. Eckhaus, W., Boundary layers in linear elliptic singular perturbation problems, SIAM Rev., Vol. 14, 1972, pp. 225-270.

2. Kellogg, R. B., Shubin, G. R., and Stephens, A. B., Uniqueness and the cell Reynolds number, SIAM J. Numer. Anal., Vol. 17, 1980, pp. 733-739.

3. Miranker, W. L., Numerical methods of boundary layer type for stiff systems of ordinary differential equations, Computing, Vol. 11, pp. 221-234.

4. Miranker, W. L., and Morreeuw, J. P., Semianalytic numerical studies of turning points arising in stiff boundary value problems, Math. of Comp., Vol. 28, 1974, pp. 1017-1034.

5. Kreiss, B. and Kreiss, H-O, Numerical methods for singular perturbation problems, SIAM J. Numer. Anal. Vol. 18, 1981, pp. 262-276.

6. Hughes, T. J. R., Liu, W. K., and Brooks, A., Finite element analysis of incompressible viscous flows by the penalty function formulation, J. Comp. Physics, Vol. 30, 1979, pp. 1-60.

7. Heinrich, J. C., and Zienkiewicz, O. C., Solution of nonlinear second order differential equations with significant first derivatives by a Petrov-Galerkin finite element method, in Numerical Analysis of Singular Perturbation Problems, P. W. Hemker and J. J. Miller, eds. Academic Press, New York, 1977, pp. 251-273.

8. de Groen, P. P. N., and Hemker, P. W., Error bounds for exponentially fitted Galerkin methods applied to stiff two point boundary value problems, Ibid., pp. 217-249.

9. Babuška, I., and Szymczak, W. G., An error analysis for the finite element method applied to convection diffusion problems, Tech. Note BN-962, Univ. of MD, Mar. 1981.

10. Allen, D. N. de G., and Southwell, R. V., Relaxation methods applied to determine the motion, in two dimensions, of a viscous fluid past a fixed cylinder, Quart. J. Mech. Applied Math., Vol. 8, 1955, pp. 129-145.

11. Il'in, A. M., Differencing scheme for a differential equation with a small parameter affecting the highest derivative, Mat. Zametki, Vol. 6, 1969, pp. 237-248.

12. Kellogg, R. B. and Tsan, A., Analysis of some difference approximations for a singular perturbation problem without turning points, Math. Comp., Vol. 32, 1978, pp. 1025-1039.

13. Berger, A. E., Solomon, J. M., and Ciment, M., An analysis of a uniformly accurate difference method for a singular perturbation problem, Math. Comp., Vol. 13, 1981, pp. 79-94.

14. El-Mistiakawy T. M., and Werle, M. J., Numerical method for boundary layers with blowing-the exponential box scheme, AIAA J., Vol. 16 (1978), pp. 749-751.

15. Doolan, E. P., Miller, J. J. H., and Schilders, W. H. A., Uniform numerical methods for problems with initial and boundary layers, Boole Press, Dublin, 1981.

16. Berger, A. E., Han, H., and Kellogg, R. B., Numerical solution of a singular perturbation problem with turning points, to appear.

17. Kellogg, R. B., Analysis of a difference approximation for a singular perturbation problem in two dimensions, in Boundary and Inertia Layers-Computations and Asymptotic Methods, J. J. Miller, editor, Boole Press, Dublin, 1980.

18. Dennis, S. C. R. and Hudson, J. D., Further accurate representations of partial differential equations by finite-difference methods, J. Inst. Maths Applics, Vol. 26, 1980, pp. 369-379.

19. Dennis, S. C. R., and Smith, F. T., Steady flow through a channel with a symmetrical construction in the form of a step, Proc. R. Soc. London, Vol. 372A, 1980, pp. 393-414.

Treatment of Numerical Oscillations in Heat and Mass Transfer Problems with "Fronts"

G.F. CAREY and L.J. HAYES
Texas Institute for Computational Mechanics
University of Texas at Austin

ABSTRACT

Some recent investigations concerning the numerical treatment of oscillations in solutions of evolution and boundary-value problems involving fronts and interfaces are described. The first class of problems are derived from convection dominated flows and here we show how a new variable upwind finite element scheme yields nonoscillatory solution profiles while preserving the front. We consider then a Stefan problem for heat transfer with a change of phase at an interface, which is related to permafrost modelling. A modified predictor-corrector scheme is shown to be of practical value for stabilizing oscillations in the interface position.

1. INTRODUCTION

When convection-dominated flows that involve sharp propagating fronts are modelled numerically, Gibb's-type oscillatory overshoot at the front is a common occurrence. A recent survey describes current finite element research on this topic (Hughes [1]). In the present investigation a variable-upwind finite element scheme using local eigenvalue bounds is applied to minimize dissipation of sharp fronts while suppressing oscillations. Numerical results are given on test cases to illustrate the performance of the approximate methods.

The second class of problems involves oscillations of a different kind. In practical applications to problems such as permafrost modelling, tracking the front is one source of difficulty for standard finite element formulations. In these applications, the contribution to the total energy of the system coming from the latent heat of fusion during phase change is very large, and if the location of the freeze front is not tracked very accurately in time, then ficticious cycles of freezing and thawing can develop numerically from one time step to the next. A modified predictor-corrector technique is implemented which effectively reduces oscillations in the front location.

2. METHOD AND DISCUSSION

(a) Convection-Diffusion Problem.

If standard Galerkin finite element methods are applied to convection dominated flows and the mesh is not sufficiently fine the resulting approximate solution is very oscillatory. Such oscillations are very troublesome in transport processes in which multiple components or multiple phases occur as the behavior of different solution fields are inter-related. Strong oscillations in one component can destroy the quality of the other solution components and destabilize the numerical computations.

Motivated by the success of backward differencing in finite differences, upwind finite element methods have been devised to suppress oscillations. These techniques are equivalent to adding numerical dissipation and consequently tend to smear out the true steep gradients in the solution. The variable upwind approach employed here utilizes eigenvalue bounds on the discrete operator to determine the amount of local upwinding required to suppress oscillations but still preserve the integrity of sharp fronts.

We consider the model convection-diffusion equation

$$\frac{\partial u}{\partial t} + \alpha \frac{\partial u}{\partial x} - \frac{\partial}{\partial x}\left(\beta^2 \frac{\partial u}{\partial x}\right), \quad 0 < x < 1, \quad t > 0 \tag{1}$$

where α and β^2 are smooth functions of x and t, with Dirichlet data

$$u(0,t) = \gamma_0(t), \quad u(1,t) = \gamma_1(t) \tag{2}$$

and initial value

$$u(x,0) = u_0(x) \tag{3}$$

The (weak) variational statement of (1)-(3) is to find u satisfying (2) and (3) such that

$$\int_0^1 u_t v dx + \int_0^1 \alpha u_x v dx + \int_0^1 \beta^2 u_x v_x dx = 0, \quad t > 0 \tag{4}$$

for all $v \in H_0^1(0,1)$. The finite element problem is obtained by restricting u and v in (4) to appropriate finite dimensional subspaces of H_0^1. In the upwind Petrov-Galerkin type methods the trial basis and test basis differ. Here we use a global basis $\{\phi_i\}$ of piecewise linears for u and upwind-biased quadratics $\{\chi_i\}$ for v and take ω_e as an upwind parameter which can be varied locally on element Ω_e to adjust the level of numerical dissipation from upwinding.

We then obtain from (4) the semidiscrete system

$$\underset{\sim}{B} \frac{d\underset{\sim}{u}}{dt} + \underset{\sim\sim}{A}\underset{\sim}{u} = \underset{\sim}{f} \tag{5}$$

and in numerical studies consider both the lumped and unlumped forms of the system (5).

For nonconstant coefficients α and β^2 and a non-uniform mesh the eigenvalue bounds for the discrete lumped case yield the following inequality for the upwind parameter

$$\omega_e > 3 - \frac{6\beta_e^2}{\alpha_e h_e}$$

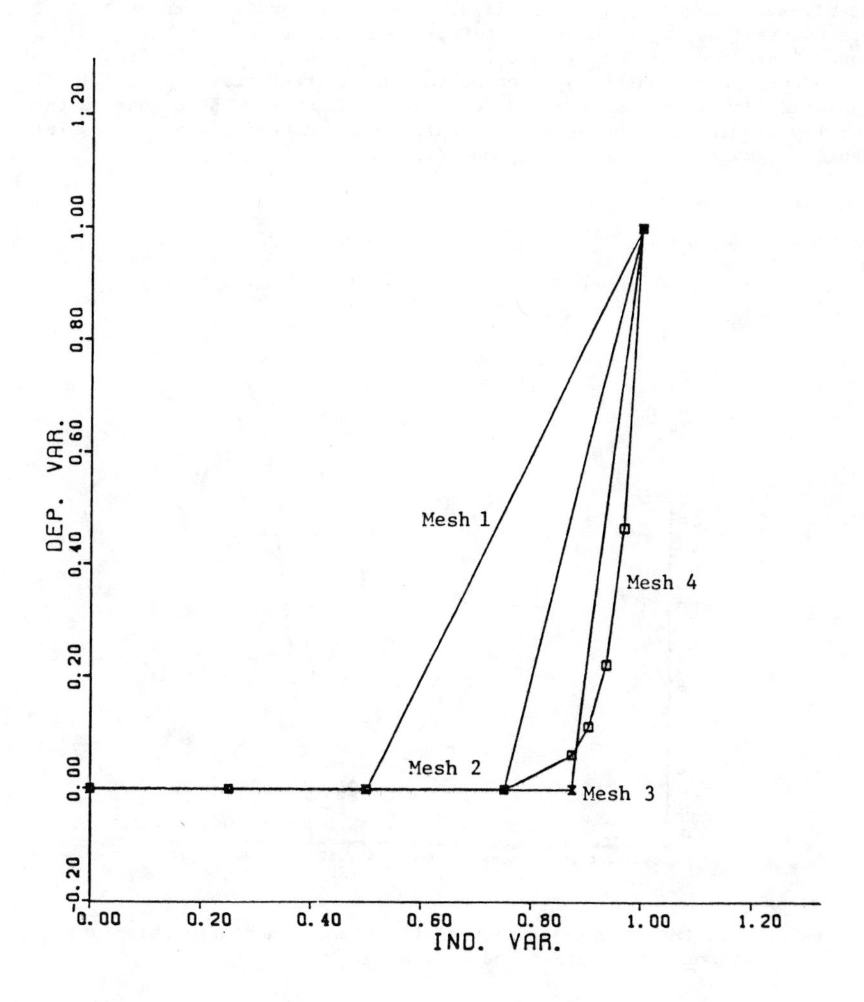

Figure 1. Finite element solution with adaptive mesh refinement and optimal local upwinding technique. Mesh numbers indicated.

for each element Ω_e .

In Figure 1 we show the finite element solution of the steady state case with $\alpha = 1$, $\beta^2 = 24$, boundary data $\gamma_0 = 0$, $\gamma_1 = 1$ and non-uniform mesh refinement with variable upwinding. Results are not oscillatory and are essentially exact on mesh 4.

Next we consider evolution of an initial profile $u(x,0) = x$ to the above steady-state boundary-layer profile. The mesh is uniform and the coefficients are constant so ω_e = constant . Representative results at t = .02, .04, .06 and .08 are indicated in Figure 2.

The approach has been extended to nonlinear problems by applying local linearization in a time step and determining ω_e from the eigenstructure of the locally linearized problem. This approach is now being used successfully for nonlinear multicomponent-multiphase transport problems.

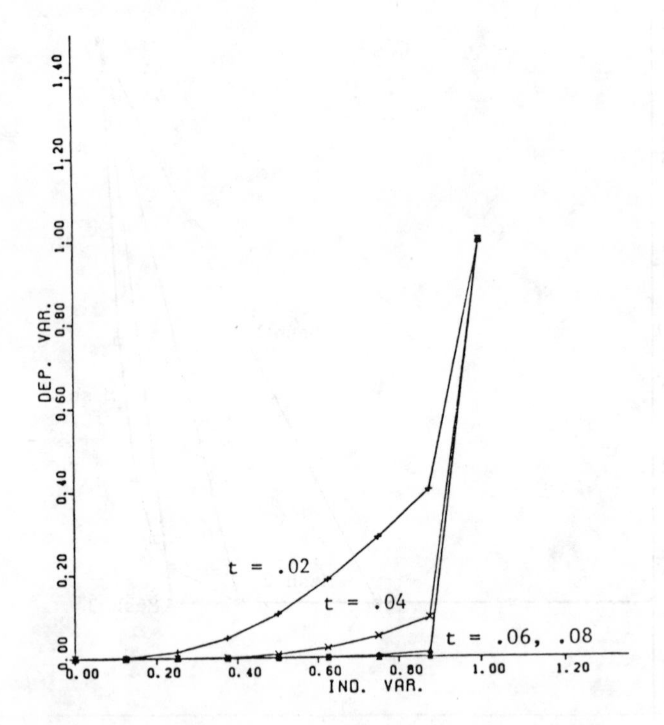

Figure 2. Finite element solution of the time dependent problem using the lumped formulation and upwinding.

(b) Stefan Problem

Stefan problems, such as those encountered in freezing and thawing, are complicated by the presence of a free boundary separating the frozen and unfrozen regions and by the presence of a latent heat source term which arises physically as the material changes state at the front [2]. The location of the front is not known in advance and oscillations in the location of the front or in the computed latent heat term can arise during numerical computations.

Mathematically, heat conduction with phase change is described by

$$\frac{\partial}{\partial t}(\rho c T + \rho\lambda) - \nabla\cdot(k\nabla T) = 0 \qquad (6)$$

where T is temperature, t is time, c is volumetric heat capacity, $\rho\lambda$ is the latent heat content, and k is the thermal conductivity. The heat capacity and the thermal conductivity vary depending on the soil type, moisture content and whether the soil is frozen or unfrozen. The latent heat term, $\partial(\rho\lambda)/\partial t$, is large and within a time step it is active only in the region which is changing phase. Either the temperature or the heat flux can be specified as boundary conditions at the surface and at remote boundaries.

Physically, latent heat of fusion is the extra energy required to thaw ice at its melting point without an increase in temperature. However, it is difficult to simulate this physical phenomenon numerically. The estimate of energy from the latent heat of fusion determines the rate of advancement of the melt front at each time step, and since the rate of movement of the melt front is not constant, the amount of latent heat involved at each time step also varies. To account for the latent heat effect, some investigators either split the region into subregions with separate conduction equations for each sub-region or they approximate the latent heat effect by an "equivalent heat capacity" derived from rapid variations of heat capacity within a narrow range of temperature at the transition zone. The location of the interface between the subregions can be determined by use of an enthalpy function or by inner iteration until the heat conduction equation is satisfied (Wheeler [3], Harlan [4], and Taylor and Luthin [5]). Gupta and Kumar [6] use internal boundary conditions to locate the freeze front. Kikuchi and Ichikawa [7] have obtained good results in a general setting using a variational inequality formulation of the boundary value problem Eq. (6), and Wheeler [3] has obtained good thermal histories using standard finite element methods with many nonlinear iterations to locate the phase change interface at each time step. We use a different approach. The goal in this work was to obtain good thermal histories using standard finite element analysis and a standard time stepping technique such as the backward difference method or the Crank-Nicolson method. In addition it was desirable that the computational work at each time step be minimized and this prohibited using many nonlinear iterations to locate the freeze front.

The extra energy absorbed by ice during melting is simulated by imposing a negative energy source at the melt front. Here latent heat of fusion will be treated as a dynamic loading "force" which moves along the melt front with magnitude which is a function of the advancement of the computed melt front at each time step. This energy term, however, produces numerical difficulties. Instead of preserving the temperature at the melting point during phase change, it actually lowers the temperature near the front. This causes numerical instability and oscillations. For brevity, results using a one-dimensional model are presented. The initial temperature of the medium is constant at 20° F, and the heat flux from a line source is assumed to be 7000 Btu/day-ft, which is simulated as a cylindrical pipeline with a two-foot radius with time dependent temperature imposed on the external surface of the pipeline. The imposed temperature was obtained by evaluating the analytical solution (Carslaw and Jaeger [8]) at a radius of two feet from the line source. The pipeline temperature and the energy flux out of the pipeline vary with time. The latent heat of fusion ($\rho\lambda$) is 3000 Btu/ft^3 and the other thermal properties are

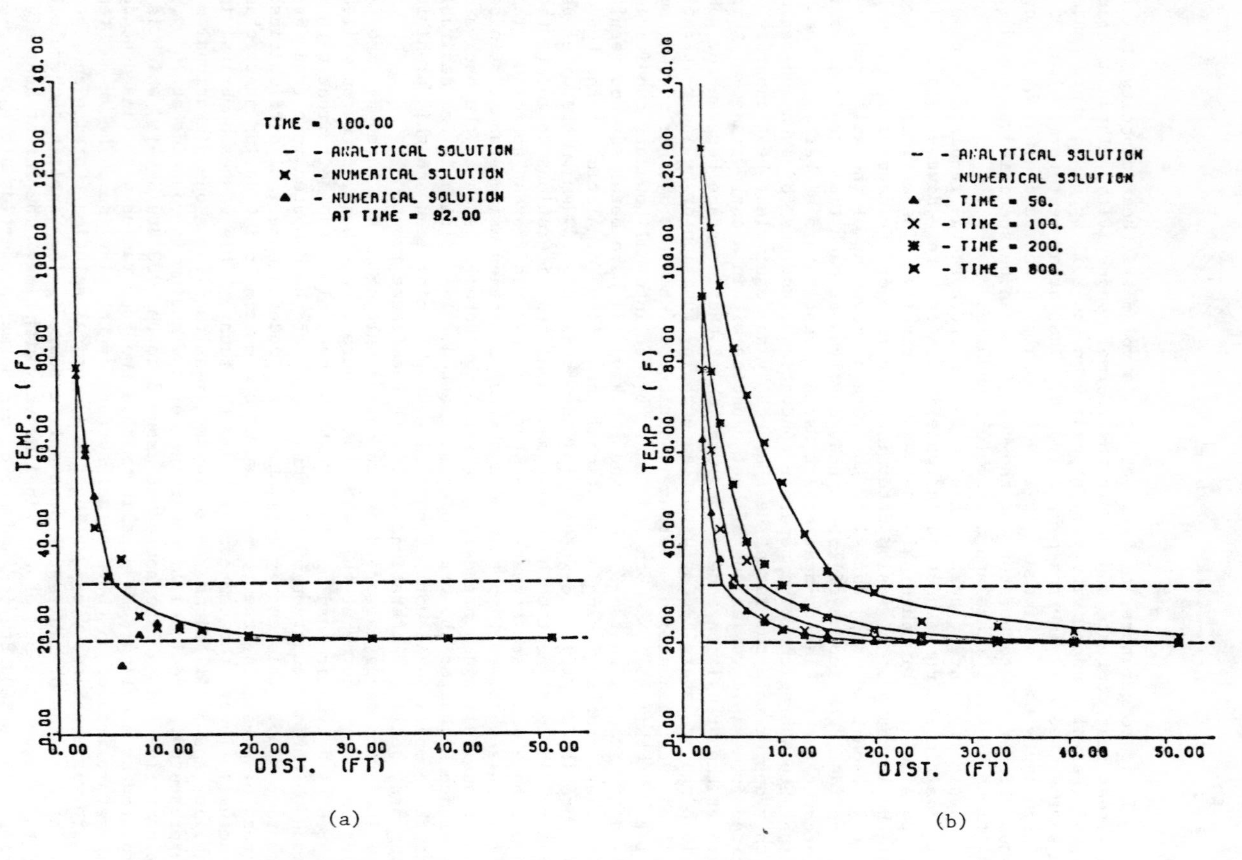

Figure 3. Temperature profiles obtained with the Crank-Nicolson method.

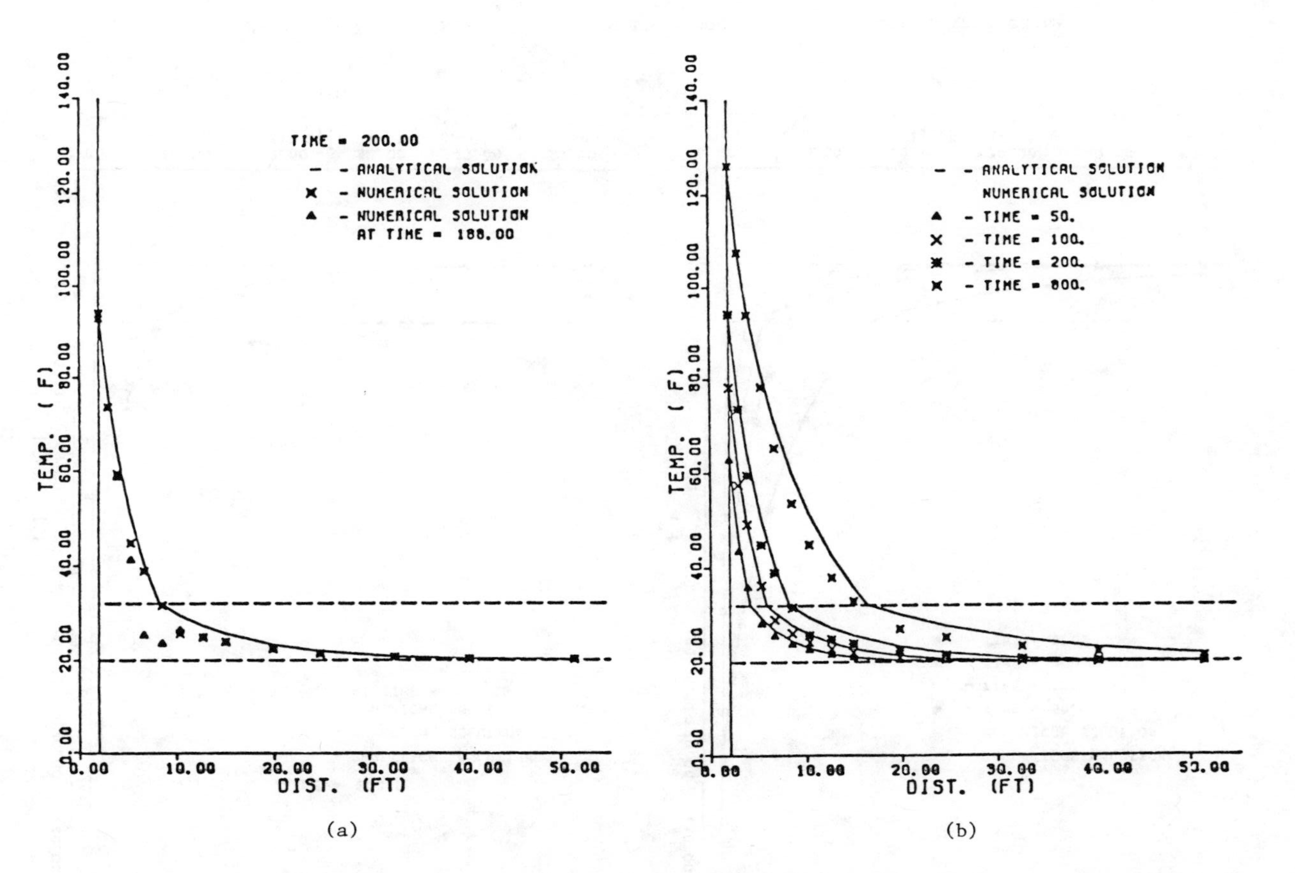

(a)

(b)

Figure 4. Temperature profiles obtained with a standard predictor-corrector method.

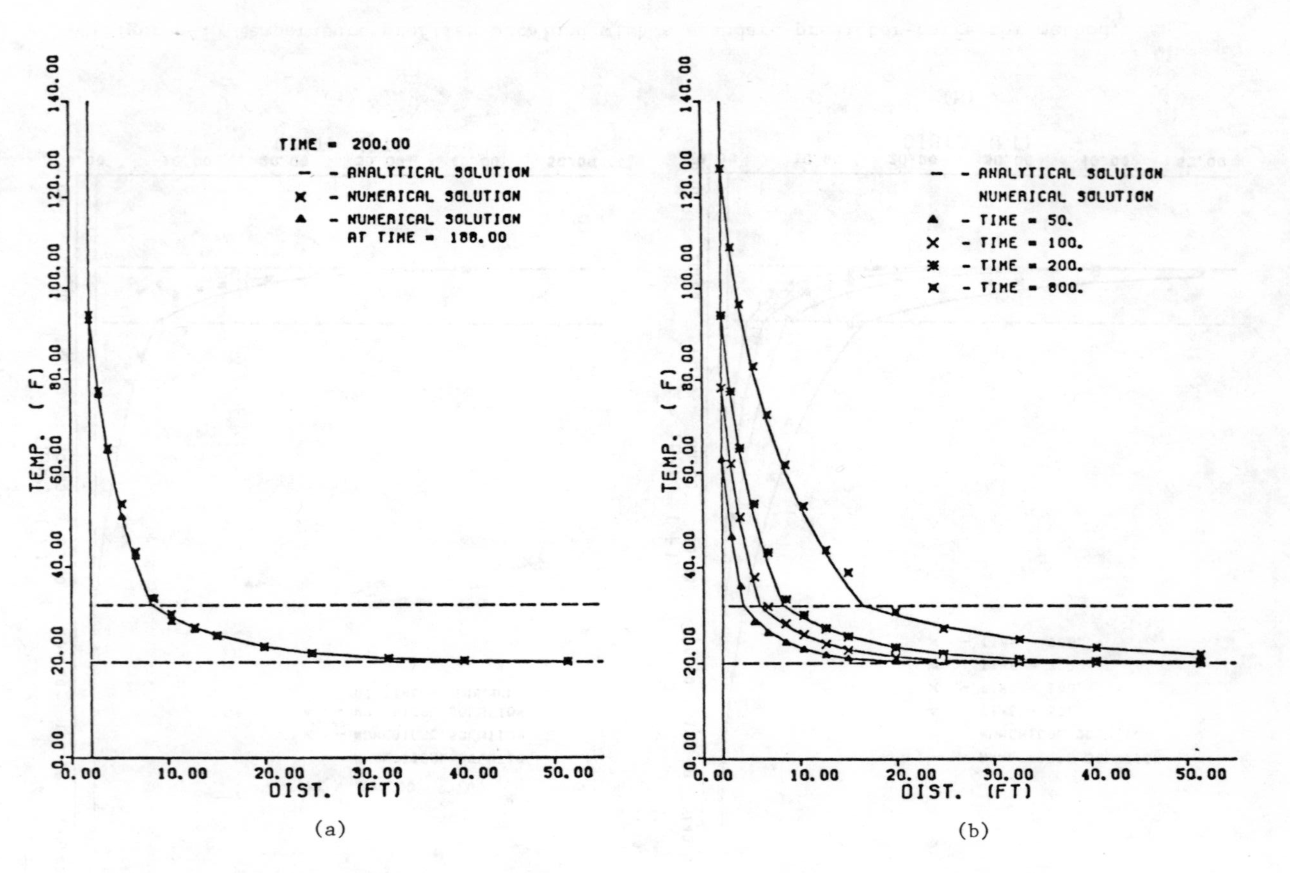

Figure 5. Temperature profiles obtained with a modified predictor-corrector method.

	Frozen	Thawed
Thermal Conductivity (Btu/day-ft-°F)	36.0	24.0
Heat Capacity (Btu/cu-ft-°F)	40.0	50.0

The analytical solution for this example is given for an infinite continuum, but we replace it with a finite region using the standard finite element method. This finite representation of an infinite continuum is fortunately feasible, since the effect of the line source decreases with increasing radial distance. A remote boundary sufficient distance away from the line source is used so that physically the heat flux across this boundary is negligible, and a zero flux boundary condition is imposed in the numerical model.

Three schemes for treating the nonlinearities are considered: (1) CN: a standard Crank-Nicolson scheme in which the front location is given by extrapolating temperatures from two previous time steps, (Douglas and Dupont, [9]); (2) PC: a standard predictor-corrector in which the corrector iterations are used to locate the front,; and (3) MPC: a modified predictor-corrector method in which the current front location is given by a weighted average of locations obtained on previous corrector iterations, (Ng, [10]). A variable time step is used.

Figure 3 shows the results using the CN method. Numerical oscillations start a few steps after the negative source is applied to the first element, and are most severe just ahead of the front. Oscillations are so bad that some of the nodal point temperatures are below the ambient temperature of 20° F of the frozen ground. However, the oscillations become smaller in amplitude when the front slows down, and a much better long term result can be obtained as seen from Figure 3.b. The improvement in numerical solutions suggests there are little accumulated errors from this oscillation.

Figure 4 shows the results using the PC method. Although cyclic oscillations occur at every other time step, good results can be obtained at the early stages and they are definitely better than those obtained with the CN method. Numerical solutions appear to be lagging behind the analytical solution, and the computed solutions become more unstable at later times.

Figure 5 shows the temperature profiles for the MPC method. The magnitude of the cyclic oscillation is comparable to the PC method at the early stages, but it is much less at a later time. The improvement in the accuracy of solutions using the MPC method can be seen by comparing Figures 4 and 5. With the MPC method there is no sudden drop in temperature beyond the front, and the change in slope of the numerical solutions at the phase change boundary is well represented.

3. CONCLUSIONS

Special techniques based on the finite element method have been presented for treating convection dominated flows and for Stefan problems with phase change. These techniques have been shown to greatly reduce oscillatory behavior in the solution for problems in which convection is important and in the location of the thaw front for Stefan problems.

ACKNOWLEDGEMENT

The authors wish to thank Mr. Timothy Plover and Mr. Y. K. Ng for their assistance in obtaining these numerical results. This work was supported in part by the U.S. Army under contract DAAG29-79-C-0081.

REFERENCES

1. Hughes, T. J. R. (ed.) (1979): Finite Element Methods for Convection-Dominated Flows, ASME Monograph AMD 34.

2. Kikuchi, N. and Ichikawa, Y. (1979): Numerical methods for two-phase Stefan problems by variatonal inequalities, Int. J. Num. Meth. Eng., 14, pp. 1221-1239.

3. Wheeler, J. A. (1973): Simulation of heat transfer from a warm pipeline buried in permafrost, 75th National Meeting of the Americal Institute of Chemical Engineers.

4. Harlan, R. L. (1973): Analysis of coupled heat-fluid transport in partially frozen soil, Water Resources Branch, Dept. of the Environment, Ottawa, Canada.

5. Taylor, G. S. and Luthin, J. N. (1980): Numeric results of coupled heat-mass flow during freezing and thawing, Proceedings, 2nd Conference on Soil-Water Problems in Cold Regions, Edmonton, Alberta.

6. Gupta, R. S. and Kumar, D. (1980): A modified variable time step method for the one-dimensional Stefan problem, Computer Methods in Applied Mechanics and Engineering, vol. 23.

7. Bathe, K. J. and Koshgaftan, M. R. (1981): On finite element analysis of nonlinear heat transfer with phase changes, in Finite Elements and Water Resources, Wang et. al. (eds.), Pentech Press, pp. 7.12-7.29.

8. Carslaw, H. S. and Jaeger, J. D. (1975): Conduction of Heat Solids, 2nd ed., Oxford University Press.

9. Douglas, J. and Dupont, J. (1970): Galerkin methods for parabolic equations, SIAM J. Numer. Anal. 7, pp. 575-626.

10. Ng, Y. K. (1981): Direct implementation of latent heat of fusion for a permafrost problem, Master's Thesis, University of Texas at Austin.

LAMINAR AND TURBULENT EXTERNAL FLOWS

Heat Transfer in Flow Past Cylinders with Variable Viscosity

M.W. CHANG, B.A. FINLAYSON and C.A. SLEICHER
Department of Chemical Engineering, BF-10
University of Washington
Seattle, Washington 98195

1. INTRODUCTION

Accurate knowledge of the overall convective heat transfer from circular cylinders is important in a number of fields, such as boiler design and hot wire anemometry. Existing Nusselt number correlations are based on experimental results which show large variations; for small Reynolds number (Re<100), the mean deviation amounts to 35%. Furthermore no reliable data exists when the cylinder is cooled rather than heated. It was first recognized by Hilpert [1] that the temperature of the surface of the cylinder can affect the heat transfer coefficient by altering the fluid properties. This effect is most pronounced for fluids with high Prandtl numbers or for situations with high temperature driving forces.

Both experimental and theoretical approaches have been used to study heat transfer and fluid flow past circular cylinders at low Re. Taneda [2] and Grove et al.[3] studied experimentally the characteristics of the wake behind the cylinder. Tritton [4] measured the drag produced by a stream of air flowing past a nearly-infinite circular cylinder. Heat transfer measurements for low Re are available only for the mean Nusselt number and for heated cylinders [5, 6, 7, 8, 9]. Numerical solutions to the problems were obtained only recently. Dennis and Chang [10] and Collins and Dennis [11] solved the flow problem using the finite difference method (FDM). Dennis et al. [12] and Krall and Eckert [13] employed the FDM to solve the coupled flow and energy equations. Taylor and Hood [14], Tuann and Olson [15] solved the flow equations by the finite element method (FEM). No FEM solutions for this problem are available for the flow and the temperature field together. The effect of the variable fluid properties on fluid flow and heat transfer for this geometry has not been carefully investigated.

A numerical simulator, HEAT, developed for modeling general fluid flow and heat transfer problems, has been used for the study. In this work, the problem is solved for either constant fluid properties or variable fluid viscosity. The constant property solution is used to compare our simulations with other solutions. Our major interest is the analysis of the effect of the viscosity variation of a real fluid on both fluid flow and heat transfer under both heating and cooling conditions.

2. PROBLEM FORMULATION

The following assumptions are made:

(1) two-dimensional, steady-state, laminar flow,
(2) incompressible, Newtonian fluid,
(3) planar geometry,
(4) Dirichlet and/or Neumann type boundary conditions,
(5) only the viscosity varies with temperature.

Under these restrictions, the governing equations describing fluid flow and heat transfer can be expressed as:

Continuity Equation: $$\nabla \cdot \underset{\sim}{u} = 0 \tag{1}$$

Momentum Equation: $$\underset{\sim}{u} \cdot \nabla \underset{\sim}{u} = -\nabla p/2 - \frac{1}{Re} \nabla \cdot \underset{\approx}{\tau} \tag{2}$$

Energy Equation: $$Pe \underset{\sim}{u} \cdot \nabla \theta = \nabla^2 \theta \tag{3}$$

The dimensionless terms involved are:

$$\underset{\sim}{u} = \underset{\sim}{u}'/u_\infty, \quad P = 2P'/\rho u_\infty^2$$
$$Re = u_\infty d/\nu_\infty, \quad \mu = \mu'/\mu_\infty \tag{4}$$
$$Pe = u_\infty d/\alpha_\infty, \quad \theta = \frac{T - T_\infty}{T_w - T_\infty}$$

where ' are dimensional terms and the free-stream temperature is chosen as the reference. For Newtonian fluids, the constitutive relation gives:

$$\underset{\approx}{\tau} = -2\mu(\Theta)\underset{\approx}{e} - \lambda (\nabla \cdot \underset{\sim}{u}) \underset{\approx}{\delta} \tag{5}$$

where $\underset{\approx}{e}$ and $\underset{\approx}{\delta}$ are the deformation tensor and identity tensor, respectively, and λ is a material function equal to $-2/3\ \mu(\theta)$ by Stokes's hypothesis. Notice that Eqs. (2), (3) are coupled through the viscosity variation with temperature in Eq. (5).

3. NUMERICAL METHODS

To pursue the solution of the Eqs. (1) ∿ (3) in general, a well-established Galerkin form of the finite element method (GFEM) is proposed. Detailed description of the method is referred to the literature [16, 17, 18]. No derivation of the equations is undertaken here. Rather the discussion is limited to a brief mention of the most important features of the numerical methods.

Nine-node Lagrangian elements are employed to discretize the continuum domain. Bilinear pressure and biquadratic velocity and temperature variables are used in each element. The system equations are solved simultaneously by performing a LU-decomposition of the assembled global matrix by means of the frontal solution method [19]. The Newton-Raphson iteration procedure is applied to the convective terms in both the momentum and energy equations, while successive substitution is used for the variable viscosity.

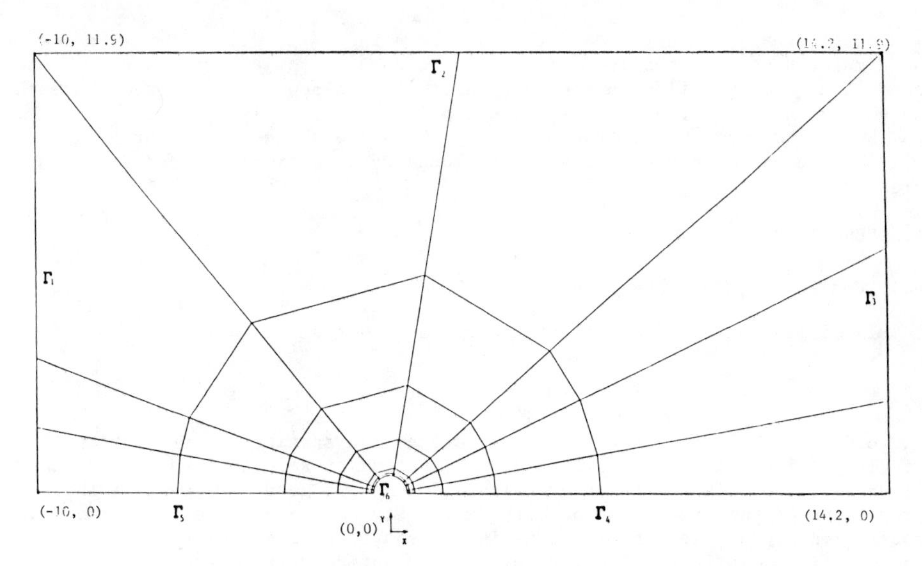

Figure 1 6 x 8 Mesh

The local Nusselt number on the surface of the cylinder is obtained by differentiating the temperature solution on the element.

$$\mathrm{Nu} \equiv \frac{hd}{k} \equiv -d \left.\frac{\partial \theta}{\partial r}\right|_{r=R} = \frac{d}{\Delta r} (3\theta_1 - 4\theta_2 + \theta_3) \qquad (6)$$

where h is the local heat transfer coefficient defined by Eq. (6), Δr is the first radial step size and θ_1, θ_2, and θ_3 are the temperatures on the cylinder and at distances $\Delta r/2$ and Δr away from the cylinder, respectively. A more accurate procedure is suggested by others [20, 21] who use an integral energy balance. The mean Nusselt number is obtained by integration azimuthally on the cylinder surface.

$$\mathrm{Nu}_m = \int_0^\pi \mathrm{Nu}\ d\phi/\pi \qquad (7)$$

The local Nusselt number is integrated using the Simpson's rule, which is consistent with the approximate solution:

$$\mathrm{Nu}_m = \frac{1}{\pi} \sum_e \Delta\phi^e \left(\frac{1}{6} \mathrm{Nu}_1{}^e + \frac{2}{3} \mathrm{Nu}_2{}^e + \frac{1}{6} \mathrm{Nu}_3{}^e \right) \qquad (8)$$

Here $\Delta\phi^e$ is the element size of the e-th element, while $\mathrm{Nu}_i{}^e$ are the local Nusselt number at the first, second and third node on the cylinder surface.

The symmetrical nature of the problem for Re<45 enables a simulation using only half of the flow field [9]. The 6 x 8 mesh was designed to insure good accuracy near the cylinder while properly representing the solution far from the cylinder (see Figure 1). The surface of the cylinder is represented exactly by 8 isoparametric quadratic Lagrangian elements. The infinite domain is approximated by imposing natural boundary conditions at the upper (Γ_2)

and outflow (Γ_3) boundaries and the symmetry lines (Γ_4, Γ_5). Large domains can be simulated using a smaller finite element domain provided the natural boundary conditions are satisfied in the integral, Galerkin sense. Here that means that no external forces or heat fluxes are applied on boundaries Γ_2, Γ_3, Γ_4 and Γ_5. On the inflow boundary we take $u = 1$, $v = 0$, $\theta = 0$ while on the surface of the cylinder we used $u = v = 0$, $\theta = 1$. No boundary conditions are necessary for pressure.

4. RESULTS

4.1 Constant Fluid Properties

The dimensionless pressure at the cylinder surface is defined as:

$$P_w = (P_w' - P_\infty')/(\tfrac{1}{2}\rho u_\infty^2) \tag{9}$$

where P_w' and P_∞' are the dimensional surface and static pressures, respectively. Azimuthal surface pressure distribution at Re = 40 is displayed in Figure 2. Comparison with other calculations shows good agreement. Other properties of the solutions including vorticity on the cylinder surface, drag coefficients, wake length are investigated and compare satisfactorily with the existing solutions. These results give confidence that the flow field is correctly determined [22].

Heat transfer results are calculated in terms of local Nusselt number for air at several Reynolds numbers (0.01<Re<50) in Figure 3. The GFEM results are in good agreement with those obtained using the finite difference method as long as centered derivatives were used [12]. Krall and Eckert [13] tried

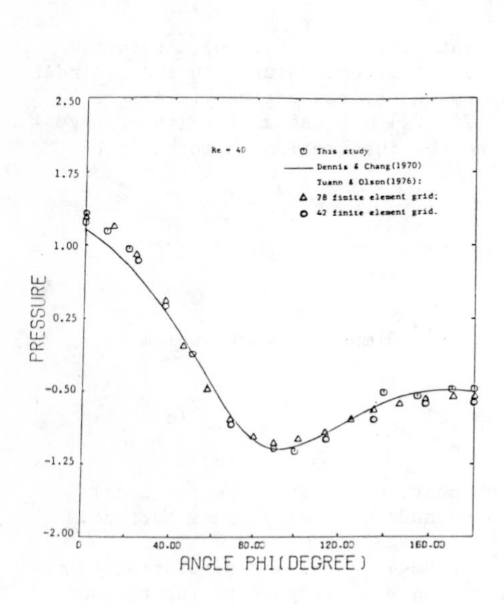

Figure 2 Azimuthal Surface Pressure Distribution

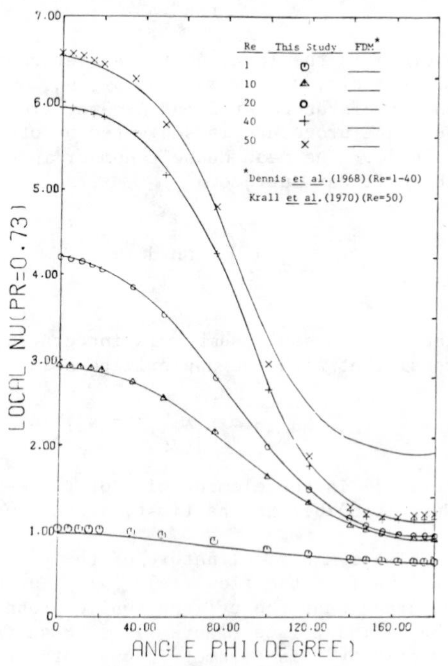

Figure 3 Azimuthal Nusselt Number Distribution for Air

to avoid numerical instability by using 'upwind differencing' in the convective term of the energy equation. This creates an artificial diffusion in the energy equation. The inception of flow separation introduces a reverse flow which creates a non-conservative error in the numerical solution [23]. In Krall and Eckert's work the error acts just like an artificial heat sink in this region. As a property of the upwind differencing scheme, this error propagates in the downstream direction [23]. Consequently, in their work the heat flux in the reverse flow region is over-estimated by about 30% (see Figure 3, Re = 50). The finite element method does a better job without upwind differencing with proper mesh refinement. For the case of air flow, with a temperature driving force less than 80°C, the effect of variable fluid properties is estimated to be less than 5% [22]. Our results in terms of mean Nusselt number are compared to experimental results in Figure 4. Generally the results differ by an average of 5% among each other.

For several Reynolds numbers, a wide range of fluids are covered in our simulation. Azimuthal local Nusselt number distributions are displayed in Figure 5 for various Prandtl numbers at Re = 1. The numerical results for mean Nusselt number are correlated in the range $0.01<Re<50$ and $7.3 \times 10^{-3}<Pr<10^4$ by:

$$Nu_m = 0.86\,(Re)^{0.42}\,(Pr)^{0.31} \qquad (10a)$$

with 9.7% mean deviation or

$$Nu_m = [0.36 + 0.58(Re)^{0.48}](Pr)^m \qquad (10b)$$
$$m = 0.29 + 0.028\,\log_{10}(Re)$$

with 4% mean deviation

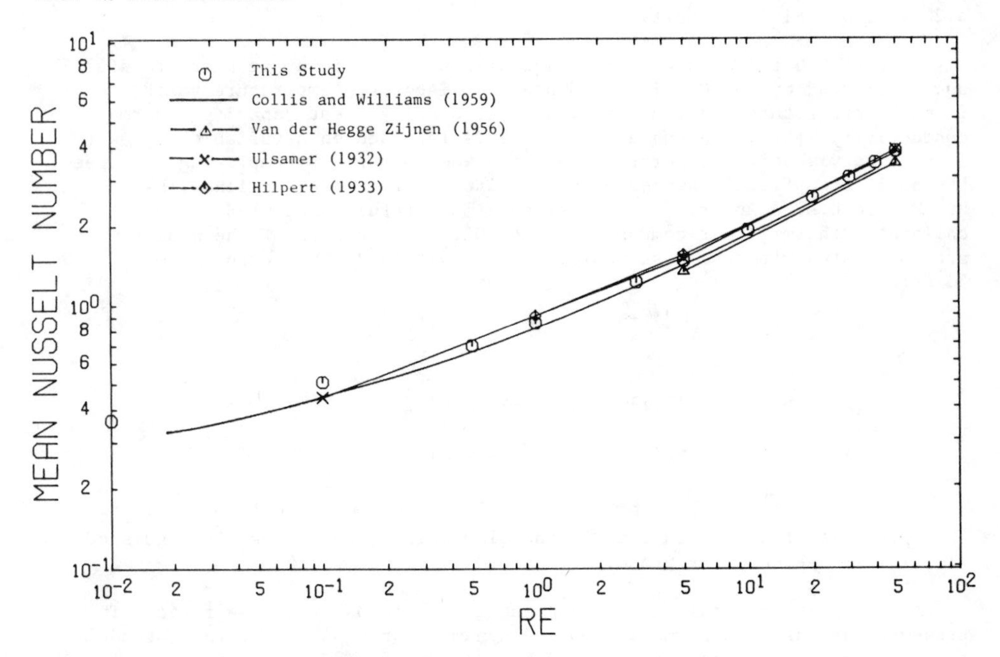

Figure 4 Mean Nusselt Number Versus Reynolds Number for Air

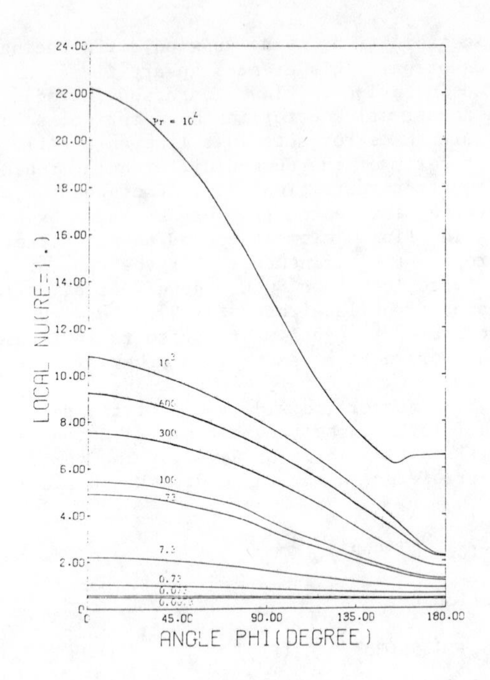

Figure 5 Azimuthal Nusselt Number Distribution for Various Fluids

4.2 Variable Fluid Property

DOWTHERM G fluid is a stable, low pressure, liquid phase heat transfer agent marketed by Dow Chemical. Since the viscosity-temperature variation is much larger than other properties (i.e. density, heat capacity, thermal conductivity) [22], the subsequent analysis is based on a variable viscosity only. The viscosity-temperature relation was measured by employing a 4-speed, LV model, Brookfield's Synchro-Lectric Viscometer in conjunction with the Brookfield U.L. Adapter. The temperature is carefully measured using a calibrated thermilinear component YSI#44202. The results of the measurement are correlated with the best empirical fit (within 2% mean error from 4°C to 50°C):

$$\mu\ (\text{c.p.}) = \left(e^{n(A_o+B_o/T)} + e^{n(A_1+B_1/T)}\right)^{1/n}$$

$$T\ (=)\ ^\circ K$$

$$A_o = -27.6902,\ B_o = 8944.2587 \qquad (11)$$

$$A_1 = -8.3878,\ B_1 = 3404.9589$$

$$n = 8.0631$$

This viscosity function is used in the simulations, which are distinguished as (T_w, T_∞) in degrees centigrade.

A cooled cylindrical surface increases the viscosity of the fluid. The pressure, acting as a normally imposed dynamic force on the surface, tends to decrease in the front portion of the cylinder (see Figure 6 for $Re_\infty = 1$).

FIGURE 6 THE VISCOSITY EFFECT ON PRESSURE DISTRIBUTION (RE=1)

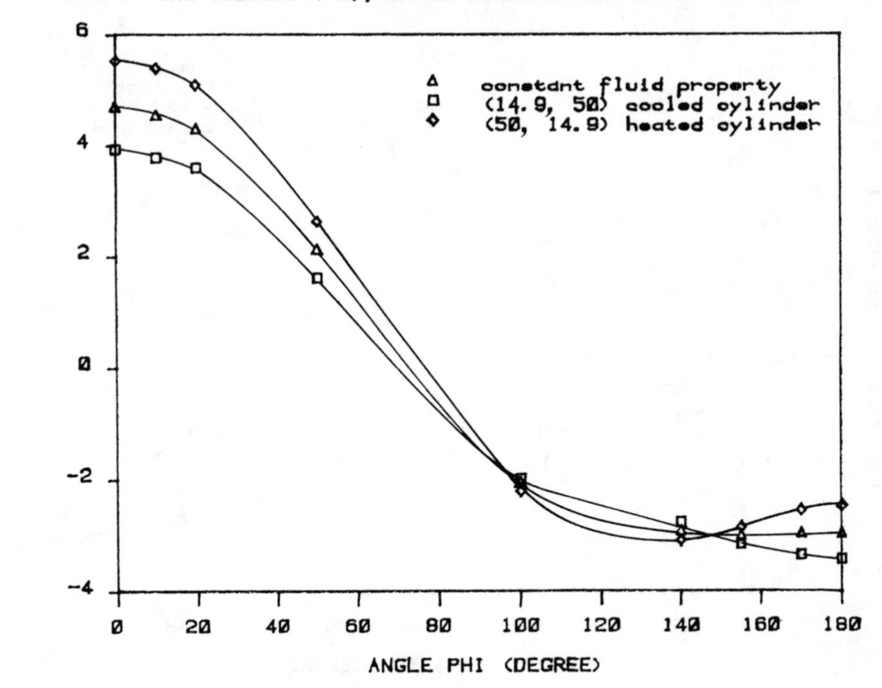

The opposite effect is observed for a heated cylinder. Notice that an adverse pressure gradient appears only at the rear portion of a heated cylinder. This is because the fluid's viscosity at the wall is only 26% that of in the free-stream. The Reynolds number based on the wall viscosity is 3.8 instead of 1.

The form drag coefficient, C_p, and shear drag coefficient, C_f, are directly related to the surface pressure and vorticity distribution, respectively. A higher viscosity near the cooled surface increases the shear drag coefficient significantly, but decreases the form drag coefficient only slightly. The reverse is true for the heated cylinder, as shown in Table I.

The local Nusselt numbers are displayed in Figure 7 for the case of variable viscosity at $Re_\infty = 1$ for both heated and cooled cylinder together with the corresponding isothermal cases. The higher viscosity of the fluid in the vicinity of the cooled cylinder reduces the velocity near the wall, consequently decreasing the convective heat flux rate. The reverse is true for a heated cylinder. Mean Nusselt numbers can be calculated and compared to the value predicted for constant fluid properties. Most correlations [7, 24, 9] are in the form:

$$Nu_m = A\, Re_\infty^{\,n}\, Pr_\infty^{\,m}\, (\mu_\infty/\mu_w)^p \qquad (12)$$

We find p=0.135 for both the heating and cooling case, which agrees nicely with the Sieder-Tate correlation having p=0.14.

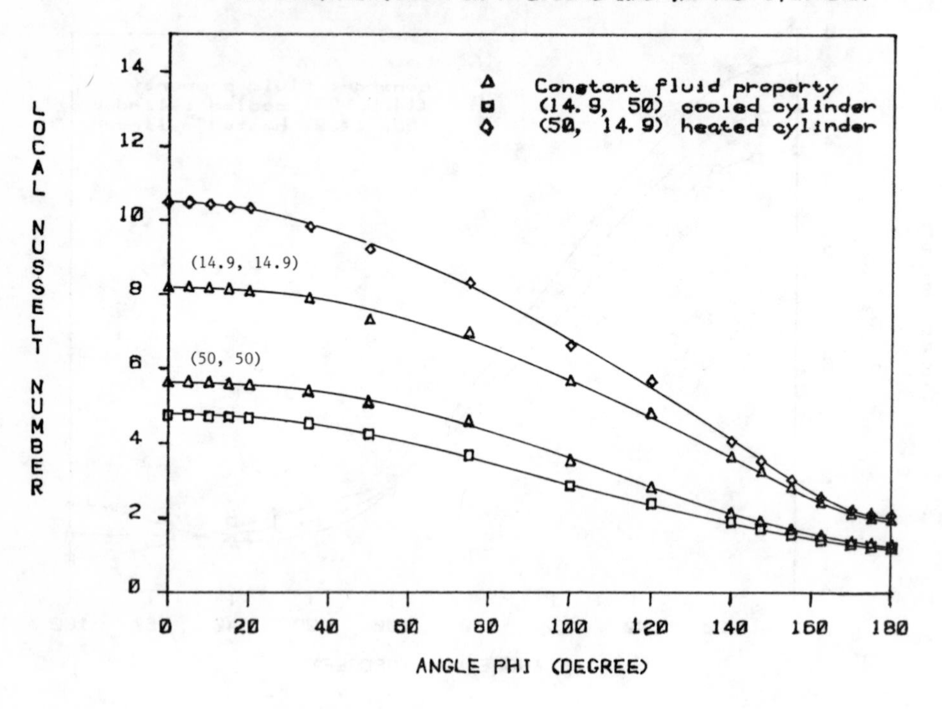

FIGURE 7

TABLE I. The Viscosity Effect on Drag Coefficients

	$Re_\infty = 1$			$Re_\infty = 10$	
(T_W, T_∞)	(50,14.9)	(14.9,50)	Const.	(7.1,20.9)	Const.
C_f	1.990(-32%)	4.044(+37%)	2.948	1.508(+16%)	1.300
C_p	3.269(+9%)	2.748(-8%)	2.989	1.635(-3%)	1.685
$^*C_D$	5.259(-11%)	6.792(+14%)	5.937	3.143(+5%)	2.985

$^*C_D = C_f + C_p$, total drag coefficient

Calculations have also been made for temperatures within the range of our experiment, (7.1, 20.9) [22]. The local Nusselt number is shown in Figure 8 for $Re_\infty = 10$. The viscosity variation has a significant similar influence on the shear drag coefficient (+16%) and the mean Nusselt number (-16%), as listed in Table II.

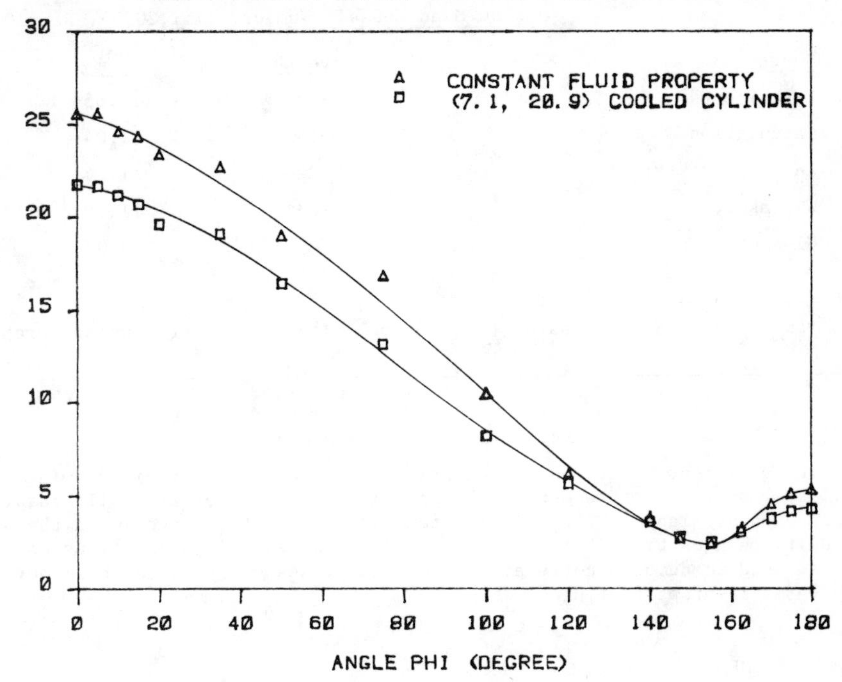

TABLE II. Results for Re_∞=10, Pr_∞=310, DOWTHERM G fluid T_w=7.1°C, T_∞=20.9°C

	C_f	C_p	C_D	L_s	ϕ_s	Nu_m
(20.9,20.9)	1.300	1.685	2.985	0.52	150°	13.1923
(7.1,20.9)	1.508	1.635	3.143	0.45	152°	11.0408
(Relative Change)	+16%	-3%	+5%	-13%	+1%	-16%

The effect on the form drag (-3%) is relatively small. Significant effects are observed on the wake length, L_s(-13%), but the separation angle, ϕ_s (+1%) hardly changes. Measurements conducted to study the wake behind the cylinder (3, 2) should be corrected for variable viscosity effects.

We can compare our results for Nu_m to those predicted by correlation of others as well as experimental data taken by us. This comparison is shown in Table III and is quite satisfactory.

TABLE III. Effect of Variable Fluid Properties* on the Mean Nusselt Number, (7.1,20.9), $Re_\infty=10$

Source	Relative Change	Nu_m
Experiment	-20% †	10.55
Calculation	-16%	11.04
Zhukauskas, $(Pr_\infty/Pr_w)^{0.25}$	-22%	11.54
Whitaker, $(\mu_\infty/\mu_w)^{0.25}$	-23%	11.78
Ulsamer		13.07

* $\mu_\infty/\mu_w = 0.35$, † compared to the simulation result for constant property

5. CONCLUSION

Finite element solutions of heat transfer to or from a fluid flowing past a cylinder show good agreement with experimental and theoretical literature values when available. The solution technique is suitable even when the viscosity changes by factors of 3 or 4. The theoretical calculations can thus be used to develop correlations for heat transfer to cooled cylinders with variable-property fluids.

ACKNOWLEDGEMENT

This research was supported in part by National Science Foundation Grant No. 80-11035.

REFERENCES

1. Hilpert,R., Wärmeabgabe von geheizten Drähten und Rohren im Luftstrom, Forsch. Geb. Ingenieurw, Vol. 4, 1933, pp. 215-224.

2. Taneda, S., Experimental Investigation of the Wakes behind Cylinders and Plates at Low Reynolds Numbers, J. Phys. Soc. Japan, Vol. 11, No. 3, 1956, pp. 302-307.

3. Grove, A.S., Shair, F.H., Petersen, E.E. and Acrivos, A., An Experimental Investigation of the Steady Separated Flow Past a Circular Cylinder, J. Fluid Mech., Vol. 19, Part 1, 1964, pp. 60-80.

4. Tritton, D.J., Experiments on the Flow Past a Circular Cylinder at Low Reynolds Numbers, J. Fluid Mech., Vol. 6, Part 4, 1959, pp. 547-567.

5. Hatton, A.P., James, D.D. and Swire, H.W., Combined Forced and Natural Convection with Low Speed Air Flow over Horizontal Cylinders, J. Fluid Mech., Vol. 42, 1970, pp. 17-31.

6. Collis, D.C. and Williams, M.J., Two-dimensional Convection from Heated Wires at Low Reynolds Numbers, J. Fluid Mech., Vol. 6, 1959, pp. 357-384.

7. Perkins, H.C. and Leppert, G., Forced Convection Heat Transfer from a Uniformly Heated Cylinder, J. Heat Transfer, Trans. ASME Series C, Vol. 8, 1962, pp. 257-263.

8. Davis, A.H., Convective Cooling of Wires in Streams of Viscous Liquids, Phil. Mag., Vol. 47, 1924, pp. 1057-1092.

9. Zhukauskas, A.A., Heat Transfer of Tubes in Crossflow, Adv. Heat Transfer, Vol. 8, 1972, pp. 93-160.

10. Dennis, S.C.R. and Chang, G.Z., Numerical Solutions for Steady Flow Past a Circular Cylinder at Reynolds Numbers up to 100, J. Fluid Mech., Vol. 42, Part 3, 1970, pp. 471-489.

11. Collins, W.M. and Dennis, S.C.R., Flow Past an Impulsively Started Cylinders, J. Fluid Mech., Vol. 60, 1973, pp. 105-127.

12. Dennis, S.C.R., Hudson, J.D., and Smith, N., Steady Laminar Forced Convection from a Circular Cylinder at Low Reynolds Numbers, Phys. of Fluids, Vol. 11, 1968, pp. 933-940.

13. Krall, K.M., Eckert, E.R.G., Heat Transfer to a Transverse Circular Cylinder at Low Reynolds Numbers Including Rarefaction Effect, Heat Transfer 1970, Vol. 3, FC. 7.5, Paris-Versallis.

14. Taylor C. and Hood, P., A Numerical Solution of the Navier-Stokes Equations Using the Finite Element Technique, Comp. Fluids, Vol. 1, 1973, pp. 73-100.

15. Tuann, S.Y., Olson, M.D., Numerical Studies of the Flow Around a Circular Cylinder by a Finite Element Method, Research Series Report No. 16 I.S.S.N. 0318-3378, Univ. of British Columbia, 1976.

16. Chang, P.W., Patten, T.W. and Finlayson, B.A., Collocation and Galerkin Finite Element Methods for Viscoelastic Fluid Flow - I. Description of Method and Problems with Fixed Geometry, Comp. Fluids, Vol. 7, 1979, pp. 267-283.

17. Chung, T.J., Finite Element Analysis in Fluid Dynamics, McGraw-Hill, New York 1978.

18. Zienkiewicz, O.C., The Finite Element Method, 3rd Ed., McGraw-Hill, London, 1977.

19. Hood, P., Frontal Solution Program for Unsymmetric Matrices, Int. J. Num. Meth. Engng., Vol. 10, 1976, pp. 379-399.

20. Marshall, R.S., Heinrich, J.C. and Zienkiewicz, O.C., Natural Convection in a Square Enclosure by a Finite-Element, Penalty Function Method Using Primitive Fluid Variables, Numerical Heat Transfer, Vol. 1, 1978, pp. 315-330.

21. Gresho, P.M., Lee, R.L. and Sani, R.L., The Consistent Method for Computing Derived Boundary Quantities when the Galerkin FEM is Used to Solve Thermal and/or Fluid Problems, UCRL-85366 Preprint, Lawrence Livermore Laboratory, 1981.

22. Chang, M.W., Finlayson, B.A., Sleicher, C.A., Heat Transfer in Flow Past Cylinders with Variable Fluid Properties, In preparation.

23. Roache, P.J., Computational Fluid Dynamics, Hermosa Publishers, 1972.

24. Whitaker, S., Forced Convection Heat Transfer Correlations for Flow in Pipes, Past Flat Plates, Single Cylinder, Single Spheres, and for Flow in Packed Beds and Tube Bundles, AIChE J., Vol. 18, 2, 1972, pp. 361-371.

25. Ulsamer, J., Die Wärmeabgabe eines Drahtes oder Rohres an einer senkrecht zur Achse Strömenden Gas-oder Flüssigkeisstrom, Forsch. Geb. Ingenieurw., Vol. 3 1932, pp. 94-98.

26. Zinjnen, B.G., Van Der Hegge, Modified Correlation Formulae for the Heat Transfers by Natural and by Forced Convection from Horizontal Cylinders, Appl. Sci. Res., Sec. A., Vol. 6, 1956-1957, pp. 129-140.

NOMENCLATURE

English and Greek Symbols:

C_D total drag coefficient $D/\frac{1}{2}\rho U_\infty^2$

C_f shear drag coefficient, shear drag force$/\frac{1}{2}\rho U_\infty^2$

C_p form drag coefficient, form drag force$/\frac{1}{2}\rho U_\infty^2$

D total drag force

d cylinder diameter

K thermal conductivity

L_s Wake length

Nu local Nusselt number hd/K

P dimensionless pressure $P'/\frac{1}{2}\rho U_\infty^2$

Pe Peclet number $U_\infty d/\alpha$

R cylinder radius

Re Reynolds number $U_\infty d/\nu$

T temperature

$\underset{\sim}{u}$ velocity vector

$\underset{\approx}{\tau}$ stress tensor

$\underset{\approx}{e}$ deformation tensor

$\underset{\approx}{\delta}$ identity tensor

μ dimensionless viscosity μ'/μ_∞

ν kinematic viscosity μ/ρ

ρ density

Θ dimensionless temperature $(T-Tw)/(T_\infty-Tw)$

ϕ azimuthal angle (ϕ=0 at leading edge)

ϕ_s separation angle (degree)

Γ simulation boundaries

α thermal diffusivity

Superscript and Subscript:

' dimensional terms

w wall characteristics

∞ free-stream characteristics

f mean-film characteristics

m mean value

The Unsteady Compressible Boundary Layer over a Semi-Infinite Flat Plate Caused by a Moving Shock

S.F. SHEN* and Y.M. CHEN**
Cornell University
Ithaca, New York 14853

1. INTRODUCTION

We consider the unsteady boundary layer over a semi-infinite flat plate in a quiescent gas caused by a normal shock moving downstream along the plate. This basic problem, as a variant of the simpler shock-tube problem treated by Mirels [1], was first studied by Lam and Crocco [2]. Their most important result is that, by using the Crocco transformation, it can again be reduced to an equivalent incompressible problem much in the same manner as for a number of steady boundary layers. However, the domain of interest now is expanding with time and the boundary layer has effectively two "leading edges", one of them being attached to the moving shock front. It was shown in [2] that for very weak shocks where $\alpha \equiv U/U_s \to 0$, U and U_s being the freestream velocity outside the boundary layer and the shock velocity, respectively, the equivalent incompressible problem is none other than the classical case of an impulsively started flat plate. Their actual computation was on the basis of a difficult integral equation, and ended up with only qualified success, the results being further limited to only the case $\alpha \to 0$. Much progress of course has since been made in the science and art of computation, especially by the finite-difference procedure. For the imcompressible boundary layer over an impulsively started flat plate, we now have excellent results, e.g. Hall [3], Dennis [4] and Williams and Rhyne [57]. Mention should also be made of Walker and Dennis [6], who computed the unsteady compressible boundary layer in a shock tube between the expansion and shock waves. The momentum and energy equations were put again into the Crocco form, but remained coupled because of the pressure gradient term. The discretization and upwinding followed [4] and a finite difference solution was successfully obtained. From the computational viewpoint, the two simultaneous equations in their case did not raise any new complications. It is generally accepted that the break-through lies in the proper account of the up-wind influence in problems of this type. Mathematically the solution behavior does involve an essential singularity as pointed out by Stewartson [7]. However, for actual computations, once recognized in designing the numerical procedure, it has so far not proved to be a serious hurdle.

This paper re-examines the Lam-Crocco problem for arbitrary shock strength and Prandtl number and provides its complete numerical solution. Instead of following the Crocco formulation, an unsteady stream-function and a Howarth

---

* Professor, Sibley School of Mechanical & Aerospace Engineering.

** Visiting Fellow; permanently, Research Associate, Institute of Mechanics, Chinese Academy of Sciences, Beijing, People's Republic of China.

transformation for the distance normal to the plate are introduced. For a linear viscosity-temeprature dependence, we again obtain the equations for momentum and energy which are decoupled from each other and identical to those for an incompressible fluid. In contrast to the Crocco form, their solution requires less cumbersome handling for the boundary conditions. In the following some of the details of the computation are discussed and typical results of the velocity and temperature profiles, as well as the Nusselt number variation along the plate are presented. We have also included cases where the Prandtl number is large, not because of their relevance to the gas dynamic problem as stated, but for showing the behavior of the thermal boundary layer in more general circumstances.

Boundary layers behind a moving front arise also in other practical problems. For instance, in the injection molding of polymers, hot fluid moves forward in a cold channel and the formation of a frozen layer along the wall is of critical interest. In such applications, the Prandtl number is much larger than unity. Other complications due to the non-Newtonian behavior notwithstanding, the basic aspects are no different from those treated here.

2. STATEMENT AND FORMULATION OF PROBLEM

The statement of the problem is schematically as in Fig. 1: the leading edge of the semi-infinite flat plate is at $x = 0$, the plate is along the x-axis, the normal shock moves to the right at shock Mach number M_s and velocity U_s, leaving behind a uniform flow of velocity U over the plate. In usual notation, the boundary layer equations are:

$$\frac{\partial \rho}{\partial t} + \frac{\partial}{\partial x}\rho u + \frac{\partial}{\partial y}\rho v = 0, \tag{1}$$

$$\rho\left(\frac{\partial u}{\partial t} + u\frac{\partial u}{\partial x} + v\frac{\partial u}{\partial y}\right) = \frac{\partial}{\partial y}\left(\mu\frac{\partial u}{\partial y}\right), \tag{2}$$

$$\rho C_p\left(\frac{\partial T}{\partial t} + u\frac{\partial T}{\partial x} + v\frac{\partial T}{\partial y}\right) = \mu\left(\frac{\partial u}{\partial y}\right)^2 + \frac{\partial}{\partial y}\left(k\frac{\partial T}{\partial y}\right). \tag{3}$$

For perfect gas:

$$\rho T = \rho_\infty T_\infty, \tag{4}$$

the subscript "∞" referring to conditions outside the boundary layer. We further assume constant C_p and constant Prandtl number $Pr \equiv \mu C_p/k$, and in addition

$$\frac{\mu}{\mu_\infty} = C\frac{T}{T_\infty}. \tag{5}$$

The shock strikes the leading edge at $t = 0$. At all $t > 0$, the boundary conditions are therefore:

$$\begin{aligned} &u = v = 0,\ T = T_w \quad \text{on } y = 0; \\ &u = U,\ T = T_\infty \quad \text{as } y \to \infty. \end{aligned} \tag{6}$$

The solution is sought in the wedge-shaped domain in x,t-plane, between the lines $x = 0$ and $x = U_s t$.

Lam and Crocco [2] showed that in Crocco variables Eqs. (1) - (5) are

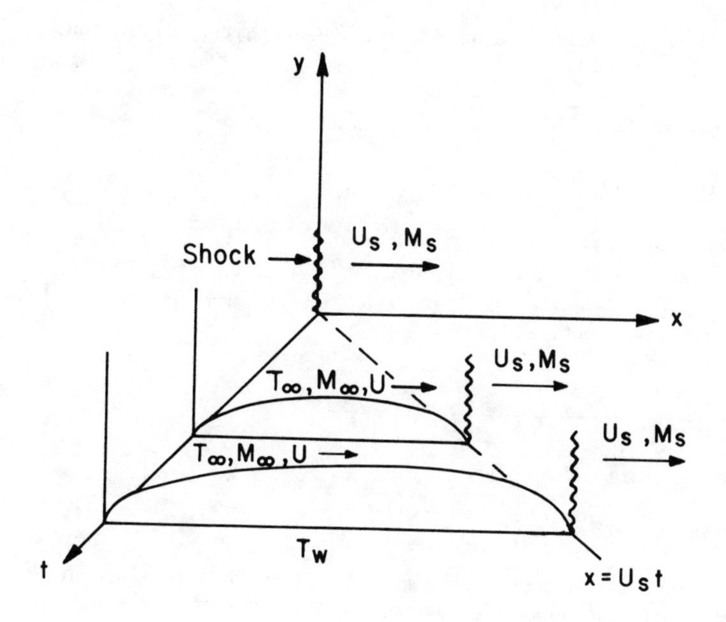

Figure 1.

reducible to a set of two equations without explicit compressibility effects. We propose now to achieve the same in an alternate form which may be more convenient for computation. An "unsteady streamfunction" $\psi(x,y,t)$ is first introduced to satisfy the continuity equation, Eq. (1),

$$\frac{\partial\psi}{\partial y} = \frac{\rho}{\rho_\infty}u, \quad -\frac{\partial\psi}{\partial x} = \frac{\rho}{\rho_\infty}v + \frac{\partial}{\partial t}\int_0^y \frac{\rho}{\rho_\infty}\, dy \,. \tag{7}$$

The independent variables are next given a Howarth transformation,

$$\xi = x, \quad \eta = \int_0^y \frac{\rho}{\rho_\infty}\, dy, \quad t = t \,. \tag{8}$$

Consequently, Eq. (7) becomes

$$\frac{\partial\psi}{\partial\eta} = u, \quad -\frac{\partial\psi}{\partial\xi} = \frac{\rho}{\rho\infty}v + \frac{\partial\eta}{\partial t} + u\,\frac{\partial\eta}{\partial x} \,.$$

It follows that, because of Eqs. (4) and (5), the momentum and energy equations are reduced to, respectively,

$$\frac{\partial^2\psi}{\partial t\partial\eta} + \frac{\partial\psi}{\partial\eta}\frac{\partial^2\psi}{\partial\xi\partial\eta} + \frac{\partial\psi}{\partial\xi}\frac{\partial^2\psi}{\partial\eta 2} = C\nu_\infty\frac{\partial^3\psi}{\partial\eta 3}, \tag{10}$$

$$\frac{\partial T}{\partial t} + \frac{\partial\psi}{\partial\eta}\frac{\partial T}{\partial\xi} + \frac{\partial\psi}{\partial\xi}\frac{\partial T}{\partial\eta} = C\,\frac{\nu_\infty}{C_p}\left(\frac{\partial^2\psi}{\partial\eta 2}\right)^2 + C\,\frac{\nu_\infty}{P_r}\frac{\partial^2 T}{\partial\eta^2}, \tag{11}$$

where $C = \rho\mu/\rho_\infty\mu_\infty$, constant. Note that Eqs. (10) and (11) are precisely the same equations for an unsteady incompressible boundary layer with no pressure gradient, except for the constant C.

Just as in the case of the impulsively started flat plate in an incompressible fluid, the boundary conditions suggest that the solution is obtainable in terms of the similarity variables

$$\zeta = \frac{\eta}{2}\sqrt{\frac{U}{C\nu_\infty\xi}}, \quad \tau = \frac{\xi}{Ut}. \tag{12a}$$

Further, write

$$\psi = 2\sqrt{C\nu_\infty U\xi}\, f(\zeta,\tau), \qquad \frac{T-Tw}{T_\infty - Tw} = \theta(\zeta,\tau) \,. \tag{12b}$$

The governing equations are, from Eqs. (10) and 11), respectively,

$$f_{\zeta\zeta\zeta} + 2ff_{\zeta\zeta} = 4\tau[(f_\zeta - \tau)f_{\zeta\zeta} - f_{\zeta\zeta}f_\tau], \tag{13}$$

$$\frac{1}{Pr}\,\theta_{\zeta\zeta} + 2f\theta_\zeta = 4\tau[(f_\zeta - \tau)\theta_\tau - \theta_\zeta f_\tau] - Kf_{\zeta\zeta}^{\;2}, \tag{14}$$

where $K = (\gamma-1)M_\infty^2/(1-T_w/T_\infty)$, γ being the ratio of specific heats C_p/C_v. The appropriate boundary conditions, Eq. (6), are transformed into

$$f(0) = f_\zeta(0) = \theta(0) = 0, \qquad f_\zeta(\infty) = \theta(\infty) = 1, \qquad \text{for } 0 \le \tau \le 1/\alpha. \tag{15}$$

As $\tau \to 0$, i.e., near the leading edge, Eqs. (13) and (14) degenerate into

$$f_{\zeta\zeta\zeta} + 2ff_{\zeta\zeta} = 0, \quad \frac{1}{P_r}\theta_{\zeta\zeta} + 2f\theta_\zeta = -Kf_{\zeta\zeta}^2, \tag{16}$$

which, with Eq. (15), are readily recognized to be the classical steady Blasius boundary-layer over a flat plate and the associated heat transfer problem. At the other limit of $\tau \to \frac{1}{\alpha}$, i.e., near the moving shock, we anticipate the Mirels solution of [1] written in a left-handed coordinate system moving with the shock. For this purpose, let

$$\xi' = U_s t - \xi, \quad \eta' = \eta, \quad t' = t, \qquad U' = U_s - U, \quad u' = U_s - u. \tag{17}$$

Using again the quantities defined by Eqs. (12a) and (12b), we get

$$\zeta' = \sqrt{\frac{\tau(1-\alpha)}{1-\alpha\tau}}, \qquad \tau' = \frac{1-\alpha\tau}{1-\alpha}, \tag{18}$$

and should recover Eqs. (13) and (14) when all the variables are replaced by the "primed" ones. The boundary conditions Eq. (15), meanwhile, should be written as

$$f'(0) = 0, \quad f'_\zeta(0) = \frac{1}{1-\alpha}, \quad f'_\zeta(\infty) = 1, \qquad \theta'(0) = 0, \quad \theta'(\infty) \to 1, \tag{19}$$

for $0 \le \tau' \le 1/(1-\alpha)$. In particular, near $\tau' = 0$, the equations corresponding to Eq. (16) are

$$f'_{\zeta'\zeta'\zeta'} + 2f'f'_{\zeta'\zeta'} = 0, \quad \frac{1}{Pr}\theta'_{\zeta'\zeta'} + 2f'\theta'_{\zeta'} = -K'f'^2_{\zeta'\zeta'} \tag{20}$$

where $K' = (1-\alpha)K/\alpha$. Eqns. (19) and (20) together give, of course, the Mirels solution.

Both Eqs. (13) and (14) are parabolic if f_ζ and θ, respectively, are regarded as the dependent variable, but singular because the effective diffusion coefficient changes sign when the factor $f_\zeta - \tau$ does. In the corresponding equations for the primed quantities, the assertion can be made that the Mirels solution, independent of τ', should in fact hold for $0 \le \tau' < 1$, since it has the property $f'_{\zeta'} \ge 1$. In contrast, from Eq. (13) the Blasius solution at $\tau = 0$ cannot extend its validity to $\tau > 0$ however small, the sign change of $f_\zeta - \tau$ near the wall being unavoidable. In the (ζ,τ)-plane, we must therefore determine the solution of Eqs. (13) and (14) in a strip $(0 \le \zeta < \infty,\ 0 \le \tau \le 1)$, with specified data on all four boundaries like an elliptic problem.

The suddenly started flat plate in an incompressible fluid corresponds to the special case $\alpha \to 0$, and is known to require the Rayleigh solution at $\tau = 1$. To see that the Mirels solution (in the primed coordinates) would go over to the Rayleigh (in the unprimed coordinates) in the limit, it is only necessary to recognize the definition

$$u = Uf_\zeta = U_x - U'f'_{\zeta'},$$

and Eq. (20) can be written for the unprimed quantities as

$$f_{\zeta\zeta\zeta} + \frac{2\tau}{1-\alpha\tau}(\zeta - \alpha f)\, f_{\zeta\zeta} = 0,$$

$$\frac{1}{P_r}\theta_{\zeta\zeta} + \frac{2\tau}{1-\alpha\tau}(\zeta - \alpha f)\theta_\zeta = - Kf^2_{\zeta\zeta}, \tag{21}$$

with boundary conditions $f(0) = f_\zeta(0) = 0$, $f_\zeta(\infty) \to 1$, and $\theta(0) = 0$, $\theta(\infty) \to 1$. We require Eq. (21) to apply at $\tau'^{\zeta} = \tau = 1$. Now, by the shock relations

$$\alpha = \frac{2}{\gamma+1}\left(1 - \frac{1}{M_s^2}\right), \quad \gamma = C_p/C_v,$$

hence α varies between 0 and $\frac{2}{\gamma+1}$ as M_s varies between 1 and ∞. Setting $\alpha = 0$ in Eq. (21) gives the familiar equation for the Rayleigh solution.

3. METHOD OF COMPUTATION AND RESULTS

From the above formulation, the computational problem of Eq. (13) is seen to be identical to that treated in [4] [5], except for the parameter α, $0 < \alpha < \frac{2}{\gamma+1}$. Our choice of the computational domain is as sketched in Fig. 2. Once the velocity profile $f_\zeta(\zeta,\tau)$ is determined, the temperature profile $\theta(\zeta,\tau)$ can be similarly integrated. The main feature requiring careful handling is the presence of the locus $f_\zeta - \tau = 0$, a priori of unknown location, across which the analytical nature of the solution is different although all derivatives are continuous. Basically, we set-up a finite- difference program for f_ζ using conventional central differencing but incorporating the upwinding formula for $\frac{\partial}{\partial\tau} f_\zeta$ as in [5] - schematically shown in Fig. 2. Iteration is, of course, necessary to determine the locus $f_\zeta - \tau = 0$. Starting with an initial approximation the general procedure is to sweep in the τ-direction, and update after each iteration with a relaxation factor, until the relative error of successive values is less than a pre-determined amount, say 0.1%.

More specifically, if $f_\zeta^{(n)}(i,j)$ denotes the value of the f_ζ at the grid point $\zeta = ih_1$, $\tau = jh_2$ after n iterations, the discretized Eq. (13) is written as

$$\frac{\overline{f}_\zeta^{(n+1)}(i+1,j) + \overline{f}_\zeta^{(n+1)}(i-1,j) - 2\overline{f}_\zeta^{(n+1)}(i,j)}{h_1^2} +$$

$$2\left[f^{(n)}(i,j) + 2\tau\, \frac{f^{(n)}(i,j+1) - f^{(n)}(i,j-1)}{2h_2}\right].$$

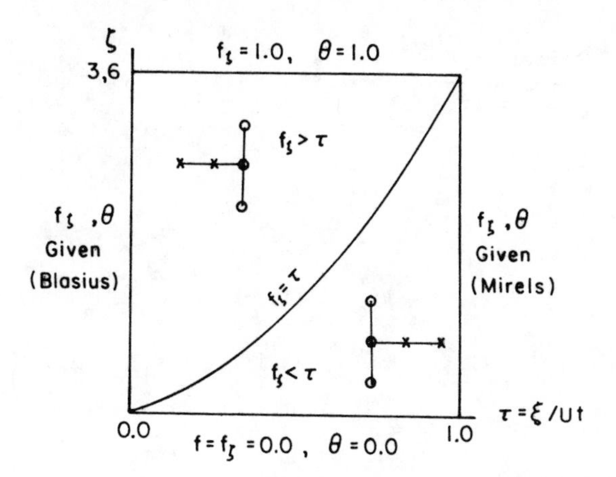

Figure 2.

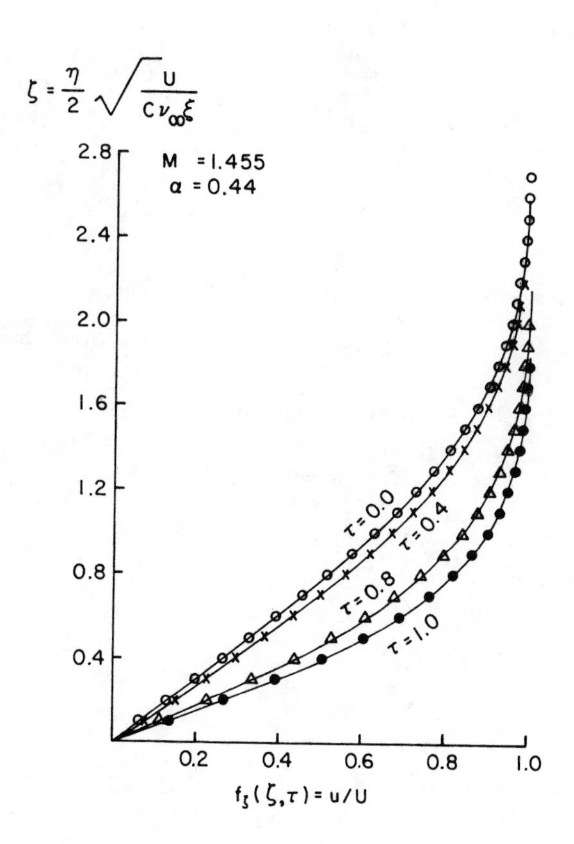

Figure 3.

$$\left[\frac{\bar{f}_\zeta^{(n+1)}(i+1,j) - \bar{f}_\zeta^{(n+1)}(i-1,j)}{2h_1}\right] = 4\tau[f_\zeta^{(n)}(i,j) - \tau]\,\frac{\Delta_\tau f_\zeta}{2h_2}\,, \tag{22}$$

where, if $f_\zeta^{(n)}(i,j) > \tau$,

$$\Delta_\tau f_\zeta = \begin{cases} 3\bar{f}_\zeta^{(n+1)}(i,j) - 4f_\zeta^{(n+1)}(i,j-1) + f_\zeta^{(n+1)}(i,j-2)\ , \text{ for } j = 2, \\ 2\bar{f}_\zeta^{(n+1)}(i,j) - 2f_\zeta^{(n+1)}(i,j-1), \text{ for } j = 2. \end{cases} \tag{23a}$$

and, if $f^{(n)}(i,j) < \tau$,

$$\Delta_\tau f_\zeta = -3\bar{f}_\zeta^{(n+1)}(i,j) + 4f_\zeta^{(n)}(i,j+1) - f_\zeta^{(n)}(i,j+2). \tag{23b}$$

Here the overbar denotes the value prior to relaxation. At the last two j-points at and next to the right end boundary, $f_\zeta^{(n)}$ in (23b) are known from the Mirels solution. The coefficient matrix of $\bar{f}_\zeta^{(n+1)}$ is tri-diagonal, and the unknown are readily solved when $f_\zeta^{(n)}$ are given. The updated $f_\zeta^{(n+1)}$ is then taken to be

$$f_\zeta^{(n+1)}(i,j) = \omega\bar{f}_\zeta^{(n+1)}(i,j) + (1-\omega)f_\zeta^{(n)}(i,j),$$

ω being the relaxation factor to be chosen from trial computation. ($\omega \simeq 0.7$ was chosen for most cases in actual computation.) The procedure is repeated until the desired convergence criterion is satisfied. Our experience shows that faster convergence is achieved by sweeping in alternate directions, i.e. from $\tau=0$ to $\tau=1$ followed by $\tau=1$ to $\tau=0$, etc.

To start the iteration, we first construct a zeroth approximation $f_\zeta^{(0)}$ and $\theta^{(0)}$ which embody the essential features of the desired solution. By treating τ as a parameter only, a simplified model satisfying Eq. (16) for $f_\zeta \geq \tau$ and Eq. (21) for $f_\zeta < \tau$ is the following:

$$\begin{aligned} &f_{\zeta\zeta\zeta}^{(0)} + \frac{2\tau f_{\zeta\zeta}^{(0)}}{1-\alpha\tau}(\zeta - \alpha f^{(0)}) = 0,\ 0 \le f_\zeta \le \tau, \\ &f_{\zeta\zeta\zeta}^{(0)} + 2f^{(0)}f_{\zeta\zeta}^{(0)} = 0,\ \tau \le f_\zeta \le 1\ , \\ &f^{(0)}(0) = f_\zeta^{(0)}(0) = 0,\quad f_\zeta^{(0)}(\infty) \to 1\ , \end{aligned} \tag{24a}$$

and, likewise for the thermal layer,

$$\frac{1}{Pr}\theta_{\zeta\zeta}^{(0)} + \frac{2\tau\theta_\zeta^{(0)}}{1-\alpha\tau}(\zeta - \alpha f^{(0)}) = -K{f_{\zeta\zeta}^{(0)}}^2,\ 0 \le f_\zeta \le \tau\ ,$$

$$\frac{1}{Pr}\theta^{(0)}_{\zeta\zeta} + 2f^{(0)}\theta^{(0)}_{\zeta} = -Kf^{(0)^2}_{\zeta\zeta}, \qquad \tau \le f_{\zeta} \le 1, \tag{24b}$$

$$\theta^{(0)}(0)=0, \quad \theta^{(0)}(\infty)\to 1.$$

The solution can be found by trial and error, adjusting guessed values of $f^{(0)}_{\zeta\zeta}(0)$ and $\theta_{\zeta}^{(0)}(0)$ until the conditions at infinity are reproduced. It proves to be a good approximation and serves to accelerate the convergence of the iteration procedure.

Numberical results have been obtained for f at several values of the parameter , and for θ at several Prandlt numbers but a single value of $K \equiv \frac{(\gamma-1)M_\infty^2}{1 - T_w/T_\infty} = 1.059$. As an example, for $M_s = 1.455$ and $\gamma=1.4$, $\alpha = 0.44$, the variation of the velocity distribution along the plate, invariant with respect to Pr, is shown in Fig. 3. The temperature profiles under the same conditions and K = 1.059, i.e. $T_w/T_\infty = 0.88$, are shown in Fig. 4 for Pr = 0.7 (air) and in Fig. 5 for the hypothetical case of Pr = 10. Although the latter has no relevance to the gas dynamic problem, it exhibits the interesting feature of an appreciable temperature overshoot due to the viscous heating which prevails both within and beyond the thin thermal layer.

Particularly simple is the special case Pr = 1, for which it is easily verified that Eqs. (10) and (11) are satisfied by the Crocco integral just as in the steady case, i.e.,

$$C_pT + \frac{u^2}{2} = a\,u + b \tag{25}$$

a and b being constants, provided that the boundary conditions permit. If the wall is insulated, a = 0 and $b = C_pT + \frac{U}{2} = C_pT_{ad}$, T_{ad} being the adiabatic wall temperature. By replotting the velocity profiles in Fig. 3 we obtain the temperature distributions along the wall in Fig. 6. To get the profiles in (x,y), the conversion is straight-forward, i.e. $x = \xi$ and $y = \int_0^\eta \frac{\rho_\infty}{\rho}\,d\eta$. If the wall temperature T_w is assigned as in the rest of our computations, Reynolds' analogy again follows from Eq. (25), and the instantaneous local skin friction and heat transfer coefficients are always proportional to each other. This is in general not true when Pr $\neq$ 1. In Fig. 7 are presented the calculated heat transfer coefficients along the plate, at several values of Pr including Pr = 1.

4. DISCUSSION AND CONCLUSIONS

By introduction an unsteady stream function and the Howarth transformation well-known for steady compressible boundary layers, the unsteady compressible boundary-layer equations with zero pressure gradient are once more turned into an equivalent incompressible problem. To be sure, certain key approximations of the gas properties that allow such a reduction for the steady case have been retained, and the unsteady streamfunction no longer defines the streamlines. Nevertheless, at least for numerical calculations, the difficulty is much reduced and techniques already developed for the incompressible case can be readily borrowed. The title problem, first treated by Lam and Crocco [2], is equivalent to a generalized version of the incompressible boundary layer problem over a

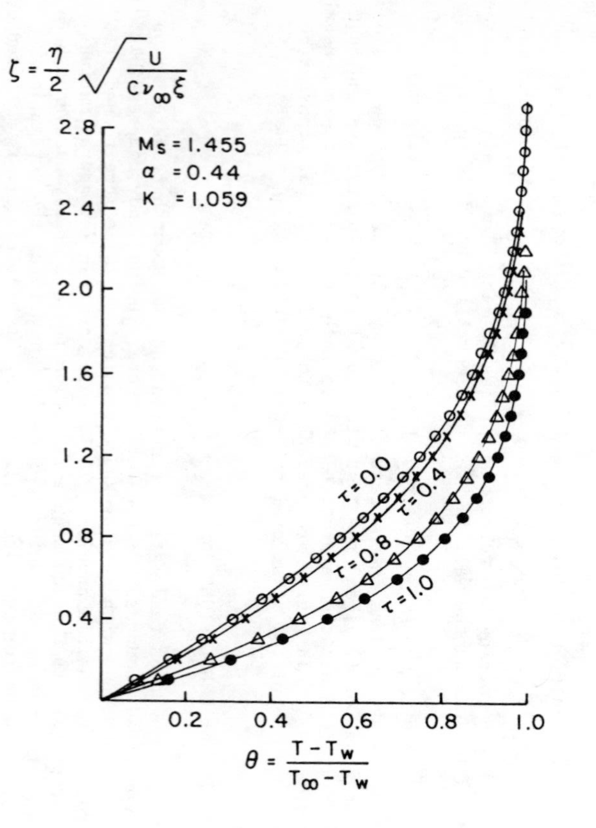

Figure 4.

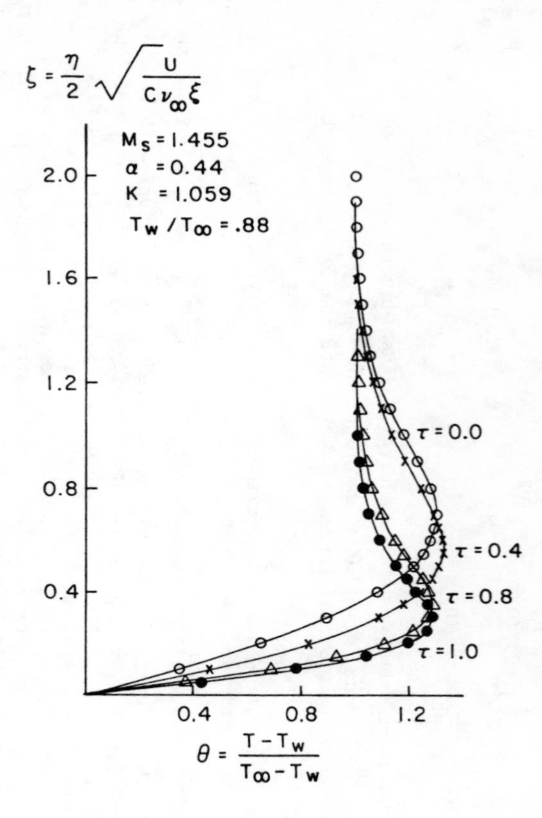

Figure 5.

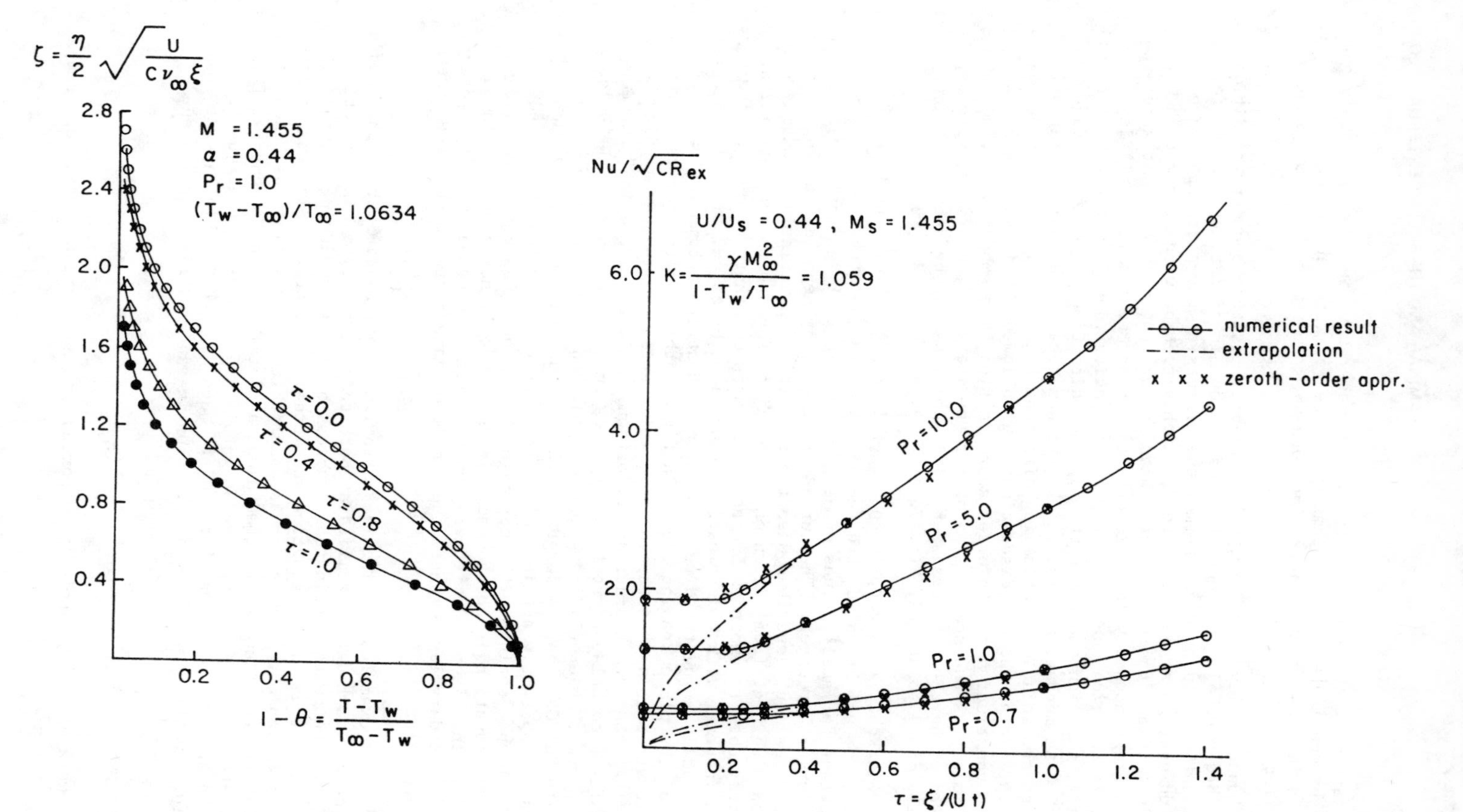

Figure 6.

Figure 7.

suddenly started flat plate. For the latter case, the finite-difference procedures used by Dennis [4] and Williams and Rhyne [5] were successful. These have been adapted in this paper to determine both the velocity and thermal boundary-layer behavior.

As a boundary layer problem, the peculiarity is that boundary conditions are prescribed over all the boundaries of the domain of interest, as if for an elliptic equation. In physical terms, the effects of the plate leading edge propagate downstream at particle speed, which varies between zero and the free stream value. Since the shock moves ahead faster, to an observer attached to the shock a fresh boundary layer is created behind, eventually ($\tau>1$) described by the Mirels solution unaware of the plate leading edge. In the computational domain $o\leq\tau\leq1$, the sign change of the "upwind" direction is to acknowledge the presence of both mechanisms. Thus, like the numerical solution for transonic flow with shock, solutions satisfying different equations must be patched along an interface, except that no discontinuity is allowed. This consideration also leads us to construct a zeroth order approximation that embodies such a feature. It serves mainly as the starting point for the iteration, but seems also capable of predicting the heat transfer fairly well, as may be seen in the comparison with the final solutions, Fig. 7.

More remarkable, however, is the general trend in Fig. 7 that, at least in the example, for all Pr calculated the heat transfer parameter $Nu/\sqrt{CRe_x}$ remains nearly constant for small values of τ and turns relatively abruptly to follow a different curve thereafter. The curve for Pr = 1, by Reynolds' analogy and after proper scaling, describes also the skin friction variation, and may thus be compared with Fig. 1 of [2] which was obtained for $\alpha=0$ in our definition. Qualitatively they resemble each other. It turns out that the part of the curve showing an increase with τ is closely approximated by calculating with Eq. (21) only, essentially using the Mirels solution without any accommodation of the influence of the plate leading edge. In Fig. 7, the results of this approximation are referred to as "extrapolation", which evidently is even simpler to construct than the zeroth order approximation. The "extrapolation" curve certainly is far from being correct as τ becomes small. At least in the calculated example, however, an excellent estimate of the heat transfer would be to take the quantity $Nu/\sqrt{CRe_x}$ as the larger of the Blasius and the Mirels values. The Blasius value apparently applies only relatively close to the leading edge, in a region of τ that shrinks with increasing Pr. From hindsight, the dominance of the Mirels equation is not too surprising, since it needs correction only when $f_\zeta > \tau$. In this problem the region $f_\zeta > \tau$ is synonymous with the outer part of the boundary layer, where the conditions are close to the free stream for moderate values of τ.

In several examples of singular parabolic equations similar to the present problem, namely with data specified at both ends of the time-like direction, Tayler [8] has met with considerable success by simply employing central differencing throughout as if the equation was actually elliptic. Since mathematically the solution may be regarded as a composite of two solutions, each satisfying a parabolic equation but patched along a certain internal boundary, Tayler's method of attack cannot be accepted as infallible without further justification. At least theoretically, proper "upwinding" such as used in this paper seems preferable, and the risk of running into unpleasant surprises is lessened.

ACKNOWLEDGMENT

This work has been partially supported by the Office of Naval Research, Grant No. N0014-77-C-0033.

NOMENCLATURE

f	dimensionless unsteady streamfunction, Eq. (25b).
h_1, h_2	mesh sizes in ζ- and τ-directions, respectively.
i, j	index denoting the grid points in ζ and τ directions, respectively.
k	coefficient of thermal conductivity.
n	iteration number, used as superscript.
t	time.
u, v	velocity components in x- and y-directions, respectively.
x, y	Cartesian coordinates along and normal to the plate, respectively.
C	constant, defined in connection with Eqs. (10) and (11).
K	constant, defined in connection with Eqs. (13) and (14).
M	Mach number.
T	temperature.
U	velocity of free stream.
C_p, C_v	specific heats at constant pressure and volume, respectively.
Nu	Nusselt number $Nu \equiv x \frac{\partial T}{\partial y}\Big\|_o / (T_w - T_\infty)$.
Re_x	Reynolds number $Re_x \equiv U_\infty x / \nu_\infty$.
α	velocity ration U/U_s.
γ	ratio of specific heats, $\gamma = C_p/C_v$.
ζ	similarity variable, Eq. (12a).
η	transformed distance from wall, Eq. (8).
θ	dimensionless temperature, Eq. (12b).
μ	viscosity coefficient.
ν	kinematic viscosity coefficient.
ξ	distance along the plate, Eq. (8).
ρ	density.
τ	similarity variable, Eq. (12a).
ψ	unsteady streamfunction, Eq. (12b).
ω	relaxation factor.

SUBSCRIPTS

s	shock.
w	wall.
∞	outside of boundary layer.
ad	adiabatic.
ζ	partial derivative with respect to ζ.
τ	partial derivative with respect to τ.

Primed quantities are the same variable, or parameter, when similarly defined in the set of left-handed Cartesian coordinates (x',y') with origin at the foot of the moving shock.

FIGURE CAPTION

Figure 1: Boundary layer at different times.
Figure 2: Computational domain, boundary conditions and difference schemes.
Figure 3: Typical velocity distributions.
Figure 4: Typical temperature distributions, T_w/T given, $Pr = 0.7$.
Figure 5: Typical temperature distributions, T_w/T given, $Pr = 10$.
Figure 6: Typical temperature distributions, adiabatic wall, $Pr = 1$.
Figure 7: Local heat transfer coefficient at different Pr.

REFERENCES

1. Mirels, H. 1955. Laminar boundary layer behind shock advancing into stationary fluid. NACA TN 3401.

2. Lam, S.H. and Crocco,L. 1959. Note on the shock-induced unsteady laminar boundary layer on a semi-infinite flat plate. J. Aero/Space Sci, Vol 26, pp 54-56.

3. Hall, M.G. 1969. The boundary layer over an impulsively started flat plate. Proc. Roy. Soc., London, Vol A310, pp 401-414.

4. Dennis, S.C.R. 1972. The motion of a viscous fluid past an impulsively started semi-infinite flat plate. J. Inst. Math. Applications, Vol 10, pp 105-116.

5. Williams, J.C. and Rhyne, T.B. 1980. Boundary layer development on a wedge impulsively set into motion. SIAM J. Appl. Math., Vol 38, pp 215-225.

6. Walker, J.D.A. and Dennis, S.C.R. 1972. The boundary layer in a shock tube. J. Fluid Mech., Vol 56, pp 19-47.

7. Stewartson, K. 1951. On the impulsive motion of a flat plate in a viscous fluid. Quart. J. Mech. Appl. Math., Vol 4, pp 182-198.

Heat Transfer Calculation for Hypersonic Flows over Blunt Noses Using an Unsteady Implicit Scheme

TSUYING HSIEH
Naval Surface Weapons Center
Silver Spring, Maryland 20910

ABSTRACT

Axisymmetric hypersonic viscous flows over blunt noses are simulated by solving the unsteady Navier-Stokes equations with thin layer approximation using an implicit factored scheme. The flow is assumed to be inviscid at the shock which is tracked. For simplicity, the shock and body boundary conditions are imposed explicitly. The steady solution is obtained asymptotically in time. Laminar results have been obtained for an adiabatic wall hemisphere-cylinder and an isothermal wall sphere-cone with a Courant number of 75. Comparison of results are made with other numerical solutions, experimental data and boundary layer calculation.

1. INTRODUCTION

Prediction of aerodynamic heating for blunt noses is important in high speed reentry vehicle design because it is directly related to the phenomena of ablation. When the nose geometry is sufficiently smooth to guarantee that the flow is everywhere attached to the body, an inviscid flow calculation coupled with boundary layer solution will give satisfactory results for prediction of the aerodynamic heating. As the nose shape changes because of ablation, the resulting indented nose shape will cause flow separation in the indented area. Then the conventional technique of coupled inviscid flow calculation and boundary layer theory is incapable of providing reliable aerodynamic and heat transfer information. Therefore, for nose shape with possible of flow separation a solution to the Navier-Stokes equations is required.

In the numerical solution of time-dependent, compressible Navier-Stokes equations, it is well known that implicit method has the advantage of using a relative large time step than the explicit method. The latter has a severe stability bound (i.e., Courant number must be less than 1) which limits the time step that can be orders of magnitude smaller than that required for accuracy; as a consequence, it leads to long computing times. The development of efficient non-iterative algorithms for systems of conservation laws by authors like Lindemuth and Killeen [1], McDonald and Briley [2] and Beam and Warming [3] further enhence the implicit scheme to be applicable to more general problems of engineering interest. Among the many application oriented papers [4,5,6], the work of Kutler et al [4] describes the application of Beam and Warming method to calculate the flowfield for an indented nosetip by solving the time-dependent compressible Navier-Stokes equations. After extensive application of Kutler's computer code, it was found that his code works well for inviscid flow [7] but not very satisfactory in computing viscous flow [8], particularly in the calculation of temperature field. This leads to a reanalysis of the entire numerical procedure and completely rewritten all the subroutines related to the viscous portion. Significant difference in heat transfer results are found between present calculation and that of Ref. [4]. In this paper, a full description of the governing equations, the numerical algorithm and the boundary conditions are given. Laminar results obtained from present calculations are compared with (i) that of Refs. [4,9] for temperature field about a hemisphere-cylinder with adiabatic wall and (ii) with Kutler's code, experimental data [10] and boundary layer calculation [10] for heating rate in terms of Stanton number for a sphere-cone with isothermal wall.

In the calculation of high Reynolds number flows, the viscous effects are generally most pronounced in a thin layer near the body surface. Therefore, a highly stretched mesh must be used near the vorticity-generating surface in order to resolve the large gradient of the flow there. The grid spacing in the normal direction to surface is generally several orders smaller than that in the streamwise direction. Consequently, the diffusion terms involving derivatives in the streamwise direction just cannot be resolved in the real calculation. For this reason, thin-layer approximation to the Navier-Stokes equations by neglecting the diffusion terms in the streamwise (or parallel to the surface directions in three dimensional flows) have been introduced by many authors [4,5,11] to simplify the unnecessary coding and computing time. This approximation will also be made in this paper. It should be mentioned that an implicit method with Newton iterative scheme for solving time-dependent Navier-Stokes equations with thin-layer-like approximations has been reported in Ref. [13].

2. GOVERNING EQUATIONS

The time-dependent compressible Navier-Stokes equations in the cylindrical coordinates (x,y,ϕ), Fig. 1, for axisymmetric flow can be written in dimensionless, conservation-law form for a perfect gas without external force as follows [12]:

$$\bar{U}_t + \bar{E}_x + \bar{F}_y + (\bar{F} + \bar{H})/y = \frac{1}{R_e}\left[\bar{R}_x + \bar{S}_y + (\bar{S} + \bar{T})/y\right] \tag{2.1}$$

where

$$\bar{U} = \begin{bmatrix} \rho \\ \rho u \\ \rho v \\ e \end{bmatrix}, \quad \bar{E} = \begin{bmatrix} \rho u \\ p+\rho u^2 \\ \rho u v \\ (e+p)u \end{bmatrix}, \quad \bar{F} = \begin{bmatrix} \rho v \\ \rho u v \\ p+\rho v^2 \\ (e+p)v \end{bmatrix}, \quad \bar{H} = \begin{bmatrix} 0 \\ 0 \\ -p \\ 0 \end{bmatrix}$$

$$\bar{R} = \begin{bmatrix} 0 \\ \tau_{xx} \\ \tau_{xy} \\ \frac{\gamma}{Pr}\kappa\varepsilon_x + u\,\tau_{xx} + v\,\tau_{xy} \end{bmatrix}, \quad \bar{S} = \begin{bmatrix} 0 \\ \tau_{xy} \\ \tau_{yy} \\ \frac{\gamma}{Pr}\kappa\varepsilon_y + u\,\tau_{xy} + v\,\tau_{yy} \end{bmatrix}, \quad \bar{T} = \begin{bmatrix} 0 \\ 0 \\ -\tau_{\phi\phi} \\ 0 \end{bmatrix}.$$

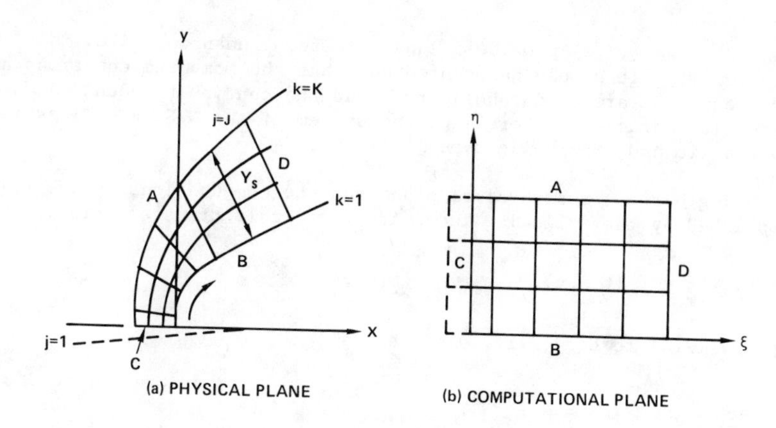

Fig. 1 Coordinate system

and

$$R_e = \frac{\rho_\infty q_\infty L}{\mu_\infty} \frac{1}{\sqrt{\gamma} M_\infty} = R_{e_\infty} \left(\frac{1}{\sqrt{\gamma} M_\infty} \right)$$

$$Pr = \mu_\infty \overline{C}_p / \kappa_\infty$$

$$\tau_{xx} = (\lambda + 2\mu) u_x + \lambda v_y + \lambda \frac{v}{y}$$

$$\tau_{xy} = \mu (u_y + v_x)$$

$$\tau_{yy} = (\lambda + 2\mu) v_y + \lambda u_x + \lambda \frac{v}{y}$$

$$\tau_{\phi\phi} = (\lambda + 2\mu) \frac{v}{y} + \lambda (u_x + v_y)$$

In Eq. (2.1), the reference quantities used to nondimensionalize the flow variables are: the length L, the velocity $\frac{a_\infty}{\sqrt{\gamma}}$, the density ρ_∞, the viscosity μ_∞ and the thermal conductivity κ_∞. The time is nondimensionalized by $\sqrt{\gamma}\, L/a_\infty$, the total energy per unit volume e and pressure p by p_∞ $(=\rho_\infty a_\infty^2/\gamma)$ and the viscous stress term τ_{xx} etc. by $\mu_\infty a_\infty^2/(L\sqrt{\gamma})$. For perfect gas, the equation of state gives

$$p = (\gamma - 1) [e - \tfrac{1}{2}\rho(u^2 + v^2)] \tag{2.2}$$

and

$$e = \rho[\varepsilon + \tfrac{1}{2} (u^2 + v^2)] \tag{2.3a}$$

$$\varepsilon = \bar{C}_v T \tag{2.3b}$$

Equations (2.1) and (2.2) provide 5 equations for 5 unknowns, i.e. ρ,u,v,e,p (or T). It should be pointed out that the momentum equations and the energy equation are of parabolic type and the continuity equation carrys the hyperbolic character. Therefore, the system of the N.S. equations is of hybrid parabolic and hyperbolic type [12].

A mapping between the physical plane and the computational plane (Fig. 1) is accomplished by the following independent variable transformation:

$$\tau = t, \quad \xi = \xi\ (t,x,y), \quad \eta = \eta\ (t,x,y) \tag{2.4}$$

Applying Eq. (2.4) to Eq. (2.1), one obtains

$$U_\tau + E_\xi + F_\eta + H = \frac{1}{R_e}\,(R_\xi + S_\eta + T) \tag{2.5}$$

where

$$\begin{aligned}
U &= \overline{U}/J \\
E &= (\xi_t\ \overline{U} + \xi_x\ \overline{E} + \xi_y\ \overline{F})/J \\
F &= (\eta_t\ \overline{U} + \eta_x\ \overline{E} + \eta_y\ \overline{F})/J \\
H &= (\overline{F} + \overline{H})/(yJ) \\
R &= (\xi_x\ \overline{R} + \xi_y\ \overline{S})/J \\
S &= (\eta_x\ \overline{R} + \eta_y\ \overline{S})/J \\
T &= (\overline{S} + \overline{T})/(yJ)
\end{aligned}$$

with metrics of transformation given by

$$\begin{aligned}
\xi_t &= (x_\eta\ y_\tau - y_\eta\ x_\tau)J\ , & \eta_t &= (y_\xi\ x_\tau - x_\xi y_\tau)J \\
\xi_x &= y_\eta J & , \quad \eta_x &= -y_\xi J \\
\xi_y &= -x_\eta J & , \quad \eta_y &= x_\xi J \\
J^{-1} &= x_\xi\ y_\eta - y_\xi\ x_\eta\ .
\end{aligned} \tag{2.6}$$

In general, the metrics of Eq. (2.6) are not known analytically and must be determined numerically at each step of integration procedure.

The viscous vectors may be rewritten as follows:

$$R \text{ or } S = \frac{1}{J}\begin{bmatrix} 0 \\ (\ )_x\ \tau_{xx} + (\ )_y\ \tau_{xy} \\ (\ )_x\ \tau_{xy} + (\ )_y\ \tau_{yy} \\ (\ )_x \left(\frac{\gamma}{Pr}\kappa\varepsilon_x + u\ \tau_{xx} + v\ \tau_{xy}\right) + (\ )_y \left(\frac{\gamma}{Pr}\kappa\varepsilon_y + u\ \tau_{xy} + v\ \tau_{yy}\right) \end{bmatrix}$$

(2.7)

where ( ) = ξ for R and ( ) = η for S. And

$$T = \frac{1}{Jy}\begin{bmatrix} 0 \\ \tau_{xy} \\ \tau_{yy} - \tau_{\phi\phi} \\ \frac{\gamma}{Pr}\kappa\varepsilon_y\eta_y + u\,\tau_{xy} + v\,\tau_{yy} \end{bmatrix} \tag{2.8}$$

with

$$\tau_{xx} = \frac{4}{3}\mu\,(u_\eta\,\eta_x + u_\xi\,\xi_x) - \frac{2}{3}\mu\,(\eta_y\,v_\eta + \xi_y\,v_\xi) - \frac{2}{3}\mu\,\frac{v}{y}$$

$$\tau_{xy} = \mu(\xi_y\,u_\xi + \eta_y\,u_\eta + \xi_x v_\xi + \eta_x\,v_\eta)$$

$$\tau_{yy} = \frac{4}{3}\mu(\xi_y\,v_\xi + \eta_y\,v_\eta) - \frac{2}{3}\mu(\xi_x\,u_\xi + \eta_x\,u_\eta + \frac{v}{y})$$

$$\tau_{\phi\phi} = -\frac{2}{3}\mu(\xi_x\,u_\xi + \eta_x\,u_\eta + \xi_y\,v_\xi + \eta_y\,v_\eta) + \frac{4}{3}\mu\,\frac{v}{y}$$

In Eqs. (2.7) and (2.8), the Stokes hypothesis, i.e. $3\lambda + 2\mu = 0$ was used. Equations (2.7) and (2.8) may be rewritten by separating terms with flow variables differentiating with respect to ξ and η as follows:

$$R = R_1 + R_2 \tag{2.9}$$

$$S = S_1 + S_2 \tag{2.10}$$

$$T = T_1 + T_2 \tag{2.11}$$

where

$$S_1 = \frac{1}{J}\begin{bmatrix} 0 \\ C_2 u_\eta + C_3\,v_\eta - C_6\eta_x v \\ C_3 u_\eta + C_4\,v_\eta - C_6\eta_y v \\ C_5\varepsilon_\eta + (C_2 u + C_3 v)\,u_\eta + (C_3 u + C_4 v)v_\eta - C_6 v\,(u\,\eta_x + v\eta_y) \end{bmatrix} \tag{2.12}$$

$$T_1 = \frac{1}{Jy}\begin{bmatrix} 0 \\ \mu(\eta_y\,u_\eta + \eta_x\,v_\eta) \\ 2\mu\eta_y\,v_\eta - 2\,\mu\,\frac{v}{y} \\ C_7\,\varepsilon_\eta + \mu\,[\eta_y(uu_\eta + \frac{4}{3}\,vv_\eta) + \eta_x(uv_\eta - \frac{2}{3}\,vu_\eta)] - \frac{2}{3}\,\mu\,\frac{v^2}{y} \end{bmatrix} \tag{2.13}$$

and

$$C_2 = \mu\left(\frac{4}{3}\eta_x^{\ 2} + \eta_y^{\ 2}\right) \quad , \quad C_3 = \mu\left(\frac{1}{3}\eta_x\eta_y\right)$$

$$C_4 = \mu\left(\eta_x^{\ 2} + \frac{4}{3}\eta_y^{\ 2}\right) \quad , \quad C_5 = \frac{\gamma\kappa}{Pr}\left(\eta_x^{\ 2} + \eta_y^{\ 2}\right) \qquad (2.14)$$

$$C_6 = \mu\,\frac{2}{3}\,\frac{1}{y} \quad , \quad C_7 = \frac{\gamma\kappa}{Pr}\,\eta_y \quad .$$

Expressions for R_1, R_2, S_2, T_2 are given in the Appendix. Equations (2.5) are the governing equations to be solved with the boundary and initial conditions described in section 4. When thin layer approximation is made, i.e. $\frac{\partial}{\partial\xi}(\ ) \ll \frac{\partial}{\partial\eta}(\ )$ for all diffusion terms, then one sets $R_1 = R_2 = S_2 = T_2 = 0$.

3. NUMERICAL ALGORITHM

The numerical algorithm described in this section is based on the work of Ref. [3]. It is intended to solve the full Navier-Stokes equations, Eq. (2.5). However, the thin-layer approximation will be made at the end.

Rewritten Eq. (2.5) as follows:

$$U_\tau + E_\xi + F_\eta + H = \frac{1}{R_e}\Big[R_1(U,U_\xi)_\xi + R_2(U,U_\eta)_\xi + S_1(U,U_\eta)_\eta$$

$$+ S_2(U,U_\xi)_\eta + T_1(U,U_\eta) + T_2(U,U_\xi)\Big] \qquad (3.1)$$

A single step temporal scheme for advancing the solution of Eq. (3.1) is

$$\Delta U^n = \frac{a'\Delta\tau}{1+b'}\frac{\partial}{\partial\tau}\Delta U^n + \frac{\Delta\tau}{1+b'}\frac{\partial}{\partial\tau}U^n + \frac{b'}{1+b'}\Delta U^{n-1} +$$

$$0\left[\left(a' - \frac{1}{2} - b'\right)\Delta\tau^2 + \Delta\tau^3\right] \qquad (3.2)$$

where $U^n = U(n\Delta t)$ and $\Delta U^n = U^{n+1} - U^n$. Substituting U_τ from Eq. (3.1) into Eq. (3.2) one obtains

$$\Delta U^n = \frac{a'\Delta\tau}{1+b'}\Bigg[\left(-\Delta E + \frac{\Delta R_1 + \Delta R_2}{R_e}\right)^n_\xi + \left(-\Delta F + \frac{\Delta S_1 + \Delta S_2}{R_e}\right)^n_\eta - \Delta H^n +$$

$$\frac{\Delta T_1^n + \Delta T_2^n}{R_e}\Bigg]$$

$$+ \frac{\Delta\tau}{1+b'}\Bigg[\left(-E + \frac{R_1 + R_2}{R_e}\right)^n_\xi + \left(-F + \frac{S_1 + S_2}{R_e}\right)^n_\eta - H^n +$$

$$+ \frac{T_1 + T_2}{R_e}\Bigg] + \frac{b'}{1+b'}\Delta U^{n-1} + 0\left[\left(a' - \frac{1}{2} - b'\right)\Delta\tau^2 + \Delta\tau^3\right] \qquad (3.3)$$

where $E^{n+1} = E\ (U^{n+1})$, $\Delta E = E^{n+1} - E^n$. A local linearization can be achieved by the Taylor series expansion:

$$E^{n+1} = E^n + \left(\frac{\partial E}{\partial U}\right)^n \left(U^{n+1} - U^n\right) + 0\ (\Delta\tau^2)$$

or

$$\Delta E^n = A^n \Delta U^n + 0\ (\Delta\tau^2). \tag{3.4a}$$

where $A^n = (\frac{E}{U})^n$ is the Jacobian matrix. Similarly,

$$\Delta F^n = B^n\ \Delta U^n + 0\ (\Delta\tau^2) \tag{3.4b}$$

$$\Delta H^n = K^n\ \Delta U^n + 0\ (\Delta\tau^2) \tag{3.4c}$$

$$\Delta R_1^n = \left(\frac{\partial R_1}{\partial U}\right)^n \Delta U^n + \left(\frac{\partial R_1}{\partial U_\xi}\right) \Delta U_\xi^n + 0\ (\Delta\tau^2)$$

$$= \overline{L}^{\,n}\ \Delta U^n + P^n\ \Delta U_\xi^n + 0\ (\Delta\tau^2)$$

$$= L^n\ \Delta U^n + (P\Delta U)_\xi^n + 0\ (\Delta\tau^2). \tag{3.4d}$$

where $L^n = \left(\frac{\partial R_1}{\partial U} - P_\xi\right)^n$ and $P^n = \left(\frac{\partial R_1}{\partial U_\xi}\right)^n$.

$$\Delta S_1^n = M^n\ \Delta U^n + (Q\Delta U)_\eta^n + 0\ (\Delta\tau^2) \tag{3.4e}$$

where $M^n = \left(\frac{\partial S_1}{\partial U} - Q_\eta\right)^n$ and $Q^n = \left(\frac{\partial S_1}{\partial U_\eta}\right)^n$.

$$\Delta T_1^n = N_1^n\ \Delta U^n + (W_1\Delta U)_\eta^n + 0\ (\Delta\tau^2) \tag{3.4f}$$

where $N_1 = \left(\frac{\partial T_1}{\partial U} - W_{1\eta}\right)^n$ and $W_1 = \left(\frac{\partial T_1}{\partial U_\eta}\right)^n$.

$$\Delta T_2^n = N_2^n\ \Delta U^n + (W_2\Delta U)_\xi^n + 0\ (\Delta\tau^2) \tag{3.4g}$$

where $N_2 = \left(\frac{\partial T_2}{\partial U} - W_{2\xi}\right)^n$ and $W_2 = \left(\frac{\partial T_2}{\partial U_\xi}\right)^n$.

The cross-derivative terms are treated explicitly

$$\Delta R_2^n = \Delta R_2^{n-1} + 0\,(\Delta\tau^2) \tag{3.5a}$$

$$\Delta S_2^n = \Delta S_2^{n-1} + 0\,(\Delta\tau^2) \tag{3.5b}$$

All the Jacobian matrices are given in the Appendix. In the analytical derivation of Jacobian matrices for viscous portion, it is assumed that transport coefficients are locally constant, i.e. $\mu_\xi = \kappa_\xi = \mu_\eta = \kappa_\eta = 0$.

By substituting Eqs. (3.4) and (3.5) into (3.3), one obtains the spatially factored form:

$$\left\{I + \frac{a'\Delta\tau}{1 + b'}\left[\left(A - \frac{L}{R_e}\right)^n_\xi - \left(\frac{P}{R_e}\right)^n_{\xi\xi} - \frac{1}{R_e}\left(N_2 - W_{2\xi}\right)^n\right]\right\}$$

$$\times\left\{I + \frac{a'\Delta\tau}{1 + b'}\left[\left(B - \frac{M}{R_e}\right)^n_\eta - \frac{1}{R_e}Q^n_{\eta\eta} + K^n + \frac{1}{R_e}\left(N_1 - W_{1\eta}\right)^n\right]\right\}\Delta U^n$$

$$= \frac{\Delta\tau}{1 + b'}\left[\left(-E^n + \frac{R^n}{R_e}\right)_\xi + \left(-F^n + \frac{S^n}{R_e}\right)_\eta - H^n + \frac{T^n}{R_e}\right]$$

$$+ \frac{a''\Delta\tau}{1 + b'}\left[\left(\Delta R_2\right)^{n-1}_\xi + \left(\Delta S_2\right)^{n-1}_\eta\right] + \frac{b'}{1 + b'}\Delta U^{n-1}$$

$$+ 0\left[\left(a' - \frac{1}{2} - b'\right)\Delta\tau^2,\ \left(a'' - a\right)\Delta\tau^2,\ \Delta\tau^3\right] \tag{3.6}$$

where a" has been introduced in the coefficient of the cross-derivative terms for notation convenience [3]. For second-order-accurate schemes, a" should be set equal to a'. However, for first-order-accurate scheme ($a' \neq \frac{1}{2} + b'$) it is consistent to set a" equal to zero. Now, Eq. (3.6) has the same temporal accuracy as Eq. (3.3) but is linear in ΔU^n. In practice, Eq. (3.6) is implemented by the sequence

$$\left\{I + \frac{a'\Delta\tau}{1 + b'}\left[\left(A - \frac{L}{R_e}\right)^n_\xi - \frac{1}{R_e}P^n_{\xi\xi} - \frac{1}{R_e}\left(N_2 - W_{2\xi}\right)^n\right]\right\}\Delta U^{*n}$$

$$= \text{RHS of Eq. (3.6)} \tag{3.7a}$$

$$\left\{ I + \frac{a'\Delta\tau}{1+b'} \left[\left(B - \frac{M}{R_e} \right)_\eta^n - \frac{1}{R_e} Q_{\eta\eta}^n - \frac{1}{R_e} (N_1 - W_{1\eta})^n \right] \right\} \Delta U^n = \Delta U^{*n} \tag{3.7b}$$

From now on, it is assumed that thin-layer approximation is applicable. Also the first-order-accurate Euler implicit scheme (a' = 1, a" = 0 and b' = 0) is chosen for the time integration. As described in Refs. [3,6], it is necessary to add the fourth-order explicit dissipation terms in order to damp high-frequency growth and thus serve to control nonlinear instability. Also the addition of the second-order implicit dissipation terms will extend the linear stability bound of the fourth order terms. Therefore, the final form of Eq. (3.7) for thin-layer approximation of the time-dependent compressible Navier-Stokes equations using Euler implicit time differencing scheme may be written as follows:

$$\left[I + \Delta\tau A_\xi^n - \varepsilon_I (J^{-1} \nabla_\xi \Delta_\xi J)^n \right] \Delta U^{*n}$$

$$= - \Delta\tau \left[E_\xi^n + F_\eta^n + H^n - \frac{1}{R_e} (S_{1\eta}^n + T_1^n) \right] - \varepsilon_E \left[J^{-1} (\nabla_\xi \Delta_\xi)^2 JU \right]^n \tag{3.8a}$$

$$\left[I + \Delta\tau \left(B - \frac{M}{R_e} \right)_\eta^n - \frac{1}{R_e} Q_{\eta\eta}^n + K^n - \frac{1}{R_e} (N_1 - W_{1\eta})^n - \varepsilon_I (J^{-1} \nabla_\eta \Delta_\eta J)^n \right] \Delta U^n$$

$$= \Delta U^{*n} - \varepsilon_E \left[J^{-1} (\nabla_\eta \Delta_\eta)^2 JU \right]^n . \tag{3.8b}$$

The spatial derivatives appearing in Eqs. (3.8) or (3.7) are approximated by three-point second-order-accurate finite difference

$$(f_\xi)_{j,k} \approx \frac{1}{2\Delta\xi} (f_{j+1,k} - f_{j-1,k}) \tag{3.9a}$$

$$\nabla_\xi \Delta_\xi f_{j,k} = (f_{\xi\xi})_{j,k} \approx \frac{1}{\Delta\xi^2} (f_{j+1,k} - 2f_{j,k} + f_{j-1,k}) \tag{3.9b}$$

$$(\nabla_\xi \Delta_\xi)^2 f_{j,k} = \frac{1}{\Delta\xi^4} (f_{j+2,k} - 4f_{j+1,k} + 6f_{j,k} - 4f_{j-1,k} + f_{j-2,k}) \tag{3.9c}$$

With the finite difference approximation of Eq. (3.9), a block-tridiagonal system of the differenced equations is formed. It should be noted that Eq. (3.9c) is applied to the RHS of Eq. (3.8a) only, therfore will not affect the block tridiagonal system (use parabolic extrapolation for j = 2 and (J-1)). For the ξ-sweep, one obtains

$$\tilde{\phi}_{j-1}\,\Delta U^*_{j-1} + \Gamma_j\,\Delta U^*_j + \psi_{j+1}\,\Delta U^*_{j+1} = (\mathrm{RHS})_j,\quad j = 2\cdots J-1 \tag{3.10}$$

where the $(\mathrm{RHS})_j$ is a column matrix which are computed with known flow variables over the entire grid points and $\tilde{\phi}, \Gamma$ and ψ are 4x4 (m x 1) matrix. As described in the next section, the boundary conditions at the axis of symmetry and the outflow plane are imposed implictly. This is done by modifying the coefficient in the matrix at j = 2 and j = J - 1, thus Eq. (3.10) will produce a bock tridiagonal system as follows:

$$\begin{bmatrix} \Gamma_2 & \psi_3 & & & \\ \tilde{\phi}_2 & \Gamma_3 & \psi_4 & & \\ & \ddots & \ddots & \ddots & \\ & & \tilde{\phi}_{J-3} & \Gamma_{J-2} & \psi_{J-1} \\ & & & (\tilde{\phi}_{J-2}-\psi_J) & \Gamma_{J-1} \end{bmatrix} \begin{bmatrix} \Delta U^*_2 \\ \Delta U^*_3 \\ \vdots \\ \Delta U^*_{J-2} \\ \Delta U^*_{J-1} \end{bmatrix} = \begin{bmatrix} (\mathrm{RHS})_2 \\ (\mathrm{RHS})_3 \\ \vdots \\ (\mathrm{RHS})_{J-2} \\ (\mathrm{RHS})_{J-1} \end{bmatrix} \tag{3.11}$$

where, for Eq. (3.8),

$$\Gamma_2 = I + \frac{\Delta\tau}{2} A_2^n - \varepsilon_I\,(J_2^{-1}\,J_1 - 2)\,I \qquad \text{for } m = 1, 2, 4$$

$$\Gamma_2 = I - \frac{\Delta\tau}{2} A_2^n + \varepsilon_I\,(J_2^{-1}\,J_1 + 2)\,I \qquad \text{for } m = 3$$

$$\Gamma_j = (1 + 2\varepsilon_I)I,\quad j = 3 \cdots J-2$$

$$\Gamma_{J-1} = I + \Delta\tau\,A_J^n - 2\varepsilon\,(J_{J-1}^{-1}\,J_{J-1})^n\,I$$

$$\tilde{\phi}_{j-1} = \frac{\Delta\tau}{2} A_{j-1}^n - \varepsilon_I\,(J_j^{-1}\,J_{j-1})^n\,I,\quad j=3 \cdots J-2$$

$$\psi_{j+1} = \frac{\Delta\tau}{2} A_{j+1}^n - \varepsilon_I\,(J_j^{-1}\,J_{j+1})^n\,I,\quad j=2 \cdots J-2$$

Equation (3.11) applies to k from 2 to K-1. The solution of the block triagonal system is obtained by the non-pivoted LU decompotition method.

Once ΔU^* are obtained, it is ready to perform the η-sweep. As described in the next section, the boundary conditions at the shock and the body surface are imposed explicitly, thus the flow variables in these two boundaries (k = 1 and K) are updated first and treated as known. The block tridiagonal system is

$$\begin{bmatrix} \Gamma'_2 & \psi'_3 & & & & \\ \tilde{\phi}'_2 & \Gamma'_3 & \psi'_4 & & & \\ & \ddots & \ddots & \ddots & & \\ & & & \tilde{\phi}'_{K-3} & \Gamma'_{K-2} & \psi'_{K-1} \\ & & & & \tilde{\phi}'_{K-2} & \Gamma'_{K-1} \end{bmatrix} \begin{bmatrix} \Delta U^n_2 \\ \Delta U^n_3 \\ \vdots \\ \Delta U^n_{k-2} \\ \Delta U^n_{k-1} \end{bmatrix} = \begin{bmatrix} \Delta U^{**}_2 \\ \Delta U^*_3 \\ \vdots \\ \Delta U^*_{K-2} \\ \Delta U^{**}_{K-1} \end{bmatrix} \tag{3.12}$$

where

$$\Gamma'_k = (1 + 2\varepsilon_I)\, I + \Delta\tau\, K^n_k - \frac{\Delta\tau}{R_e} N^n_k, \quad k = 2 \cdots K-1$$

$$\tilde{\phi}'_{k-1} = \frac{\Delta\tau}{2} B^n_{k-1} - \frac{\Delta\tau}{R_e} M^n_{k-1} - \varepsilon_I\, (J^{-1}_k\, J_{k-1})^n\, I, \quad k=2 \cdots K-1$$

$$\psi'_{k+1} = \frac{\Delta\tau}{2} B^n_{k+1} - \frac{\Delta\tau}{R_e} M^n_{k+1} - \varepsilon_I\, (J^{-1}_k\, J_{k+1})^n\, I, \quad k=2 \cdots K-1$$

$$\Delta U_2^{**} = \Delta U^*_2 + \tilde{\phi}'_1$$

$$\Delta U_{k-1}^{**} = \Delta U^*_{k-1} - \psi'_1$$

$$\tilde{\phi}_1 = \frac{\Delta\tau}{2} B^n_1 - \frac{\Delta\tau}{R_e} M^n_1 - \varepsilon_1\, (J^{-1}_2\, J_1)^n\, I$$

$$\psi_1 = \frac{\Delta\tau}{2} B^n_k - \frac{\Delta\tau}{R_e} M^n_k - \varepsilon_I\, (J^{-1}_{K-1}\, J_K)^n\, I$$

Equation (3.12) applies to j = 2 to J - 1. The same block tridiagonal solver is used to solve (3.12). This completes one full integration per time step.

4. BOUNDARY AND INITIAL CONDITIONS

As shown in Fig. 1, one would like to compute the flowfield enclosed by the four boundaries A,B,C, and D, where A is the bow shock, B is the body surface, C is the axis of symmetry and D is the outflow boundary. In implementing the boundary conditions, one intuitively expects implicit boundary conditions to be more stable than explicit one. However, according to many authors [4,5,6,] this has not been their experience. Since treating the boundary conditions explicitly is far more simpler to implement than to do it implicitly, the shock points and body points boundary conditions are imposed explicitly according to the method described by Kutler [4] and are briefly given in the following.

4.1 Shock Points

The flow in the vicinity of the bow shock is assumed to be inviscid and the Rankine-Hugoniot relations are satisfied or the shock is tracked. Since the final location of the shock must come from the solution, so it is allowed to move. A quasi-steady propagation of the shock is assumed. The pressure behind the shock is first determined by integrating the energy equation in nonconservative form as follows:

$$p_\tau = -\tilde{u}p_\xi - \tilde{v}p_\eta - \rho a^2(u_\xi\xi_x + v_\xi\xi_y + u_\eta\eta_x + v_\eta\eta_y + \frac{v}{y}) \qquad (4.1)$$

where

$$\tilde{u} = \xi_t + \xi_x u + \xi_y v \quad ,$$

$$\tilde{v} = \eta_t + \eta_x u + \eta_y v \quad .$$

Because explicit method is used, the time step $\Delta\tau_s$ for shock integration, Eq. (4.1) is restricted by the CFL condition (CN = 1), or

$$\Delta\tau_s = (0.9/\sigma_{max}) \qquad (4.2)$$

where σ_{max} is the maximum of the eigenvalues of the matrices A and B of all the nodel points at shock wave, or

$$\sigma_{1,2} = k_o + uk_1 + vk_2 \ ,$$

$$\sigma_{3,4} = k_o + uk_1 + vk_2 \pm a(k_1^2 + k_2^2)^{1/2} \qquad (4.3)$$

where for A: $k_o = \xi_t$, $k_1 = \xi_x$, $k_2 = \xi_y$; and for B: $k_o = \eta_t$, $k_1 = \eta_x$, $k_2 = \eta_y$;

and the constant 0.9 is a safety factor which must be less than 1. It should be noted that $\Delta\tau_s$ is different from the $\Delta\tau$ used in the integration of the interior points, this means that the calculation cannot be time-accurate. However, this does not prevent one to obtain steady state solution.

Knowing the pressure, the shock velocity can be determined as follows (see Fig. 2):

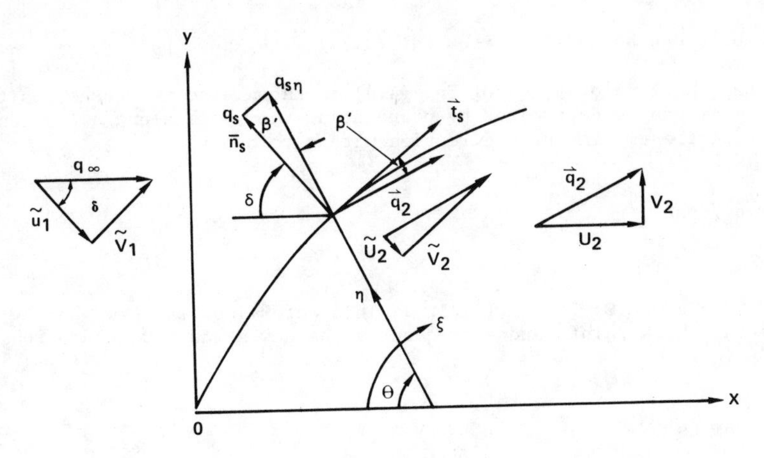

Fig. 2 Notation for shock point boundary condition

$$q_s = a_\infty M_x - \tilde{u}_1 \tag{4.4}$$

where

$$M_x = \left\{ \frac{1}{2\gamma} \left[\frac{p_2}{p_\infty} (\gamma + 1) + (\gamma - 1) \right] \right\}^{\frac{1}{2}}$$

$$\tilde{u}_1 = q_\infty \cos\delta$$

$$a_\infty = (\gamma p_\infty / \rho_\infty)^{\frac{1}{2}} \quad .$$

The shock angle δ is a function of the metrics

$$\delta = \tan^{-1}(-\eta_y/\eta_x)_{\text{shock}} \tag{4.5}$$

where η_y and η_x are defined in Eq. (2.6). From the Rankine-Hugoniot relations the density behind the shock can be determined by

$$\rho_2 = \rho_\infty \left(\frac{p_2}{p_\infty} + \frac{\gamma-1}{\gamma+1} \right) \Big/ \left(1 + \frac{\gamma-1}{\gamma+1} \cdot \frac{p_2}{p_\infty} \right) \tag{4.6}$$

The velocity components behind the shock in cylindrical coordinates are:

$$\begin{aligned} u_2 &= q_\infty \sin^2\delta + \tilde{u}_2 \cos\delta \\ v_2 &= q_\infty \sin\delta\cos\delta - \tilde{u}_2 \sin\delta \quad . \end{aligned} \tag{4.7}$$

where

$$\tilde{u}_2 = 2(1 - M_x^2)\, a_\infty \Big/ \left[(\gamma + 1) M_x \right] + \tilde{u}_1 \quad .$$

The value of e can be obtained from Eq. (2.3a) with known p_2, ρ_2, u_2, v_2.

Once the shock velocity q_s of Eq. (4.4) is known, the new shock position at time $\tau + \Delta\tau$ can be determined by propagating the shock along a ξ = constant line, or equivalently in the η direction with a velocity

$$q_{s_\eta} = q_s/\cos\beta' \tag{4.8}$$

where $\beta' = \Theta - \delta$ and $\Theta = \tan^{-1}(\xi_x/\xi_y)$. This determines the new x and y values of the shock points and subsequently the new x and y values of the interior points.

4.2 Body Points

On body surface, the no-slip boundary condition requires

$$\tilde{u} = \tilde{v} = 0 \tag{4.9}$$

when the body surface is not moving, Eq. (4.9) also implies u = v = 0. To determine the surface pressure, it is assumed that the normal pressure gradient over the first 3 grid points above the body surface is zero, or

$$p_n = \frac{1}{(\eta_x^2 + \eta_y^2)^{1/2}} \left[(\xi_x\eta_x + \xi_y\eta_y)p_\xi + (\eta_x^2 + \eta_y^2)p_\eta \right] = 0 \tag{4.10}$$

Similarly, for an adiabatic wall boundary condition, the temperature may be determined by

$$(\xi_x\eta_x + \xi_y\eta_y)\,T_\xi + (\eta_x^2 + \eta_y^2)T_\eta = 0 \tag{4.11}$$

The ξ and η derivatives in Eqs. (4.10) or (4.11) are differenced using a second-order central difference formula for the ξ-derivatives and a three-point one-sided formula for the η-derivatives. This results in a tri-diagonal system of equations which can be solved to yield the pressure and temperature. For a constant temperature wall, the temperature along the wall is kept constant at its initialized value throughout the entire convergence process. Once pressure and temperature are known, the density is determined from the equation of state.

4.3 Plane of Symmetry

The axis of symmetry line is bypassed by choosing the first two ξ = constant lines to straddle the axis or stagnation streamline. The plane of symmetry boundary is then enforced by the reflection principle. The flow variables are either even or odd functions with respect to the plane of symmetry, or

$$\rho(1,k) = \rho(2,k), \qquad v(1,k) = -v(2,k)$$
$$u(1,k) = u(2,k), \qquad e(1,k) = e(2,k) \quad . \tag{4.12}$$

The boundary conditions at the plane of symmetry is imposed implicitly.

4.4 Outflow Points

Since velocity at majority of the grids in this plane is supersonic, a simple linear extrapolation of the conservative variables is used. For those points near the surface, the flow is subsonic there, thus some error is introduced. The supersonic outflow boundary condition is imposed implicitly, or

$$Q(J,k) = 2Q(J-1,k) - Q(J-2,k) \tag{4.13}$$

4.5 Initial Conditions

To start the calculation, an initial flowfield must be provided. A good initial guess of the flow variables over the computation region will speed up the convergence of the solution. Fortunately, inviscid flows over sphere are well known, thus the shock location for a given free stream Mach number may be represented by empirical equations. This will give the flow variables at shock. On the body surface, Newtonian pressure distribution is a good approximation for high Mach number flow and the rest flow variable on the surface may be obtained by the isentropic relations. With flow variables approximated at shock and on body their values at the rest grid points are obtained by interpolation. For the details of providing initial conditions, please refer to Ref.[8].

5. RESULTS AND DISCUSSIONS

A computer code to carry out the integration as described in the previous sections has been obtained by modifying the Kutler's computer code. The major differences are in the viscous subroutines which are rewritten according to the equations presented in this paper. Results have been obtained for two cases: The first case is a hemisphere-cylinder with adiabatic wall at Mach number M_∞ of 2.94, Reynolds number Re_∞ of 2.2×10^5 and free stream stagnation temperature of 293°K; this case has been studied by Vivand and Ghazzi [9] and Kutler et al. The second case is a sphere-cone (cone half angle equals 9.75 deg) with isothermal wall ($T_w/T_\infty = 4.4$) at M_∞ of 5.92 and Re_∞ of 10^6. Before discussing the results, a brief description of the computational mesh, the criterion of convergence, and the determination of time integration step and the dissipation coefficients will be given.

Computational Mesh. A body-normal computational mesh is used for all the calculations. A uniform distribution of grid points on the body surface in the streamwise direction is used. In the normal direction, a grid point clustering scheme used by Kutler et al is followed:

$$\frac{\bar{n}}{Ys} = 1 + \beta\left[1 - \left(\frac{\beta+1}{\beta-1}\right)^{1-b''}\right] \Big/ \left[1 + \left(\frac{\beta+1}{\beta-1}\right)^{1-b''}\right] \tag{5.1}$$

where $b'' = (k-1)/(K-1)$. Equation (5.1) clusters coordinate surfaces closer to the body as the free parameter β approaches unity. Three sets of mesh A, B and C are used for hemisphere-cylinder and mesh D is used for sphere-cone as shown in Table 1. It is noted that the minimum spacing near the surface for Mesh C is about 4 times smaller than that for Mesh B and about 8 times smaller than that for Mesh A.

TABLE 1

Mesh	β	Points 0.1Ys	J x K	First 6 points					
				n_1/Ys	n_2/Ys	n_3/Ys	n_4/Ys	n_5/Ys	n_6/Ys
A	1.01	12	25 x 25	.0025	.0055	.0093	.014	.0199	.0271
B	1.005	17	25 x 32	.0011	.0024	.0039	.0058	.0081	.0109
C	1.001	20	25 x 32	.0003	.0006	.0011	.0017	.0024	.0033
D	1.005	17	28 x 32	.0011	.0024	.0039	.0058	.0081	.0109

Criterion for Convergence. The convergence of solution is judged by the convergence of shock speed. From experience, when the non-dimensional shock speed reaches 10^{-3} to 10^{-5}, all the flow variables remain essentially constant and the residue of the solution, which is given by the RHS of Eq.(3.6), is in the order of 10^{-5} to 10^{-7} over all the grid points. The shock speed does not converge monotonously, it will oscillate but decrease in the averaged magnitude. For all cases computed in this paper, a converged solution may be obtained in about 300 to 1000 time steps depending on the mesh selected. In general, the convergence rate slows down rapidly for a strongly clustered mesh such as Mesh C, see Table 2 for the hemisphere-cylinder case.

TABLE 2

Mesh	Number of Time Integrations	Shock Speed	Remark
A	300	$.51 \times 10^{-4}$	CN = 75 and final ε_E = 0.02 and $\varepsilon_I \equiv 3\,\varepsilon_E$ for all cases.
B	600	$.68 \times 10^{-4}$	Mesh C starts with ε_E = 0.1 for 400 steps.
C	1000	$.16 \times 10^{-2}$	

Time Steps and Dissipation Coefficients. The time step $\Delta\tau$ used for each time integration is determined from the input Courant number according to

$$\Delta\tau = \frac{CN}{\sigma_{max}} \tag{5.2}$$

where σ_{max} is given by Eq. (4.3) and is the maximum eigenvalues of the matrices A and B over all the interior points. The allowable Courant number, CN, for a calculation is problem dependent and also related to the dissipation coefficients ε_E and ε_I used. In the present calculation $\varepsilon_E = 0.02$ and $\varepsilon_I \equiv 3\varepsilon_E$ are used and a CN of 75 has been achieved (can also run for CN = 150 if let $\varepsilon_E = 0.1$). In some situation, a large value of ε_E is required at the beginning of the convergence process (because the initial flowfield is far off) and may be reduced afterward as the flowfield gradually approaching the final solution. Experiments about the effects of dissipation coefficients on the solution were conducted for the case of hemisphere-cylinder calculation. After obtained a converged solution with $\varepsilon_E = 0.02$, the calculation was continued for 200 more time steps with $\varepsilon_E = 0.001$. No significant change in the solution, which was also converged, was detected. However, if let $\varepsilon_E = \varepsilon_I = 0$, the calculation diverged. Thus, it is necessary for the dissipation terms to be presented in the calculation and $\varepsilon_E = 0.02$ is then used for all results presented in this paper. For a mesh of 25 x 32 the CPU time required for one time integration is 0.68 sec, or $0.85 \times 10^{-3}/\Delta\tau$/mesh point, using CDC-7600 computer.

Hemisphere-Cylinder. The results for hemisphere-cylinder with adiabatic wall at M_∞ of 2.94, Re_∞ of 2.2×10^5 and T_o of 293°K are given in Figs. 3 to 5. Figure 3 shows the temperature distribution T/T_∞ over the body surface. It is seen that the results obtained from Mesh B and C agree quite well but not that given by Mesh A which provides not enough points in the viscous layer. As shown in Table 1, the distribution of mesh point differs significantly between Mesh B and C and the solutions agree well (temperature is a more sensitive variable than other variables). Thus, it is necessary to provide sufficient grid points to resolve the viscous effects near the surface, such as that given by Mesh B or C. Also plot in Fig. 3 is the solution of Viviand and Ghazzi [9] who solved the full Navier-Stokes equation and slight differences are found in the area near the shoulder between his and the present solution. It was unable to produce the results of Kutler et al as given in Fig. 7 of Ref. [4] from the copy of computer code supplied by him. The result of T/T_∞ given by Kutler's code using Mesh B is shown in dotted line which is obviously wrong. Kutler et al [4] also indicated that temperature is a mesh dependent variable, it is not so as seen from the present results of Mesh B and C given in Fig. 3.

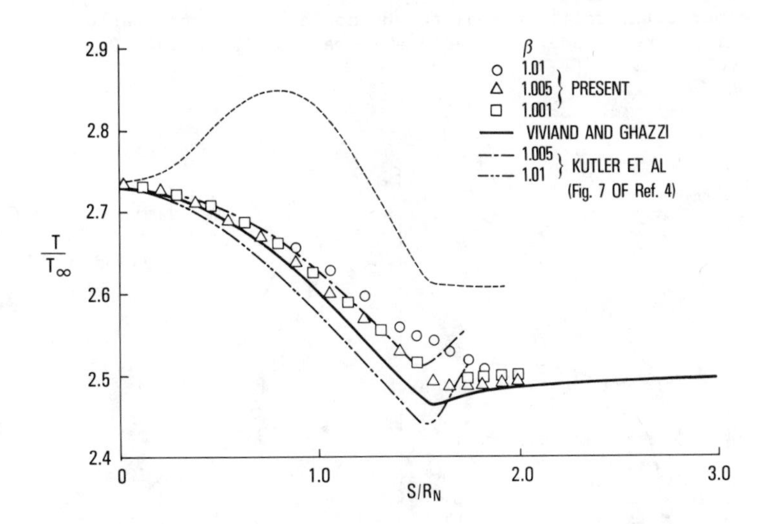

Fig. 3 Surface temperature distribution for hemisphere-cylinder with adiabatic wall at $M_\infty = 2.94$, $Re_\infty = 2.2 \times 10^5$ and $T_o = 293°K$

The temperature profile at three stations obtained from Mesh B and C are shown in Fig. 4, the agreement with the solution of Viviand and Ghazzi at slightly different station (given in parenthesis) is good. The shock shape and surface pressure are plotted in Fig. 5. It is interesting to note that these two quantities are not as sensitive as temperature and all solutions, including the one obtained using the code of Kutler et al, agree well.

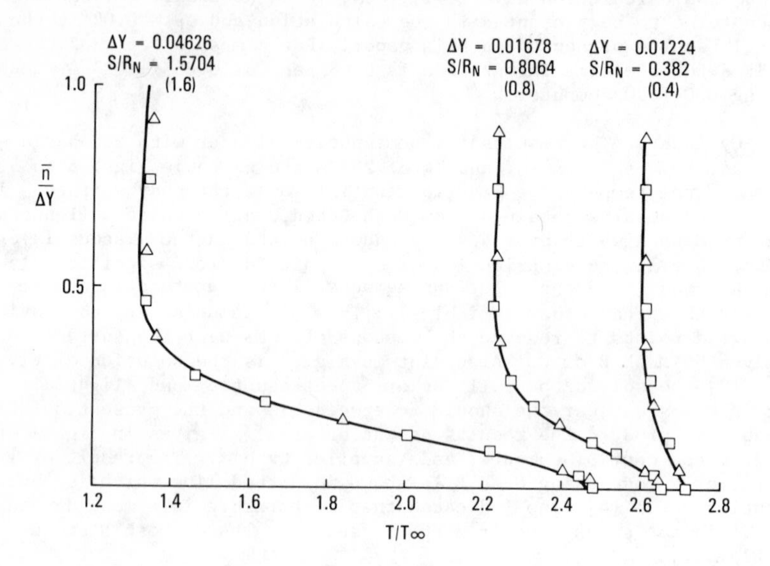

Fig. 4 Temperature profile normal to surface at different stations for hemisphere-cylinder with adiabatic wall at $M_\infty = 2.94$, $Re_\infty = 2.2 \times 10^5$ and $To = 293^oK$

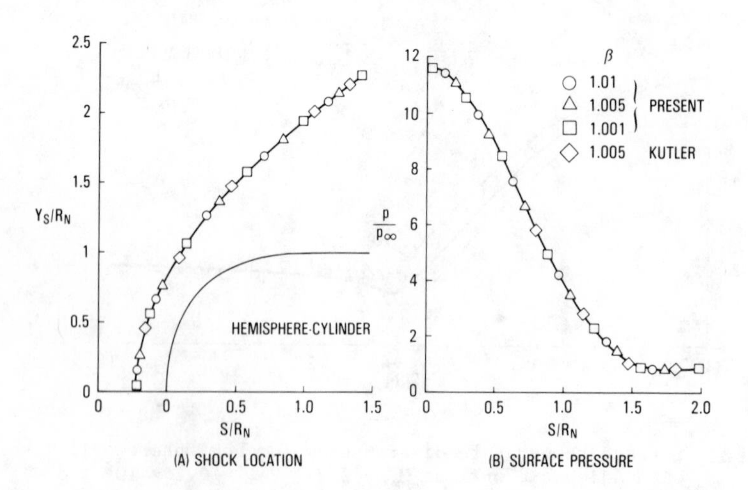

Fig. 5 Comparison of shock location and surface pressure for hemisphere-cylinder with adiabatic wall at $M_\infty = 2.94$, $Re_\infty = 2.2 \times 10^5$ and $To = 293^oK$

Sphere-Cone. The results for sphere-cone with cone half angle of 9.75 deg and with isothermal wall of $Tw/T_\infty = 4.4$ at $M_\infty = 5.92$ and $Re_\infty = 10^6$ are shown in Fig. 6-8. In hemisphere-cylinder calculation, it is noted that Mesh B gives as accurate results as Mesh C but with much less computing time, thus the same value of $\beta = 1.005$ is chosen for sphere-cone calculation. In order to compare heat transfer with boundary layer calculation, it is important that the surface pressure used for the boundary layer calculation must be consistent with that obtained from the present solution. In Fig. 6 a comparison is made for the surface pressure between the present solution and that inviscid surface pressure solution (using a blunt body code developed at NSWC) used in the boundary layer calculation. The agreement is excellent except at the shoulder where slight difference is shown. The Stanton number distribution is given in Fig. 7. It is seen that the agreement between present solution and the boundary layer calculation is surprisingly good up to the shoulder, from there on slight difference (because of pressure difference near the shoulder) is shown. The solution of Kutler et al gives overall higher values of ST. Because of wide spread in the experimental data, all calculations seem to fall within the experimental error band.

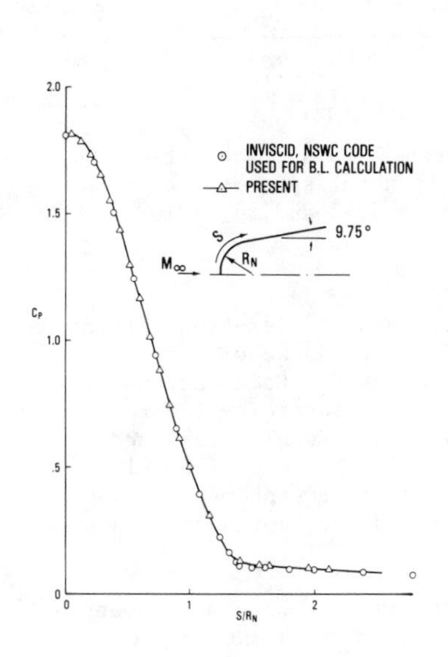

Fig. 6 Comparison of surface pressure used for boundary layer calculation and present solution for sphere-cone with isothermal wall of $Tw/T_\infty = 4.4$ at $M_\infty = 5.92$ and $Re_\infty = 10^6$

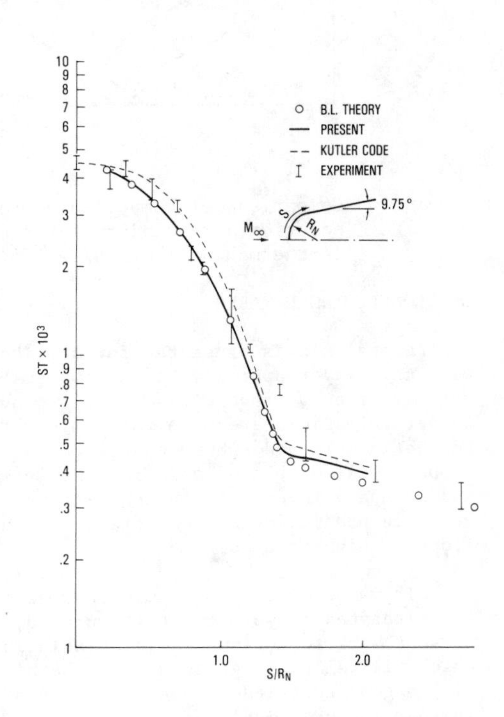

Fig. 7 Heat transfer distribution in terms of Stanton Number for sphere-cone with isothermal wall of $Tw/T_\infty = 4.4$ at $M_\infty = 5.92$ and $Re_\infty = 10^6$

A comparison of temperature profile at several stations between present calculation and that of boundary layer calculation (station given in parenthesis) is given in Fig. 8. The agreement is good. At station $S/Rn = 1.4$, i.e., the shoulder, again the difference is larger. The good agreement of present calculation with boundary layer calculation is to be expected since the surface pressure in both calculations agree well.

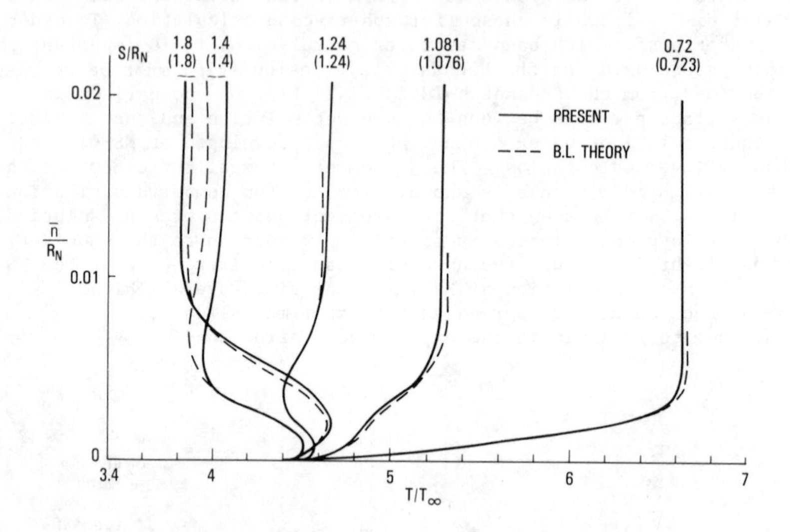

Fig. 8 Comparison of temperature profile normal to surface between present solution and boundary layer calculation for sphere-cone with isothermal wall of $T_w/T_\infty = 4.4$ at $M_\infty = 5.92$ and $Re_\infty = 10^6$

6. CONCLUDING REMARKS

An analysis is presented for solving the unsteady Navier-Stokes equations with thin-layer approximation using an implicit factored scheme for axisymmetric hypersonic viscous flows over blunt noses. Calculations of temperature field are made for laminar flow over hemisphere-cylinder with adiabatic wall and sphere-cone with isothermal wall. Results obtained compare well with available full Navier-Stokes solution, experimental data and boundary layer calculation. It is believed that present method gives reliable prediction of heat transfer and flow field for laminar unseparated flows at high Mach numbers.

It is necessary to examine how satisfactory is the calculation method for separated flows. For that purpose, it is necessary to extend the present work to include: (i) a solution to the full Navier-Stokes equation which will allow large separation bubble to appear in the flowfield and (ii) a good turbulence model, because after separation the flow is no more laminar in most cases.

ACKNOWLEDGEMENTS

The author would like to thank Dr. P. Kutler of NASA Ames Research Center for providing a copy of their research computer code as described in Ref. [4] and Dr. W. C. Ragsdale of Naval Surface Weapons Center for providing the experimental data and boundary layer calculations for the sphere-cone case. This work is partially funded by the Reentry Aerodynamic Program of NSWC at White Oak, monitored by Drs. A. M. Morrison and W. C. Lyons and by the Fluid Mechanics Program of Naval Air Systems Command at Washington, DC monitored by Mr. D. E. Hutchins.

Notations

a	Speed of sound
a', a'', b'	Parameters used in temporal differencing, Eq. (3.2) and (3.6)
A, B, K, L, M, N, P, Q	Jacobian Matrices, see Appendix
b_n, C_n	Coefficients appeared in Eq.(2.14) and (A.1)
CN	Courant number, Eq. (5.2)
Cp	Pressure coefficient, $(p - p_\infty)/\frac{1}{2}\rho_\infty q_\infty$
$\bar{C}p$, $\bar{C}v$	Specific heat at constant pressure and volume respectively
e	Total energy per unit volume
E, F, H, R, S, T	Functions of U
j, k	Grid index in ξ and η directions respectively
I	Identity matrix
J, K	Maximum grid point in ξ and η directions respectively
J	Jacobian of transformation from (x,y) to (ξ,η)
ℓ, m	Row and column of a matrix
L	Reference length
M	Mach number
n	Number in time integration
$\bar{n}$	Normal distance
p	Pressure
Pr	Prandtle number
q	Total velocity, or $(u^2 + v^2)^{\frac{1}{2}}$
q_s	Shock velocity
q_{s_η}	Velocity along ξ = constant line
Re	Reynolds number
R_N	Nose Radius
S	Arc length
St	Stanton number, $\frac{\mu/\mu_\infty}{Re_\infty Pr}\left[\frac{To}{T_\infty} - \frac{Tw}{T_\infty}\right]^{-1}\frac{\partial(T/T_\infty)}{\partial(\bar{n}/L)}$
t	Time
T	Temperature
u, v	Velocity components in cylindrical coordinates
$\tilde{u}, \tilde{v}$	Contravariant velocity components, Eq. (4.1)
U	Vector of conservative variables
x, y	Coordinates in the physical plane
Ys	Thickness of shock layer along body normal direction
β	Clustering parameter, Eq. (5.1)

β'	Angle between shock normal and ξ = constant line, See Fig. 2
γ	Ratio of specific heat $\bar{C}p/\bar{C}v$
Γ,ϕ,ψ	
Γ',ϕ',ψ'	Matrices in block tridiagonal system, Eqs. (3.11) and (3.12)
δ	Angle between shock normal and x-axis, see Fig. 2
ε	Internal energy of a gas, Eq. (2.3b)
$\varepsilon_E,\varepsilon_I$	Explicit and Implicit dissipation coefficients respectively
θ	Angle between axis and ξ = constant line
κ	Coefficient of thermal conductivity of a gas
μ,λ	First and second coefficients of viscosity
ξ,η	Coordinates in the computational plane
ρ	Density
σ	Eigenvalue
τ	Time after transformation
τ_{xx}, τ_{yy}, τ_{xy}, $\tau_{\phi\phi}$	Viscous stress terms

Substripts

∞	Free stream condition
1	Upstream of shock
2	Downstream of shock
w	Wall

Superscript

*	Intermediate value between ξ and η sweep

REFERENCES

1. Lindemuth, I. and Killeen, J., Alternating Direction Implicit Techniques for Two Dimensional Magnetohydrodynamic Calculations, J. of Computational Physics, Vol. 13, Oct. 1973, pp. 181-208.

2. Briley, W. R. and McDonald, H. Solution of Three Dimensional Compressible Navier-Stokes Equations by an Implicit Technique. Proceeding of the Fourth International Conference on Numerical Methods in Fluid Dynamics, Lecture notes in Physics, Vol. 35, Spring-Verlag, Berlin, 1975, pp. 105-110.

3. Beam, R. M. and Warming, R. F., An Implicit Factored Scheme for the Compressible Navier-Stokes Equations, AIAA Journal, Vol. 16, No. 4., April 1978, pp. 393-402.

4. Kutler, P., Chakravarthy, S. R. and Lombard, C. P., Supersonic Flow Over Ablated Nosetips Using an Unsteady Implicit Numerical Procedure, AIAA Paper 78-213, January 1978.

5. Steger, J. L., Implicit Finite Difference Simulation of Flow About Arbitrary Geometries with Application to Airfoils, AIAA Paper 77-665, June, 1977.

6. Pulliam, T. H. and Steger, J. L., Implicit Finite-Difference Simulations of Three Dimensional Compressible Flow, AIAA Journal, Vol. 18, No. 2, February 1980, pp. 159-167.

7. Hsieh, T., Numerical Investigation of Flowfield About a Series of Indented Nosetips, AIAA Paper 81-0077, January 1981.

8. Hsieh, T., Calculations of Flowfield About Indented Nosetips, NSWC report in preparation.

9. Viviand, H. and Ghazzi, W., Numerical Solution of the Navier-Stokes Equations at High Reynolds Numbers with Application to the Blunt Body Problem, Lecture notes in Physics, No. 59, Proceddings of the Fifth International Conference on Numerical Methods in Fluid Dynamics, 1976.

10. Ragsdale, W. C. and Morrison, A. M., IAP 202 Heat Transfer and Pressure Tests in the NSWC/WOL Hypersonic Tunnel, Private Communication, 1980.

11. Baldwin, B. S. and Lomax, H., Thin-Layer Approximation and Algebraic Model for Separated Turbulent Flows, AIAA Paper 78-257, 1978.

12. Peyret, R. and Viviand, H., Computations of Viscous Compressible Flows Based on the Navier-Stokes Equations, AGARD-AG-212, 1975.

13. Golovachov, Y. P., Numerical Investigation of Supersonic Nonequilibrium Carbon Dioxide Flow Past Blunt Bodies, Int. J. of Heat and Mass Transfer, Vol. 24, No. 4, pp. 649-657, 1981.

APPENDIX

The expressions for R_1, R_2, S_2 and T_2 are listed in the following:

$$R_1 = \frac{1}{J}\begin{bmatrix} 0 \\ b_2 u_\xi + b_3 v_\xi - c_6 \xi_x v \\ b_3 u_\xi + b_4 v_\xi - c_6 \xi_y v \\ b_5 \varepsilon_\xi + (b_2 u + b_3 v) u_\xi + (b_3 u + b_4 v) v_\xi - c_6 v (u\xi_x + v\xi y) \end{bmatrix} \tag{A.1}$$

$$R_2 \text{ or } S_2 = \frac{1}{J}\begin{bmatrix} 0 \\ b_8 u_{()} + b_{10} v_{()} \\ b_q u_{()} + b_{11} v_{()} \\ b_7 \varepsilon_{()} + (b_8 u + bqv) u_{()} + (b_{10} u + b_{11} v) v_{()} \end{bmatrix} \tag{A.2}$$

where ( ) = η for R_2 and ( ) = ξ for S_2.

$$T_2 = \frac{1}{Jy}\begin{bmatrix} 0 \\ u(\xi_y u_\xi + \xi_x v_\xi) \\ 2\mu \xi_y v_\xi \\ b_6 \varepsilon_\xi + \mu\xi_y (uu_\xi + \frac{4}{3} vv_\xi) + \mu\xi_x (uv_\xi - \frac{2}{3} vu_\xi) \end{bmatrix} \tag{A-3}$$

and

$$\begin{aligned}
b_2 &= \mu\left(\frac{4}{3}\xi_x^{\,2} + \xi_y^{\,2}\right), & b_3 &= \frac{1}{3}\mu\xi_x \xi_y \\
b_4 &= \mu\left(\xi_x^{\,2} + \frac{4}{3}\xi_y^{\,2}\right), & b_5 &= \frac{\gamma k}{Pr}(\xi_x^{\,2} + \xi_y^{\,2}) \\
b_6 &= \frac{\gamma k}{Pr}\xi_y, & b_7 &= \frac{\gamma k}{Pr}(\xi_x \eta_x + \xi_y \eta_y) \\
b_8 &= \frac{4}{3}\xi_x \eta_x + \xi_y \eta_x, & b_9 &= \xi_x \eta_y - \frac{2}{3}\xi_y \eta_x \\
b_{10} &= -\frac{2}{3}\xi_x \eta_y + \xi_y \eta_x, & b_{11} &= \xi_x \eta_x + \frac{4}{3}\xi_y \eta y
\end{aligned} \tag{A-4}$$

The Jocobian matrices used in Eq. (2.7) are listed in the following:

$$
A \text{ or } B = \begin{bmatrix}
k_o & k_1 & k_2 & 0 \\
k_1 c_1 - u(k_1 u + k_2 v) & k_o - k_1(\gamma-2)u + k_1 u + k_2 v & -k_1(\gamma-1)v + k_2 u & k_1(\gamma-1) \\
k_2 c_1 - v(k_1 u + k_2 v) & k_1 v - k_2(\gamma-1)u & k_o - (\gamma-2)k_2 v + k_1 u + k_2 v & k_2(\gamma-1) \\
(k_1 u + k_2 v)(2c_1 - \frac{\gamma e}{\rho}) & (\frac{\gamma e}{\rho} - c_1)k_1 - (\gamma-1)(k_1 u + k_2 v)u & (\frac{\gamma e}{\rho} - c_1)k_2 - (\gamma-1)(k_1 u + k_2 v)v & k_o + (k_1 u + k_2 v)
\end{bmatrix} \tag{A.5}
$$

where $c_1 = (\gamma-1)(u^2+v^2)$ and k_o, k_1 and k_2 can be found in Eq. (4.3).

$$
K = \frac{1}{y} \begin{bmatrix}
0 & 0 & 1 & 0 \\
-uv & v & u & 0 \\
-v^2 & 0 & 2v & 0 \\
v[c_1 - (e+p)/\rho] & -uv(\gamma-1) & \frac{1}{\rho}(e+p) - (\gamma-1)v^2 & \gamma v
\end{bmatrix} \tag{A.6}
$$

$$
L \text{ or } M = \frac{C_6}{\rho} \begin{bmatrix}
0 & 0 & 0 & 0 \\
v(\ )_x & 0 & -(\ )_x & 0 \\
v(\ )_y & 0 & -(\ )_y & 0 \\
2v\ u(\ )_x + v(\ )_y & -v(\ )_x & -u(\ )_x + 2v(\ )_y & 0
\end{bmatrix} \tag{A.7}
$$

where $(\ ) = \xi$ for L and $(\ ) = \eta$ for M.

$$
P \text{ or } Q = \frac{1}{\rho}\begin{bmatrix} 0 & 0 & 0 & 0 \\ \hline -(\ )_2u-(\ )_3v & (\ )_2 & (\ )_3 & 0 \\ \hline -(\ )_3u-(\ )_4v & (\ )_3 & (\ )_4 & 0 \\ \hline -(\ )_5(\varepsilon-\frac{u^2+v^2}{2}) & -(\ )_5u+(\ )_2u & -(\ )_5v+(\ )_4v & (\ )_5 \\ -(\ )_2u^2-2(\ )_3uv & +(\ )_3v & +(\ )_3u & \\ -(\ )_4v^2 & & & \end{bmatrix} \tag{A.8}
$$

where ( ) = b for P and ( ) = c for Q.

$$
N_1 = \frac{1}{J\rho}\begin{bmatrix} 0 & 0 & 0 & 0 \\ \hline 0 & 0 & 0 & 0 \\ \hline 3c_6v & 0 & -3c_6 & 0 \\ \hline 2c_6v^2 & \frac{5}{3}d_2v_\eta & -\frac{5}{3}d_2u_\eta-2c_6v & 0 \end{bmatrix} \tag{A.9}
$$

$$
N_2 = \frac{1}{\rho J}\begin{bmatrix} 0 & 0 & 0 & 0 \\ \hline 0 & 0 & 0 & 0 \\ \hline 0 & 0 & 0 & 0 \\ \hline 0 & \frac{5}{3}d_2v_\xi & -\frac{5}{3}d_2u_\xi & 0 \end{bmatrix} \tag{A.10}
$$

where $d_2 = \mu\eta_x$ for N_1 and $d_2 = \mu\xi_x$ for N_2.

$$W_1 \text{ or } W_2 = \frac{1}{Jy\rho}\begin{bmatrix} 0 & 0 & 0 & 0 \\ -(d_1 u + d_2 v) & d_1 & d_2 & 0 \\ -2d_1 v & 0 & 2d_1 & 0 \\ \begin{array}{l} -d_3\left(\varepsilon - \frac{u^2+v^2}{2}\right) \\ -d_1\left(u^2 + \frac{4}{3}v^2\right) \\ -d_2\frac{uv}{3} \end{array} & \begin{array}{l} -(c_7 - d_1)u \\ -\frac{2}{3}d_2 v \end{array} & \begin{array}{l} -(c_7 - \frac{4}{3}d_1)v \\ +d_2 u \end{array} & c_7 \end{bmatrix} \qquad \text{(A.11)}$$

where for W_1: $d_1 = \mu\eta_y$, $d_2 = \mu\eta_x$, $d_3 = c_7$ and for W_2: $d_1 = \mu\xi_x$, $d_2 = \mu\xi_x$, $d_3 = b_6$.

Numerical Solutions for Flow and Heat Transfer of a Plane Turbulent Oblique Impinging Jet

JACK C. HWANG and F.K. TSOU
Drexel University
Philadelphia, Pennsylvania

ABSTRACT

A two-equation model of turbulence was applied to obtain the solution of elliptic equations that govern the flow and heat transfer of an incompressible, plane, turbulent jet impinging obliquely on a flat surface. The case of $H/D = 30$, $Re = 45000$, $\alpha = 70°$ and constant wall temperature boundary condition was considered. The results of computation including velocity profiles, friction coefficients and Nusselt numbers are in good agreement with available data.

1. INTRODUCTION

In recent years, there has been an increasing interest in studying impinging jet flow and heat transfer problems because several new engineering applications have been found. The applications include ground effects in VTOL Aircrafts [1], jets issuing from hydraulic outlet works and weirs [2], and heat exchangers employing multiple impinging jets for the purpose of improving significantly the heat transfer rates [3]. In the latter case, the jets are arranged close to each other such that the large heat transfer coefficient in the stagnation region can be fully utilized.

When multiple jets issuing from a VTOL Aircraft impinge on the ground or on the deck of a ship, the interaction of the jets and the ground is a very complicated phenomenon. The important features of the interaction are: (a) Suck-down results when turbulent jet entrainment induces a flow about the aircraft. Such a flow will lead to a pressure below ambient and give rise to a negative lift of the aircraft. (b) An upward fountain flow results from the interaction of the neighboring wall jets. The fountain flow will heat up the underside of the aircraft. (c) Ingestion of the hot exhaust gas leads to a lower thermal efficiency, and (d) the heating of the deck is excessive and protection of human beings and equipment is required.

To analyze this complicated system, it would be appropriate to start from a simple case, e.g. a single impinging jet. The normal impingement of plane turbulent jet on a flat surface was considered earlier. The governing elliptic equations with two-equation models of turbulence were solved numerically.

The present studies were sponsored under Navy Contract No. N68335-79-C2055, Program Manager, Robert Black, Naval Air Engineering Center, Lakehurst, NJ.

The results indicate that the flow velocity and pressure are in good agreement with data [1].

The general problem, however, is an oblique impingement of the turbulent jet, which this paper is concerned with. Past work of the oblique impingement is few in existence. Let us describe briefly in the following:

Data of velocity and heat transfer for large $^H/D$ was reported by Schauer and Eustis [4]. Turbulence properties near stagnation points were measured with various impingement angles [5]. Simple empirical methods were developed to predict the properties of an oblique jet [6]. Analytical solution for rotational viscous oblique case was obtained by Rubel [7]. The results from this solution give a good prediction on the static pressure distribution on the impinging surface and on the location of the stagnation points. An interesting technique has been newly developed for the visualization of the stagnation lines of water impinging jets [8]. The technique utilizes fluorescein-sodium, a fluorescent dye, as the tracer fluid illuminated from the source of a laser beam.

Like the case of normal impingement, the oblique impinging jets have established themselves the existence of three distinct flow regions. There is a free jet region starting from the exit of the slot to some distance above a solid surface. The center line velocity of the free jet may decrease. The flow, however, has not been affected by the presence of the solid surface. The flow velocity is further decreased accompanying an increase in static pressure and eventually the velocity is reduced to zero at the stagnation point. This is referred to as impingement region. The stagnation pressure is significantly higher than the ambient resulting in a favorable pressure gradient that turns the flow to a direction parallel to the solid surface. A wall jet flow is formed with a pressure close to the ambient. The entire flow field is not symmetrical with unknown location of the stagnation point.

In this paper, the flow and heat transfer for a turbulent impinging jet with the oblique angle, 70°, are solved numerically. The elliptic equations governing stream function, vorticity and temperature as well as the two-equation model of turbulence [9] were utilized. The two-equation model is adopted because of the inadequacy of the one-equation model discussed in Ref. 1. In the following sections the analytical models, boundary conditions, use of wall functions, computational procedures and results, and comparison of some results with existing data will be described.

2. ANALYTICAL MODELS

Consider an incompressible, two-dimensional turbulent jet flow issued from an inclined slot impinging on a flat surface (Fig. 1).

The differential equations of elliptic type which govern the stream function ψ, the vorticity ω, the kinetic energy of turbulence k, the turbulence dissipation rate ε and the temperature T can be written as follows [10]:

$$a[\frac{\partial}{\partial x}(\phi\frac{\partial\psi}{\partial y}) - \frac{\partial}{\partial y}(\phi\frac{\partial\psi}{\partial x})] - \frac{\partial}{\partial x}[b\frac{\partial(c\phi)}{\partial x}] - \frac{\partial}{\partial y}[b\frac{\partial(c\phi)}{\partial y}] + S = 0, \quad (1)$$

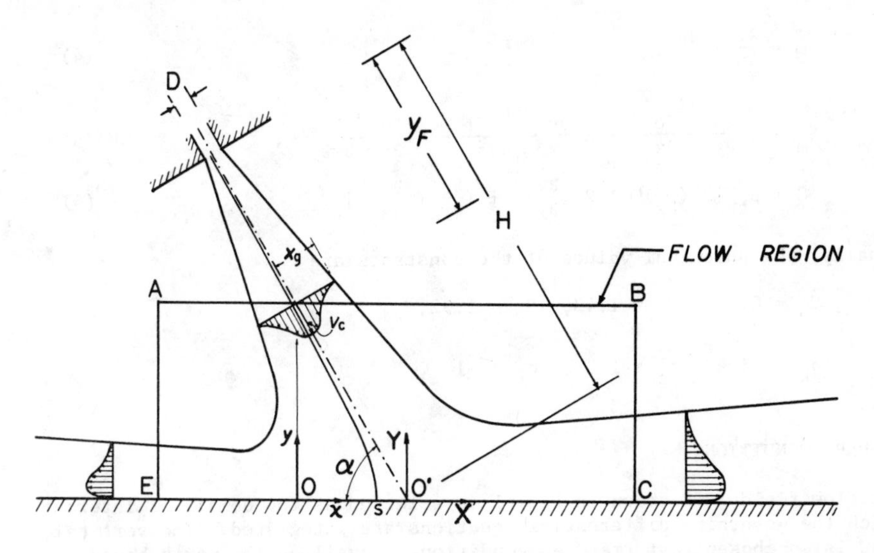

FIGURE 1. ANALYTICAL MODEL OF OBLIQUE IMPINGING JET FLOW

where ϕ stands for any one of the unknowns, ψ, ω, k, ε, T and the coefficients, a, b, c, and S are given in Table 1.

Table 1 Coefficients of a, b, c and S

ϕ	a	b	c	S
ω	1	1	μ_{eff}	$-S_\omega$
ψ	0	$1/\rho$	1	$-\omega$
k	1	μ_{eff}/σ_k	1	$-G+\rho\varepsilon$
ε	1	$\mu_{eff}/\sigma_\varepsilon$	1	$-C_1 G\frac{\varepsilon}{k}+C_2\rho\frac{\varepsilon^2}{k}$
T	1	$\rho(\alpha+\frac{\nu_t}{\sigma_h})$	1	0

The definition of functions appearing in the table are given as

$$\mu_{eff} = \mu + \mu_t = \mu + C_\mu \rho \frac{k^2}{\varepsilon} , \tag{2}$$

$$u = \frac{1}{\rho}\frac{\partial\psi}{\partial y} , \quad v = -\frac{1}{\rho}\frac{\partial\psi}{\partial x} , \tag{3}$$

$$\omega = \frac{\partial v}{\partial x} - \frac{\partial u}{\partial y} , \tag{4}$$

$$S_\omega = 2 \frac{\partial u}{\partial y} \frac{\partial^2 \mu_{eff}}{\partial x^2} + 2 \frac{\partial v}{\partial x} \frac{\partial^2 \mu_{eff}}{\partial y^2} - 4 \frac{\partial v}{\partial y} \frac{\partial^2 \mu_{eff}}{\partial x \partial y} , \tag{5}$$

$$G = \mu_t \left[2 \left(\frac{\partial u}{\partial x}\right)^2 + 2 \left(\frac{\partial v}{\partial y}\right)^2 + \left(\frac{\partial u}{\partial y} + \frac{\partial v}{\partial x}\right)^2\right] . \tag{6}$$

Finally, the numerical values of the constants are

$$C_\mu = 0.09, \quad C_1 = 1.43, \quad C_2 = 1.92,$$

$$\sigma_k = 1 , \quad \sigma_\varepsilon = 1.3 , \quad \sigma_h = 1 .$$

3. BOUNDARY CONDITIONS

The flow field ABCE shown in Fig. 1 is selected as the domain of interest over which the governing differential equations are integrated. The vertical extent BC is so chosen that free jet conditions prevail on the north boundary AB. The flow is obviously not symmetrical. Thus, the domain of interest covers both the downstream and upstream side of the impinging jet. The horizontal extent is chosen such that on the east and west boundaries any property gradient along x-coordinate is ignored. A detailed account of the boundary conditions is given below:

North Boundary AB

The distribution of the free stream function ψ across the boundary is based on the solution of plane turbulent jet [11]. In terms of (x,y) coordinates shown in Fig. 1, one obtains

$$\psi = 0.1043 \rho v_c \sqrt{y_F M} \tanh \left(\frac{M}{N}\right) , \tag{7}$$

where

$$M = y_F + (H - y_F) \sin^2 \alpha + x \cos \alpha - y \sin \alpha ,$$

$$N = 7.67 \left[x \sin \alpha - (H - y_F) \sin \alpha \cos \alpha + y \cos \alpha\right] .$$

The centerline velocity v_c and the reference length x_g are determined from the measurements [4],

$$v_c = 2.35 \, v_o / \sqrt{y_F/D} , \tag{8}$$

$$x_g = 0.22 \, y_F , \tag{9}$$

where v_o is the jet velocity at slot exit and y_F is indicated in Fig. 1.

The velocity along the boundary AB is then calculated from Eqs. (3) and (7). The remaining properties are prescribed below:

$$k = 0.04 \, v_c^2 , \tag{10}$$

$$\varepsilon = 0.0374\ v_c^{\ 3}/x_g\ , \tag{11}$$

$$T = T_\infty\ \text{(constant)}. \tag{12}$$

Equations (10) and (11) are obtained from the work of Bower, et al. [12] and Patankar [13]. The value of AB and BC for the present computation are selected as

$$AB = 35x_g \text{ and } BC = 2.5x_g . \tag{13}$$

West Boundary AE and East Boundary BC

The properties are independent of x on these boundaries, i.e.,

$$\frac{\partial \omega}{\partial x} = \frac{\partial \psi}{\partial x} = \frac{\partial k}{\partial x} = \frac{\partial \varepsilon}{\partial x} = \frac{\partial T}{\partial x} = 0. \tag{14}$$

Wall Boundary EC

The stream function ψ at the wall is constant and must be equal to that of the stagnation streamline. The relation of the stagnation streamline with the oblique angle as obtained by Rubel [7] has the form,

$$\cos\alpha = 1.3327\ \psi_s\ (1 - 0.2652\psi_s^{\ 2}). \tag{15}$$

This equation compared well with experimental data [4,6] and hence, is used to calculate ψ on the boundary EC.

The wall vorticity can be expressed in terms of stream function with the assumption that the derivative of ψ along x-coordinate is small compared with $\partial\psi/\partial y$. The resulting form is [1],

$$\omega = \frac{-3(\psi_A - \psi)}{d_A^{\ 2}} - \frac{\omega_A}{2}. \tag{16}$$

To treat the remaining unknowns, k, ε and T, one utilizes the wall-function approach. It is noted that the k-ε model used in the present work is applicable only to flows or flow regions with high turbulence Reynolds number R_t. In the region near the wall, i.e., viscous sublayer, the effect of molecular viscosity governs and the turbulence Reynolds number is small. Thus, k, ε and T have to be obtained at a location just outside the sublayer in order to satisfy the requirement of high turbulence Reynolds number.

The basic assumptions used in the wall-function approach include: (a) the velocity component just outside the sublayer follows the usual logarithmic law of wall and (b) the turbulence is in local equilibrium. With these assumptions, the quantities, u_A, k_A and ε_A at a point with distance d_A from the wall just outside the sublayer can be related with the friction velocity u_τ in the form [9]

$$\frac{u_A}{u_\tau} = \frac{1}{\kappa}\ \ell n\ [E\ \frac{u_\tau d_A}{\nu}]\ , \tag{17}$$

$$k_A = \frac{u_\tau^{\ 2}}{C_\mu}\ , \tag{18}$$

$$\varepsilon_A = \frac{u_\tau^3}{\kappa d_A}, \tag{19}$$

where $u_\tau = \sqrt{\tau_w/\rho}$.

Similarly the thermal wall function [14] is used to relate the heat flux from the wall with the wall temperature and the temperature just outside of sublayer as

$$\rho C_p C_\mu^{\frac{1}{4}} k_A^{\frac{1}{2}} \left(\frac{T_w - T_A}{q_w}\right) = \frac{\sigma_h}{\kappa} \ln\left[E \frac{u_\tau d_A}{\nu}\right]$$

$$+ \sigma_h \frac{\pi/4}{\sin \pi/4} \left(\frac{A}{\kappa}\right)^{\frac{1}{2}} \left(\frac{\sigma_{h,\ell}}{\sigma_h} - 1\right) \left(\frac{\sigma_h}{\sigma_{h,\ell}}\right)^{\frac{1}{4}}, \tag{20}$$

where

A = Van Driest constant, equal to 26 for a smooth wall,
σ_h = effective Prandtl number of fully turbulent fluid, taken as unity,
$\sigma_{h,\ell}$ = Prandtl number taken as 0.73,
q_w = wall heat flux,
E = 9,
κ = 0.4.

Equation (20) is used for calculation of Nusselt number with constant wall temperature boundary condition.

4. COMPUTATIONAL PROCEDURES

The numerical scheme used in the present work is based on that described in Refs. 1 and 10, which employs Gauss-Seidel iterative procedures, finite-difference upwind scheme for the convective terms and the linearization of the source terms appearing in the k and ε equations. In the near wall nodes, the velocity gradient is obtained by differentiating the wall function.

A 16 x 50 nonuniform grid system was used for computation. Initially, a value of 10^{-6} was assigned for ω, ψ and T and a value of 10^{-2} for k and ε. The values on the non-iterative boundary nodes are based on the afore-mentioned boundary conditions. In performing the computations, all unknowns and properties appearing in the equations are made dimensionless.

In addition to these five unknowns, the velocity components u and v, the length scale and the effective viscosity μ_{eff} were also computed at each grid point. Equations (3) and (2) are used to obtain u, v and μ_{eff}, and the length scale is calculated from the relation

$$\ell = C_\mu \frac{k^{3/2}}{\varepsilon}. \tag{21}$$

At the end of each iteration new values for ω, ψ, k, ε and T at all interior nodes were calculated. Then the wall function is applied to obtain u_τ and $(\partial u/\partial y)_A$ at the near wall nodes. With these values available, k and ε at the near wall nodes are then recalculated. As mentioned in the foregoing, the wall function is applicable for large turbulence Reynolds number, the recommended value of which is between 100 and 400 [13]. An adjustment of the distance d_A is needed in order to satisfy this condition.

The computation is said to be convergent if the residual of each of the five variables is less than 10^{-3}. The residual of a variable, ϕ, is defined as

$$\beta = \left(\frac{\phi_n - \phi_o}{\phi_o}\right)_{max} , \qquad (22)$$

where the subscripts "n" and "o" refer to new and old values of ϕ, respectively. The residual β represents the maximum ratio throughout the flow field. Under relaxation is required for k and ε, particularly in the early iterations. This convergence criterion was checked at the end of each iteration. All five variables were converged after 1000 iterations. The computations were performed on a Hewlett-Packard 1000 mini-computer. In the present system, energy equation is not coupled with the other equations. There is no need, however, to solve the energy equation separately after the flow field solution is obtained since the saving of computation time is small.

5. PRESENTATION OF RESULTS

The results of numerical computation for the two-dimensional oblique impinging jet described in the foregoing is presented in this section. The computation is for the case of Re = 45000, H/D = 30, α = 70° and constant wall temperature boundary condition. The computer output for ψ, ω, k, ε, ℓ, and T is arranged in the form of contour plots while the remaining quantities such as velocity profiles, friction coefficient and Nusselt number are plotted in order to facilitate data comparison. It has to be noted that the distances x and y in Fig. 2 through Fig. 7 refer to the coordinate system of x and y indicated in Fig. 1 and the (X,Y) system is used in the remaining figures.

Contour Plots

There are six contour plots (Fig. 2 through Fig. 7) reported herein. In each plot, the horizontal extent, x/x_g, is large compared with the vertical extent, y/x_g. The scale of the former is therefore compressed for convenience of presentation. Figure 2 shows the distribution of the streamline functions, $\psi/\rho v_c x_g$. The stagnation point s indicated in the figure is shifted to the left of the point o', the intersecting point of the jet centerline with the flat surface (c.f. Fig. 1). The streamlines are close to each other along the mainstream of the jet. In the horizontal direction, the distribution appears even both in the region near the surface and in the region away from it. In the case of the normal impinging jet, however, the streamlines are very close to each other in the region near the surface [1], indicating large velocity gradients and friction coefficients.

The vorticity distribution, $\omega x_g/v_c$, is shown in Fig. 3. In the region very near to the surface, the absolute value of the vorticity is large. There is a sign change at a distance not far from the surface. Fig. 4 indicates the distribution of kinetic energy of turbulence, k/v_c^2. It is observed that k is small near the surface and increases in the direction away from it until some maximum value is reached. Near the stagnation point, there is a large increase in k along the vertical coordinate, y, as expected. The rate of dissipation, $\varepsilon x_g/v_c^3$ is given in Fig. 5, which shows a large dissipation near the

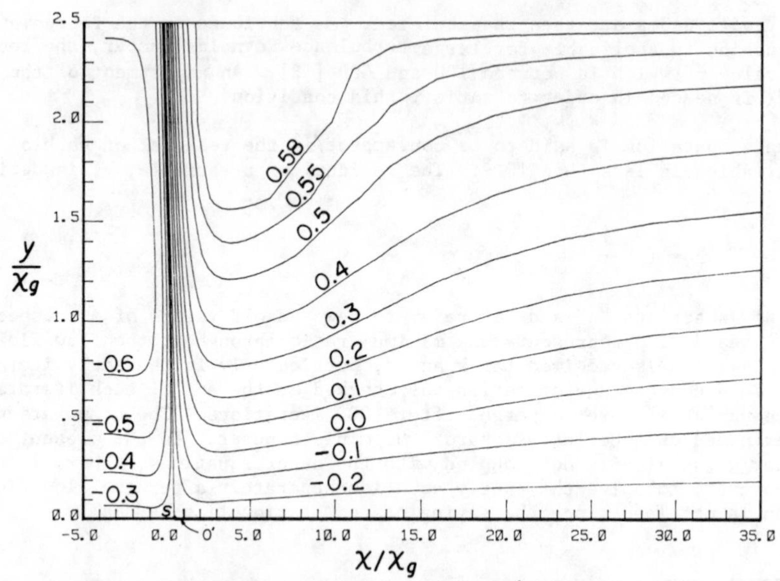

Fig. 2, Distribution of Streamline Function, $\psi/\rho V_c \chi_g$
Angle = 70 Deg., H/D = 30, Re = 45000

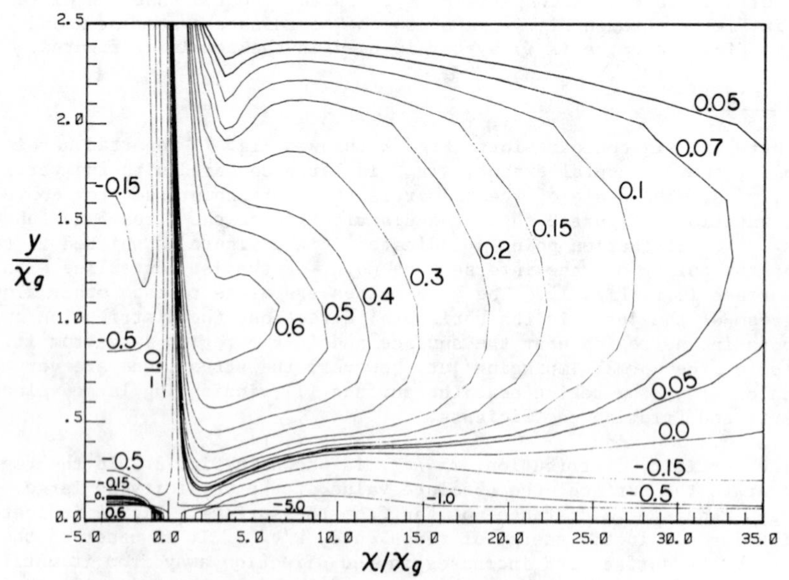

Fig. 3, Distribution of Vorticity, $\omega \chi_g / V_c$
Angle = 70 Deg., H/D = 30, Re = 45000

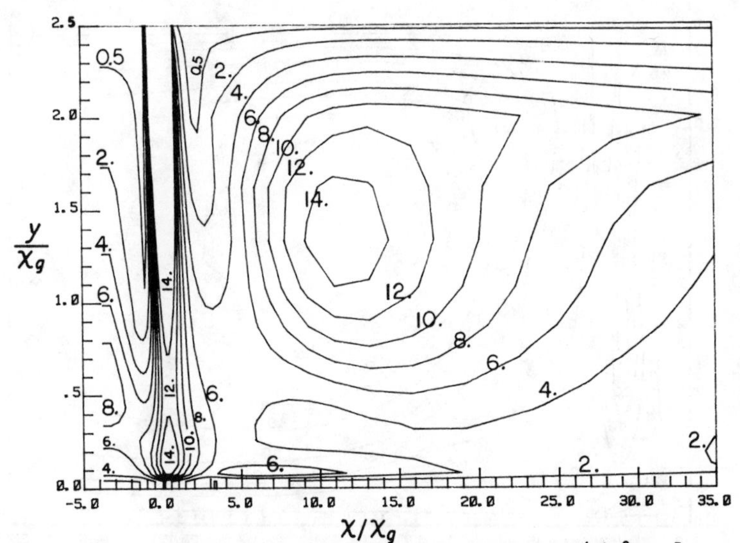

Fig. 4, Distribution of Kinetic Energy of Turbulence, $(k/V_c^2)\times10^3$
Angle = 70 Deg., H/D = 30, Re = 45000

surface and decreases along y until some minimum value is obtained. Along the jet flow, ε decreases up to the neighborhood of the stagnation point. It is interesting to examine the distribution of length scale, ℓ/x_g, shown in Fig. 6. Near the surface, the line labeled 1.0 appears parallel to the surface, i.e., ℓ is independent of x. The usual concept that ℓ is linear with y in this region seems to apply. Away from the surface, ℓ distribution indicated in the figure, like the other variables, is so complicated that any estimation using algebraic relations becomes unrealistic. Thus, a one-equation model using such relations may give erroneous results. The dimensionless temperature field,

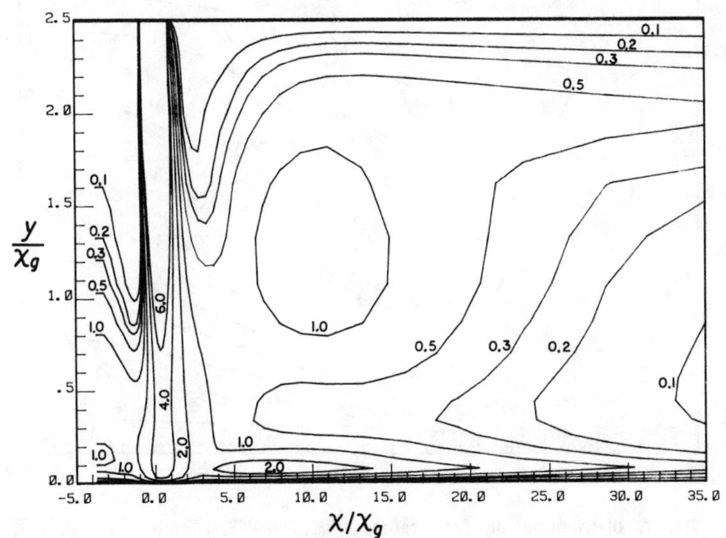

Fig. 5, Distribution of Dissipation Rate of Turbulence, $(\epsilon X_g/V_c)\times10^3$
Angle = 70 Deg., H/D = 30, Re = 45000

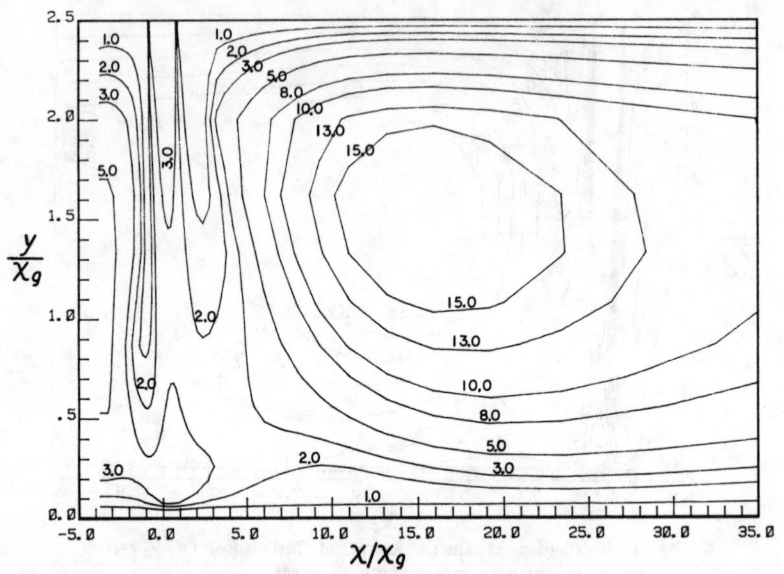

Fig. 6, Distribution of Length Scale, $(\ell/X_g)\times10^3$
Angle = 70 Deg., H/D = 30, Re = 45000

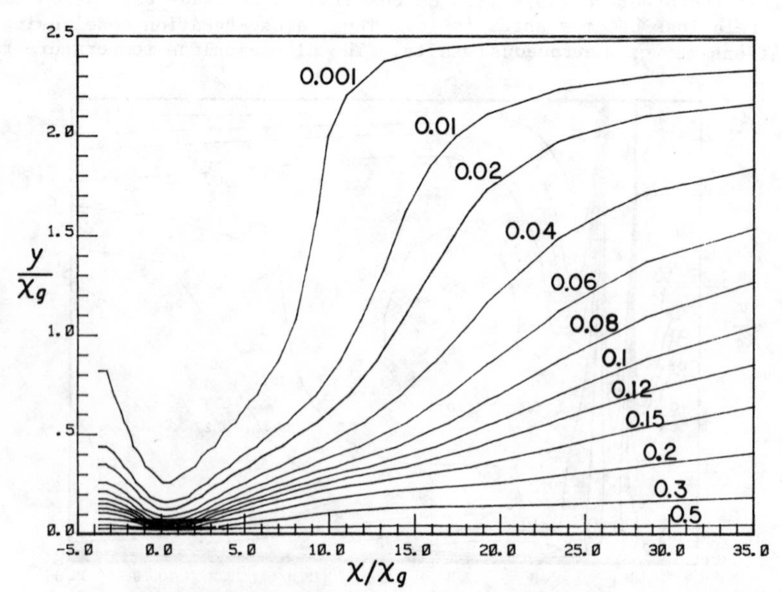

Fig. 7, Distribution of Temperature with Const. Wall Temp., $(T-T_\infty)/(T_w-T_\infty)$
Angle = 70 Deg., H/D = 30, Re = 45000

$T-T_\infty/T_W-T_\infty$, shown in Fig. 7 extends only a small vertical distance in the stagnation region. This distance becomes large for large x. It was considered that the temperature of the jet at the jet exit is the same as ambient, T_∞ and the wall temperature, T_W is constant.

Comparison with Data

Further results from the numerical computation are presented in this paragraph. A comparison with the experimental data [4] in Fig. 8 through Fig. 11 is made. In plotting these figures, the (X,Y) coordinate system with origin o' (Fig. 1) was employed. Figure 8 shows the velocity profiles of the wall jet calculated for three different stations. These profiles reveal slight deviation from a single similar profile. The normalizing factor Y_5 in the figure represents the distance of Y where the X-component velocity, u = 1/2 u_{max}. The data points show a fairly good agreement with calculated results. The calculated maximum velocities u_{max} of the wall jet also compare well with measured velocities (Fig. 9). At stagnation point, u_{max} is reduced to zero.

Figure 10 compares the computed friction coefficient, C_f, with the measured one. For small x, the computed C_f appears smaller than the measured C_f. The calculated maximum C_f is located to the right of the stagnation point. The results of Nusselt number is given in Fig. 11. An excellent agreement of the computed Nu with the measured Nu is observed. It is also seen that the maximum Nu from the computation is at the stagnation point. The location of the maximum Nu is therefore different from that of the maximum C_f. The concept of the Reynolds analogy does not seem to apply in this stagnation.

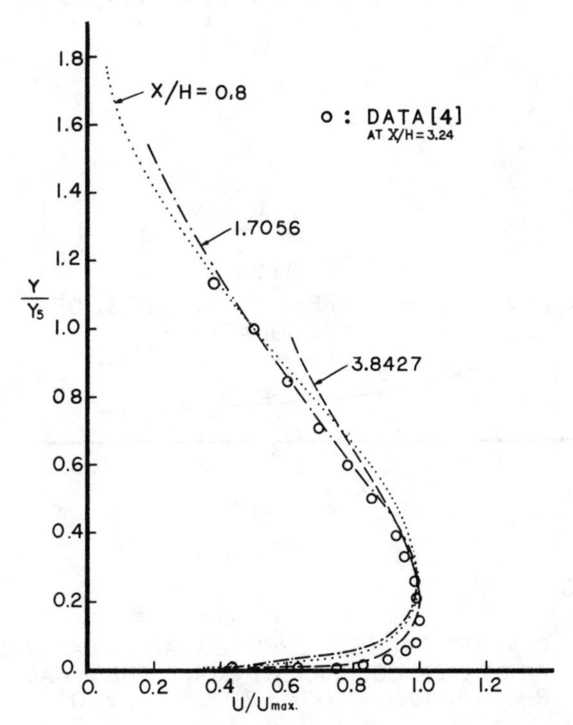

FIGURE 8. IMPINGING JET VELOCITY PROFILES.

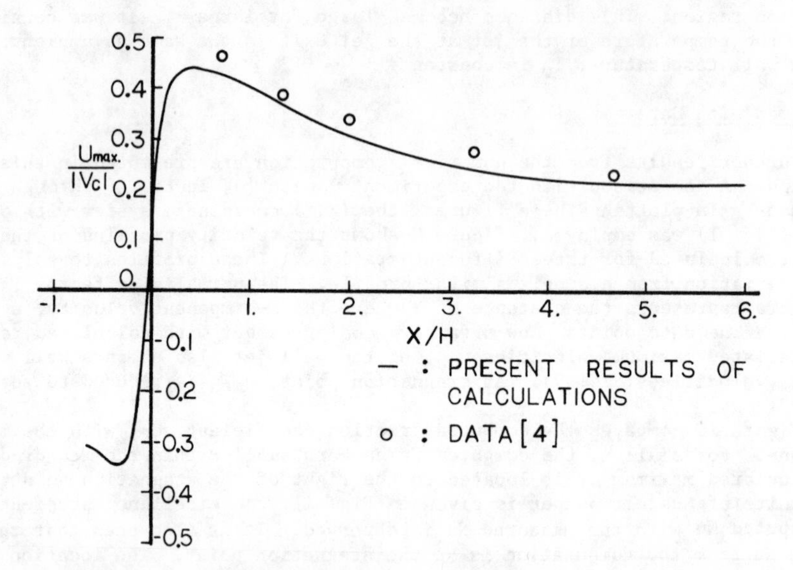

FIGURE 9. COMPARISON OF COMPUTED AND MEASURED MAX. VELOCITY ALONG THE WALL. Re = 45000, H/D = 30, $\alpha = 70°$

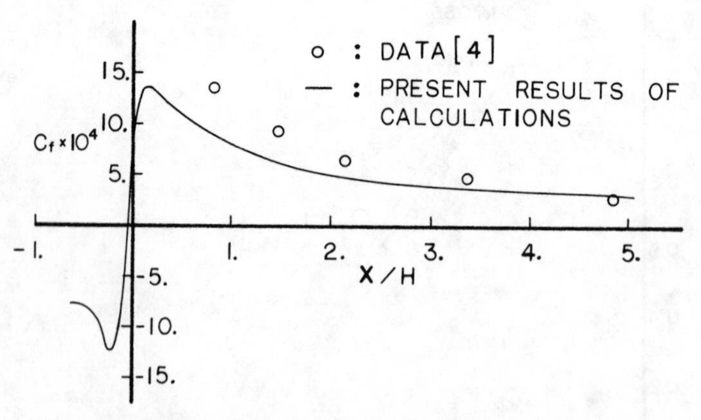

FIGURE 10. COMPARISON OF COMPUTED AND MEASURED FRICTION COEFFICIENT ON THE WALL. Re = 45000, H/D = 30, $\alpha = 70°$

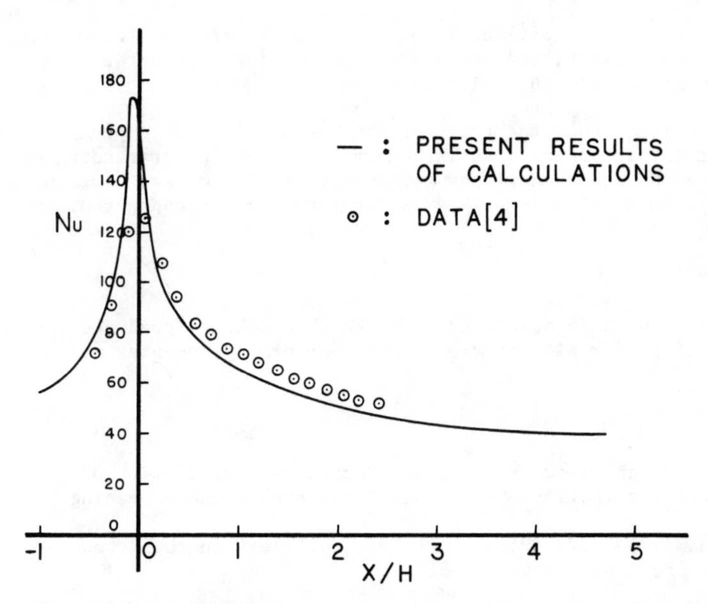

FIGURE II. COMPARISON OF COMPUTED AND MEASURED NUSSELT NUMBER FOR CONST. WALL TEMP. $Re = 45000$, $H/D = 30$, $\alpha = 70$

6. SUMMARY AND CONCLUSION

The numerical solution was obtained for flow and heat transfer of a two-dimensional, turbulent jet impinging obliquely on a flat surface. The numerical scheme, derived from the governing elliptic equations and utilized to obtain the solution, includes: (a) the use of a k-ε model of turbulence and (b) the application of wall functions for flow and temperature at the near wall node. It is adopted in the present work because of its application to the case of the normal impinging jet reported earlier [1].

There are three parameters in the oblique impinging jet, namely, Reynolds number Re, height and slot width ratio $^{H}/_{D}$, and the angle of impingement α. The results from the present work for Re = 45000, $^{H}/_{D}$ = 30, and α = 70° are summarized below:

(1) There is a shift of the stagnation point to the left of the intersecting point of the jet centerline with the surface.

(2) The vorticity and dissipation rate is large near the surface and decreases away from it while the kinetic energy of turbulence changes in the opposite direction.

(3) The length scale in the region very near the surface is independent of x. The usual concept of the linear relation with y appears reasonable. Away from the surface, its distribution is complicated. Approximation using algebraic relations will result in error.

(4) There is an extended area of temperature distribution. The thin thermal boundary layer does not seem to exist.

(5) The velocity profiles and the maximum velocities of the wall jet, the friction coefficient, and the Nusselt number for constant wall boundary condition compare well with available data.

It may conclude that the test for the k-ε model used to predict oblique impinging jet is, in general, satisfactory. A better understanding of the oblique jet can be achieved if the parametric studies of Re, $^H/_D$, and α using numerical experimentation described in the foregoing is conducted.

ACKNOWLEDGEMENT

The authors wish to acknowledge Mr. Woncheol Cho, a graduate student at Drexel University, for his contribution of performing computer calculations.

REFERENCES

1. Hwang, J. C. and Tsou, F. K. 1981. "Numerical calculation of jet-induced ground effects in VTOL," AIAA 19th Aerospace Sciences Meeting, St.Louis,MO.

2. Rajaratnam, N. 1967. Plane turbulent wall jets on rough boundaries. Water Power, London, pp. 149-153.

3. Martin, H. 1977. Heat and mass transfer between impinging gas jets and solid surfaces. Advances in Heat Transfer, Vol. 13.

4. Schauer, J. J. and Eustis, R. H. 1963. "The flow and heat transfer characteristics of plane turbulent impinging jets," Tech. Rept. No. 3, Stanford University, Department of Mechanical Engineering.

5. Kamoi, A. and Tanaka, H. 1972. Measurements of wall shear stress, wall pressure and fluctuations in the stagnation region produced by oblique jet impingement. Fluid Dynamic Measurements. Conference Papers. Leicester University Press, Vol. 1, pp. 217-227.

6. Beltaos, S. 1976. Oblique impingement of plane turbulent jets. ASCE Jour. of Hydraulic Div. HY9, pp. 1177-1192.

7. Rubel, A. 1978. Computation of jet impingement on a flat surface. AIAA 16th Aerospace Science Meeting, Huntsville, Alabama.

8. Saripalli, K. R. 1981. Visualization of multi-jet impingement flow. AIAA/SAE/ASME 17th Joint Propulsion Conference, Colorado Srings, Colorado.

9. Rodi, W. 1981. Progress in turbulence modeling for incompressible flows. AIAA 19th Aerospace Science Meeting, St. Louis, Missouri.

10. Gosman, A. D. and Pun, W. M. and Runchal, A. K. and Spalding, D. B. and Wolfstein, M. 1969. Heat and mass transfer in recirculating flows. Academic Press.

11. Schlichting, D. 1979. Boundary layer theory. McGraw-Hill Co.

12. Bower, W. W. and Kotansky, D. R. and Hoffman, G. H. 1977. Computation and measurements of two-dimensional turbulent jet impingement flow fields. Symposium on Turbulent Shear Flows.

13. Patankar, S. V. 1980. Numerical heat transfer and fluid flow. McGraw-Hill Co.

14. Launder, B. E. and Spalding, D. B. 1974. The numerical computation of turbulent flows. Computation Method in App. Mech. and Engr. Vol. 3, pp. 269-289.

NOMENCLATURE

A	Van Driest constant
a,b,c	coefficients in Eq. (1)
C_1, C_2	constant
C_μ	constant
C_p	specific heat at constant pressure
C_f	friction coefficient
D	slot width of the jet nozzle
d	distance between near wall node and the wall
E	constant defined in Eq. (19)
G	generation of turbulence kinetic energy
H	distance between the nozzle exit and the surface along jet centerline
k	turbulence kinetic energy
ℓ	turbulence length scale
q_w	wall heat flux
Nu	Nusselt number
Re	Reynolds number based on slot width and exit velocity at the nozzle
R_t	turbulence Reynolds number, $\rho\sqrt{k}\ell/\mu$
S	source term in Eq. (1)
T	temperature
T_w	wall temperature
T_∞	ambient temperature
u,v	velocity components along x,y
u_{max}	local maximum velocity
u_τ	friction velocity
v_c	jet centerline velocity at north boundary AB
v_o	jet velocity at nozzle exit
x_g	reference length indicated in Fig. 1
x,y	rectangular coordinates with origin 0
X,Y	rectangular coordinates with origin 0'
y_F	distance indicated in Fig. 1
Y_5	half width of the wall jet
α	thermal diffusivity in Table 1
α	oblique angle
β	residual
ε	turbulence dissipation rate
κ	Von Karman constant
ν	kinematic viscosity
μ	dynamic viscosity
μ_t	turbulent viscosity = $\rho\sqrt{k}\ell$
μ_{eff}	effective viscosity
ρ	density
σ_k	turbulent Prandtl number for k
σ_ε	turbulent Prandtl number for ε
σ_h	turbulent Prandtl number for T
$\sigma_{h,\ell}$	laminar Prandtl number
τ_w	wall shear stress
ϕ_n	new point value of variable ϕ
ϕ_o	old point value of variable ϕ
ψ	stream function
ω	vorticity

Subscript:

A	denotes the condition at the near wall node

TWO-PHASE FLOWS

Developments in the IPSA Procedure for Numerical Computation of Multiphase-Flow Phenomena with Interphase Slip, Unequal Temperatures, Etc.

D. BRIAN SPALDING
Computational Fluid Dynamics Unit
Imperial College of Science and Technology
London SW7 2AZ, England

ABSTRACT

A review is made of developments in, and additions to, the interphase slip algorithsm IPSA. A fully symmetrical volume-fraction equation has been adopted. The treatment of the stratified-flow and 'particle-packing' problems has been unified. A donor-acceptor version has been developed. Applications with interphase heat and mass transfer have been successfully made. A simple technique for the approximate calculation of the mass-transfer-influenced particle-size distribution has been devised. Preliminary thought has been given to the incorporation of turbulent mixing, based on new hypotheses.

1. INTRODUCTION

1.1 Background

IPSA (≡ Interphase-Slip Algorithm) is a numerical procedure for solving the equations which govern the motion of several interspersed and mutually slipping phases. It was first described in a lecture delivered in 1976; and it has been further adumbrated in several publications by the author and his colleagues[1]. During the course of time, the procedure has been modified, by way of both simplifications and extensions; and it has been subjected to extensive tests. However, no single report collects the modifications together, or provides a succinct summary of the procedure as it now stands.

1.2 Purpose and Content of the Present Paper

An up-to-date summary of the IPSA procedure is provided in the following sections of this paper. The presentation is by way of assertion rather than argument; and no account is given of the various stages through which IPSA passed before reaching its current one, or of the intermediate experiences which guided or motivated the development.

It is not to be expected that the development has yet reached its culmination; but this is all the more reason for reviewing the present situation; this can be summarised, from the operational viewpoint, as follows:

---

(1) See Bibliography, Section 10, for references to these and other works mentioned in the paper.

a. For fully-dispersed flow, the procedure works well, having been employed for such diverse flow situations as:

- water suspended in steam;
- steam bubbles in water;
- coal gasification;
- the combustion of gun propellants;
- various chemical processes.

b. Success has also been achieved with gravity-stratified flow, and with other situations in which a distinction must be made between the local pressures in the two phases.

c. The degeneration of the problem which occurs when interphase friction is high, and the so-called 'homogeneous model' is valid, has been successfully handled.

d. The same is true of the degeneration resulting from the existence of a sharp interface between the two phases, on a scale large compared with the computational grid. However, the most sophisticated forms of 'donor-acceptor' technique have not yet been tried out.

e. Interphase heat and mass transfer have been encountered in many of the problems which have been solved; and IPSA succeeds in procuring solutions, provided minor and rather obvious devices are added. However, so numerous are the kinds of interphase transport process which may occur, that it cannot yet be asserted confidently that the future will be entirely free from difficulties.

f. The account for turbulent mixing in two-phase mixtures remains primitive. This is not because of numerical difficulties but because of lack of both experimental knowledge and theoretical guidance. This aspect of IPSA deserves attention.

g. Although the full allowance for particle-size variations in a suspended phase is a more expensive matter than can usually be contemplated, a method has been developed which allows at least the local average size of particle to be accounted for.

All the above topics will be mentioned in the following sections of the paper.

2. DISPERSED FLOW

2.1 Nomenclature

Let lower- and upper-case letters pertain to the first and second (eg lighter and heavier) phases respectively.

Let r and R thus represent the volume fractions of the two phases, so that:

$$r + R = 1 \qquad .(2.1\text{-}1)$$

Let $\dot{m}$ and $\dot{M}$ represent the mass-transfer rates into their respective phases, from the other, for a given computational space-time cell, so that:

$$\dot{m} + \dot{M} = 0 \qquad .(2.1\text{-}2)$$

Let f and G stand for either:

(i) the product of density (d or D), normal velocity (u or U) and cell-face area (a, no distinction being needed between the phases, the cell geometry being shared); or

(ii) the product of density (d or D) and cell volume (v, no V being needed for obvious reasons), divided by time interval (t, the same for both phases). Thus:

$$g \equiv aud, \text{ or } vd/t \qquad ;(2.1\text{-}3)$$

$$G \equiv aUD, \text{ or } vD/t \qquad .(2.1\text{-}4)$$

Let subscripts i and o denote respectively inflow and outflow, by reference to the computational space-time cell in question. In respect of fluxes (g's, G's) associated with the time interval, 'inflow' signifies 'from the past' and 'outflow' signifies 'towards the future'.

2.2 Phase-Conservation Equations

With the above nomenclature, the mass-conservation equations for the individual phases take the form:

$$\sum_o rg = \sum_i rg + \dot{m} \qquad ,(2.2\text{-}1)$$

$$\sum_o RG = \sum_i RG + \dot{M} \qquad .(2.2\text{-}2)$$

In simple circumstances (no turbulence or donor-acceptor features), it is recommended that:

(i) g and G be taken as time-average values over the areas and volumes in question;

(ii) the volume fractions to be associated with the fluxes are those prevailing in the 'upwind' or 'donor' cell.

With these conventions, equations (2.2-1) and (2.2-2) become:

$$r_c \sum_o g = \sum_i (r_n\, g) + \dot{m} \qquad ,(2.2\text{-}3)$$

$$R_c \sum_o G = \sum_i (R_n\, G) + \dot{M} \qquad .(2.2\text{-}4)$$

wherein $\sum_o$ and $\sum_i$ denote summations over all outflow and inflow 'faces' respectively, while subscript c refers to the 'in-cell' value and n refers to the 'neighbour-cell' value.

2.3 The Recommended Equations for r_c and R_c

Equation (2.2-3) can be rearranged to yield:

$$r_c = \left(\sum_i (r_n\, g) + \dot{m}\right)/\sum_o g \qquad ,(2.3\text{-}1)$$

which can be used, during the course of the numerical computation, to 'up-date' the values of r_c at the grid points.

This practice is not recommended. What is preferred is removal of $\sum_o g$ from its over-crucial place, by reference to the equation formed from (2.2-1), (2.2-3) and (2.2-4), namely:

$$(\sum_o g).(\sum_o G) = (\sum_o G)\ \{\sum_i (r_n\ g) + \dot{m}\} + (\sum_o g)\ \{\sum_i (R_n\ G) + \dot{M}\} \qquad .(2.3\text{-}2)$$

The resulting equation, recommended for solution to yield r_c, is:

$$r_c = \frac{(\sum_o G)\ \{\sum_i (r_n\ g) + \dot{m}\}}{(\sum_o G)\ \{\sum_i (r_n\ g) + \dot{m}\} + (\sum_o g)\ \{\sum_i (R_n\ G) + \dot{M}\}} \qquad .(2.3\text{-}3)$$

The corresponding equation for R_c is obvious.

2.4 The Pressure-Correction Equation

In simple dispersed-flow situations, it suffices to consider that there is a single pressure, p, at each cell, its effects being 'shared' by the two phases. However, this pressure is not known a priori; it must be computed by a guess-and-correct procedure.

The test of whether a guessed pressure is correct is that the densities and velocities which result from it, and the volume fractions which result from them, also satisfy 'the' continuity equation. Since there are now two continuity equations, it is questionable as to how these should be combined.

Let them be added, after division by weighting factors, w and W, as follows:

$$\{r_c \sum_o g - \sum_i (r_n\ g) - \dot{m}\}\ /w + \{R_c \sum_o G - \sum_i (R_n\ G) - M\}\ /W = 0 \qquad .(2.4\text{-}1)$$

From this equation, the pressure can be computed by taking note of the ways in which all terms except the volume fractions depend upon pressure changes. Thus, a pressure-correction equation can be deduced from:

$$\{r_c \sum_o g' - \sum_i (r_n\ g') - \dot{m}'\}/w + \{R_c \sum_o G' - \sum_i (R_n\ G') - \dot{M}'\}/W =$$

$$-\{r_c \sum_o g^* - \sum_i (r_n\ g^*) - \dot{m}^*\}/w - \{R_c \sum_o G^* - \sum_i (R_n\ G^*) - \dot{M}^*\}/W \qquad .(2.4\text{-}2)$$

wherein g', $\dot{m}'$, G' and M' can all be expressed linearly in terms of the pressure corrections, p'_c and p'_n at in-cell and neighbour grid points. The result is a system of simultaneous equations for the p''s, to be solved in any convenient manner.

Although there are some theoretical advantages in using $\sum_o g$ and $\sum_i G$ as weighting factors, most practical experience has been gained with the use of the formulae:

$$w = d, \quad \text{and} \quad W = D \qquad .(2.4\text{-}3)$$

This 'density weighting' implies that it is the 'volumetric continuity equation' which is corrected at each stage of pressure-field adjustment. Then the individual 'phase-mass continuity equations' are brought into satisfaction by the next stage of adjustment of r's and R's.

3. THE TWO-PRESSURE PROBLEM

3.1 Particles in Contact

There are two circumstances in which it is necessary to regard the two phases as having distinct pressures. In the first, one of the phases consists of a compressible solid, the individual particles of which come into contact when their volume fraction attains a critical 'packing' value, R_p. For larger values of R, this phase can be regarded as having an 'extra' pressure P, given by:

$$P = K\,(R - R_p) \qquad .(3.1\text{-}1)$$

Here K is a kind of 'rigidity constant', which may in fact be dependent upon P.

3.2 Stratified Flow

The second two-pressure circumstance arises when the two phases are separated, for example by gravitational effects, and when the dimensions of the domain in the direction of separation are such as to render unecessary a detailed account for the corresponding momentum equation. Then the lower fluid has a (vertically-averaged) pressure which is greater than that of the upper fluid at the same horizontal location; and its pressure excess, P, is given by:

$$P = a_{grav}\,(ZD + zd) \qquad ,(3.2\text{-}1)$$

wherein a_{grav} is the gravitational acceleration, Z and z are the heights of the centroids of the phase cross-sections <u>below</u> the interface (so that z is negative), and D and d are the local phase densities, as before.

If the two phases share a space, of wide horizontal extent, having total height h_{tot}, and if the height of the interface above the bottom of the space is h_{int}, the following relations serve to link P, through Z and z, with the volume fraction of second phase, R:

$$R = h_{int}/h_{tot} \qquad ,(3.2\text{-}2)$$

$$Z = 1/2\ h_{int} \qquad ,(3.2\text{-}3)$$

$$z = 1/2\ (h_{tot} - h_{int}) \qquad ,(3.2\text{-}4)$$

which can be inserted in equation (3.2-1) to yield:

$$P = 1/2\ a_{grav}\ h_{tot}\ \{d + R\,(D - d)\} \qquad .(3.2\text{-}5)$$

If the fluids flow in a duct of which the cross-section varies with horizontal position (eg a circular-sectioned pipe), a different $P \sim R$ relation is appropriate; but the qualitative nature is usually the same: P increases with R.

There is thus a similarity between the particles-in-contact and stratified-fluid problems; and it is necessary to modify IPSA so that it can handle a general $P \sim R$ relation.

3.3 Modifications to IPSA

The equation (2.3-3), and its counterpart for R_c, do not require to be modified because of the presence of the second pressure; for they remain valid. It is however useful, if the values of $\partial P/\partial R$ resulting from equations (3.1-1), (3.2-5) or more general $P \sim R$ relations are large, to introduce an 'R-correction stage' into the computation between the solutions for r_c and R_c and the subsequent correction of the pressure p. This proceeds as follows.

Equation (2.2-4) is written in terms of 'guessed' (starred) and 'correction' (primed) values, thus:

$$(R_c{}^* + R_c{}') \sum_o (G^* + G') = \sum_i \{R_n (G^* + G')\} + \dot{M} \qquad .(3.3\text{-}1)$$

Rearrangement, and neglect of products of primed quantities, leads to:

$$R_c{}' \sum_o G^* + R_c{}^* \sum_o G' - \sum_i R_n G' = \sum_i R_n G^* + M - R_c{}^* \sum_o G^* \qquad .(3.3\text{-}2)$$

Now the G' quantities are changes in the G's which are associated with the change in R_c, viz $R_c{}'$, and are caused by the resulting changes in the excess pressure, P'. Values of $\partial G/\partial R_c{}'$ can thus be computed by way of the momentum equations, which yield $\partial G/\partial P$, and the $P \sim R$ relation which yields $\partial P/\partial R_c$. Insertion of these values into equation (3.3-2) yields an equation for R_c, namely:

$$R_c = \frac{\sum_i R_n G^* + \dot{M} - R_c{}^* \sum_o G^*}{\sum_o G^* + R_c{}^* \sum_o (\partial G/\partial R_c) - \sum_i R_n (\partial G/\partial R_c)} \qquad .(3.3\text{-}3)$$

This equation forms the basis of a point-by-point R-correction procedure, to be conducted after the R-solution stage and before the p-correction stage of IPSA. In some circumstances it is useful to make the solution procedure 'more implicit' by allowing for the simultaneous adjustments of the R's. Then a system of simultaneous linear equations is set up which is similar to that from which the p''s are computed in the pressure-correction stage. This is especially desirable when the $\partial P/\partial R$ values are large.

4. HOMOGENEOUS FLOW

4.1 Definition of the Problem

Sometimes it is desired to presume that 'slip' between the phases is negligible, and to gain the diminutions of computer time and storage which result from taking the second-phase velocities to be equal to those of the first phase, and so not solving for the former.

In these circumstances, the hydrodynamic part of the computation is solved as through the fluid were one of homogeneous phase, having a density $\bar{d}$ given by:

$$\bar{d} = rd + RD \qquad .(4.1\text{-}1)$$

The question now is: how, in these circumstances, are the distributions of r and R to be determined?

4.2 Recommended Procedure

Equation (2.3-3), for r_c, is still valid; but it requires some rearrangement before it can be used.

First, because the velocities of the phases are equal, the ratio $\sum_0 G/\sum_0 g$ is equal to D/d. Thus, equation (2.3-3) can be reduced to:

$$r_c = \left[1 + \frac{d}{D} \cdot \frac{\sum_i (R_n\ G) + \dot{M}}{\sum_i (r_n\ g) + \dot{m}} \right] \qquad .(4.2\text{-}1)$$

This equation can still not be used directly, however, because (at least if the most obvious homogeneous-model procedure is used) neither d nor $r_n g$ will be available, their places having been taken by $\bar{d}$, defined above, and by $\bar{g}_n$, the mass inflow rate of mixture from neighbour cells.

It is therefore necessary to recover d from $\bar{d}$ and D (which must be computed) by way of equation (4.1-1); and $\sum_i (r_n\ g)$ must be deduced from $\sum_i \bar{g}_n$ and $\sum_i (R_n\ G)$ by way of:

$$\sum_i \bar{g}_n = \sum_i (r_n\ g) + \sum_i (R_n\ G) \qquad .(4.2\text{-}2)$$

The necessary further algebraic steps, leading to usable formulae for r_c and R_c, are too obvious to require display.

5. WELL-SEPARATED FLOW

It is not necessary, when the two phases are fully separated (as for example in water-wave-impact problems), to use a two-velocity-field treatment and the IPSA algorithm; and, because it is wasteful to store two fields of values when one will do, it is probably undesirable to do so.

Nevertheless, in the vicinity of the interface, the two fluids must have the same normal velocity; but their tangential velocities can be very different. It is therefore sometimes necessary to use a two-velocity-field treatment, and IPSA also, in this restricted region.

The problem which arises then is that, unless some departure is made from 'upwind-differencing', what starts as a sharp interface does not remain as one, as a consequence of 'numerical diffusion'.

The author recommends, for the solution of this problem, an adaptation of the so-called 'donor-acceptor' procedure. This concerns the way in which the value of r in the product rg (and of R in RG) is to be chosen.

In 'upwind' differencing, the value of r to enter the produce is always the value prevailing in the cell from which the fluid flows. In donor-acceptor differencing, however, different rules are obeyed, of which the simplest set is indicated in the following table. Here r_{up} stands for 'r on the upwind side', r_{down} stands for 'r on the downwind side', and r_g stands for 'the r which multiplies g'. ∿ stands for 'between zero and unity'.

Case	1	2	3	4	5	6	7	8	9
If r_{up} is	1	0	1	0	∿	0	1	∿	∿
and r_{down} is	1	0	0	1	∿	∿	∿	0	1
set r_g =	r_{up}	r_{up}	r_{up}	r_{up}	r_{up}	r_{up}	r_{up}	r_{down}	r_{down}

As the table shows, only in two cases out of the possible nine is it appropriate to depart from the upstream rule. This small departure suffices to keep the interface from becoming diffused.

More elaborate donor-acceptor techniques are available, taking account of more r values than the two on the upwind and downwind side of the interface; and these have the merit of preserving the interface shape with greater precision than the 9-case rule-set can do. The author lacks experience of these, however.

6. HEAT AND MASS TRANSFER

6.1 Heat Transfer Without Mass Transfer

Suppose that it is desired to calculate the temperatures of two interspersed phases, taking account of their thermal interactions. Then algebraic equations must be solved, of the kind:

$$\tau_c = \frac{\Sigma b\tau_n + \dot{q}}{\Sigma b} \quad ,(6.1\text{-}1)$$

$$T_c = \frac{\Sigma BT_n + \dot{Q}}{\Sigma B} \quad .(6.1\text{-}2)$$

Here τ and T represent the temperatures of the lighter and heavier phases, b and B represent the cell-to-cell coefficients accounting for the influences of convection and of conduction, while $\dot{q}$ and $\dot{Q}$ represent the heat-transfer rates into each phase. Supscripts c and n distinguish in-cell and neighbour-cell values as before.

In order to avoid needless distraction, it will be supposed that $\dot{q}$ and $\dot{Q}$ are equal and opposite, ie that the heat transfers in question are from one phase to the other. Further, the heat-transfer rate will be taken as proportional to the temperature difference; thus:

$$\dot{q} = -\dot{Q} = \beta(T - \tau) \quad .(6.1\text{-}3)$$

The recommended procedure for determining the temperature is to substitute (6.1-3) into (6.1-1) and (6.1-2) and so deduce:

$$\tau_c = \frac{(\Sigma b\tau_n)\ (\Sigma B + \beta) + \beta(\Sigma BT_n)}{(\Sigma b)\ (\Sigma B) + \beta(\Sigma b + \Sigma B)} \quad ,(6.1\text{-}4)$$

with a corresponding expression for T_c.

It will be noted that, as a consequence of algebraic elimination, T_c is absent from the τ_c equation; correspondingly, τ_c will be found to make no appearance in the equation for T_c.

It is interesting to note that, when β is very large compared with b and B, equation (6.1-4) reduces to:

$$\tau_c = \frac{\Sigma b\tau_n + \Sigma BT_n}{\Sigma b + \Sigma B} \quad ;(6.1\text{-}5)$$

and the same expression appears on the right-hand side of the correspondingly reduced equation for T_c.

The implication is clear: when the interphase heat-transfer coefficient is high, τ and T are everywhere equal; so it is necessary to solve for only one of them; and the relevant equation is (in terms of τ):

$$\tau_c = \frac{\Sigma(b + B)\,\tau_n}{\Sigma(b + B)} \qquad .(6.1\text{-}6)$$

6.2 Mass Transfer Determined by Heat Transfer

With steam and water, or some other vapour-liquid pair having the same chemical composition, it is common for temperature differences between the phases to occasion mass transfer between them.

In many circumstances, the liquid and vapour are in thermodynamic equilibrium at the interface; and the temperature of this interface, $\tau_{int} = T_{int}$, is a function of the local pressure.

Further to be considered is the latent heat of phase change, λ.

The relevant relations are then:

$$\dot{q} = e\,(\tau_{int} - \tau) \qquad ,(6.2\text{-}1)$$

$$\dot{Q} = E\,(T_{int} - T) \qquad ,(6.2\text{-}2)$$

$$\dot{m} = -\,(\dot{q} + \dot{Q})/\Lambda \qquad ,(6.2\text{-}3)$$

$$\Lambda = \lambda + c(\tau - \tau_{int}) + C(T_{int} - T) \qquad .(6.2\text{-}4)$$

Here e and E are heat-transfer coefficients; c and C are specific heats.

These equations can be combined with the cell energy balances in various ways. The formulae which are recommended for use in numerical computations are:

$$\tau_c = \frac{\Sigma b\tau_n + \{e + c\,|\dot{m}|\}\,\tau_{int}}{\Sigma b + e + c\,|\dot{m}|} \qquad ,(6.2\text{-}5)$$

$$T_c = \frac{\Sigma BT_n + \{E + C\,|\dot{M}|\}\,T_{int}}{\Sigma B + E + C\,|\dot{M}|} \qquad ,(6.2\text{-}6)$$

$$\dot{m} = -\dot{M} = \frac{e\tau_c + ET_c - (e + E)\,\tau_{int}}{\Lambda} \qquad .(6.2\text{-}7)$$

to be solved successively cell by cell.

6.3 Other Mass-Transfer ∿ Heat-Transfer Interrelations

When the two phases are related to each other as reactant to product, as when solid-propellant particles move within a body of gas formed from its combustion products, the situation differs from the above in that the interface temperature is ordinarily not a function of pressure alone. Instead, it is more likely to be a function of the mass-transfer rate itself; and, as often as not, a non-linear one.

In these circumstances, if numerical computations are not to become either unstable (when long time steps are used) or excessively expensive (because short time steps are employed so as to secure stability), the interface temperature must be eliminated from equations (6.2-5), (6.2-6) and (6.2-7) by reference to the $\dot{m} \sim \tau_{int}$ relation, which must probably be linearized for the occasion.

There are other circumstances in which like uncertainty prevails as to the magnitude of τ_{int}. These include:

- vaporisation of water into moist air;
- condensation of water from a steam $\sim$ air mixture;
- combustion of carbon particles in air.

In each case, the guiding rule is the same: conduct sufficient algebraic elimination between the equations relating to the temperatures (and indeed concentrations) at a computational cell to ensure that the temperatures of the two phases are not excessively dependent upon each other. This was the principle which led to preference for (6.1-4) over (6.1-1); and it should be followed, mutatis mutandis, in all the other circumstances.

6.4 Linkages with the Pressure-Correction Equations

Equation (2.4-2) contains the quantities $\dot{m}'$ and $\dot{M}'$. These represent the changes in the interphase mass-transfer rates which result from changes in the local pressure.

It is now possible to see how these quantities can be evaluated. Thus, equation (6.2-7) can be differentiated to yield:

$$\frac{\partial \dot{m}}{\partial p} = \frac{-(e + E)}{\Lambda} \frac{\partial \tau_{int}}{\partial p} \qquad ;(6.4\text{-}1)$$

and $\partial\tau_{int}/\partial p$ is of course a thermodynamic property of the materials in question. Then $\dot{m}'$ is related to p' by:

$$\dot{m}' = \frac{\partial m}{\partial p} \cdot p' \qquad .(6.4\text{-}2)$$

It is not necessary to allow for this variation; and, if the $\dot{m}'$ term is small compared with others in the pressure-correction equation, it may not be computationally worthwhile to do so. After all, the advantage of working with corrections, and proceeding iteratively, is that it suffices to make corrections in the right direction, and of the right order of magnitude; a succession of such corrections will lead to the desired solution.

It is therefore wise to consider each case on its own merits: account of the $\dot{m} \sim p$ linkage should be taken only when significantly shorter computation times result therefrom.

7. TURBULENT MIXING

7.1 The Problem

In recent years, the turbulent flow of single-phase fluids has been made amenable to numerical computation by the devising and employment of the so-called 'turbulence models'. These are systems of equations purporting to describe how such statistical properties of turbulence as energy, dissipation rate and length scale are convected, diffused, created and destroyed throughout the flow domain; and how these quantities interact with the flow field by affecting momentum, heat and mass transfer from one part of the flow to another.

Such turbulence models have many known shortcomings, acknowledged by their originators from the start (though sometimes given scant attention by turbulence-model users, it must be admitted); and, when the attempt is made to extend them to two-phase flows, the shortcomings are thrown into strong focus.

A central feature of the most popular single-phase turbulence models is that the transport of a mixture component by time-average (convection) and random (diffusion) motion is expressed as:

$$\overline{r_j \, d_j \, \vec{u}_j} = \bar{m}_j \, \bar{d} \, \vec{u} - \Gamma_j \, \text{grad} \, \bar{m}_j \qquad ,(7.1\text{-}1)$$

wherein:

- subscript j denotes the j'th species in the mixture;
- lack of a subscript indicates that the mixture as a whole is referred to;
- an over-bar denotes a time-average;
- Γ_j is regarded as an 'effective' diffusion coefficient, the value of which is calculable from the turbulence-model variables;
- m_j is the mass of species j per unit mass of mixture, related to the volume fraction r_j by:

$$m_j \, d = r_j \, d_j \qquad .(7.1\text{-}2)$$

The 'effective-diffusion' concept, which is just adequate to describe single-phase turbulent-mixing phenomena, ceases to be so when two phases are present, as the following example will reveal.

If separate streams of oxygen and nitrogen gases enter steadily one end of a long pipe, and the flow is turbulent, it is found that, at the pipe outlet, the variation of gas composition with radius is negligible. This is a consequence of the workings of the $\Gamma \text{grad} \, \bar{m}$ term, which ensures that, unless the gradient of $\bar{m}$ is zero, there will be a movement of material from high concentration regions to low. If, on the other hand, it were not a second gas but a stream of sand particles which entered the duct along with the oxygen, the distribution of sand across the outlet would NOT be found to be uniform. This implies that, since the components of $\overline{r_j \, d_j \, \vec{u}_j}$ and of $\bar{m}_j \, \bar{d} \, \vec{u}$ in the radial direction must be zero in the fully-developed (far-downstream) condition, because there can be no net radial transport of either component of the two-phase mixture, the term $-\Gamma_j$ grad $\bar{m}_j$

cannot properly represent the diffusional contribution to the transport of sand.

The question now to be considered is: what expression is it reasonable to employ, in an exploratory fashion, to represent the diffusional transport of a particulate phase, flowing in a two-phase stream?

7.2 The 'Modified Mixing-Length' Hypothesis

When considering the question just propounded, it is useful to recall the basic ideas which underly the use of the conventional expression, $\Gamma_j \text{ grad } \bar{m}_j$. They are:

(a) the phase possesses, over and above its time-average velocity $\bar{\vec{u}}$, a randomly-oriented fluctuating velocity, u_{rand}, say.

(b) Consequently, across the interface separating two points in the field, there is an extra flux, $(rdu_{rand})_\ell - (rdu_{rand})_r$, where ℓ and r stand for 'left' and 'right', and overbars have been omitted for clarity.

(c) If the average distance L between the left and right locations, ie the 'mixing length', is small compared with the distance over which $\bar{d}$ and u_{rand} vary, this extra flux can be taken as:

$$\{(\frac{rd}{\bar{d}})_\ell - (\frac{rd}{\bar{d}})_r\} \, \bar{d} \, u_{rand} \quad ,$$

where $\bar{d}$ stands for the mixture density.

This expression is nothing but:

$$(m_\ell - m_r) \, \bar{d} \, u_{rand} \quad ;$$

and, if L is introduced as both multiplier and divisor, the expression can be written as:

$$- (\bar{d} \, u_{rand} \, L) \text{ grad } m \quad .$$

(d) It remains to give $(\bar{d} \, u_{rand} \, L)$ a symbol of its own, namely Γ; and the concept is complete.

A crucial step in the argument is the presumption, appearing in paragraph (c), that L is small compared with the scale of variation of $\bar{d}$ and u_{rand}. Suppose it is not; then the formula which must be employed for the 'diffusional flux' is:

$$\text{flux} = -L \text{ grad } (rdu_{rand}) \quad .(7.2\text{-}1)$$

This formula can be regarded as the starting point of a 'modified mixing-length hypothesis', having rather greater prospects than conventional turbulence modelling of fitting the facts about turbulent two-phase flows.

Equation (7.2-1) implies that, in the postulated pipe flow, the volume-fraction profile would tend to show that the r's are largest near the axis, where the <u>random</u> velocity, as distinct from the time-average velocity, is the smallest. There are experimental data confirming this expectation; but no systematic study of the modified mixing-length hypothesis has yet been made.

7.3 Recommendation

The only recommendation that can safely be made to computer modellers wishing to represent turbulent mixing of two-phase mixtures is: 'Proceed cautiously; you are on your own'. This is an area of research deserving much more attention that it is currently receiving.

8. Particle-Size Calculation

8.1 The Problem

In many two-phase-flow problems, it is necessary to be able to calculate the distribution throughout the field of the average size of the particulate phase. For example, in coal combustors, the rate of burning, ie of interphase mass transfer, depends strongly upon the size of the coal particles; and this size diminishes, of course, as the coal is consumed.

A complete treatment of the problem involves treating the flow as a <u>multi-phase</u> one, the coal being divided into sub-groups characterised by having particle sizes lying between prescribed values. Then the particle-size <u>distribution</u> can be computed; and, if so desired, each sub-group can be treated as having its own temperature and set of velocity components.

Such a multiphase analysis involves much computation, and is necessarily expensive. There is, therefore, a need for an approach which permits the <u>average</u> particle size to be computed more directly.

8.2 The 'Shadow' Solution

A convenient solution to the problem is to compute a 'shadow' volume fraction, that is to say the volume fraction which the solid phase would have possessed, at each point, if interphase mass transfer had not taken place, the velocities, however, being the same as the phase actually possesses.

If the symbol $\tilde{R}$ is adopted for this 'shadow' volume fraction, an equation from which it can be computed is:

$$\tilde{R}_c \sum_o G = \sum_i (\tilde{R}_n G) \qquad ,(8.2\text{-}1)$$

which differs from equation (2.2-4) by the absence of the mass-transfer rate $\dot{M}$. However, to make the treatment of $\tilde{R}$ more closely parallel to that of R, substitution for $\sum_o G$ from equation (2.3-2) is recommended, with the result:

$$\tilde{R}_c = \frac{(\sum_o g) \sum_i \tilde{R}_n G}{(\sum_o G)\{\sum_i (r_n g) + \dot{m}\} + (\sum_o g)\{\sum_i (R_n G) + \dot{m}\}} \qquad .(8.2\text{-}2)$$

The particle <u>size</u> can now be deduced from:

$$\frac{s}{s_o} = \left(\frac{R_c}{\tilde{R}_c}\right)^{1/3} \qquad ,(8.2\text{-}3)$$

wherein s stands for some linear dimension of the particle, and s_o is the value of s for the particles which enter the flow domain.

Knowledge of s then permits the local values of interphase heat-transfer coefficient, interphase friction coefficient, and of mass-transfer rate to be determined.

8.3 Discussion

This technique can be employed for liquid fuels as well as for solid ones; it is only a question of employing the appropriate mass-transfer-rate law.

It can also be utilised when the particles increase in size (for example because of condensation of a vapour), rather than diminish; for there is no reason why $R/\tilde{R}$ should not exceed unity.

In general, however, the problem of predicting the variation through space of the typical fragment size of the discontinuous phase is too complex to be handled by this technique. Steam-bubble sizes in water, for example, are determined by break-up and coalescence at least as much as by vaporisation and condensation; and there appears to be no way by which the 'shadow' technique can even approximately predict the results of these.

9. Conclusions

The foregoing review of the recent developments of the IPSA approach to the numerical computation of multiphase flow allows the following conclusions to be drawn:

(a) The recommended volume-fraction equations, (2.3-3) and its counterpart for the second phase, are satisfyingly 'symmetrical' yielding volume fractions which necessarily sum to unity.

(b) There is an instructive parallelism, between the R-correction equation of the two-pressure problem and the generally applicable pressure-correction equation, which can guide the numerical analyst to correct action when steep $P \sim R$ relations are encountered.

(c) The transition from two-phase flows with unequal velocities and temperatures for the two phases to those which are 'homogeneous' is a smooth one, accomplished by setting the interphase friction and heat-transfer coefficients to large numbers; but computational economy can be effected, when the homogeneous model is indeed appropriate, by dispensing with the solution for the velocities and temperature for one of the phases.

(d) Donor-acceptor forms of IPSA are available for well-separated flows.

(e) Interphase heat- and mass-transfer processes, and associated particle-size changes, have been satisfactorily incorporated.

(f) Turbulence models for two-phase flows are still at the speculative stage; but there is no difficulty about incorporating the additional transport terms, likely to be physically realistic, into the volume-fraction equations and the solution procedure.

10 Bibliography

(a) Descriptions of the IPSA Procedure

1. Spalding D Brian 1977
'The Calculation of Free-Convection Phenomena in Gas-Liquid Mixtures'
ICHMT Seminar Proceedings 'Turbulent Buoyant Convection' Editors: N Afgan D Brian Spalding, Hemisphere Publishing, Washington DC, pp 569-586 also as CFDU* Report 76/11

2. Spalding D Brian 1981
'Numerical Computation of Multiphase Flows. A Course of 12 Lectures, with GENMIX 2P Listing and 5 Appendices'
CFDU Report 81/8

3. Spalding D Brian 1981
'Numerical Computation of Two-Phase Flow in Gun Barrels'
US Army Workshop on Multiphase Flow, Aberdeen Proving Ground, Maryland, USA
CFDU Report 81/6

4. Spalding D Brian 1981
'GENMIX 2P: Notes and Listing' CFDU Report 81/1

5. Spalding D Brian 1981
'Numerical Computation of Multiphase Fluid Flow and Heat Transfer'
Recent Advances in Numerical Methods in Fluids, Editors: C Taylor and K Morgan, Pineridge Press, pp 139-167

6. Moult A Pratap V S and Spalding D Brian 1978
'Calculation of Unsteady One-Dimensional Two-Phase Flows'
Proceedings First International Conference on PhysicoChemical Hydrodynamics Advance Publications UK, vol 2, pp 805-814

7. Baghdadi A H A Rosten H I Singhal A K Spalding D Brian and Tatchell D G 1979
'Finite-Difference Predictions of Waves in Stratified Gas-Liquid Flows'
ICHMT Seminar Proceedings 'Two-Phase Momentum, Heat and Mass Transfer'
Editors: F Durst, N Afgan and G Tsiklauri, Hemisphere Publishing, Washington DC, vol 1, pp 471-483

8. Kurosaki Y and Spalding D Brian 1979
'One-Dimensional Unsteady Two-Phase Flows With Interphase Slip: A Numerical Study'
2nd Multiphase Flow and Heat Transfer Symposium Workshop, 'Multiphase Transport: Fundamentals, Reactor Safety, Applications', Hemisphere Publishing, Washington DC, vols 1-5

(b) Two-Phase Flows with Sharp Interfaces (Donor-Acceptor)

1. Ramshaw J D and Trapp J A 1976
'A Numerical Treatment for Low-Speed Homogeneous Two-Phase Flow With Sharp Interfaces' J Computational Physics, vol 21, pp 438-453

2. Spalding D Brian
'Numerical Computation of Flows of Two Phases Separated by A Moving Interface'
CFDU Report 80/4

---

* CFDU Reports may be obtained by writing to the Author's Imperial College Office. A cost-covering charge is made.

(c) Applications of IPSA to Steam-Generator and Other Flows

1. Spalding D Brian 1980
'Multiphase Flow Prediction in Power-System Equipment and Components'
Int J Multiphase Flow, vol 6, pp 157-168

2. Singhal A K and Spalding D Brian 1980
'Numerical Modelling of Two-Phase Flow in Steam Generators'
2nd Multiphase Flow and Heat Transfer Symposium, 'Multiphase Transport: Fundamentals, Reactor Safety, Applications', Hemisphere Publishing, Washington DC, vols 1-5, pp 373-406

3. Marchand E O Singhal A K and Spalding D Brian 1980
'Parametric Computations for Thermal Hydraulic Performance of a PWR Steam Generator', Proceedings ANS/ASME/NRC Nuclear Reactor Thermal Hydraulics Meeting, NUREG/CP-0014, vol 1, pp 482-503

4. Keeton L W Singhal A K and Spalding D Brian 1980
'Predictions of Thermal Hydraulics of a PWR Steam Generator by Using the Homogeneous and Two-Slip-Flow Models'
19th National Heat Transfer Conf, AIChE Symposium Series 199, vol 76, pp 45-55

5. Marchand E O Singhal A K and Spalding D Brian 1980
'Predictions of Operation Transients for a Steam Generator of a PWR Nuclear Power System', ASME Nuclear Engineering Conference, ASME Paper Number ASME 80-C2/NE-5

(d) Two-Phase Turbulence

1. Lumley J L 1978
'Two-Phase and Non-Newtonian Flows' in 'Turbulence' Editor: P Bradshaw, Springer, Berlin, Heidelberg, New York, pp 290-324

A Numerical Method for Steam-Water Two-Phase Flow Heat Transfer Simulation

S.S. WANG, R.E. FERGUSON, and J.H. STUHMILLER
Fluid Dynamics Group
JAYCOR
San Diego, California 92138

ABSTRACT

Heat transfer in steam-water two-phase flows involves instantaneous local conduction, convection and energy and mass exchanges across the interface. A numerical method is used to simulate the microscale transient of such flows by modeling the constituent fundamental processes and the interfacial configurations evolution. The bubble dynamics and the liquid temperature distribution are calculated using the fourth order Runge-Kutta scheme in time and the control volume approach in space. The technique has a potential in industrial applications.

1. INTRODUCTION

Steam-water two-phase heat transfer problems are of concern in the areas of power generation, energy conversion and reactor safety. Due to the complexity of the phenomena, many problems still exist which defy prediction from a basic point of view. Among them, a fundamental problem is the nucleate boiling on a solid surface. Despite numerous investigations in this field [1-7], there remain many uncertainties. In particular, one has little confidence in extrapolating the available information to the situations involving new geometries, varied pressure or different flow configurations. This paper presents a new approach, which is able to follow the flow regime development and is relatively independent of the geometric and the pressure conditions, for the nucleate wall boiling simulation.

Work in the nucleate boiling related areas in the past was mostly empirical, which tended to overlook the detailed processes. The empirical approach generally formulates a correlation to fit the experimental data of a certain parameter of interest in a specific configuration [8-9]. Although such correlations are easy to use in engineering designs, they are usually limited in the range of application. Extending one correlation to predict the behavior of a different system may result in substantial error [10]. In addition, the correlation is generally flow-regime dependent. A designer will have to know the flow regime before choosing the proper correlations for his system. Unfortunately, the flow regime information is not precisely known a priori in many cases, one can only rely on past experience.

The present approach emphasizes the phenomenology of the process and therefore differs fundamentally from the empirical approach. It takes into account the detailed, microscale processes and their time development so that the real phenomena can be more closely followed. Since the method is not restrictive with respect to the surface geometry or the pressure, it becomes possible to simulate a wide range of boiling devices under various pressure conditions. This method can handle bubbly, churn turbulent and slug flows and their transitions in the vertical direction. Successful comparisons of the calculated transition with two groups of experimental data [11] have been obtained.

The essence of our approach is to keep track of the microscopic boiling dynamics so that the macroscopic phenomena will emerge as a natural consequence. In the nucleate boiling, heat transfers into the liquid through the solid wall. Steam bubbles will grow from distributed nucleation sites, eventually depart from the wall and evolve in the two-phase flow. The major difficulties in analyzing such a system are the need to trace a large number of interacting bubbles and to calculate the local liquid velocity field. Material property and the surface condition may add more complications, for their small variations could change the boiling characteristics drastically [12]. To cope with these difficulties, the present technique traces each individual bubble motion and its interfacial heat and mass transfer in a deterministic way. This is in contrast to Saha et al.'s model [13], in which the interfacial area density is related to the local void fraction. Our model computes each bubble's surface area and volume in order to evaluate the interfacial transfer rate and the void distribution in space. A bubble wake model is also implemented to account for the bubble-bubble interaction and coalescence which can result in the boiling crisis and the flow regime transition. To model the flow field, each bubble wake is superimposed on a turbulent velocity field. The turbulent effect on the bubble motion and the velocity effect on the interfacial heat and mass transfer are incorporated. The bubble geometry is limited to a set of definite shapes and the bubble shape evolution resulting from continuous mass transfer and bubble coalescence is dynamically modeled. The material property and the surface condition are represented by the active nucleation site density under the heat flux and pressure conditions.

The models used in our technique cover the processes from the bubble inception in nucleation sites to the evolving two-phase flow. From the given surface property, we first determine the active nucleation site distribution on the surface. In each time step, the liquid temperature distribution as a result of the instantaneous wall heat flux, the inlet liquid temperature and liquid flow rate as well as the local interfacial heat transfer will be calculated. When the incipience boiling condition is met, steam bubble will grow from the local nucleation sites. Subsequently, the buoyancy and the flow effects can cause the bubbles to detach from the wall. While ascending upward, interacting with other bubbles, they will continue to grow or collapse depending on the local liquid temperature. The detailed models for these processes are described in the next section.

2. SIMULATION MODELS

2.1 Bubble Dynamic Equations

This method solves the following equations to determine the motion, interaction, and thermodynamic variation of each bubble in the system. The coordinate system used has x vertically upward with y and z in the horizontal cross plane. The corresponding velocity components are u, v, w for the bubble and U, V, W for the liquid. The bubble momentum equation has the components

$$M_b \frac{du}{dt} = B - D_x \quad , \tag{1}$$

$$M_b \frac{dv}{dt} = S_y - D_y \quad , \tag{2}$$

$$M_b \frac{dw}{dt} = S_z - D_z \quad , \tag{3}$$

where $M_b = m_b + m_a$ is the total inertia of the bubble, m_b is the mass contained in the bubble and m_a is the added mass of the surrounding liquid; D_x, D_y, D_z are the components of the drag force due to relative motion; B is the buoyancy force; and S_y, S_z are the lateral forces due to mean velocity shear. Equations (1), (2) and (3) are integrated in time starting with the initial conditions u(0), v(0), w(0) for each bubble.

The bubble position evolves according to the kinematic relations

$$\frac{dx_g}{dt} = u + u' \quad , \tag{4}$$

$$\frac{dy_g}{dt} = v + v' \quad , \tag{5}$$

$$\frac{dz_g}{dt} = w + w' \quad , \tag{6}$$

where x_g, y_g, and z_g are the components of the bubble displacement and u', v', and w' are appropriate turbulent velocities to be specified later. Equations (4), (5), and (6) are integrated in time to determine the instantaneous displacement from its initial position $x_g(0)$, $y_g(0)$ and $z_g(0)$.

The bubble mass changes are assumed to be heat diffusion limited in the liquid phase and therefore vary with time according to

$$\frac{dm_b}{dt} = \dot{q}_{fg} A_b / h_{fg} \quad , \tag{7}$$

where h_{fg} is the latent heat of evaporation, $\dot{q}_{fg}$ is the evaporation heat flux flowing into the bubble from the liquid, and A_b is the total bubble surface area. The bubble mass can be calculated by integrating Eq. (7) with an initial condition of $m_b(0)$.

Since the phase change processes are so rapid and the rates are generally not well understood, we assume that saturation is achieved in a shorter time scale than the fluid motions so that

$$T_g = T_{sat}(p) \quad , \tag{8}$$

where T_g is the bubble steam temperature, $T_{sat}(p)$ is the saturation temperature at the local pressure p.

Equations (1)-(8) are the basic dynamic equations describing the thermal and mechanical evolution of each bubble in the system. To close these equations certain constitutive relations concerning single bubbles and certain properties of the continuous phase must be supplied. These relations are discussed below.

2.2 Mechanical Constitutive Relations

The drag force due to relative motion can be written as

$$\vec{D} = \frac{1}{2} \rho_f (\vec{u} - \vec{U})|\vec{u} - \vec{U}| \; C_D \pi r_e^2 \quad , \tag{9}$$

where C_D is a dimensionless drag coefficient and r_e is the equivalent radius defined by $4/3\pi r_e^3 = V_b = m_b/\rho_g$. The buoyancy force is

$$B = (\rho_f - \rho_g) g V_b \quad , \tag{10}$$

where g is the acceleration due to gravity. A useful quantity is the terminal velocity of a single bubble, U_∞, defined as

$$\frac{1}{2} \rho_f U_\infty^2 C_D \pi r_e^2 = B \quad . \tag{11}$$

With the total bubble inertia written as

$$M_b = (\rho_g + \mu \rho_f) V_b \quad , \tag{12}$$

where μ is the added mass coefficient which varies from 0.5 to 1.0 for oblate spheroids, we can combine the above equations with (1) and obtain

$$\frac{du}{dt} = - \frac{(1 - \rho_g/\rho_f) g}{(\mu + \rho_g/\rho_f) U_\infty^2} (u - U - U_\infty)(u - U + U_\infty) \quad . \tag{13}$$

This becomes the bubble momentum equation in the longitudinal direction. The lateral force due to the mean liquid shear is of the form [15]

$$\vec{S} = - \rho_f (u - U) \nabla \vec{U} \; R_b \pi r_e^2 \quad , \tag{14}$$

where R_b is a half of the linear dimension in the cross section for various bubble shapes. Combined with the drag expression, the lateral equations of motion become

$$\frac{dv}{dt} = - \frac{(1 - \rho_g/\rho_f)}{(\mu + \rho_g/\rho_f)} \frac{g}{U^2} (u - U) \left[v \left(- \frac{2}{C_D} \right) - \frac{dU}{dy} \right] R_b \quad , \tag{15}$$

$$\frac{dw}{dt} = - \frac{(1 - \rho_g/\rho_f)}{(\mu + \rho_g/\rho_f)} \frac{g}{U^2} (u - U) \left[w \left(- \frac{2}{C_D} \right) - \frac{dU}{dz} \right] R_b \quad , \tag{16}$$

where

$$C_D = \frac{8}{3}\left(1 - \rho_g/\rho_f\right)\frac{g_{r_e}}{U_\infty^2} .$$

2.3 Thermal Constitutive Relations

In the heat and mass transfer equations, the key quantity is the vaporization heat flux at the steam-water interface. It depends on the physical process as well as the local pressure and temperature conditions. This heat flux is related to the heat transfer coefficient h and the local liquid and gas temperature difference by

$$\dot{q}_{fg} = h\left(T - T_g\right) . \tag{17}$$

Therefore, when T and T_g are calculated and the heat transfer coefficient h is modeled, $\dot{q}_{fg}$ can be determined. The following sections describe the model for h under two flow conditions.

Steam bubble without translatory motion. Stationary vapor bubble growth or collapse in uniformly superheated or subcooled liquids has been studied extensively and analytical solutions exist that can model the process. Scriven [16] solved the heat diffusion equation in liquid surrounding a spherical bubble and obtained a general solution

$$r_e = 2\beta\left(Kt\right)^{0.5} , \tag{18}$$

where K is the thermal diffusivity of the liquid, t is time and the growth constant β is a function of Jakob number J_a. For large J_a, the solution coincides with that obtained earlier by Plesset and Zwick [17] using a thin thermal layer approach. Our model applies Plesset, Zwick and Prosperetti's idea of a time-varying heat transfer coefficient

$$h(t) = \frac{2\sqrt{3/\pi}\, K}{\sqrt{K\left(t + t_d\right)}} , \tag{19}$$

where k is the liquid thermal conductivity and t_d is the time delay in the order of a few milliseconds for an initial growth when inertia effect is not negligible. After the initial growth, the interfacial mass transfer is essentially heat diffusion limited. Comparisons of the simulated bubble growth with the experimental data have shown satisfactory agreement [18]. This model will be used for homogeneous nucleate boiling in a stagnant flow.

Steam bubble with translatory motion. The heat and mass transfer rate is generally enhanced when the steam bubble is in relative motion to the liquid. In solving the convective diffusion equation in a potential flow around a spherical bubble, Ruckenstein and Davis [19] found that the heat transfer coefficient should be

$$h = 0.7976\, k \left(\frac{u - U}{r_e K}\right)^{0.5} . \tag{20}$$

This coefficient is valid only if the flow is laminar, e.g., $R_e \lesssim 2300$ for a pipe flow. Calculations of mass transfer using this coefficient exhibited good agreement with experimental data [20]. For turbulent flows, we deduce from a set of experimental results [18] an average heat transfer coefficient

$$h = 2.7 \frac{k}{r_e^{0.66}} \left(\frac{u - U}{K}\right)^{0.34} . \tag{21}$$

The relations described above complete the closure of the dynamic equations in terms of the dependent variables related to each bubble. We must supply thermodynamic, geometric, and continuous phase flow properties to complete the whole model.

2.4 Thermodynamic Properties

The local pressure in a two-phase gas-liquid system is determined by the quasi-steady relation

$$p(x) = p_T + \int_x^{x_T} \left\{ g\left[(1 - \alpha)\rho_f + \alpha\rho_g\right] + \frac{1}{2} \rho_f \frac{C_W}{R_H} \left(\frac{Q}{A}\right)^2 \right\} dx \quad , \tag{22}$$

where p_T is the applied pressure at the top of the liquid, α is the local void fraction, $C_W = 0.005$ is a wall drag coefficient, R_H is the hydraulic radius and Q/A is the liquid flow velocity. Corresponding to each local pressure, a set of thermodynamic variables will be defined. They include the saturation temperature T_{sat}, the latent heat of vaporization h_{fg}, the thermal diffusivity K, the specific heat at constant pressure for the liquid C_p and the steam and liquid densities ρ_g and ρ_f. Since the thermodynamic properties are pressure dependent, the method can be applied to a wide range of pressure conditions.

2.5 Bubble Geometry

A bubble can assume the geometry of a sphere, an ellipsoid, a spherical cap and a Taylor bullet-shaped bubble depending on the bubble volume V_b and the geometry of the boundary. Relations can be found for the geometric factors μ, U_∞, and A_b. Details are included in reference 21.

A single bubble growth simulation was carried out using the models described above. The result is compared with Kosky's [22] experimental data in Figure 1, where the geometric variation is shown alongside the slug length growth. Single bubble collapse in subcooled water was also calculated and a comparison with Florschuetz and Chao's data [23] is shown in Figure 2.

2.6 Liquid Velocity Field

The liquid velocity field could be determined at a variety of levels of sophistication from assuming a constant value to solving a separate, time dependent multi-dimensional two-phase flow problem. The present approach uses a parameterized distribution function based on single phase flow experiments to model the velocity field in a circular tube. For a laminar flow, Re $\lesssim$ 2300, we use the Hagen-Poiseulle velocity profile [15]

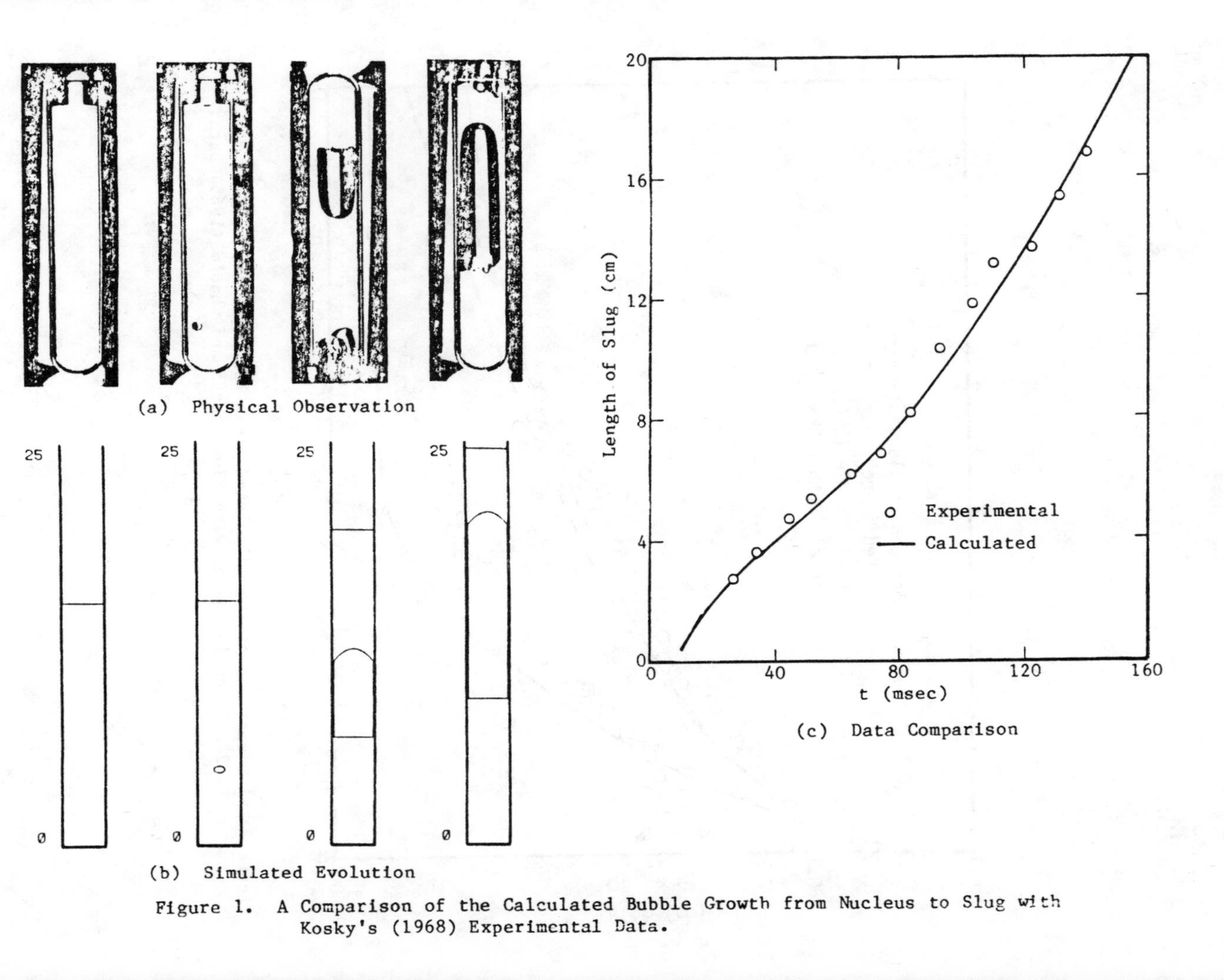

Figure 1. A Comparison of the Calculated Bubble Growth from Nucleus to Slug with Kosky's (1968) Experimental Data.

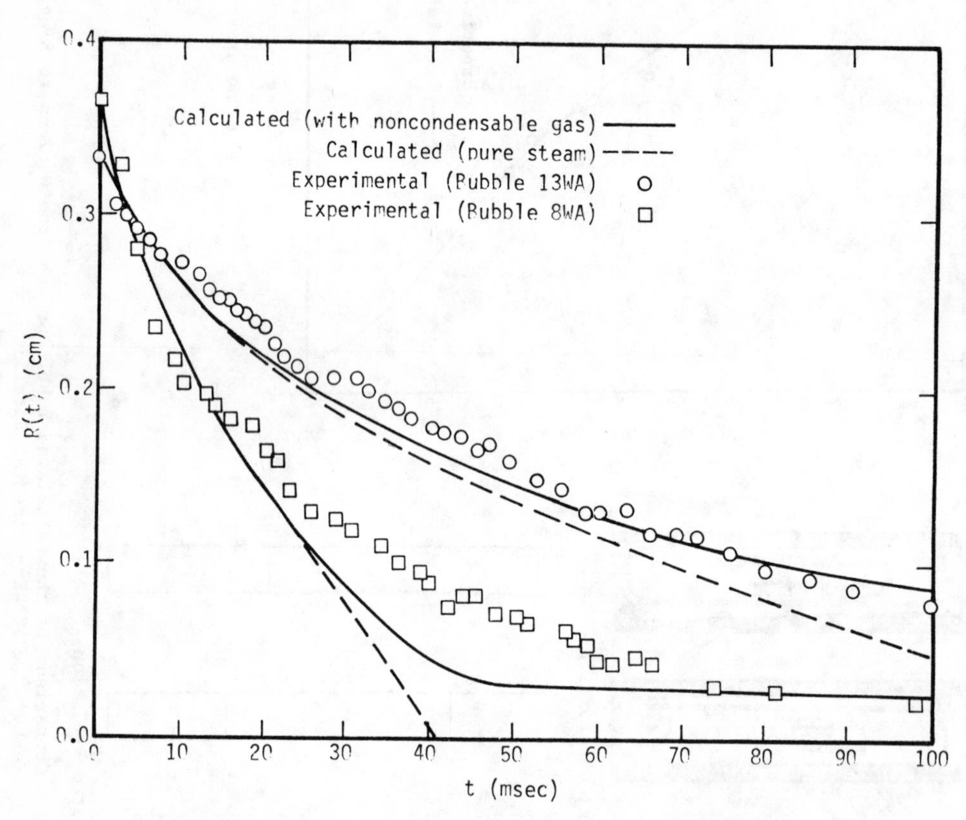

Figure 2. A Comparison of the Calculated Steam Bubble Collapses in 5.2°C and 12.2°C Subcooled Water with Florschuetz and Chao's (1965) Data.

$$U(r) = \frac{2Q}{\pi R_p^2}\left(1 - \frac{r}{R_p}\right)^2 , \tag{23}$$

where Q is the local liquid volume flow rate and R_p is the pipe radius. On the other hand, a general turbulent velocity distribution

$$U(r) = v_*\left(5.75 \log \frac{R_p - r}{k_s} + B'\right) \tag{24}$$

is used when Re > 2300 in a rough pipe with a surface roughness k_s. The friction velocity v_* and parameter B' are obtained following Schlichting's derivation [24].

2.7 Turbulent Bubble Wake

The turbulent velocity components in u', v', and w' in Equations (4)-(6) include a bubble wake and a small random perturbation. The perturbation is modeled by a random walk procedure. The bubble wake which determines the bubble-bubble interaction is taken to be in a similar form,

$$u_w(x,r) = U_w(x)\ e^{-[r/r^*(x)]^2} , \tag{25}$$

where $U_w(x)$ is the centerline wake velocity reduced from experimental data and $r^*(x)$ is the radial scaling length for wake. The bubble-bubble interaction thus arises from the local liquid velocity change due to the wake effect of the bubbles moving ahead of the current bubble. The bubble mutual interaction can cause bubble coalescence and statistical distribution of physical variables. Figure 3 demonstrates that good agreement has been achieved between the calculated and the measured slug volume and slug velocity distributions in a 1 inch diameter air-water experiment.

2.8 Liquid Temperature Field

The temperature of the liquid is obtained by solving the time-dependent energy transport equation

$$\rho_f C_p \frac{dT}{dt} = k\ \nabla^2 T + \dot{q} , \tag{26}$$

where $\dot{q}$ is the local heat source, including wall heat flux and the interfacial heat exchange. The inlet liquid temperature will serve as a boundary condition. See the control volume scheme described in Section 3.

2.9 Wall Nucleation

Wall nucleation involves a collection of models on site distribution, cavity size, growth rate, and detachment criteria.

Nucleation sites distribution model. During nucleation boiling, steam bubbles will grow from specific sites which are cavities or scratches that can trap vapor. The active site density depends on the surface material and condition and the heat flux level [25,26]. Recent experimental measurement

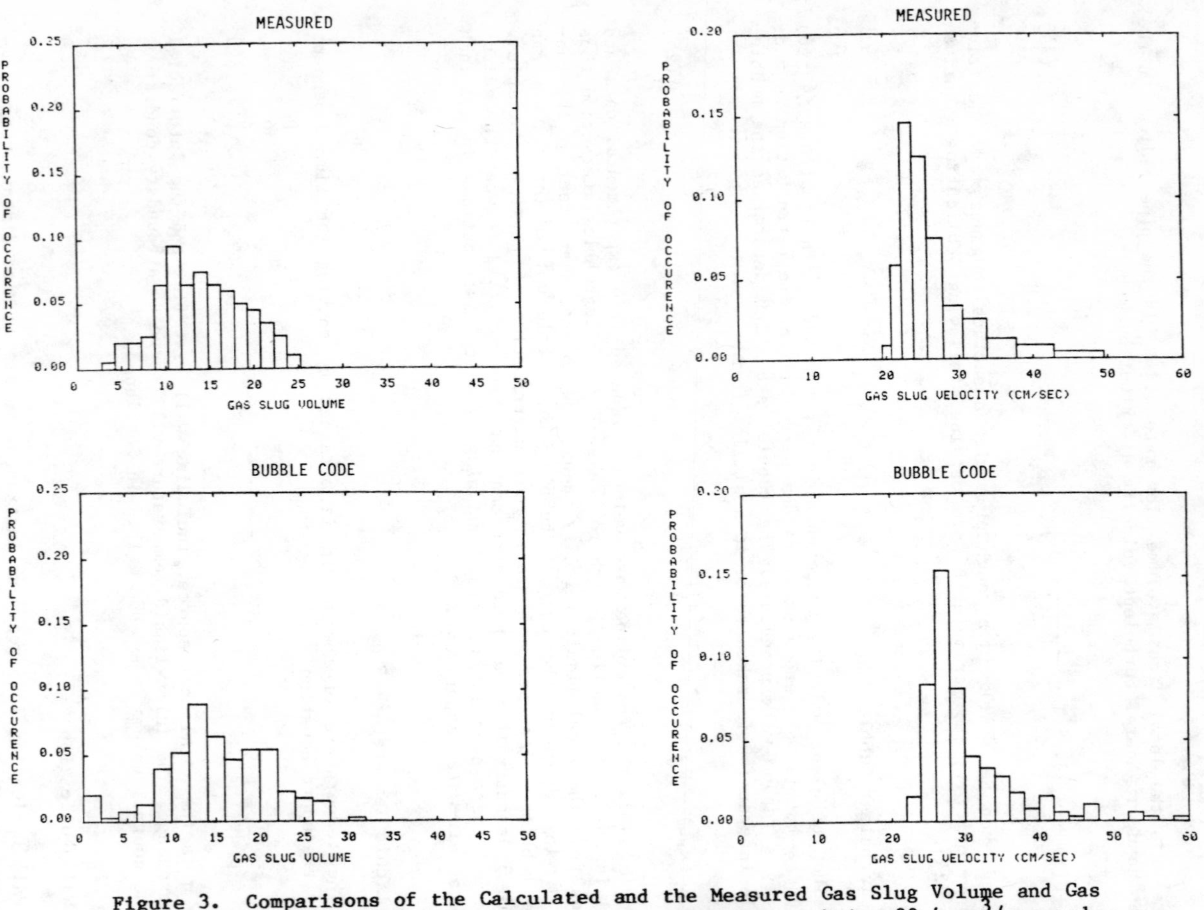

Figure 3. Comparisons of the Calculated and the Measured Gas Slug Volume and Gas Slug Velocity Distributions with Air Flow Rate being 22.4 cm^3/sec and No Liquid Flow Rate. Tube radius is 1.27 cm and the entrance distance is 75 cm.

showed that the statistical spatial distribution of the nucleation sites forms a Poisson curve [25]. In our method, when the mean site density is given, a random number generator and a Poisson function are used to determine the site locations, which become the initial positions $x_g(0)$, $y_g(0)$ and $z_g(0)$'s for the steam bubbles. An example is the calculated site distribution on a 1" × 1" specimen of copper as illustrated in Figure 4(a). Its probability density function is compared with the Poisson distribution in Figure 4(b). They look similar to the measured results [25]. Since these site locations can be assigned on an arbitrary three-dimensional surface, there is essentially no geometric limitation on the present technique.

Cavity size distribution model. The incipience of boiling is closely related to the cavity size distribution [27] which was found to be a Gaussian-like function. When its mean and standard deviation are known, the distribution can be computed and a size assigned to each cavity. The initial bubble volume $V_b(0)$ is in proportion to such cavity size.

Model for bubble growth on a wall. We use Mikic, Rohsenow and Griffith's model [28] for the bubble growth on a solid wall. The growth of the average bubble radius in time t follows the equation

$$r_e = \frac{2B^2}{3A}\left[(t^* + 1)^{3/2} - (t^*)^{3/2} - 1\right] , \tag{27}$$

where

$$A = \frac{\pi}{7}\left[\frac{(T_w - T_{sat})h_{fg}\rho_g}{T_{sat}\rho_f}\right]^{1/2} ,$$

$$B = \frac{12}{\pi} K^{1/2} \frac{(T_\infty - T_{sat})C_p\rho_f}{h_{fg}\rho_g} ,$$

$$t^* = A^2 t/B^2 ,$$

and, T_w, T_∞ are wall temperature and liquid temperature respectively. The model is able to predict the experimental results with reasonable accuracy [28].

Bubble departure radius and departure velocity models. Bubble departure radius from a vertical wall is essentially determined by a balance of buoyancy, surface tension and the flow effect. Levy's model [29] is used here for the departure radius

$$r_e = \left[\frac{C_s\alpha}{C_B g(\rho_f - \rho_g) + C_F \frac{\Gamma_w}{D_H}}\right]^{1/2} , \tag{28}$$

where C_s, C_B and C_F are proportionality constants in surface tension, buoyancy and frictional forces; σ is the surface tension and Γ_w is the wall shear stress and D_H is the flow diameter.

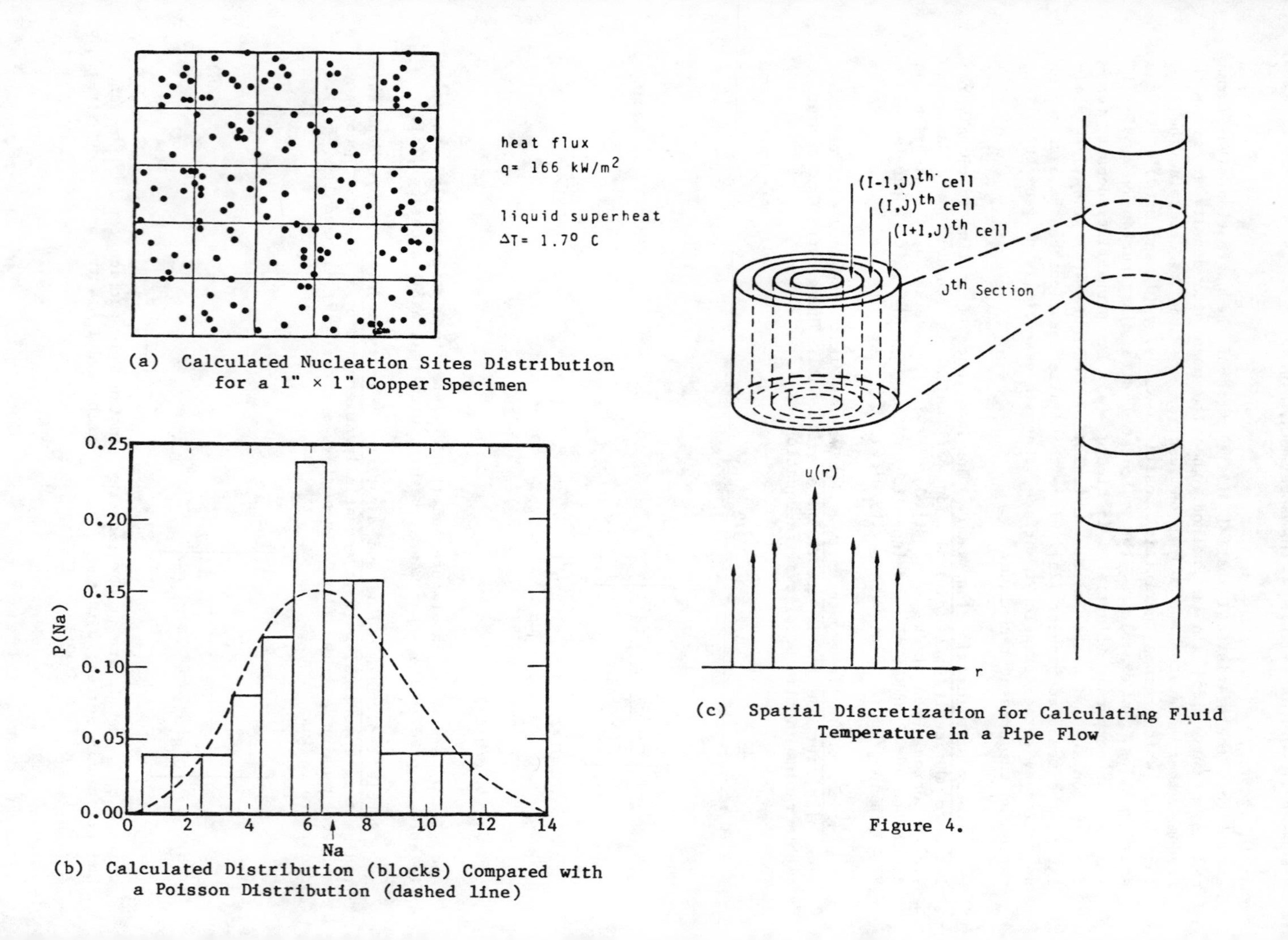

(a) Calculated Nucleation Sites Distribution for a 1" × 1" Copper Specimen

(b) Calculated Distribution (blocks) Compared with a Poisson Distribution (dashed line)

(c) Spatial Discretization for Calculating Fluid Temperature in a Pipe Flow

Figure 4.

For the bubble departure velocity, we employ Hamburger's [30] departure formula

$$v_0 = 0.166\ \theta^{1/2}[\delta g(\rho_f - \rho_g)/\rho_f^2]^{1/4} \quad , \tag{29}$$

where θ is bubble-wall contact angle in sexagesimal degree. The value of v_0 becomes the initial velocity magnitude of the bubble and the direction of the velocity is along the local surface normal.

Incipience of boiling model. Bergles and Rohsenow [31] have derived a relation which can predict the incipience of boiling under different pressures and wall temperatures. It is used in our model, that is

$$\dot{q}_i = 15.6\ p^{1.156}\ (T_w - T_{sat})^{2.3/p^{0.0234}} \quad , \tag{30}$$

where $\dot{q}$ in Btu/hr-ft^2 is the heat flux corresponding to the onset of local nucleate boiling, p in psia is the local pressure and T_w in °F is the local wall temperature. For a given wall temperature T_w, if the heat flux is higher than q_i, boiling will take place and part of the heat flux will go to the generation and the growth of the steam bubbles.

3. NUMERICAL METHOD

To solve the dynamic equations (7), (13), (15)-(16), and (26), we use the control volume finite difference method for spatial differencing and the fourth order Runge-Kutta scheme for time differencing. The former assures the energy conservation in each control volume and the latter a high accuracy in time integration. An example for illustration here is to solve the liquid energy transport equation (26) in a circular pipe. The r-z spatial discretization is shown in Figure 4(c). The finite-differenced representation of (26) in the $(i,j)^{th}$ control volume is

$$\rho_L C_p V_{i,j} \frac{\partial T_{i,j}}{\partial t} = \rho_L C_p A_i u_i (T_{i,j-1/2} - T_{i,j+1/2})$$

$$- k \left[\frac{T_{i,j} - T_{i-1,j}}{\Delta r_{i-1/2}} Ar_i + \frac{T_{i,j} - T_{i+1,j}}{\Delta r_{i+1/2}} Ar_{i+1} \right.$$

$$\left. + \frac{T_{i,j} - T_{i,j-1}}{\Delta r_{j-1/2}} A_i + \frac{T_{i,j} - T_{i,j+1}}{\Delta r_{j+1/2}} A_i \right] + \dot{Q}_{i,j} \quad , \tag{31}$$

where $V_{i,j}$ is the cell volume, $T_{i,j}$ is the liquid temperature of the cell, $T_{i,j-1/2}$ and $T_{i,j+1/2}$ are the temperatures defined at the lower and upper cell boundaries, A_i is the cross section area of the ith concentric cell, Ar's are the radial cell surface area, Δr, Δz's are the distances between the neighboring cell centers in the r and z directions, and $\dot{Q}_{i,j}$ is the heat source in the cell which contains the wall heat flux in a boundary cell and the heat transfer rate due to all the bubbles in the cell. In a turbulent pipe flow situation, a turbulent thermal diffusivity in the order of 1 cm^2/sec should be used in place of the molecular thermal diffusivity.

The standard fourth-order Runge-Kutta scheme [32] is used to advance time step. When combined with the control volume spatial difference, a stable solution procedure under Courant and the diffusion time step limits [33] is attained. An interesting implication is that an efficient ordinary differential equation solution procedure could be applied to solve certain types of partial differential equations. Boeing Computer Service's EASY5 package is an example.

4. CALCULATION RESULTS

The results described below include a superheated boiling and a subcooled forced convection boiling simulation, and a parameter study of the liquid temperature distribution. These results are considered to be qualitative for no direct comparison with experimental data has been made. Nevertheless, these qualitative results already indicate that the technique is capable of handling different flow, subcooling and heating conditions.

The first calculation describes nucleate boiling on a stainless steel tube wall at a heat flux of 55 watts/cm^2. The tube radius is 0.404 cm and the length is 2.54 cm. Assume the liquid flow rate is zero and the liquid temperature is initially uniform. The system is suddenly depressurized at time zero to achieve a liquid superheat of 1.7°C everywhere in the liquid. The wall temperature is maintained at 7.45°C higher than the saturation temperature. For better visualization purpose, we limited the nucleation site distribution in two narrow longitudinal regions, each spanned by an azimuthal angle of 30°. Steam bubbles are observed to grow on the tube wall in time as shown in Figure 5. They also continuously grow in liquid after their detachment from the wall. The average departure radius and the departure velocity are 0.024 cm and 18 cm/sec, respectively. The bubbles also coalesce to form larger bubbles as seen in Figure 5(d).

The second calculation adds both the flow and the temperature field effects on the nucleate boiling simulation. A high subcooling of 60°C liquid enters with a flow rate of 135 cm^3/sec at the inlet. A few steam bubbles start to grow and depart from the wall under a high heat flux condition even when the core liquid temperature is still subcooled. Bubbles are observed to collapse in the core region while moving downstream in the flow field as illustrated in Figure 6(b) and 6(c). A similar process was recorded experimentally by Abdelmessih et al. [34] as shown on the five movie frames in Figure 6(a).

Since the liquid temperature can significantly affect the bubble heat and mass transfer, it is necessary to accurately calculate the liquid temperature under various wall heat flux, inlet subcooling and liquid flow rate conditions. In the following, only one of the three key parameters is allowed to vary with all the other conditions held constant. The results could reveal the influence of each parameter on the liquid temperature distribution and hence the boiling process. Let a standard condition be that the liquid flow rate is 158.3 cm^3/sec in a 0.69 cm radius tube, subcooling be 15°C and the wall heat flux at 4.77×10^2 watts/cm^2. The calculated single phase liquid temperature as a function of the distance from the wall is plotted at entrance distances of 5.08, 10.16, 15.24 and 20.32 cm in Figure 7(a). Higher temperatures near the wall than those around the core are the result of the wall heating and the energy diffusion. On the other hand, the temperature increase downstream is mainly determined by the convection heat transfer. Results from the parameter variation will be compared with this temperature distribution. First, the inlet liquid subcooling, dashed line results in Figure 7(b) are due to 30°C subcooling. They show a consistent decrease of the liquid temperature as expected. From a collection of calculations with varied subcoolings, we can plot the

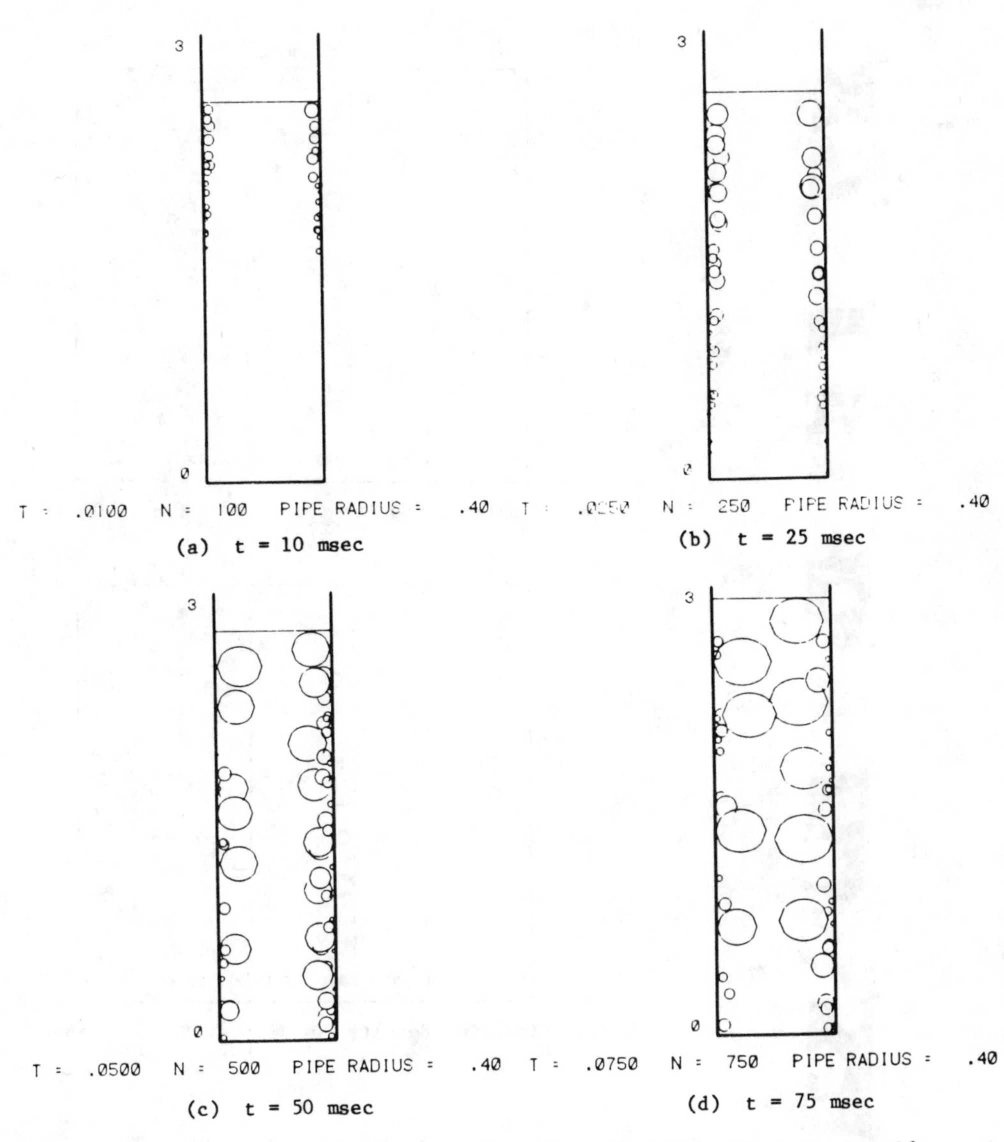

(a) t = 10 msec

(b) t = 25 msec

(c) t = 50 msec

(d) t = 75 msec

Figure 5. Calculation Results for Tube Wall Boiling When the Liquid is 1.7°C Superheated.

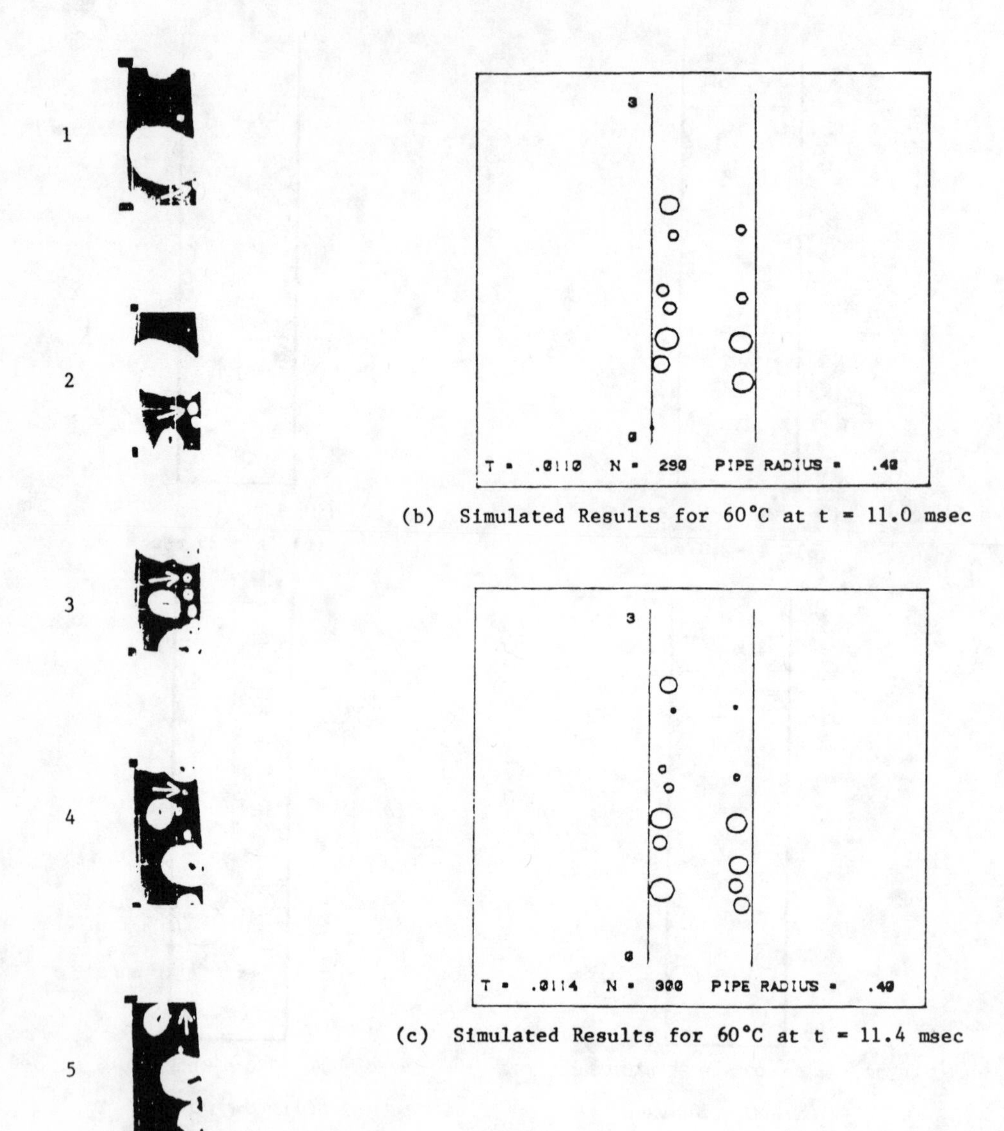

(a) Experimental Results from Abdelmessih, Hooper and Nangia (1973)

(b) Simulated Results for 60°C at t = 11.0 msec

(c) Simulated Results for 60°C at t = 11.4 msec

Figure 6. Bubble Collapse in Subcooled Forced Convection Flow

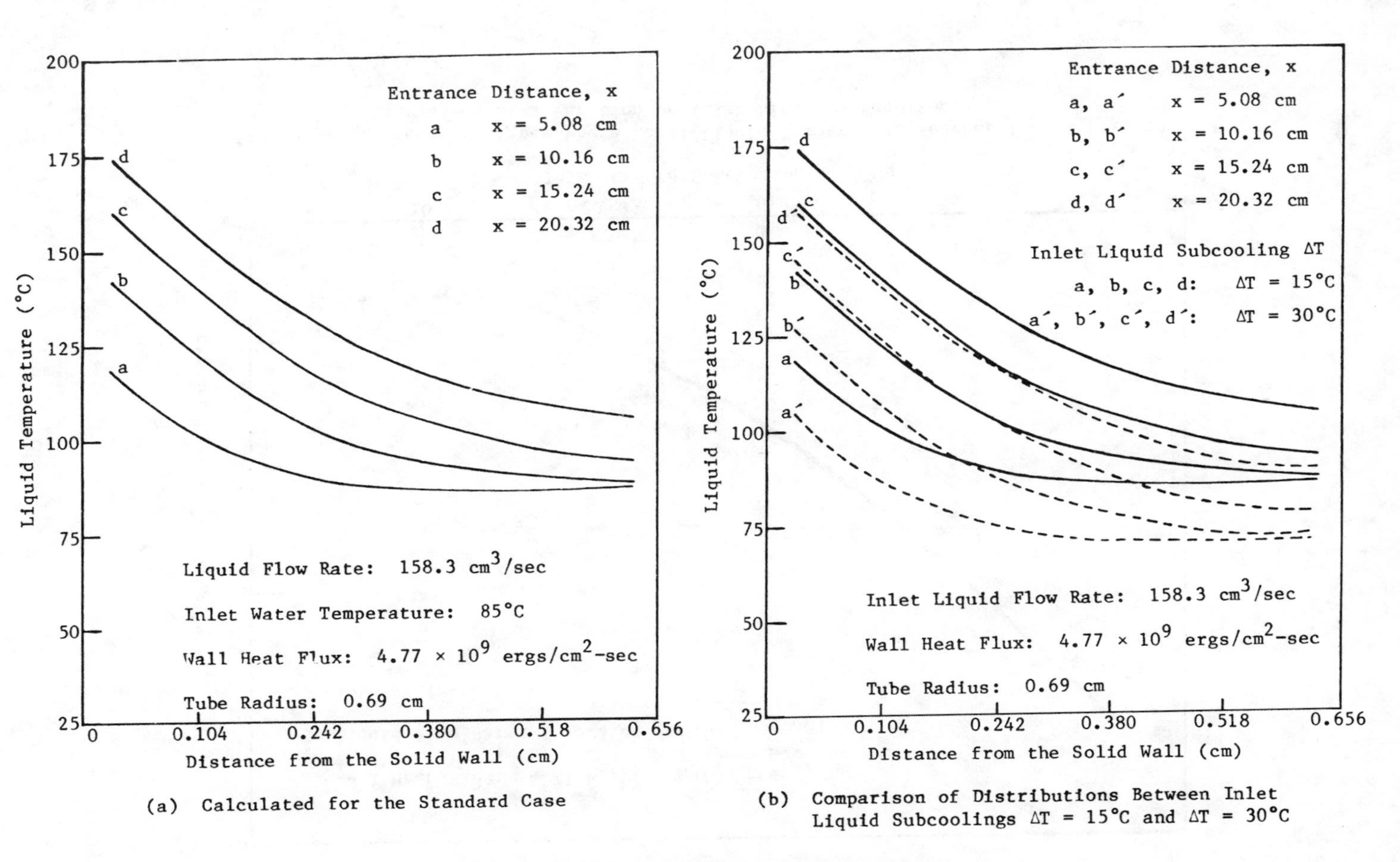

(a) Calculated for the Standard Case

(b) Comparison of Distributions Between Inlet Liquid Subcoolings $\Delta T = 15°C$ and $\Delta T = 30°C$

Figure 7. Liquid Temperature Distributions.

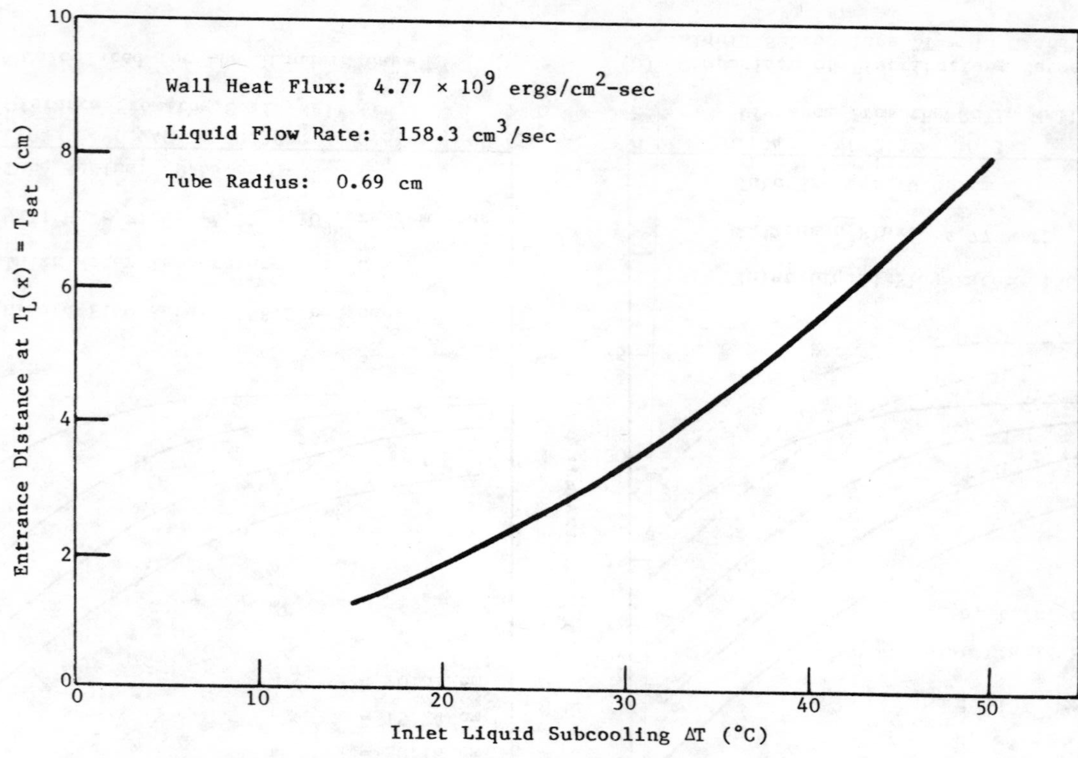

Figure 8. Entrance Distance Where Local Liquid Temperature Reaches the Saturation Temperature as a Function of Inlet Liquid Subcooling.

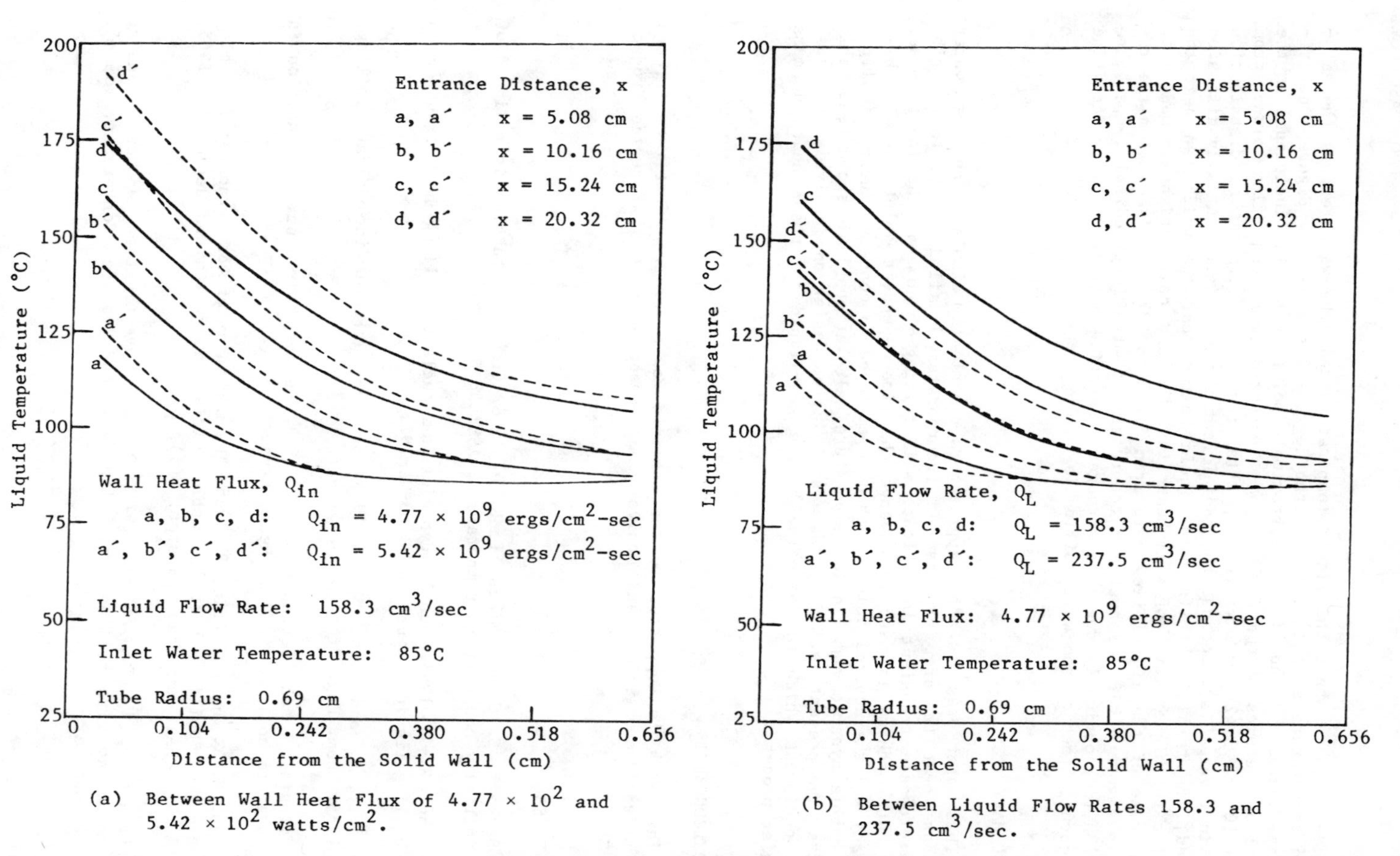

(a) Between Wall Heat Flux of 4.77 × 10^2 and 5.42 × 10^2 watts/cm^2.

(b) Between Liquid Flow Rates 158.3 and 237.5 cm^3/sec.

Figure 9. Comparison of the Liquid Temperature Distribution.

entrance distance where the liquid temperature near the wall reaches the saturation temperature as a function of the degree of subcooling. Figure 8 quantifies the increase trend of this approximate point of boiling incipience as the subcooling becomes larger. Next, we increased the heat flux alone from 4.77×10^2 to 5.42×10^2 watts/cm^2, obtaining a new temperature distribution shown in Figure 9(a). Because the radial heat transfer is essentially diffusion limited, the result exhibits more liquid heatup near the wall than near the core for the higher level of wall heat flux. The last calculation was made with an increase of the liquid flow rate from 158.3 to 237.5 cm^3/sec. From the result in Figure 9(b), we observe a compression of the longitudinal temperature distribution, obviously due to a stronger convective heat transfer process. The consequent effect on the wall boiling is self-evident.

5. SUMMARY

This paper presents a new approach to numerically simulate the steam-water two-phase heat transfer process. It incorporates detailed models to describe the microscale transient in nucleate wall boiling phenomena. The fourth order Runge-Kutta scheme is used to advance the time-dependent solutions with high accuracy and the control volume method is employed to conserve energy. Qualitative bubble dynamic and liquid temperature calculations have shown reasonable results. The present technique can assist in the design and analysis of industrial equipment which is dominated by the gas-liquid two-phase heat and mass transfer process.

ACKNOWLEDGEMENTS

This work is supported by the Electric Power Research Institute through the Nuclear Power Safety and Analysis Department as part of Research Project RP888-1.

REFERENCES

1. Bankoff, S. G. and Mikesell, R. D. 1958. Growth of bubbles in a liquid of initially non-uniform temperature, ASME 58-WA-105.

2. Yang, W.-J. 1963. Bubble dynamics and nucleate boiling heat transfer in boiling liquid mixture, ASME 63-WA-197.

3. Corty, C. and Foust, A. S. 1955. Surface variables in nucleate boiling, 1955. Chem. Eng. Prog. Symp. 51, 17, 1-12.

4. Moissis, R. and Berenson, P. J. 1963. On the hydrodynamic transition in nucleate boiling, ASME J. Heat Transfer, 85C(3), 221-229.

5. Han, C. Y. and Griffith, P. 1965. The mechanism of heat transfer in nucleate pool boiling, Part 1, Bubble initiation, growth and departure. 1965. Int. J. Heat and Mass Transfer, 8(6), 887-904.

6. Baranenko, V. I., et al. 1974. Optical investigation of heat transfer mechanism with boiling, Proc. 5th Int. Heat Transfer Conference, Vol. 5, Hemisphere.

7. Swanson, J. L. and Bowman, H. F. 1974. Transient surface temperature behavior in nucleate pool-boiling nitrogen, Proc. 5th Int. Heat Transfer Conf., Hemisphere.

8. Levy, S. 1959. Generalized correlation of boiling heat transfer, Trans. ASME, Series C, 81(1), p. 37.

9. Janssen, E. and Kirvinen, J. A. 1963. Burnout conditions for non-unformly heated rod in annular geometry, water at 1000 psia, GEAP 3899.

10. Hewitt, G. F. 1981. Two phase flow and its applications, past, present and future, D. Q. Kern lecture, ASEM, AIChE 20th Nat. Heat Transfer Conf.

11. Stuhmiller, J. H., Ferguson, R. E., Wang, S. S. and Agee, L. J. 1981. Two-phase flow regime modeling, Third CNSI Specialist Meeting on Transient Two-Phase Flow, C.I.T.

12. Shoukri, M. and Judd, R. L. 1978. On the influence of surface conditions in nucleate boiling - the concept of bubble flux density, Trans. of the ASME, Vol. 100, pp. 618-623.

13. Saha, P., Abuaf, N. and Wu, B. J. C. 1981. A nonequilibrium vapor generation model for flashing flows, ASME 81-HT-84.

14. Wang, S. S. and Stuhmiller, J. H. 1979, Numerical simulation of two-phase flows in a producing gas saturated well, SIAM annual meeting 1979, Houston.

15. Batchelor, G. K. 1970, Fluid Dynamics, Cambridge Press.

16. Scriven, L. E. 1959. On the dynamics of phase growth, Chem. Eng. Sci., 10(1), pp. 1-13.

17. Plesset, M. S. and Zwick, S. A. 1954. Growth of vapor bubbles in superheated liquids, J. Applied Phys., 24 (4), 493-500.

18. Wang, S. S., Stuhmiller, J. H. and Ferguson, R. E. 1980. Numerical simulation of steam bubbles in a vertical tube, ASME Basic Mechanisms in Two-Phase Flow and Heat Transfer, pp. 79-86.

19. Ruckenstein, E. and Davis, E. J. 1971. The effect of bubble translation on vapor bubble growth in a superheated liquid, Int. J. Heat and Mass Transfer, Vol. 14, pp. 939-952.

20. Moalem, D. and Sideman, S. 1973. The effect of motion on bubble collapse, Int. J. Heat and Mass Transfer, Vol. 16, pp. 2321-2329.

21. Stuhmiller, J. H. and Ferguson, R. E. 1980. The role of microscale processes in the modeling of two-phase flow, EPRI NP-1325.

22. Kosky, P. G. 1968. Bubble growth measurements in uniformly superheated liquid, Chem. Eng. Sci., Vol. 23, pp. 695-706.

23. Florshuetz, L. W. and Chao, B. T. 1965. On the mechanics of vapor bubble collapse, J. Heat Transfer, pp. 209.

24. Schlichting, H. 1960. Boundary layer theory, Chapter XX, McGraw-Hill.

25. Sultan, M. and Judd, R. L. 1978. Spatial distribution of active site and bubble flux density, Trans. ASME, Vol. 100, pp. 56-62.

26. Gaertner, R. F. 1961. Distribution of active sites in nucleate boiling of liquids, G. E. Report No. 61-RL-2826C.

27. Griffith P. and Wallis, J. D. 1960. The role of surface condition in nucleate boiling, Chem. Eng. Prog. Symp. Ser. 56, 30, pp. 49-63.

28. Mikic, B. B., Rohsenow, W. M. and Griffith, P. 1970. On bubble growth rates, Int. J. Heat and Mass Transfer, Vol. 13, pp. 657-666.

29. Levy, S. 1967. Forced convection subcooled boiling - prediction of vapor volumetric fraction, Int. J. Heat and Mass Transfer, Vol. 10, pp. 951-965.

30. Hamburger, L. G. 1965. The growth and rise of individual vapor bubbles in nucleate pool boiling, Int. J. Heat and Mass Transfer, Vol. 8, pp. 1369-1386.

31. Bergles, A. E. and Rohsenow, W. M. 1964. The determination of forced-convection surface boiling heat transfer, J. Heat Transfer, pp. 365-372.

32. Isaacson, E. and Keller, H. B. 1966. Analysis of numerical methods, pp. 400-405, Wiley.

33. Roache, P. J. 1972. Computational fluid dynamics, Chapter 2, Hermosa Publishers.

34. Abdelmessih, A. H., Hooper, F. C. and Nangia, S. 1973. Flow effects on bubble growth and collapse in surface boiling, Int. J. Heat and Mass Transfer, Vol. 15, pp. 115-125.

NOMENCLATURE

A_i cross section area of ith cell, cm^2

Ar_i radial surface area of ith cell, cm^2

A_b bubble surface area, cm^2

B buoyancy force, dyne

C_D drag coefficient

C_p specific heat at constant pressure for liquid, erg/g °C

C_B proportionality constant

C_F proportionality constant

C_s proportionality constant

C_w wall drag coefficient

D bubble drag force due to liquid, has components D_x, D_y and D_z, dyne

D_H hydraulic diameter, cm

g acceleration due to gravity, 980 cm/sec^2

h heat transfer coefficient, erg/cm^2-sec-°C

h_{fg} latent heat of evaporation, erg/g

J_a Jakob number = $\rho_f C_p (T_\infty - T_{sat})/\rho_g h_{fg}$

k liquid thermal conductivity, erg/cm-sec-°C

K liquid thermal conductivity, cm^2/sec

k_s surface roughness parameter, cm

M_b total bubble inertia, g

m_a bubble added mass, g

m_b bubble steam mass, g

p pressure, dyne/cm^2 [psia in Eq. (30)]

p_T pressure at the free surface, dyne/cm^2

Q liquid flow rate, cm^3/sec

$\dot{Q}_{i,j}$ heat generation source in cell i,j, erg/sec

$\dot{q}$ heat source, erg/cm^3-sec

$\dot{q}_{fg}$ heat flux due to evaporation, erg/cm^2-sec

r_e equivalent bubble radius, cm

r^* radial scale length for wake, cm

r radial displacement, cm

Δr cell size in the radial direction, cm

R_p pipe radius, cm

Re Reynolds number

R_H hydraulic radius, cm

S bubble lateral force, has components S_y, S_z, dyne

t time, sec

T liquid temperature, °C

T_{sat} saturation temperature for a given pressure, °C

T_w wall temperature, °C

T_∞ liquid temperature, °C

u,v,w bubble velocity components, cm/sec

u´,v´,w´ liquid turbulent velocity components, cm/sec

U,V,W liquid velocity components, cm/sec

U_∞ bubble terminal velocity, cm/sec

u_w axial wake velocity, cm/sec

U_w centerline wake velocity, cm/sec

V_b bubble volume, cm^3

$V_{i,j}$ liquid volume in cell i,j, cm^3

v_0 magnitude of the initial bubble velocity, cm/sec

x,y,z displacement components, cm

x_g, y_g, z_g bubble displacement, cm

α void fraction

β bubble growth constant

σ surface tension, dyne/cm

Γ_w wall shear stress, $dyne/cm^2$

μ added mass coefficient

ρ density, g/cm^3

θ sexagesimal degree

Subscripts

g gas

f fluid

d time delay

b bubble

w wake

Numerical Methods for the Transient Behavior of Two-Phase Flow Heat Transfer in Evaporators and Condensers

JOOST J. BRASZ and KENNETH KOENIG
Research Division
Carrier Corporation
Carrier Parkway
Syracuse, New York 13221

ABSTRACT

A fast computer simulation has been established that describes the main heat transfer phenomena in heat pump evaporators and condensers during start-up and shutdown operation. The various finite-difference methods, which have been applied to solve the original set of nonlinear partial differential equations describing the transient behavior of a two-phase flow heat transfer system, were all too slow for use in an overall heat pump simulation program. The simulation time has been decreased by model reduction neglecting dynamic pressure waves which are of minor importance for a heat transfer analysis, while still preserving fluid compressibility and thermal expansion. The choice of independent state variables had a decisive effect on the simulation speed.

NOMENCLATURE

a	acoustic velocity
e	specific internal energy
h	specific enthalpy
F	frictional pressure loss per unit length
G	mass flux
P	pressure
Q	rate of heat added per unit volume
t	time
x	distance
ρ	density

1. INTRODUCTION

In the heat pump and air conditioning industry, steady-state, full-load evaluation procedures allow for the capacity determination necessary for properly sizing the unit to match the building load. At current energy prices, unit selection has to be based on real life-cycle cost analysis. Therefore, heat pump performance at part-load conditions has to be determined as well. Part-load operation of a heat pump is normally realized by on-off cycling of the compressor. The energy consumption under these circumstances is determined by calculating the relative lengths of the on-and-off periods and corresponding compressor and fan power requirements. The current state-of-the-art is to obtain this data from a dynamic computer simulation of the complete system including heat pump, building, and outdoor environment. In such dynamic models, the capacity of the heat pump unit itself is modeled as a first-order system with separate time constants for start-up and shutdown [1]. It has been found experimentally that, due to phenomena such as rapid pressure equalization after shutdown, the shutdown time constant is much smaller than the start-up time constant. Due to this nonlinear dynamic behavior, the actual cooling or heating capacity of a heat pump is smaller than would follow from the ratio of the lengths of the on-and-off periods (Fig. 1). As a result, part-load performance and, hence, seasonal energy efficiency ratios may deteriorate as much as 10 percent for air conditioners and 25 percent for heat pumps. Consequently, the determination of those design factors which contribute to seasonal energy efficiency ratios being lower than steady-state energy efficiency ratios (cycling losses) are a major concern for the air conditioning industry.

In order to arrive at a better understanding of the heat pump operation and efficiency under transient conditions, an experimental and theoretical research program has been initiated. The aim of the theoretical studies is to develop a detailed dynamic heat pump computer model for the calculation of energy efficiencies during part-load conditions with on/off cycling. Since the major dynamic elements of a heat pump are the evaporator and the condenser, the theoretical work first concentrates on the establishments of a fast computer simulation describing the relevant heat transfer phenomena in parallel tube heat pump evaporator and condenser heat exchangers during start-up and shutdown. Eventually, these component simulations will form an integral part of an overall heat pump system model.

This paper describes the development of a finite-difference solution for a fast simulation of the transient behavior of two-phase flow heat transfer in condensers and evaporators. Stability criteria and convergence requirements for common finite-difference solution schemes applied to the original set of partial differential equations limited the integration time-step size to very small values, resulting in excessive computer time for the simulation of a complete on-off cycle. This problem has been solved by subsequently simplifying the model equations and finding a time-effective numerical solution.

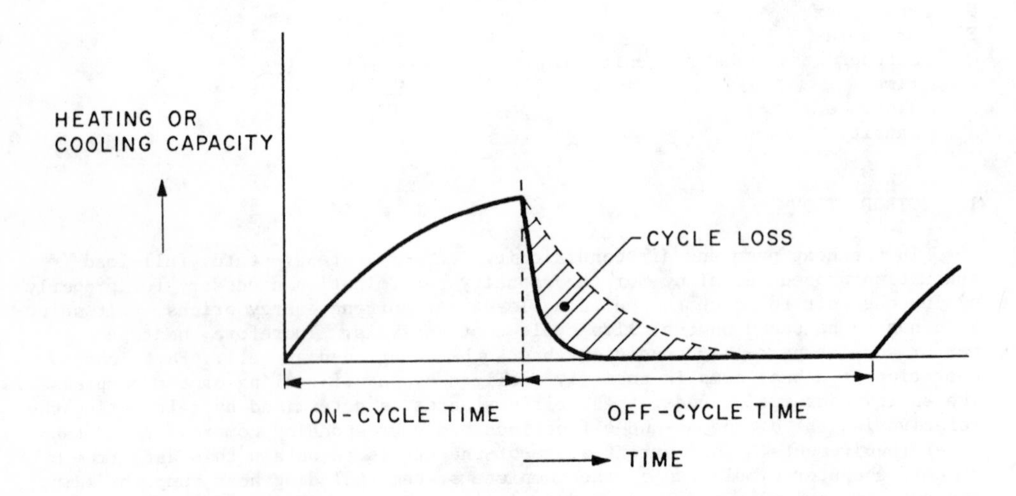

Fig. 1 Heating Capacity as a Function of Time under Part-load Conditions

2. MATHEMATICAL MODEL

The transient behavior of two-phase flow heat transfer can be described by a set of nonlinear, coupled partial differential equations representing the conservation laws of mass, momentum, and energy. Under the assumption of one-dimensional homogeneous flow and thermodynamic equilibrium, and neglecting gravitational pressure effects, these conservation laws take the following form [2]:

Mass Balance: $$\frac{\partial \rho}{\partial t} + \frac{\partial G}{\partial x} = 0, \tag{1}$$

Momentum Balance: $$\frac{\partial G}{\partial t} + \frac{\partial}{\partial x}\frac{G^2}{\rho} + \frac{\partial P}{\partial x} + F = 0, \tag{2}$$

Energy Balance: $$\frac{\partial}{\partial t}\left(\rho e + \frac{G}{2\rho}\right) + \frac{\partial}{\partial x}\left(Gh + \frac{G^3}{2\rho^2}\right) = Q. \tag{3}$$

This system of equations is closed with appropriate boundary conditions; constitutive equations for friction pressure loss, F, and heat input, Q; and an equation-of-state giving, for example, pressure, P, and enthalpy, h, as a function of density, ρ, and internal energy, e.

Pressure drop and heat transfer correlations are used to determine F and Q for the various flow regimes.

Equations (1) to (3), which describe single-phase as well as two-phase fluid flow, are valid for a homogeneous flow. However, unequal density and viscosity of liquid and vapor in a two-phase flow system usually force the vapor to attain a relative velocity or "slip" with respect to the liquid (nonhomogeneous flow). The occurrence of slip between the two phases can be modeled by a two-fluid model with separate conservation equations for liquid and gas, and appropriate interphase coupling terms; but such an approach is computationally complicated, and the interphase terms are often unknown. A common practical approach is to allow only the velocity to differ for the two phases while the conservation equations are still written for the combined flow as in the case of the homogeneous flow model where equal gas and liquid velocities are assumed. As is shown in [3], the original homogeneous form of the conservation equations can then be preserved by the introduction of mixture variables. In this way, the inclusion of slip in a two-phase flow model can be made through minor modifications of terms in the single-phase energy and momentum conservation equations. This approach also simplifies the modeling of fluid-flow conditions at transition boundaries between single- and two-phase flow, as encountered in heat pump evaporators and condensers. It also guarantees that the inclusion of slippage does not change the stability and convergence requirements of the numerical solution method applied to the conservation equations.

The system of Equations (1) through (3) form a set of nonlinear hyperbolic partial differential equations which have been solved for various nuclear engineering applications [3,4,5,6] mainly dealing with nuclear safety analysis. Although the numerical methods for solving these equations are correct, they suffer in requiring excessive computer time. Model reduction is clearly necessary.

Some simplified models in the literature; e.g., [7], assume the permissibility of linearization or constant pressure as a function of time. Such approximations are useful for control studies when only minor variations around a steady-state operating point occur or for applications where the change in pressure is relatively small so that density and enthalpy are barely affected.

However, for start-up and shutdown simulations, linearization is not permitted, neither can it be assumed that pressure remains constant.

Work reported so far on start-up/shutdown of heat pump and refrigeration systems [8,9,10] neglects spatial effects of the evaporator and condenser. The evaporator and condenser are modeled as a single ideally-mixed tank, thus reducing the partial-differential equations to ordinary differential equations. Dynamic effects related to the finite residence time of the refrigerant in the component are lost.

For our purpose of a transient energy analysis, a simplified model is desired where heat transfer and compressibility effects need to be included, while acoustic effects are of minor importance and should be neglected if this improves computer speed.

3. CHARACTERISTIC DIRECTIONS

The characteristic directions of the original set of partial differential equations define lines in the time-space solution domain across which derivatives may be continuous, relating physically to the paths of traveling waves. By examining these directions, the consequences of eliminating some terms in the original set of equations can be investigated. Specifically, the effect of eliminating the dynamic and steady-state acceleration terms in the momentum balance together with corresponding terms in the energy equation will be studied. The symbols δ_1 and δ_2 will be introduced to represent the presence or absence of these terms depending on whether their value is 1 or 0. The set of Equations (1) to (3) is rewritten as:

$$\frac{\partial \rho}{\partial t} + \frac{\partial G}{\partial x} = 0, \tag{4}$$

$$\delta_1 \frac{\partial G}{\partial t} + \delta_2 \frac{\partial \, G^2/\rho}{\partial x} + \frac{\partial P}{\partial x} + F = 0, \tag{5}$$

$$\frac{\partial}{\partial t}\left(\rho e + \delta_1 \frac{G^2}{2\rho}\right) + \frac{\partial}{\partial x}\left(Gh + \delta_2 \frac{G^3}{2\rho^2}\right) = Q. \tag{6}$$

By using the following relationship for the enthalpy:

$$h = e + \frac{P}{\rho}, \tag{7}$$

and rewriting the spatial pressure gradient as:

$$\frac{\partial P}{\partial x} = \frac{\partial P}{\partial \rho}\frac{\partial \rho}{\partial x} + \frac{\partial P}{\partial e}\frac{\partial e}{\partial x}, \tag{8}$$

Equations (4) to (6) can be written in matrix form as:

$$\begin{bmatrix} 1 & 0 & 0 & 1 & 0 & 0 \\ \left(-\frac{2G\delta_2}{\rho}\right) & \left(\frac{\partial P}{\partial \rho} - \frac{G^2\delta_2}{\rho^2}\right) & \delta_1 & 0 & 0 & \partial P/\partial e \\ \left(\frac{P}{\rho} - \frac{G^2(\delta_1-\delta_2)}{2\rho^2}\right) & \left(-\frac{PG}{\rho^2}\right) & 0 & 0 & \rho & G \\ dt & dx & 0 & 0 & 0 & 0 \\ 0 & 0 & dt & dx & 0 & 0 \\ 0 & 0 & 0 & 0 & dt & dx \end{bmatrix} \begin{bmatrix} \partial\rho/\partial t \\ \partial\rho/\partial x \\ \partial G/\partial t \\ \partial G/\partial x \\ \partial e/\partial t \\ \partial e/\partial x \end{bmatrix} = \begin{bmatrix} 0 \\ -F \\ Q + GF/\rho \\ \rho \\ G \\ e \end{bmatrix}. \quad (9)$$

The characteristic lines are along those dx/dt values that make the determinant of the coefficient matrix zero. When all terms are included, ($\delta_1 = \delta_2 = 1$), solving the above matrix yields:

$$\left(dx - vdt\right)\left[dx^2 - 2vdxdt + \left(v^2 - \frac{P}{\rho^2}\frac{\partial P}{\partial e} - \frac{\partial P}{\partial \rho}\right) dt^2\right] = 0, \quad (10)$$

or

$$\frac{dx}{dt} = v \pm a \text{ and } v, \quad (11)$$

where $v = \frac{G}{\rho}$ is the fluid transport velocity and $a = \left(\frac{P}{\rho^2}\frac{\partial P}{\partial e} + \frac{\partial P}{\partial \rho}\right)^{\frac{1}{2}}$ is the sonic speed of a two-phase mixture.

In case the dynamic acceleration terms are omitted, the determinant becomes:

$$\left(dt\right)\left[dx^2 - \tfrac{1}{2}\left(3v - \frac{a^2}{v} + \frac{v}{2\rho}\frac{dP}{de}\right)dxdt + \tfrac{1}{2}\left(v^2 - a^2\right)dt\right] = 0, \quad (12)$$

and there are only two characteristics (the third one is dt=0) which are difficult to evaluate in a general sense since the quadratic cannot be factored. Assuming that v=0.1a, the two characteristics for Freon 22 in gaseous state become:

$$\frac{dx}{dt} = 1.006v, \ -4.95a. \quad (13)$$

One characteristic is almost exactly equal to the fluid transport velocity, while the other is a supersonic backward traveling wave.

When both the dynamic and steady-state acceleration terms are omitted, the determinant simplifies to a single characteristic line representing the fluid velocity:

$$\frac{dx}{dt} = v, \quad (14)$$

and all acoustic effects are eliminated.

4. FINITE DIFFERENCE METHODS

In the one-dimensional finite difference formulation, the fluid conservation equations given by Equations (1) through (3) are spatially discretized by defining the dependent variable along a discrete spatial mesh. The mesh is comprised of a series of mesh points numbered i = 1, ..., I at locations x_i (see Fig. 2). Each mesh point, i, is located at the center of a cell which has a length, Δx_i. The cells are connected by junctions which are numbered using half integers.

Thus, the junction between cells i and i-1 is numbered $i-\frac{1}{2}$ and located at $x_{i-\frac{1}{2}}$. The length of the cell i is defined by:

$$\Delta x_i = x_{i+\frac{1}{2}} - x_{i-\frac{1}{2}}, \tag{15}$$

and the distance between mesh points i and i-1 by:

$$\Delta x_{i-\frac{1}{2}} = x_i - x_{i-1}. \tag{16}$$

The spatial differencing method can be illustrated by the cell-centered discretization of Equation (1). In the case of uniform channel flow area, this is given by:

$$\frac{\partial}{\partial t}\rho_i = -\left(\frac{\partial G}{\partial x}\right)_i = \frac{G_{i-\frac{1}{2}} - G_{i+\frac{1}{2}}}{\Delta x_i}, \tag{17}$$

where cell-centered differencing is used for the mass convection term. Similar differencing schemes are used for Equations (2) and (3).

For time discretization of the fluid conservation equations, time step n is designated by the discrete increment:

$$\Delta t^n = t^{n+1} - t^n, \tag{18}$$

where superscripts n and n+1 refer to previous and advanced-time values, respectively. Time weighting of terms in the finite-difference equations is accomplished by use of the θ-differencing scheme. The time discretized form of Equation (17) over time increment Δt^n, for example is:

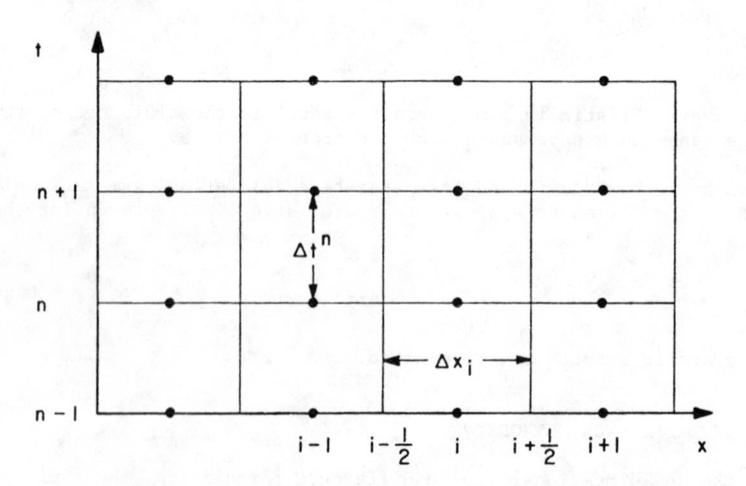

Fig. 2 Spatial and Time Mesh Notation. State variables are calculated at mesh points and flow variables are calculated at corners.

$$\frac{\rho_i^{n+1} - \rho_i^n}{\Delta t^n} = -\theta \left(\frac{\partial G}{\partial x}\right)_i^{n+1} - (1-\theta) \left(\frac{\partial G}{\partial x}\right)_i^n , \tag{19}$$

where $0 \leq \theta \leq 1$.

By assigning θ a value from 0 to 1, we can obtain any degree of time weighting on the right side of Equation (19), including purely implicit (θ=1), time-centered (θ=½), and purely explicit (θ=0).

The variable time-weighting capability can be used to improve numerical stability or reduce truncation error in the finite-difference solution for time-dependent fluid flow.

Finite-difference equations corresponding to Equations (1) through (3) are derived using the space and time-discretization models above for mesh point i and time step Δt^n. The difference equations corresponding to mass, momentum, and energy conservation, respectively, are written as:

$$\rho_i^{n+1} = \rho_i^n - \frac{\Delta t^n}{\Delta x_i}\left[\theta \left(G_{i+\frac{1}{2}}^{n+1} - G_{i-\frac{1}{2}}^{n+1}\right) + (1-\theta) \left(G_{i+\frac{1}{2}}^{n} - G_{i-\frac{1}{2}}^{n}\right)\right], \tag{20}$$

$$G_{i+\frac{1}{2}}^{n+1} = G_{i+\frac{1}{2}}^{n} - \frac{\Delta t^n}{\Delta x_{i+\frac{1}{2}}}\left[\theta \left\{\frac{\left(G_{i+1}^{n+1}\right)^2}{\rho_{i+1}^{n+1}} - \frac{\left(G_{i}^{n+1}\right)^2}{\rho_{i}^{n+1}}\right\} + (1-\theta)\left\{\frac{\left(G_{i+1}^{n}\right)^2}{\rho_{i+1}^{n}} - \frac{\left(G_{i}^{n}\right)^2}{\rho_{i}^{n}}\right\}\right.$$

$$\left. + \theta \left(P_{i+1}^{n+1} - P_{i}^{n+1}\right) + (1-\theta) \left(P_{i+1}^{n} - P_{i}^{n}\right)\right]$$

$$- \Delta t^n \left[\theta\, F_{i+\frac{1}{2}}^{n+1} + (1-\theta)\, F_{i+\frac{1}{2}}^{n}\right], \tag{21}$$

and

$$(\rho e)_i^{n+1} = (\rho e)_i^n + \frac{\left(G_i^n\right)^2}{2\rho_i^n} - \frac{\left(G_i^{n+1}\right)^2}{2\rho_i^{n+1}} - \frac{\Delta t^n}{\Delta x_i}\left[\theta \left[G_{i+\frac{1}{2}}^{n+1}\left\{h_{i+\frac{1}{2}}^{n+1}\right.\right.\right.$$

$$\left.\left. + \frac{1}{2}\left(\frac{G_{i+\frac{1}{2}}^{n+1}}{\rho_{i+\frac{1}{2}}^{n+1}}\right)^2\right\} - G_{i-\frac{1}{2}}^{n+1}\left\{h_{i-\frac{1}{2}}^{n+1} + \frac{1}{2}\left(\frac{G_{i-\frac{1}{2}}^{n+1}}{\rho_{i-\frac{1}{2}}^{n+1}}\right)^2\right\}\right]$$

$$+ (1-\theta)\left\{G_{i+\frac{1}{2}}^{n}\left\{h_{i+\frac{1}{2}}^{n} + \frac{1}{2}\left(\frac{G_{i+\frac{1}{2}}^{n}}{\rho_{i+\frac{1}{2}}^{n}}\right)^2\right\} - G_{i-\frac{1}{2}}^{n}\left\{h_{i-\frac{1}{2}}^{n}\right.\right.$$

$$\left.\left.\left. + \frac{1}{2}\left(\frac{G_{i-\frac{1}{2}}^{n}}{\rho_{i-\frac{1}{2}}^{n}}\right)^2\right\}\right]\right] + \Delta t^n \left[\theta\, Q_i^{n+1} + (1-\theta)\, Q_i^n\right], \tag{22}$$

where $0 \leq \theta \leq 1$.

The finite difference form of the mass and energy equations involving time derivatives of state variables are cell-centered, while the corresponding form of the momentum equation with the time derivative of the flow variable is staggered or junction centered. In this way, most of the variables at the right-hand side of Equations (20) through (22) are calculated at the correct position for the next calculation step. The definition of some state variables (h and P) and the flow variable G at both cell centers and junctions makes it necessary to introduce additional equations relating cell and junction quantities. When we define:

$$G^n_{i+\frac{1}{2}} = G^n_i, \tag{23}$$

$$h^n_{i+\frac{1}{2}} = h^n_i, \tag{24}$$

and

$$\rho^n_{i+\frac{1}{2}} = \rho^n_i, \tag{25}$$

which basically comes down to the introduction of a spatial backward difference approximation, the explicit numerical solution method which is obtained by setting θ=0 in Equations (20) through (22) (which implies a forward difference time differential approximation) corresponds to the numerical scheme presented in [4]. The values defined by Equations (23) to (25) are used in the right-hand side of Equations (20) to (22) for both the linear and nonlinear terms.

In this way, the set of Equations (20) through (25), together with the equation of state, has been solved for initial and boundary conditions in the two state variables, ρ and h, and the flow variable, G. The initial conditions are obtained from a steady-state solution of Equations (1) through (3) giving:

$$h^{n=0}_i = h(x=x_i,\ t=0),$$

$$P^{n=0}_i = P(x=x_i,\ t=0),$$

and

$$G^{n=0}_i = G(t=0).$$

Boundary conditions for h and G are specified at the inlet:

$$G^n_{i=0} = G(x=0,\ t=n\Delta t),$$

$$h^n_{i=0} = h(x=0,\ t=n\Delta t),$$

and for P at the outlet

$$P^n_{i=I} = P(x=X,\ t=n\Delta t).$$

Figures 3 and 4 show some simulation results obtained with this numerical scheme where, for the sake of clarity, zero heat input, Q, and frictional pressure drop, F, were assumed. Figure 3 shows pressure and mass flux profiles for a 20-ft long evaporator with refrigerant Freon R-22 with initial conditions (G = 50 lbm/ft^2-sec, h = 72 Btu/lbm, P = 158.6 psi) at different times after a sudden step disturbance (10 lbm/ft^2-sec) in inlet mass flow rate at t=0.

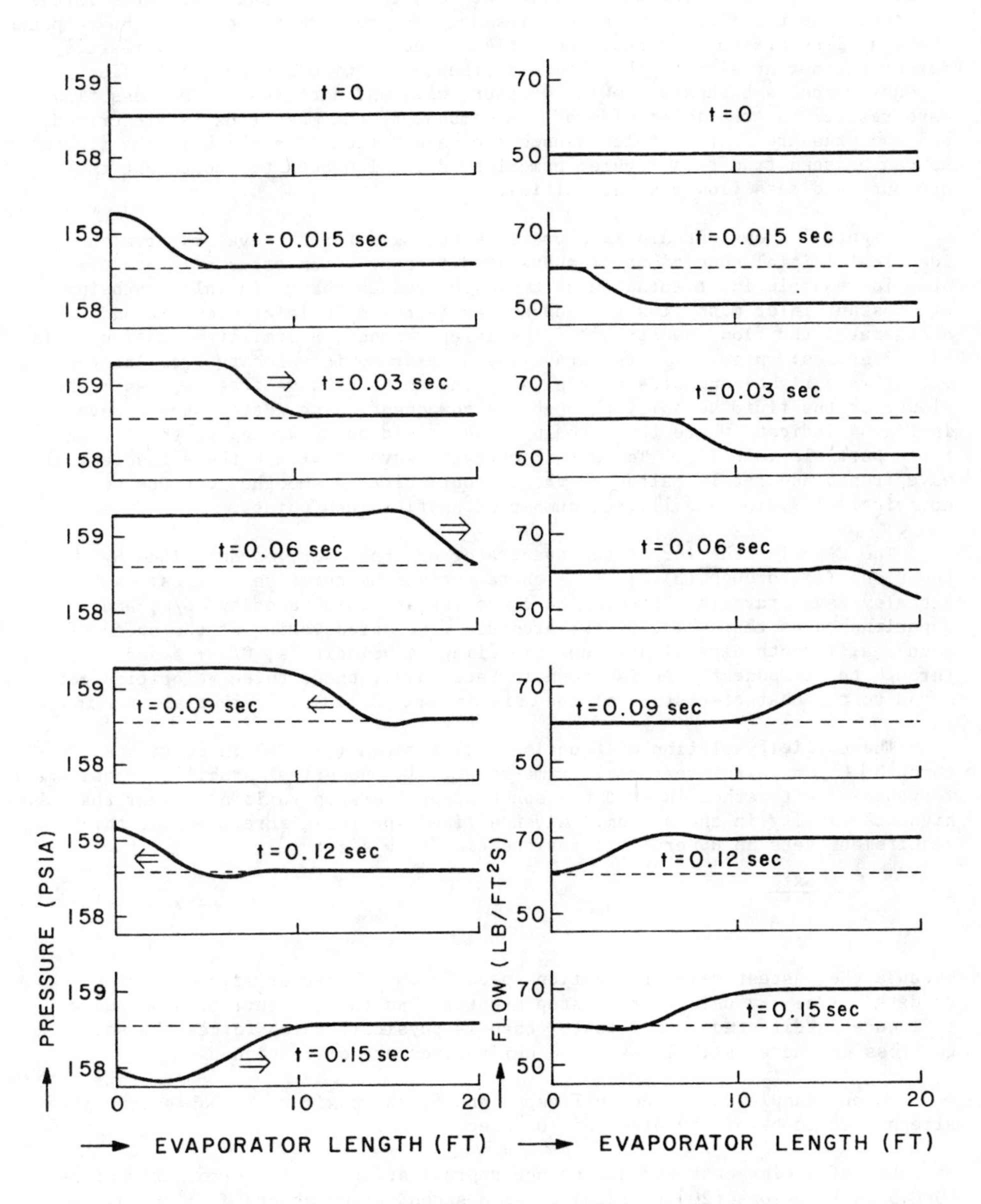

Fig. 3 Pressure and flow profiles at various moments after an inlet disturbance in mass flow rate

Owing to the compressibility of the two-phase flow medium, a wave propagates towards the outlet end at near sonic velocity. The fluid behind the wave front is at a high pressure and a high flow rate due to the necessary pressure forces to accelerate the fluid. When the pressure wave reaches the exit of the component where a fixed pressure boundary condition is defined, the resulting pressure forces further accelerate the flow disturbance to twice its original value. As a consequence, a backward flowing pressure wave and a corresponding mass flow wave result. At the inlet side of the component, the mass flux is prescribed; and the pressure is free which causes the wave reflections shown in the figure. As can be seen from this figure, numerical diffusion acts to smooth out the pressure and mass flow discontinuities.

Figure 4 shows enthalpy and pressure profiles for the evaporator with identical initial conditions as above at different times after a 10 Btu/lbm step increase in inlet enthalpy at t=0. The sudden change in inlet enthalpy at constant inlet mass flow rate causes an increase in inlet pressure and accelerates the flow downstream of the inlet. Hence, a similar situation as in Fig. 3 arises: pressure waves traveling at near sonic velocity from inlet to outlet (see right-hand side of Fig. 4). The enthalpy wave itself moves much slower at the fluid velocity through the component. The dotted square waves in Fig. 4 indicate where the enthalpy wave should be according to the average fluid particle velocity. The actual enthalpy waves approach these theoretical wave fronts accurately, although the discontinuity is smoothed out due to numerical diffusion and limited number of spatial mesh points.

The dynamic behavior of the evaporator or condenser, as described by Equations (1) through (3), is thus characterized by three velocities: an enthalpy wave traveling through the component at fluid velocity, G/ρ, and superimposed on that velocity two pressure waves propagating at the speed of sound, a, in both directions; thus traveling at velocities, $G/\rho + a$ and $G/\rho - a$, through the component. As is shown in Section 3., these three velocities correspond to the characteristics of the original set partial differential equations.

The explicit solution of Equations (1) through (3) (θ=0 in Equations [20] through [22]) requires very small time-steps. The numerical stability requirement for an explicit method is that the space step/time-step ratio be larger than the highest velocity in the system. Given a fixed spatial discretization, this requirement sets an upper limit for the time-step size:

$$\Delta t < \frac{\Delta x}{\left|\frac{G}{\rho}\right| + a} , \tag{26}$$

because the fastest wave propagation speed is the characteristic direction $dt/dx = v + a$. By using a time-step greater than this criterion, a boundary influence is directed inward faster than is physical, which forces the solution to cross characteristic lines where derivatives are discontinuous.

In our sample case used in Figs. 3 and 4, the maximum allowable time-step size proved to be of the order of 10^{-4} sec.

Use of a time-centered difference approximation for the time derivatives (θ=0.5 in Equations [20] to [22]) gives a second-order accurate solution. An explicit difference formulation of this method can be obtained by introducing a staggered grid of mesh points (see Fig. 5). In this method, the state variables, ρ and e, and the flow variable, G, are calculated at alternate time-steps. The state variables are still calculated on mesh points and the flow variable at junctions; but a two-time-step cycle is required for a completely new set of ρ, e, and G. However, this centered difference solution

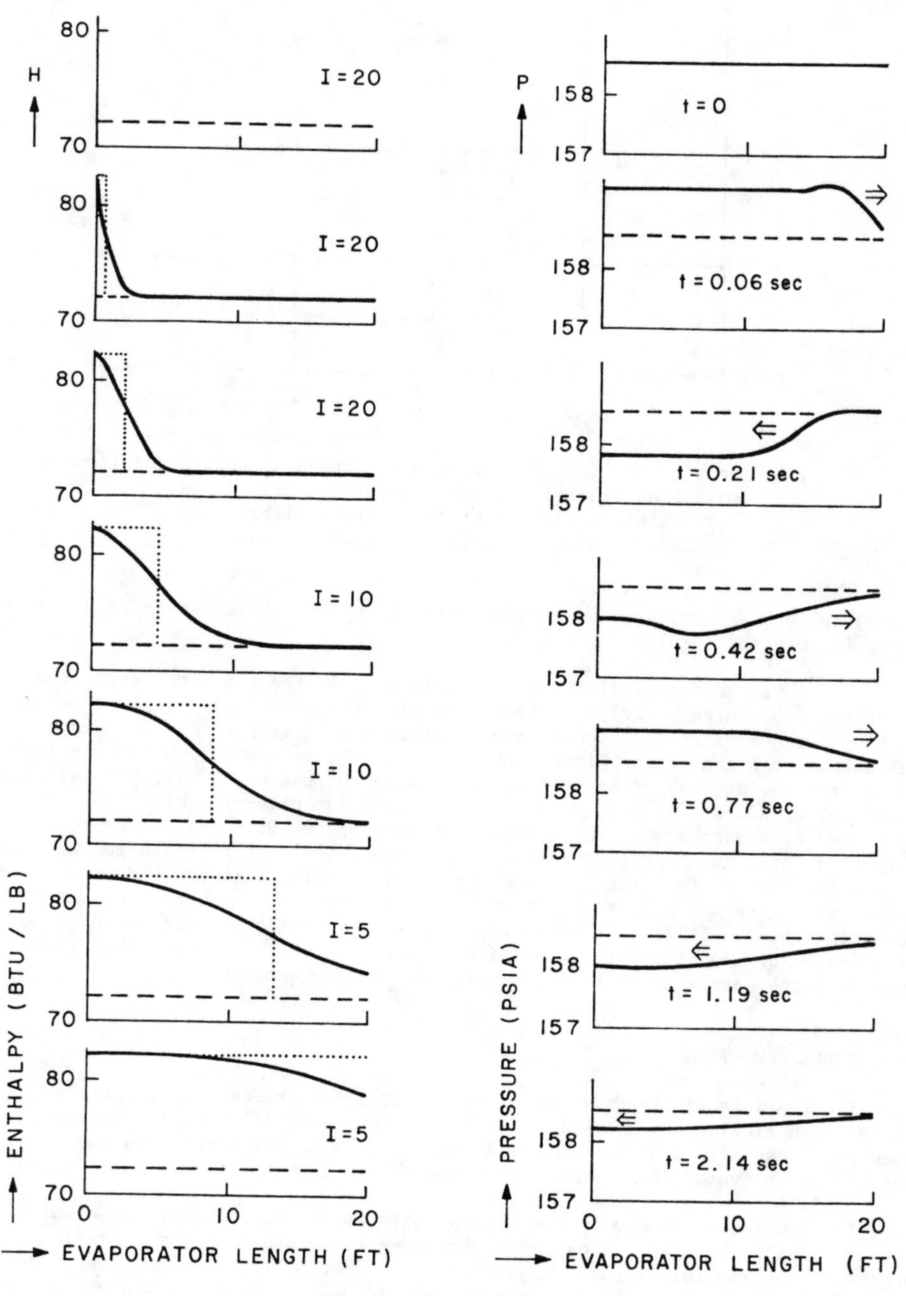

Fig. 4 Enthalpy and pressure profiles after an inlet disturbance in inlet enthalpy. I is the number of spatial mesh points.

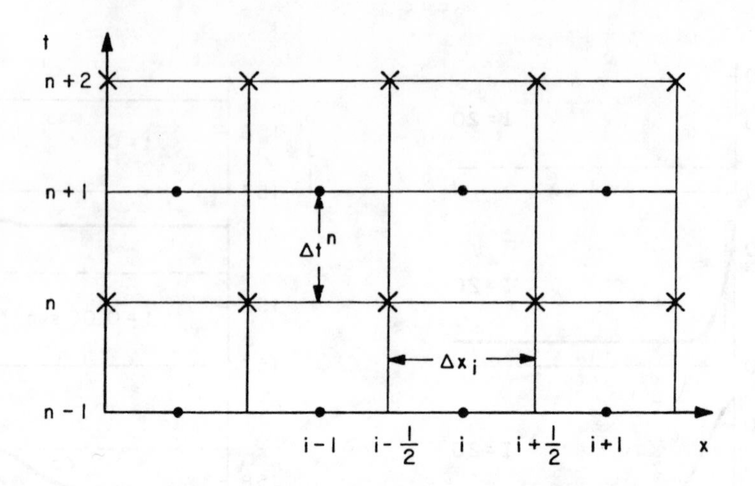

Fig. 5. Spatial and Time Staggered Mesh Notation. State and flow variables are calculated at alternate time-steps. · indicates mesh point for state variable and x indicates corner point for flow variable.

proved to be even more susceptible to instability than the first-order accurate explicit solution (θ=0).

To remove the numerical stability limit (26) on the time-step size, the Equations (20) through (22) were made implicit by setting θ=1. The problem of an implicit numerical solution method is to find a first guess of the state variables and a convergent iteration scheme. Old values were used as a first guess, and the average of the old and new values of the state variables was the input for each new iteration step. In this way, the time-step size could be increased by a factor 40. The improvement in computer CPU time, however, was only a factor 7 due to the iteration steps taken. Further increase in time-step size increased the CPU time of the solution, indicating that the benefit of the larger time-step was more than offset by the penalty for the larger number of iteration steps. Still further increase in time-step size caused convergence problems. More sophisticated iteration procedures like Newton's method [4] involve large matrix inversions and were therefore abandoned.

5. MODEL REDUCTION

The implicit finite difference method described in Section 4. was the fastest numerical scheme for the solution of Equations (1) to (3). However, even this most efficient method still results in a solution which is too slow for use in an overall heat pump system simulation program.

The problem is caused by the high velocities of the acoustic waves which require small time-steps in order to guarantee convergence of the iteration scheme of the implicit method. Therefore, speeding up the simulation by model reduction has been attempted. The model should be reduced in such a way as to neglect the dynamic pressure waves while still preserving fluid compressibility associated with varying density and thermal expansion of the fluid due to heating.

An obvious way to speed up the simulation seems to be the replacement of the dynamic momentum (partial differential) equation by its quasi-steady-state (ordinary differential) approximation, neglecting the dynamic acceleration term (the first term in Equation (2)). However, contrary to our expectations, smaller time-steps were required to guarantee convergence of the implicit solution method in this case.

The solution itself showed two characteristic velocities: The positive fluid velocity for enthalpy disturbances and a negative extraneous speed with a numerical value an order of magnitude larger than the speed of sound for pressure disturbances. The latter supersonic wave, which does not represent a real physical phenomenon, is obviously caused by the quasi-steady-state approximation for the momentum balance. This supersonic velocity has also been found analytically as one of the two characteristic roots of the mass and energy partial differential equations (see Equation (13)). This high velocity explains the very small time-steps necessary for convergence of the implicit finite difference solution technique. Furthermore, model reduction of the dynamic momentum balance to a quasi-steady-state equation did not improve the computation time of the explicit solution method either.

By neglecting both the dynamic and static acceleration terms in the momentum equation (the first two terms in Equation (2)), the number of partial differential equations is reduced from 3 to 2. With this approximation, the solution showed only one characteristic velocity: the positive fluid velocity for enthalpy disturbances (see Equation (14)).

Very small time-steps are required in order to maintain convergence. The solution procedure is as follows (see Fig. 6): new values of internal energy

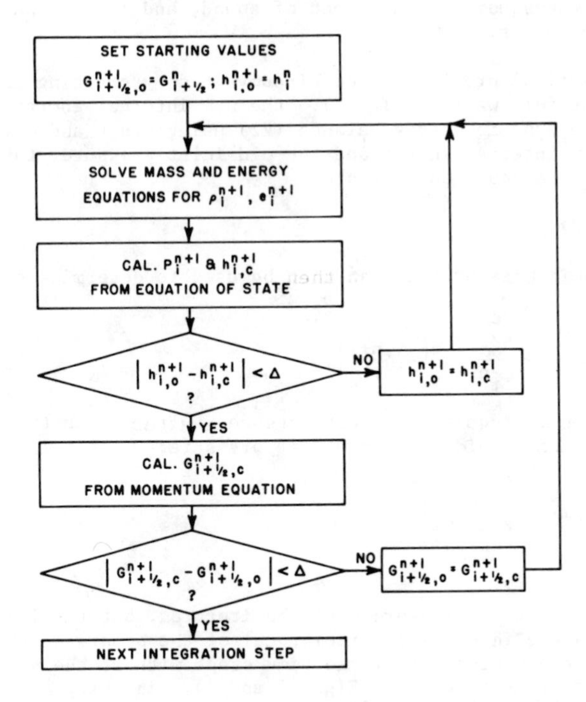

Fig. 6 First Numerical Flow Chart

and density are calculated from the dynamic mass and energy balances (20) and (22). Subsequently, the new pressure and enthalpy are determined from the equation of state:

$$P = P(e,\rho) \text{ and } h = e + P/\rho \tag{27}$$

and the steps iterated until h converges. The new mass flux is calculated from the steady-state momentum equation:

$$\frac{dP}{dx} + F = 0, \tag{28}$$

where the frictional pressure loss depends on the mass flux as follows:

$$F = K\,\frac{G^2}{2g\rho}\;. \tag{29}$$

Therefore, Equation (21) is replaced by:

$$G_{i+\frac{1}{2}}^{n+1} = \left(\frac{2g\rho_{i+\frac{1}{2}}^{n+1}}{K}\,\frac{P_i^{n+1} - P_{i+1}^{n+1}}{\Delta x_{i+\frac{1}{2}}}\right)^{\frac{1}{2}}. \tag{30}$$

The calculated mass flux in Equation (30) is converged by repeating all prior steps.

The numerical convergence problem of this solution is caused by the large sensitivity of the pressure to changes in density in Equation (27), which is on the order of the square of the speed of sound, and is not inherent to the set of equations themselves.

This numerical problem can be circumvented by changing the order of calculation as follows (see Fig. 7): the new internal energy is calculated first from the dynamic energy balance (22) using old P and G values initially. Given this new internal energy and the old inlet pressure, the new density is determined by the equation of state:

$$\rho = \rho(e,P) \tag{31}$$

The dynamic mass balance can then be used to determine the leaving mass flux:

$$G_{i+\frac{1}{2}}^{n+1} = G_{i-\frac{1}{2}}^{n+1} + \frac{\Delta x_i}{\Delta t^n}\left(\rho_i^n - \rho_i^{n+1}\right), \tag{32}$$

where iteration is required for convergence, after which the steady-state momentum equation provides the new exit pressure:

$$P_{i+1}^{n+1} = P_i^{n+1} - K\,\frac{\left(G_{i+\frac{1}{2}}^{n+1}\right)^2}{2g\rho_{i+\frac{1}{2}}^{n+1}}\;. \tag{33}$$

At this point the pressure could be iterated, but the insensitivity of the density to changes in pressure (reciprocal of the square of the sonic speed) enables the use of relatively large time steps without the necessity of this iteration. In our sample case (Figs. 3 and 4), time step sizes of 0.1 sec could now be taken without numerical problems; thus making this solution a useful one for inclusion in an overall heat pump simulation.

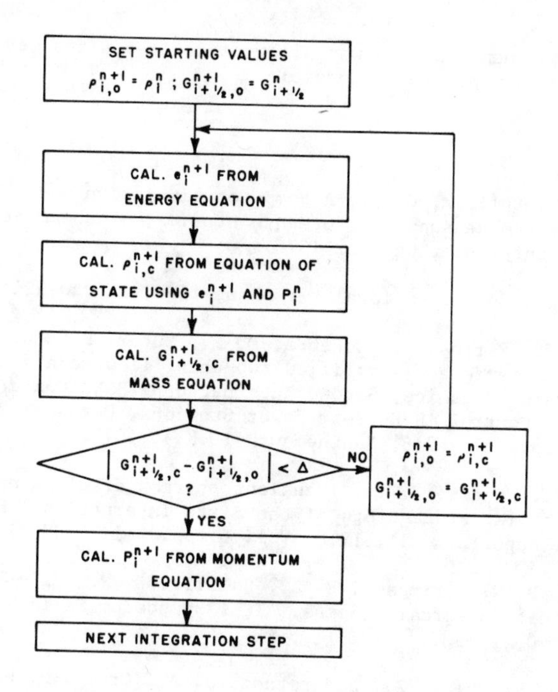

Fig. 7 Second Numerical Flow Chart

Simulation results obtained with this quick solution of the approximate model (Equations (1), (3), and (28)) have been compared to solutions obtained with the original model (Equations (1) to (3)) for similar disturbances in boundary conditions. The model responses were found to be almost identical except for the high-speed pressure waves in the first 50 milliseconds after an imposed disturbance. Therefore, it can be concluded that this simplified model is a useful, practical description of the physical phenomena taking place during transient evaporation or condensation.

6. CONCLUSIONS

An efficient numerical solution method has been found for the equations describing the main heat transfer and fluid flow phenomena in heat pump evaporators and condensers. This solution is based on:

-- an implicit finite difference technique

-- neglect of the acceleration terms in the model equations which are of minor importance while still preserving the major two-phase flow characteristics of fluid compressibility and thermal expansion

-- an appropriate choice of the independent variables (in this case, pressure and internal energy, as opposed to density and internal energy) which are calculated by the finite difference equations such that the form of the equation of state to be used is relatively insensitive to numerical discretization errors.

The solution found in this way allows time-step sizes several orders of magnitude larger than otherwise possible.

REFERENCES

1. Groff, G. C., Bullock, C. E., A computer simulation model for air-source heat pump system seasonal performance studies, Oklahoma State Heat Pump Technology Conference, October 1976.

2. Wallis, G. B., One-dimensional two-phase flow, McGraw-Hill, New York, 1969.

3. Dupont, J. F., Sarlos, G., LeFebre, D. M., Suter, P., Numerical comparison between a reference and simplified two-phase flow models as applied to steam generator dynamics, Second International BNES Conference on Boiler Dynamics and Control in Nuclear Power Stations, October 23 - 25, 1979, Preprints, pp. 207 - 216, Bournemouth (U.K.), 1979.

4. Banarjee, S., Hancox, W. T., Transient thermohydraulics analysis for nuclear reactors, Proceedings of the Sixth International Heat Transfer Conference, August 7 - 11, 1978, Vol. 6, pp. 311 - 338, Toronto, Canada, 1978.

5. Lyczkowski, R. W., Grimesey, R. A., Solbrig, C. W., Pipe blowdown analysis using explicit numerical schemes, AIChE Symposium Series 174, Vol. 74, pp. 129 - 140, 1978.

6. Lee, J. C., Akcasu, A. Z., Duderstadt, J. J., Crump, M. W., Fortino, R., Transient modeling of steam generator units in nuclear power plants: computer code, TRANSG-01, EPRI NP-1368, March 1980.

7. Bhat, B. L., Wedekind, G. L., Transient and frequency response characteristics of two-phase condensing flows: with and without compressibility, ASME Journal of Heat Transfer, Vol. 102, pp. 495 - 500, 1980.

8. Dhar, M., Soedel, W., Transient analysis of a vapor compression refrigeration system: Part I - The mathematical model, XV International Congress of Refrigeration, Paper B2-4, Venice, September 23 - 29, 1979.

9. Josiassen, N. J., Simulation of condition sequence during start-up of an evaporation refrigeration system, Proceedings of the 1978 Purdue Compressor Technology Conference, pp. 309 - 316, July 19 - 21, 1978.

10. Chi, J., Didion, D. A., A simulation model of a heat pump's transient performance, to be published in International Journal of Refrigeration.

THERMAL RADIATION

Numerical Methods in Radiation Heat Transfer

D.K. EDWARDS
University of California
Los Angeles, California

ABSTRACT

The general radiation heat transfer problem is reviewed. Radiant intensity, radiant flux, and radiant flux divergence (the volume heat sink or source due to thermal radiation) are related to the equation of transfer. In a numerical approach the requisite spherical angular integration is replaced by a sum. Fixed "discrete ordinates" (directions) may be used, or a Monte Carlo unbiased selection of ordinates made. Either selection can be used to compute volume-to-volume transfer factors for a finite-domain representation of the radiant volume heat source at mesh point i by summation over all other mesh points j. In the case of discrete ordinates, the full matrix of transfer factors may be avoided by introducing the radiant intensity (or partial flux) in each discrete direction as an additional dependent variable. This multiflux approach results in multiple radiation transfer matrices, but those matrices are banded.

Spectral integration is made numerically by summing over narrow or wide bands. Narrow- or wide-band scaling is then employed to account for nonhomogeneities (variations in radiant properties with temperature, pressure, and/or composition). Such scaling is easily incorporated into an iterative transfer factor volume-heat-source calculation scheme. In the multiflux approach, however, change in flux with an increment of path does not depend merely upon the magnitude of the flux and the conditions in the path increment, but upon the history of the flux as determined by path integrals, and radiation matrices lose their banded nature.

Special techniques for special circumstances include use of slab band absorptance and axial band absorptance in plane and circular duct flows. Numerical solutions for duct flows obtained using these quantities are summarized.

1. INTRODUCTION

The problem of incorporating radiation heat transfer within a participating medium into a reasonably general numerical model of convective fluid mechanics and heat transfer is a difficult one. On the one hand, the action-at-a-distance nature of radiation introduces geometrical difficulty. On the other hand, the rapid spectral variation in the gas absorption coefficient property introduces difficult physics. Neglect or oversimplification of either difficulty at best saps the resulting numerical model of its generality, and, at worst, renders the results erroneous and misleading.

The geometrical difficulty arises from the fact that radiation contributing to heating of a volume element arrives from all directions, and the intensity in a given direction is the integrated effect of a source function at each increment along the path. The spectral difficulty arises from the fact that the radiant heating is contributed by photons of all wavenumbers, and gas radiant properties often vary greatly and rapidly with wavenumber.

One way to attack numerically the directional problem is to select a set of fixed directions and approximate the integral over all directions by a sum over the chosen set of directions. This mode of attack goes by names such as "discrete ordinates" or "multifluxes" and "finite quadrature". In contrast is the Monte Carlo approach, in which the directions are not fixed but are randomly chosen. The random selection avoids inadvertant bias but requires a large number of random ordinates to achieve reasonable accuracy.

The usual way to attack numerically the spectral problem is to employ a "narrow band model" and invoke "narrow band scaling". At times a "wide band model" and "wide band scaling" are invoked to reduce the number of spectral calculations. A Monte-Carlo calculation scheme can readily accommodate narrow-band scaling to produce a workable radiation code. In the case of high-albedo scattering, a hybrid Monte-Carlo matrix-inversion technique appears attractive.

In a finite-domain approach, it appears necessary to use a two-level mesh, a coarse level for radiation, and a finer level for convection, for even when the geometrical and spectral problem are resolved, the radiation matrix is a full rather than diagonally-banded one. A three-dimensional 12 x 12 x 12 mesh-point problem leads to a 1728 x 1728 matrix completely filled with 2985984 radiation transfer factors. If the radiation subdivision is reduced to 3 x 3 x 3, the resulting matrix is 27 x 27 containing a more manageable 729 terms.

In special cases, predominantly cases of simple geometry, special techniques will continue to find favor. Moment methods, spherical harmonics, and embedding are examples. Of particular interest to this worker have been duct flow problems equivalent to the classical laminar and turbulent Graetz problems but including molecular radiation. There, with neglect of axial variations, good success has been achieved for both plane-parallel and circular black-walled ducts.

In what follows, there is first a review of the radiant intensity, radiant flux, and flux divergence concepts and the equation of transfer giving the radiant intensity. Discrete and Monte Carlo ordinates are discussed. An example of the type and magnitude of error in the often-used six-flux approximation is presented, and a more general multiflux approach is recommended. The discussion then turns to the spectral problem, and the concepts of narrow- and wide-band scaling are reviewed. Finally the one-dimensional radiant flux in the slab and cylinder is reviewed, and the duct flow solutions obtained to date summarized.

2. GEOMETRICAL CONSIDERATIONS

2.1 Radiant Intensity, Flux, and Flux Divergence

The spectral radiant intensity I is defined [1,2] as the power [Watts] per unit solid angle per unit area [m^2] normal to a beam, and per unit spectral band width. Spectral band width may be measured in terms of wavelength [μm], frequency [s^{-1}] or wavenumber [cm^{-1}]. The latter is usually preferred. Solid angle Ω (unitless steradians) is defined by area projected onto a sphere divided by the square of the sphere radius. In polar-azimuthal coordinates polar angle θ measures the angle of the beam from the z-axis and ϕ the angle from the projection of the beam onto the x-y plane from the x-axis. In these coordinates $d\Omega = \sin\theta d\theta d\phi$.

The z-component of the spectral radiant flux is the $\cos\theta d\Omega$ integral of radiant intensity I over 4π steradians,

$$q_z = \int_0^{4\pi} I\cos\theta d\Omega = \int_0^{2\pi}\int_0^{\pi} I\cos\theta\sin\theta d\theta d\phi \ . \tag{1}$$

For the x and y components $\cos\theta_x = \sin\theta\cos\phi$ and $\cos\theta_y = \sin\theta\sin\phi$. Accordingly

$$q_x = \int_0^{4\pi} I\cos\theta_x d\Omega = \int_0^{2\pi}\int_0^{\pi} I\sin^2\theta d\theta\cos\phi d\phi \ , \tag{2}$$

$$q_y = \int_0^{4\pi} I\cos\theta_y d\Omega = \int_0^{2\pi}\int_0^{\pi} I\sin^2\theta d\theta\sin\phi d\phi \ . \tag{3}$$

The spectral flux divergence is the volume heat sink [W/m^3] per unit band width. When one wishes to employ "scaling" as defined in Section 3, one prefers to look upon the flux divergence as the solid angle integral of the negative gradient along the beam of the incoming intensity I^-,

$$-\nabla\cdot q = \int_0^{4\pi} \frac{dI^-}{ds'} d\Omega \ , \tag{4}$$

where path s' measured along the beam locates the volume being heated and s" continues along the path to the value s at the end of the beam where it terminates at the wall of an enclosure. (If necessary an imaginary wall may be used to complete an enclosure.) The superscript on I^- denotes that the intensity is directed backwards in the direction from s to s'.

2.2 Equation of Transfer

The equation of transfer gives the change in I along slant path s'. In simplest form for local thermodynamic equilibrium and in the absence of scattering, it is

$$\frac{dI^+}{ds'} = k_a(I_b - I^+) \ , \tag{5}$$

where k_a is the spectral absorption coefficient [m^{-1}] and I_b is the Planck intensity

$$I_b = \frac{2hc^2\nu^3}{e^{hc\nu/kT}-1} \ . \tag{6}$$

Here a superscript plus is used to denote that I^+ is in the forward direction from s' to s. When scattering exists, a further extinction occurs and an additional source arises. For isotropic scattering

$$\frac{dI^+}{ds'} = -(k_a+k_s)I^+ + k_aI_b + k_sI_s \ , \tag{7}$$

where

$$I_s = \frac{1}{4\pi}\int_0^{4\pi} I^{\pm} d\Omega \; . \tag{8}$$

The solution to Eq. (5) (note that Eq. (7) is of the same form) is

$$I^+(s') = I_o e^{-\int_0^{s'} k_a ds'''} + \int_0^{s'} e^{-\int_{s''}^{s'} k_a ds'''} I_b(s'')k_a ds'' \; , \tag{9}$$

where I_o is the intensity at s' = 0. Similarly the back intensity is

$$I^-(s') = I_e e^{-\int_{s'}^{s} k_a ds'''} + \int_{s'}^{s} e^{-\int_{s'}^{s''} k_a ds'''} I_b(s'')k_a ds'' \; , \tag{10}$$

where I_e is the back intensity at the end of the path.

Integration by parts puts the back intensity in particularly convenient form,

$$I^-(s') = I_b(s') + [I_e - I_b(s)]e^{-\int_{s'}^{s} k_a ds''} + \int_{s'}^{s} e^{-\int_{s'}^{s} k_a ds''} \frac{dI_b(s'')}{ds''} ds'' \; . \tag{11}$$

Note that, if $dI_b(s'')/ds''$ is discontinuous, the integral is taken in the Stieltjes sense.

2.3 Discrete Ordinates

In special circumstances discussed in Section 4 it is possible to develop analytical expressions that incorporate or subsume the dΩ integration. But in general the integral is computed by "finite quadrature" [3,4],

$$\int_0^{4\pi} F(\theta,\phi) d\Omega = \sum_n a_n F(\theta_n,\phi_n) \; . \tag{12}$$

When azimuthal symmetry exists, the φ-integral becomes 2π, and the summation need be carried out only over θ directions. In this case just a few directions (say as few as three forward and three back [5]) suffice to give reasonable accuracy. If one is computing flux, equal weighting in dΩ is inappropriate. Usually equal weighting in cosθdΩ i.e., equal $\Delta\sin^2\theta$ increments, or Gaussian quadrature is preferred [3-6]. However, for a general 3-D case employing Eq. (4), equal weighting in dΩ does appear appropriate. Thus equal increments of Δcosθ and Δφ might be used.

2.4 An Example of a Poor Choice of On-Axis Ordinates

To gain insight into the question of ordinate selection consider a three-dimensional six-flux scheme, one in which the six directions are parallel to the forward and backward x, y, z axes. Suppose $-\nabla\cdot q$ is desired at the origin when an isothermal gas at temperature T_g is contained by black infinite parallel walls at $z = \pm\delta$. The wall temperature is T_w. Taking

$$-\nabla\cdot q \overset{?}{=} \sum_{n=1}^{6} \left(\frac{4\pi}{6}\right)\left(\frac{dI_n^-}{ds_n'}\right) , \tag{13}$$

gives in this instance

$$-\nabla\cdot q \overset{?}{=} \frac{4\pi}{3} [I_{bw}-I_{bg}]e^{-k_a\delta} . \tag{14}$$

In contrast the exact solution can be derived in terms of exponential integrals [7,2]

$$-\nabla\cdot q = 4\pi[I_{bw}-I_{bg}]E_2(k_a\delta) . \tag{15}$$

As the optical depth $t = k_a\delta$ goes to zero, both $\exp(-t)$ and $E_2(t)$ go to one. As t goes to infinity, both go to zero but $E_2(t)$ goes faster, as $\exp(-t)/t$. The grossest error, however, is the $4\pi/3$ coefficient versus the 4π exact value. The reason is not hard to discern: four of the six chosen ordinates are badly placed in the example.

In the case of a long cylinder aligned with the z-axis, a similar comparison would show that two of six ordinates aligned with the axes would be badly placed.

Remedies are to use Monte Carlo ordinates (Section 2.5 below) or place the discrete ordinates off-axis (Section 2.7). Increasing the number of ordinates, either random or fixed, generally increases accuracy.

2.5 Monte Carlo Ordinates

The Monte Carlo technique [8,9] employs a random-number (P) generator ($0 \leq P \leq 1$) to set the directions. If uniform weighting in $d\Omega$ is desired for Eq. (4), one equates

$$\cos\theta = 2P_1-1 , \tag{16}$$

$$\phi = 2\pi P_2 . \tag{17}$$

After N samplings, the sum of the N values of dI^-/ds^- (or whatever is desired) is multiplied by 4π and divided by N to yield the Monte Carlo estimate of the integral in Eq. (4). The probable deviation Δp of an outcome with probability p is related to N by [10]

$$N = (0.675/r^2)(1-p)/p , \quad r = \Delta p/p ;$$

$$\Delta p = [(0.675/N)(1-p)p]^{1/2} . \tag{18}$$

The maximum occurs when p is 0.5, and the maximum probable deviation goes as $0.41/\sqrt{N}$.

2.6 Radiation Transfer Factor Matrix

The net volume heat source at mesh point i is the sum of contributions from other mesh points j,

$$(-\nabla\cdot q)_i = \sum_j g_{i-j}(B_j-B_i) , \tag{19}$$

where

$$B_j = \pi I_{bj} . \tag{20}$$

The transfer factors g_{i-j} (or better $\mathscr{G}_{i-j} = V_i g_{i-j}$, for the $\mathscr{G}_{i-j}$ matrix is symmetric) can be found by marching backwards along the selected paths from point i. Around each mesh point j is an associated volume. A particular direction-ordinate pierces the volume from s_j' to s_j''. In the march from s_j' to s_j'', I_{bj} is taken to be $1/\pi$ (i.e., $B_j = 1$) and the contribution of dI^-/ds' at point i from the increment $s_j''-s_j'$ is g_{i-j}, given by Eqs. (4) and (11) to be

$$\Delta g_{i-j} = \frac{\Delta\Omega}{\pi} k_{ai} \left[e^{-\int_{s_i}^{s_j'} k_a ds'''} - e^{-\int_{s_i}^{s_j''} k_a ds'''} \right] . \tag{21}$$

As already stated, in a Monte Carlo calculation all the Δg_{i-j} contributions would be summed, multiplied by 4π and divided by N. Also in a Monte Carlo calculation, the source points would be randomly chosen in the associated volume around i.

Note that Eq. (21) gives the spectral transfer factor, and the equation is useful as it stands only for continuum absorption. Line effects are taken up in Section 3.

2.7 Off-Axis Multiflux Ordinates

The radiation transfer matrix generated via Eq. (21), or Eq. (45) in Section 3, is full. Thus if a 12 x 12 x 12 x-y-z grid is used, a full 1728 x 1728 matrix must be generated, and the volume heat source at each grid requires a sum over 1728 sources. An alternative, if discrete direction-ordinates are employed, is to introduce auxiliary dependent variables, the intensities or "fluxes" in each of the discrete directions. The equation of transfer, Eq. (5) or (7), for each direction is discretized and prescribes the corresponding flux. A difficulty is that the common method of computing explicitly in the downstream direction can no longer be employed, for the fluxes coming back from downstream are unknown. Hence an iterative or full implicit scheme is required.

Many alternative schemes of discretization can be imagined. Fundamental to many of them is finding the increments of Δx, Δy, and Δz associated with an increment of slant path Δs. The direction cosines of a unit vector along the slant path provides the answer. These are, as mentioned in conjunction with Eqs. (1)-(3),

$$s_{nx} = \sin\theta_n \cos\phi_n , \tag{22}$$

$$s_{ny} = \sin\theta_n \sin\phi_n , \tag{23}$$

$$s_{nz} = \cos\theta_n . \tag{24}$$

Subscript n denotes the nth of the multifluxes. For example, Eq. (5) expressed in back-difference form with linear interpolation becomes, from Eq. (9),

$$I_{n,i,j,k} = I_n' e^{-k_a \Delta s} + I_b' [1-e^{-k_a \Delta s}] , \tag{25}$$

where

$$I'_n = I_{n,i,j,k} - \frac{s_{nx}\Delta s}{\Delta x}[I_{n,i,j,k}-I_{n,i',j,k}] - \frac{s_{ny}\Delta s}{\Delta y}[I_{n,i,j,k}-I_{n,i,j',k}] - \frac{s_{nz}\Delta s}{\Delta z}[I_{n,i,j,k}-I_{n,i,j,k'}] , \tag{26}$$

and

$$i' = i-s_x , \quad j' = j-s_y , \quad k' = k-s_z , \tag{27}$$

$$s_x = s_{nx}/|s_{nx}| , \quad s_y = s_{ny}/|s_{ny}| , \quad s_z = s_{nz}/|s_{nz}| . \tag{28}$$

An expression similar to Eq. (26) with the subscript n replaced by subscript b gives I'_b. The values of Δx, Δy, Δz, and Δs are, of course, arbitrary. In a very simple numerical scheme they might all be equal to a common grid spacing h. Substitution of Eq. (26) into (25) and collection of terms completes the scheme.

The spectral value of the volume heat source due to radiation is computed from

$$(-\nabla\cdot q)_{i,j,k} = \left(\sum_n \Delta_n \Omega I_{n,i,j,k} - 4\pi I_{b,i,j,k}\right) k_a , \tag{29}$$

where the abosrption coefficient k_a is the local value at location x_i, y_j, z_k.

3. SPECTRAL CONSIDERATIONS

3.1 Continuum and Line Radiation

In a clear gas containing particulates or droplets of a condensed phase, the spectral absorption coefficient varies sufficiently slowly with wavenumber ν so that the total integrations necessary, viz.,

$$q_{Total} = \int_0^\infty q \, d\nu , \tag{30}$$

$$(-\nabla\cdot q)_{Total} = \int_0^\infty (-\nabla\cdot q) d\nu , \tag{31}$$

$$I_{n,Total} = \int_0^\infty I_n d\nu , \tag{32}$$

may be carried out numerically by summing over a number of discrete wavenumbers ν_k. In a polyatomic or asymmetric diatomic molecular gas, the same can be said at high temperatures and pressures. A gas such as CO_2 or H_2O has a few absorption bands (say 5) each having a spectral width of 10^2 or 10^3 cm^{-1}, and a few wavenumbers per band suffice. If the walls are nonisothermal, a few wavenumbers between bands are also needed. However, even when spectral integration is numerically feasible, one may wish to employ wide band scaling as described in Section 3.8 for greater economy.

Often true spectral integration is simply impossible, because the absorption coefficient varies several orders of magnitude again and again from wavenumber to wavenumber. Not only are the number of numerical calculations required too large for practical computation of a total value, but the requisite physical properties are unknown in sufficient detail. The only alternative is to employ a narrow- or wide-band model for which the band model parameters are known or can be estimated.

3.2 Narrow-Band Behavior

A narrow-band model provides the spectrally smoothed spectral transmissivity,

$$\bar{\tau} = \frac{1}{\Delta\nu}\int_{\nu-\Delta\nu/2}^{\nu+\Delta\nu/2} e^{-k_a s}\, d\nu , \tag{33}$$

in terms of the spectrally-smoothed absorption coefficient $\bar{k}_a$ and a line-width-to-spacing parameter η. The Goody model [1] prescribes

$$\bar{\tau} = \exp \frac{-\bar{k}_a s}{\sqrt{1+\bar{k}_a s/\eta}} , \tag{34}$$

where

$$\eta = \beta P_e . \tag{35}$$

The equivalent broadening pressure ratio P_e is given by [2]

$$P_e = \left\{(P/P_o)[1+(b-1)x_a]\right\}^n , \tag{36}$$

where P_o = 1 atm, b is the self-broadening coefficient, x_a is the mole fraction of absorbing species, and n is an empirically determined pressure-broadening exponent near unity. The relations account for the facts that lines are broadened by molecular collisions, and absorber-absorber collisions are more broadening than foreign-gas-absorber collisions.

The curve-of-growth, a plot of absorptivity $1-\bar{\tau}$ versus s or $X = \rho_a s$, shows marked departures from continuum behavior when the lines are narrow, that is, when η is small. In such a case, after a brief interval of linear behavior when $\bar{k}_a s$ is small compared to η, the curve of growth goes as

$$1-\bar{\tau} = 1-\exp(-\sqrt{\bar{k}_a s\beta P_e}) , \tag{37}$$

instead of

$$1-\bar{\tau} = 1-\exp(-\bar{k}_a s) , \tag{38}$$

for a continuum absorber. For example, when $\bar{k}_a s = 2$ and $\beta P_e = 0.05$, Eq. (37) gives an absorptivity of 0.27 instead of 0.86 from Eq. (38).

3.3 Curtis-Godson Approximation

The profound differences between the curves of growth for a line radiator and a continuum radiator require that the equations of Section 2 be spectrally smoothed before practical calculations be contemplated. Spectrally smoothing Eq. (10) gives

$$I^{-}(s') = I_e\bar{\tau}(s,s') + \int_{s'}^{s} -\frac{d\bar{\tau}(s'',s')}{ds''} I_b(s'')ds'' , \tag{39}$$

where $\bar{\tau}$ is the spectrally smoothed transmissivity of the nonhomogeneous gas along the slant path from s' to s. The Curtis-Godson approximation gives the nonhomogeneous gas transmissivity in terms of path-integrated quantities,

$$\xi = \int_{s'}^{s''} \bar{k}_a ds''' , \tag{40}$$

$$\zeta = \int_{s'}^{s''} \eta\bar{k}_a ds''' ; \tag{41}$$

$$\bar{\tau}(s'',s') = \exp\left\{\frac{-\xi}{\sqrt{1+\xi^2/\zeta}}\right\} . \tag{42}$$

Note that end-of-path intensity I_e must be from a continuum, or the path must be extended.

3.4 Wall-to-Gas Transfer Factor

Consider the impact of line structure upon the calculation of the wall-to-wall-to-gas transfer factors. A slant path from wall element i (at s' = 0) through the gas is traced back to its intersections with volume element j. As in Eq. (21) denote the near intersection as s_j' and the far one as s_j''. Then the contribution to $\mathcal{G}_{i-j}$ is

$$\Delta\mathcal{G}_{i-j} = A_i\varepsilon_i[\bar{\tau}(s_j',0)-\bar{\tau}(s_j'',0)] . \tag{43}$$

In a Monte Carlo calculation the points of origin and direction are chosen appropriately for a wall and the sum normalized.

After tracing back to a wall element w, a fraction $A_i\varepsilon_i\varepsilon_w\bar{\tau}(s_w,0)$ is scored to $\Delta\mathcal{G}_{i-w}$, and the specularly or diffusely reflected beam traced further, with s understood to be the combined path from original element i to the reflecting wall, and on backwards along the path to entry point s_j' and exit point s_j'' for volume element j. A further contribution is scored, according to Eq. (43) multiplied by the intervening wall reflectivity. The tracing is continued until the $\bar{\tau}\Pi\rho_w$ product is below a threshold value. Alternatively the wall reflections may be treated in the Monte Carlo sense with the wall-to-wall transfer factor scored with the full value of $\varepsilon_i\bar{\tau}(s_w,0)$ when random number P is less than ε_w or the ray regarded as wholly reflected if not.

Note that the impact of the line structure upon the calculation procedure is not great. For a continuum absorber, optical depth ξ must be integrated. With lines, both ξ and ζ are integrated.

3.5 Gas-to-Gas Transfer Factor

Differentiating Eq. (39) with respect to s' gives the gradient in I needed for Eq. (4),

$$\frac{dI^-}{ds'} = I_e \frac{d\bar{\tau}(s,s')}{ds'} - \bar{k}_a(s')I_b(s') + \int_{s'}^{s} - \frac{d^2\bar{\tau}(s'',s')}{ds'ds''} I_b(s'')ds'' . \tag{44}$$

In the increment of path from s_j' to s_j'' the source intensity $I_b(s'')$ is $1/\pi$, and the contribution to Eq. (4) is

$$\Delta \mathcal{G}_{i-j} = 4V_i \left\{ \frac{d\bar{\tau}(s_j',s')}{ds'} - \frac{d\bar{\tau}(s_j'',s')}{ds'} \right\} , \tag{45}$$

where, from differentiating Eq. (42),

$$\frac{d\bar{\tau}(s'',s')}{ds'} = \bar{k}_a(s')\bar{\tau}(s'',s') \frac{[1+\xi^3\eta(s')/\zeta^2]}{[1+\xi^2/\zeta^2]^{3/2}} . \tag{46}$$

If one compares Eqs. (45) and (46) with Eq. (21), one sees again that the main difference is the need to calculate running sums of ξ and ζ instead of just ξ.

3.6 Line Effects on Multiflux Calculations

While line effects can readily be incorporated into the calculation of transfer factors, it is not so for the intensities or multifluxes. To the Curtis-Godson approximation the forward-directed intensity is

$$I^+ = I_o\bar{\tau}(s,0) + \int_0^s \frac{d\tau(s,s')}{ds'} I_b(s')ds' , \tag{47}$$

and its derivative is

$$\frac{dI^+}{ds} = I_o \frac{d\tau(s,0)}{ds} + k_a(s)I_b(s) + \int_0^s \frac{d^2\tau(s,s')}{dsds'} I_b(s')ds' . \tag{48}$$

For continuum radiation the integral in Eq. (48) becomes identical to that in Eq. (47), so that dI/ds is related to I and I_b according to the equation of transfer. Here an incremental change in s requires recalculating the entire integral, not just adding an increment to it.

3.7 Wide-Band Models

Integration of Eq. (39) by parts for a black wall puts the equation into the form

$$I^-(s') = I_{bw}-[I_{bw}-I_b(s)][1-\bar{\tau}(s,s')] - \int_{s'}^{s} [1-\bar{\tau}(s'',s')]dI_b(s'') . \tag{49}$$

Spectral integration over isolated bands results in

$$\pi I^-_{Total}(s') = B_w - \sum_k [B_{wk}-B_k(s)]A_k(s,s') - \sum_k \int_0^s A_k(s'',s')dB_k(s'') , \tag{50}$$

where A_k is the (nonisothermal) wide band absorption [2]. The wide band absorption of the kth band is defined by

$$A_k(s'',s') = \int_{\nu_k-\Delta\nu}^{\nu_k+\Delta\nu} [1-\bar{\tau}(s'',s')]d\nu \; , \tag{51}$$

where $\Delta\nu$ can be taken to be indefinitely large without significant error. The divergence of the heat flux follows from Eq. (4),

$$-\nabla\cdot q_{Total} = \sum_k \frac{1}{\pi}\int_0^{4\pi}\left\{[B_{wk}-B_k(s)]\;\frac{dA_k(s,s')}{ds'} + \int_0^s \frac{dA_k(s'',s')}{ds'}\;dB_k(s'')\right\}d\Omega \; . \tag{52}$$

Band absorption A_k is expressed in terms of band absorptance A_k^* and band width parameter ω_k,

$$A_k = \omega_k A_k^*(t_{Hk},\eta_k) \; , \tag{53}$$

where band absorptance is a function of optical depth at the band head

$$t_{Hk} = \frac{\alpha_k X(s'',s')}{\omega_k} \; , \tag{54}$$

and line-to-width spacing parameter η_k. The quantity α_k is the integrated mean absorption coefficient on a mass basis, and X(s",s') is the integrated absorber-density-path-length product

$$X(s'',s') = \int_{s'}^{s''} \rho_a ds''' \; . \tag{55}$$

For the exponential band model with $\eta > 1$, the band absorptance becomes

$$A_k^* = ln\; t_{Hk} + E_1(t_{Hk}) + \gamma_e \; . \tag{56}$$

3.8 Wide-Band Scaling

For the nonhomogeneous gas, "scaled" values of α_k, ω_k, and η_k must be used in Eqs. (53) and (54). Scaling rules proposed by Edwards and Morizumi [11] differ somewhat from those proposed by Chan and Tien [12]. The former rules are

$$\xi_{1,k} = \int_0^X \alpha_k dX = \tilde{\alpha}_k X \; , \tag{57}$$

$$\xi_{2,k} = \int_0^{\xi_{1,k}} \omega_k d\xi_{1,k} = \tilde{\omega}_k \xi_{1,k} \; , \tag{58}$$

$$\xi_{3,k} = \int_0^{\xi_{2,k}} \eta_k d\xi_{2,k} = \tilde{\eta}_k \xi_{2,k} \; . \tag{59}$$

Use of wide-band absorption reduces the spectral integration to the sum over a few absorption bands.

3.9 Total Emissivity and Absorptivity

With reference to Eq. (50), one can define external and internal total absorptivities,

$$\alpha_e(s,s',T)\sigma T^4 = \sum_k B_k(T)A_k(s,s') \ , \tag{60}$$

$$\alpha_i(s'',s',T)4\sigma T^3 = \sum_k \frac{dB_k}{dT} A_k(s'',s') \ . \tag{61}$$

Then Eq. (52) can be written in terms of total properties, and no spectral integration remains. The difficulty is that rational total property scaling rules for the nonisothermal gas need development and validation. If one is satisfied with ascribing to the total property the characteristics of the principal band, one can write from Eqs. (57)-(59):

$$\alpha_e(s,s',T) = [\tilde{\omega}_k/\omega_k(T)]\varepsilon_e(\tilde{X},\tilde{P}_e,T) \ ; \tag{62}$$

$$\alpha_i(s,s',T) = [\tilde{\omega}_k/\omega_k(T)]\varepsilon_i(\tilde{X},\tilde{P}_e,T) \ ; \tag{63}$$

where, from equating t_{Hk}'s and η's,

$$X = [\omega_k(T)/\tilde{\omega}_k][\tilde{\alpha}_k/\alpha_k(T)]X \ , \tag{64}$$

and

$$\tilde{P}_e = \tilde{\eta}_k/\beta_k(T) \ . \tag{65}$$

Since all bands have the same $\omega_k(T)$ variation, there is no difficulty with the coefficients in Eqs. (62) and (63). However, not all the $\alpha_k(T)$ and $\beta_k(T)$ variations are the same from band to band. Nevertheless, there is an expectation of reasonable engineering accuracy from use of Eqs. (64) and (65) with k chosen to be the band that contributes the largest fraction of the total property.

4. SPECIAL GEOMETRIES

4.1 The Slab

Radiation heat transfer in a fluid contained between two parallel plates may often be treated to a good approximation as one-dimensional. When the Peclet number is large and/or volume heat sources vary slowly in the direction of flow, large streamwise x-grid increments compared to cross-stream y-grid spacings are called for, and slant paths only at very high θ-angles see upstream or downstream grid points. In such a case the slab band absorption [13] can be introduced to express spectral and solid-angle integrations in a single function. The slab band absorption is defined as

$$A_s(t_{Hk},\eta_k) = \int_{\nu_k-\Delta\nu}^{\nu_k+\Delta\nu} \frac{1}{\pi}\int_0^{2\pi}\int_0^{\pi/2} [1-\bar{\tau}(t,\eta_k)]\cos\theta\sin\theta \, d\theta \, d\phi \, d\nu \ , \tag{66}$$

where for the exponential wide-band model

$$t = (t_{Hk}/\cos\theta)\exp(-2|\nu-\nu_k|/\omega_k) \ . \tag{67}$$

For overlapped lines $\eta_k > 1$, the quantity may be expressed in terms of exponential integrals

$$A_s(t_{Hk}) = ln\ t_{Hk} + E_1(t_{Hk}) + \gamma_e + \frac{1}{2} - E_3(t_{Hk}) \ . \tag{68}$$

A particularly simple expression exists for the case of symmetrical temperature and composition profiles in a black-walled plane-parallel duct [14],

$$q_{Total} = \sum_{k=1}^{n} \int_0^\delta K^*(y,y')\omega_k B_k' \frac{\partial T}{\partial y'} dy' \ , \tag{69}$$

where B_k' denotes as before the derivative of the Planck function with respect to T at constant ν_k, and the kernel is

$$K^* = A_s^*(t_{Hk}(2-y^*-y^{*\prime})) - A_s^*(t_{Hk}|y^*-y^{*\prime}|) \ . \tag{70}$$

Here, t_{Hk} is based upon the half spacing δ between plates, and constant reference values of α_k and ω_k have been assumed.

4.2 The Cylinder

The idea of approximating radiation as one-dimensional is especially valid for a circular cylinder with high Peclet number and/or a slowly varying volume heat source. Unfortunately both angular integrations have not proved possible, but one angular integration and one spectral integration can be carried out. Wassel and Edwards [15] define and determine an axial band absorptance and give the radial heat flux in terms of it.

4.3 Numerical Solutions for Duct Flow

A number of solutions have been obtained through numerical means for flows of a radiating and conducting molecular gas flowing laminarly or turbulently in a black-walled plane-parallel or circular duct [14-24]. Entrance flow solutions were obtained by James and Edwards [23] and Balakrishnan and Edwards [24]. Radiation was treated in the linearized limit, e.g. [14], and with full nonlinearity and property variations [16,23].

If, instead of a molecular gas, one hypothesizes a gray gas and retains the one-dimensional radiation approximation, the problem becomes so simple that one can introduce complexity from another quarter, by the inclusion of scattering. For example, Sutton and Ozisik [25] have used an iterative technique and Chawla and Chan [26] a spline-collocation method. The problem of a molecular gas with scattering has only very recently been the subject of exploratory investigations, e.g. [27].

Consider the thermal entrance flow of a molecular gas for the plane-parallel duct illustrated in Fig. 1. The energy equation solved [24] in dimensionless form was

$$u^+ \frac{\partial\theta}{\partial x^*} = \frac{\partial}{\partial y^*} [\varepsilon_H^+ \frac{\partial\theta}{\partial y^*}] + R_{dm} \frac{\partial}{\partial y^*} (q^*_{Total}(y^*)) \ , \tag{71}$$

where $q_{Total}(y^*)$ is the dimensionless form of Eq. (69). The dimensionless radiative heat flux was approximated for numerical analysis by

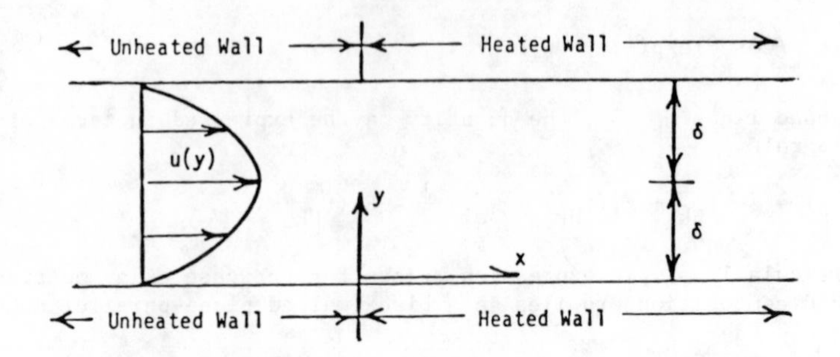

Fig. 1 Thermal Entrance Flow in a Black-Walled Plane Duct

$$q^*_{Total}(y^*_\ell) = \sum_{j=1}^{M+1} Q_{\ell,j} P_j \ , \tag{72}$$

where P_j is the y-direction central-difference temperature gradient,

$$P_j = \frac{\theta_{j+1} - \theta_{j-1}}{y^*_{j+1} - y^*_{j-1}} \ , \tag{73}$$

and $Q_{\ell,j}$ are coefficients found from

$$Q_{\ell,j} = \frac{1}{2}\,[R_{\ell,j+1} + R_{\ell,j}] \ , \tag{74}$$

$$Q_{\ell,1} = \frac{1}{2} R_{\ell,2} \ , \quad Q_{\ell,M+1} = \frac{1}{2} R_{\ell,M+1} \ , \tag{75}$$

where

$$R_{\ell,j} = \sum_{k=1}^{n} R_{\ell,j,k} \ , \tag{76}$$

$$R_{\ell,j,k} = \frac{1}{t_{Hk}} \Big\{ [S^*(t_{Hk}(2-y^*_\ell-y^*_{j-1})) - S^*(t_{Hk}(2-y^*_\ell-y^*_j))] - \left| S^*(t_{Hk}|y^*_\ell-y^*_j|) - S^*(t_{Hk}|y^*_\ell-y^*_{j-1}|) \right| \Big\} \ , \tag{77}$$

$$S^*(t) = \int_0^t A^*_s(t')dt' = t[\ln t + \gamma_e - \tfrac{1}{2}] + [1-E_2(t)] - [\tfrac{1}{3} - E_4(t)] \ . \tag{78}$$

The mesh arrangement is illustrated in Fig. 2. Fifty-one y-points, stacked more closely at the wall, were located in the half channel. The solution was marched in x, with increasing x-step sizes, and fully implicit in y. With coefficients a_j, b_j, c_j, d_j based upon values at the previous x-step, the energy equation at x_{i+1} is tridiagonal,

$$a_j\theta_{i+1,j+1} + b_j\theta_{i+1,j} + c_j\theta_{i+1,j-1} + d_j = 0 \ . \tag{79}$$

The Gauss-elimination algorithm is thus employed, marching from the wall cal-

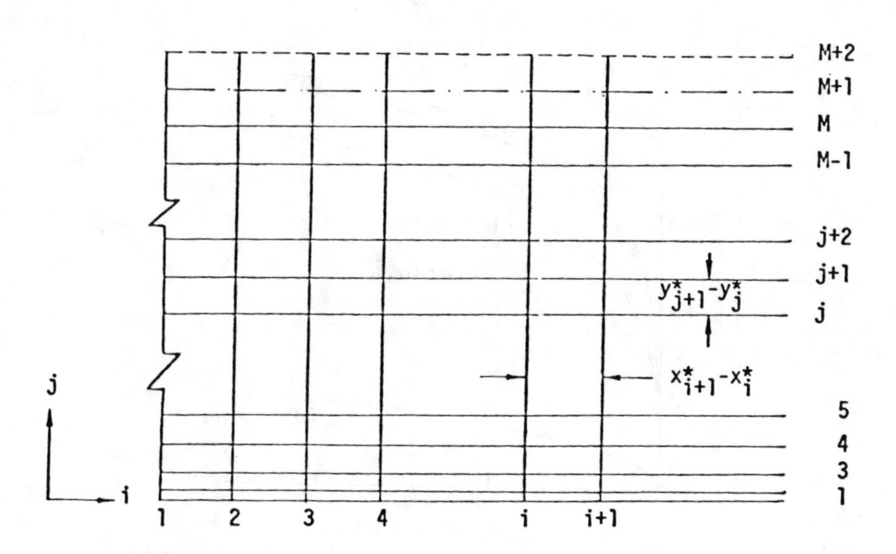

Fig. 2 Finite Difference Mesh

culating coefficients A_j, B_j and then marching back from the center calculating temperatures according to

$$\theta_{i+1,j} = A_j \theta_{i+1,j+1} + B_j \; , \tag{80}$$

where

$$A_j = \frac{-a_j}{b_j + c_j A_{j-1}} \; , \quad B_j = \frac{c_j B_{j-1} + d_j}{b_j + c_j A_{j-1}} \; , \tag{81}$$

$$A_2 = -a_2/b_2 \; , \quad B_2 = -d_2/b_2 \; . \tag{82}$$

The turn-around condition to start Eq. (80) follows from symmetry at the channel center.

Figure 3 presents sample results. At a fixed value of x*, increasing the radiation-to-conduction parameter causes the gas temperature to cool more toward the wall temperature. At the highly turbulent conditions shown, radiation thickens the wall boundary layer, so to speak, with the result that the convective (conductive) heat flux at the wall falls. Just the opposite occurs in the case of laminar flow.

In the linearized limit the inclusion of one-dimensional radiation has a rather negligible influence upon the computer-run costs. In fully-nonlinear variable-property cases the one-dimensional radiation calculations accounted for 40 per cent of the computational cost [23]. It should be emphasized that the radiation calculation included several bands of an H_2O-CO_2-N_2 combustion gas mixture whose composition as well as temperature varied in both directions.

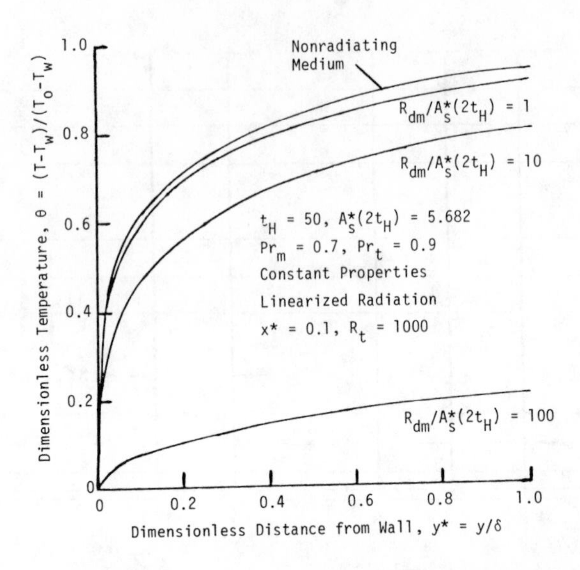

Fig. 3 Calculated Temperature Profiles

5. CONCLUSIONS

For general geometries the two main options discussed are the finite-domain (zone) approach and the multiflux approach. The former requires the computation of matrix elements in a full matrix. Such computation can be carried out, for example, with the Monte Carlo technique. In such a calculation full account can be taken of line structure at small additional cost in computation time.

The multiflux approach need not be restricted to six fluxes aligned with the principal coordinates. Examples discussed here, a thin large slab and a long cylinder, illustrate the error in doing so. Equations (22)-(29) presented here show how to apply the multiflux concept to more suitably aligned fluxes. However, it appears at this time that line structure cannot be accommodated in the multiflux approach. Even where the radiative coupling to, or influence upon, the temperature field is weak, so that an iterative approach with regard to the radiation may be taken, it is not apparent how to account correctly for line structure in the presence of diffusely reflecting walls without introducing the Monte Carlo approach.

For special geometries where one-dimensional radiation in adequate, the ability to solve the energy equation including radiation is well demonstrated. While calculations made to date have neglected line effects, the path toward doing so seems clear. When one-dimensional radiation was incorporated into plane-parallel or cylindrical duct flow problems, the additional computational cost associated with variable radiation properties and nonlinearity was found to be 40 per cent.

REFERENCES

1. R. M. Goody, Atmospheric Radiation, Oxford Press, London, 1964.

2. D. K. Edwards, Radiation Heat Transfer Notes, Hemisphere, Washington, D.C., 1981.

3. R. E. Bellman, R. E. Kalaba, and M. C. Prestrud, Invariant Imbedding and Radiative Transfer in Slabs of Finite Thickness, American Elsevier, New York, 1963.

4. T. J. Love, Radiative Heat Transfer, Merrill, Colombus, Ohio, 1968.

5. F. P. Incropera and W. G. Houf, "A Three-Flux Method for Predicting Radiative Heat Transfer in Aqueous Suspensions", J. Heat Transfer, 101, 497 (1979).

6. J. E. Rogers and D. K. Edwards, "Bidirectional Reflectance and Transmittance of a Scattering-Absorbing Medium with Rough Surface", Progr. Astronautics and Aeronautics, 49, 3 (1976).

7. V. Kourganoff, Basic Methods in Transfer Problems, Oxford Press, London 1952.

8. J. R. Howell, "Application of Monte Carlo to Heat Transfer Problems", Advances in Heat Transfer, 5, 1 (1966).

9. L. W. Stockham and T. J. Love, "Radiative Heat Transfer from a Cylindrical Cloud of Particles", AIAA Journal, 6, 1935 (1969).

10. J. V. Uspensky, Introduction to Mathematical Probability, McGraw-Hill, New York, 1937.

11. D. K. Edwards and S. J. Morizumi, "Scaling of Vibration-Rotation Band Parameters for Nonhomogeneous Gas Radiation", J. Quant. Spectrosc. Rad. Transfer, 10, 175 (1970).

12. S. H. Chan and C. L. Tien, "Total Band Absorptance of Nonisothermal Infrared Radiating Gases", J. Quant. Spectrosc. Rad. Transfer, 9, 1261 (1969).

13. D. K. Edwards and A. Balakrishnan, "Slab Band Absorptance for Molecular Gas Radiation", J. Quant. Spectrosc. Rad. Transfer, 12, 1379 (1972).

14. D. K. Edwards and A. Balakrishnan, "Nongray Radiative Transfer in a Turbulent Gas Layer", Int. J. Heat Mass Transfer, 16, 1003 (1973).

15. D. K. Edwards and A. T. Wassel, "The Radial Radiative Heat Flux in a Cylinder", J. Heat Transfer, 95, 276 (1973).

16. D. K. Edwards and A. Balakrishnan, "Self-Absorption of Radiation in Turbulent Molecular Gases", Combustion and Flame, 20, 401 (1973).

17. D. K. Edwards and A. Balakrishnan, "Radiative Cooling of a Turbulent Flame Front", J. Heat Transfer, 95, 433 (1973).

18. A. T. Wassel and D. K. Edwards, "Molecular Gas Band Radiation in Cylinders", J. Heat Transfer, 96, 21 (1974).

19. A. Balakrishnan and D. K. Edwards, "Radiative Flame Cooling for Reduction of Nitric Oxide Emissions", J. Heat Transfer, 96, 37 (1974).

20. A. Balakrishnan and D. K. Edwards, "Established Laminar and Turbulent Flow of a Radiating Molecular Gas", Heat Transfer 1974, Vol. I, pp. 93-97, 1974. (Proceedings of the Fifth International Heat Transfer Conference, Tokyo, September 3-7, 1974, published by the Japan Society of Mechanical Engineers.)

21. A. T. Wassel, D. K. Edwards, and I. Catton, "Molecular Gas Radiation and Laminar or Turbulent Heat Diffusion in a Cylinder with Internal Heat Generation", Int. J. Heat Mass Transfer, 18, 1267 (1975).

22. A. T. Wassel and D. K. Edwards, "Molecular Gas Radiation in a Laminar or Turbulent Pipe Flow", J. Heat Transfer, 98, 101 (1976).

23. R. K. James and D. K. Edwards, "Effect of Molecular Gas Radiation on a Planar, Two-Dimensional, Turbulent-Jet-Diffusion Flame", J. Heat Transfer, 99, 221 (1977).

24. A. Balakrishnan and D. K. Edwards, "Molecular Gas Radiation in the Thermal Entrance Region of a Duct", J. Heat Transfer, 101, 489 (1979).

25. W. H. Sutton and M. N. Ozisik, "An Iterative Solution for Anisotropic Radiative Transfer in a Slab", J. Heat Transfer, 101, 695 (1979).

26. T. C. Chawla and S. H. Chan, "Spline Collocation Solution of Combined Radiation-Convection in Thermally Developing Flows with Scattering", Numerical Heat Transfer, 3, 47 (1980).

27. R. O. Buckius, "Scattering Band Absorption for a Planar Medium", Am. Soc. Mech. Engrs. Paper 81-HT-61, presented at the 20th National Heat Transfer Conference, Milwaukee, August 1981.

Application of Finite Elements to Heat Transfer in a Participating Medium

MINOR L. NICE
Technical Center
Owens-Corning Fiberglas Corporation
Granville, Ohio

ABSTRACT

This paper applies finite element techniques to radiative transfer in one-dimensional systems containing an absorbing/emitting medium. The paper first considers radiative transfer without thermal conduction followed by an analysis of radiative transfer with thermal conduction included.

For the case of no conduction, it is shown that application of finite element techniques to the pure radiative problem recovers Hottel's exchange areas for one-dimensional systems, and it is concluded that the method of zoning as described by Hottel and Sarofim is, in fact, a finite element approximation to the governing integral equation.

Thermal conduction is added to the problem and, in this case, Galerkins method is applied to the governing nonlinear, integro-differential equation, and two methods are considered for the treatment of the radiation terms. The first consists of considering the temperature variable over each finite element while the second utilizes a constant temperature for evaluating the integral that appears in the radiative terms. For the variable element case, it is shown how a singularity in the kernel of the integral term of the governing equation can, with linear elements, be integrated without recourse to special numerical techniques. For the constant temperature case, the singularity poses no problem as it can be directly integrated.

1. INTRODUCTION

The transport of heat in the presence of a participating medium finds applications in many different fields. For example, the transport of heat in nuclear reactors [1] and the flow of heat in glass sheets [2,3] are two examples where absorption and emission of radiation can be important in determining the heat fluxes occurring within a system. In most instances, the equations necessary for describing the transport processes in the presence of a participating medium are known or can be derived. The difficulty that arises is solving the set of derived governing equations. This difficulty stems from the nature of the equations necessary for describing radiative processes in the presence of participating media; namely, integro-differential equations. This implies that, at any point within the solution domain, the solution is influenced by processes occurring throughout the entire solution domain. In addition, at system boundaries or interfaces, integral equations are again required to account for reflections and transmission of radiation, and the "global" nature of radiative transport again manifests itself. The net result of this "global" effect is to augment the role that geometry plays in the solution of this type of problem as compared to, for example, the solution of a set of differential equations and boundary conditions (i.e., a conventional boundary value problem). This geometry problem becomes especially acute for multidimensional systems of arbitrary geometry and is probably responsible for the lack of general purpose calculational procedures for problems involving radiative transport in an absorbing/emitting medium.

Within recent years finite element techniques have emerged and are being utilized to solve multidimensional field problems. One advantage of the technique is its capability for handling problems of arbitrary geometry, and it seems worthwhile to investigate this technique as a means for calculating radiative transport in view of the earlier discussion.

Since the author is not aware of such an application for finite elements, the simplest of problems was chosen for testing the technique. Specifically, the radiant heat transfer between parallel plates of infinite extent with a one-dimensional temperature distribution is considered. The problem of radiation between the plates both with and without conduction is addressed and only the simplest of boundary conditions are permitted--that of black walls at fixed temperatures.

2. FORMULATION

The problem considered is the heat transfer between two infinite parallel plates that bound a participating medium. The medium is considered to have a uniform absorption coefficient (independent of temperature, pressure and wavelength) and the walls are taken to be black at two different fixed temperatures. The coordinate system and geometry are shown in Fig. 1. The equation for the temperature distribution in this system has been derived elsewhere [4] and is given by

$$k_t \frac{d^2T}{dy^2} = 4\sigma a T^4(y) - 2\sigma a T_1{}^4 E_2(ay) - 2\sigma a T_2{}^4 E_2[a(D-y)] - 2\sigma a^2 \int_0^D T^4(y^*) E_1[a|y-y^*|]dy^*. \tag{1}$$

Here k_t represents the thermal conductivity and a is the absorption coefficient. T is temperature, σ the Stephan Boltzmann Constant while $E_2(aY)$, $E_2[a(D-y)]$ and $E_1[a|y-y^*|]$ are exponential integrals. T_1 and T_2 represent the two fixed wall temperatures. The boundary conditions are:

$$T = T_1 \text{ at } y = 0, \tag{1a}$$

$$T = T_2 \text{ at } y = D. \tag{1b}$$

Equation (1) can be cast into nondimensional form by defining the nondimensional variables $\Theta = T/T_1$ and $k = ay$. The resulting equation derived in [4] is

$$N\frac{d^2\Theta}{dk^2} = \Theta^4 - \frac{1}{2}E_2(k) - \frac{1}{2}\Theta_2{}^4 E_2(k_D - k) - \frac{1}{2}\int_0^{k_D} \Theta^4(k^*) E_1[|k-k^*|]dk^*. \tag{2}$$

$N = k_t a/4\sigma T_1{}^3$, $\Theta_2 = T_2/T_1$, $k_D = aD$.

In these variables the boundary conditions are

$$\Theta = 1.0 \text{ at } k = 0, \tag{2a}$$

$$\Theta \quad \Theta_2 \text{ at } k = k_D = aD. \tag{2b}$$

Two cases are now considered.

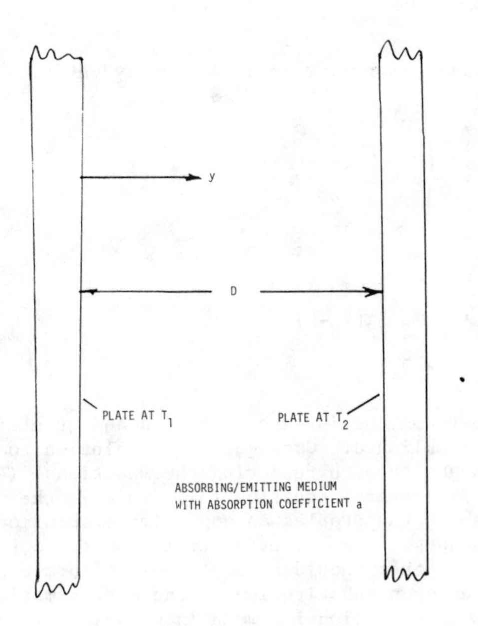

Fig. 1

2.1. Conduction Omitted

If conduction is omitted Eq. (2) becomes

$$\Theta^4(k) = \frac{1}{2}E_2(k) + \frac{1}{2}\,\Theta_2{}^4 E_2(k_D-k) + \frac{1}{2}\int_0^{k_D} \Theta^4(k^*)E_1[|k-k^*|]dk^*. \tag{3}$$

Since the equation is now an integral equation, no boundary conditions are required. Specifically, this equation is an inhomogeneous Fredholm integral equation of the second kind for the nondimensional temperature to the fourth power, Θ^4. It is to be noted that the kernel of the equation ($E_1[|k-k^*|]$) is symmetric and becomes infinite at $k = k^*$. This problem has been treated previously by various investigators [5,7] and the intent here is to approach the problem from a finite element point of view with the goal of putting this work in perspective with respect to these previous investigators. Specifically, it will be shown that using a finite element approximation for generating a solution to Eq. (3) the exchange areas utilized in Hottel's method of zoning [5] can be recovered.

Associated with Eq. (3) is a functional [6] whose stationary value yields (3). That is if

$$J = \int_0^{k_D} \int_0^{k_D} Q(k^*,k)\phi(k)\phi(k^*)dkdk^* - \int_0^{k_D} [\phi(k)]^2 dk + 2\int_0^{k_D} \phi(k)G(k)dk \tag{4}$$

with Q(k,k*) a symmetric kernel, then it is easily verified that minimizing J leads to

$$\phi(k) = G(k) + \frac{1}{2}\int_0^{k_D} Q(k,k^*)\phi(k^*)dk^* \tag{5}$$

Letting

$$\phi(k) = \Theta^4(k)$$

$$G(k) = \frac{1}{2}E_2(k) + \frac{1}{2}\Theta_2{}^4 E_2(k_D-k)$$

$$Q(k,k^*) = E_1[|k-k^*|],$$

the correspondence between the integral equation and quantities appearing in the functional are established. Consequently a solution to the problem being considered can be sought through rendering the functional (4) stationary as opposed to solving the integral equation (3). This is the path that will be followed here. To solve the problem an approximate solution is sought using finite element techniques. The criteria utilized for choosing the order of the polynomials is that they should be the simplest form consistent with the functional (4) in that upon substitution of the approximating polynomials in Eq. (4) the terms in the functional remain integrable. It is noted that no derivatives exist in the functional and that the above criteria will be satisfied for piecewise constant functions. Consequently a solution is sought by expanding the dependent variable, Θ^4, in terms of a set of piecewise constant basis functions $\psi_i(k)$. These functions have the following properties (see Fig. 2):

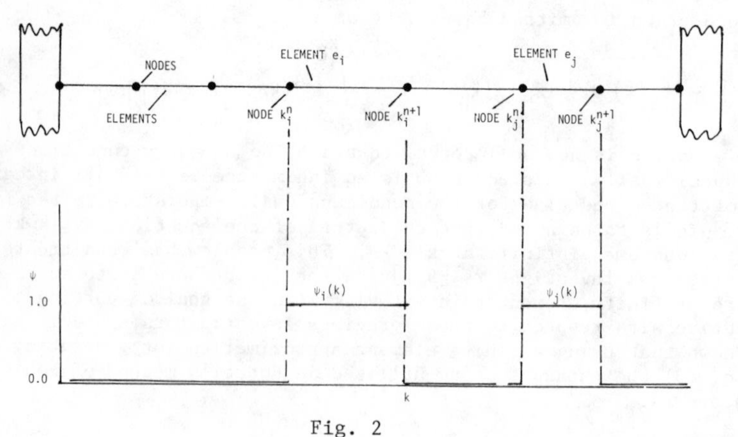

Fig. 2

$$\psi_i(k) = \begin{cases} 1.0 & k_i^n < k < k_i^{n+1} \\ 0.0 & k_i^n > k > k_i^{n+1} \end{cases}$$

at k_i^n

$$\lim_{k \to k_i^n \text{ from left}} \psi_i(k) \to 0 \quad ; \quad \lim_{k \to k_i^n \text{ from right}} \psi_i(k) \to 1$$

at k_i^{n+1}

$$\lim_{k \to k_i^{n+1} \text{ from right}} \psi_i(k) \to 0 \quad ; \quad \lim_{k \to k_i^{n+1} \text{ from left}} \psi_i(k) \to 1$$

and

$$\int_0^{k_D} \psi_i(k)\psi_j(k)dk = \begin{cases} 0 & i \neq j \\ k_i^{n+1} - k_i^n \end{cases}$$

With these definitions, the expansion for Θ^4 becomes

$$\Theta^4(k) = \sum_{i=1}^{NEL} C_i\psi_i(k). \quad NEL = \text{Number of elements.} \tag{6}$$

For clarity the functional is rewritten in the following form

$$J = \underbrace{\int_0^{k_D} \Theta^4(k) \left[\int_0^{k_D} E_1\left[\frac{|k-k^*|}{2}\right]\Theta^4(k^*)dk^* \right] dk}_{J^{(1)}} - \underbrace{\int_0^{k_D} [\Theta^4(k)]^2 dk}_{J^{(2)}} + \underbrace{2\int_0^{k_D} [\tfrac{1}{2}E_2(k) + \tfrac{1}{2}\Theta_2{}^4E_2(k_D-k)\Theta^4(k)dk.}_{J^{(3)}} \tag{7}$$

Each of the components of J, as indicated in Eq. (7), can now be evaluated by substituting the approximate solution, (6), into the functional. The final results are

$$J^{(1)} = \sum_{j=i}^{NEL} \sum_{i=1}^{NEL} C_i C_j F_{ij}, \tag{8}$$

$$F_{ij} = \int_{e_i} \int_{e_j} \frac{E_1|(k-k^*)|}{2} dk^* dk, \tag{8a}$$

$$J^{(2)} = \sum_{i=1}^{NEL} C_i^2 (k_i^{n+1} - k_i^n) \tag{9}$$

$$J^{(3)} = \sum_{i=1}^{NEL} \frac{C_i}{2} [E_3(k_i^n) - E_3(k_i^{n+1})] + \frac{C_i \Theta_2^4}{2} [E_3(k_D - k_i^{n+1}) - E_3(k_D - k_i^n)]. \tag{10}$$

Note that F_{ij} is symmetric ($F_{ij} = F_{ji}$). The complete functional is given by $J = J^{(1)} - J^{(2)} + 2J^{(3)}$ and forming $\partial J/\partial C_i = 0$, i = 1, NEL, yields the following matrix system for the unknown coefficients C_i.

$$[F]\{C\} - \lceil L \rfloor C + \frac{1}{2}\{E_3(k_i^n) - E_3(k_i^{n+1})\} + \frac{1}{2}\Theta_2^4 \{E_3(k_D - k_i^{n+1}) - E_3(k_D - k_i^n)\} = 0. \tag{11}$$

The matrix [F] is a square symmetric matrix whose elements are F_{ij} and $\lceil L \rfloor$ is a diagonal matrix of element lengths. {C} is the vector of unknown coefficients in the expansion for Θ^4. Now multiplying Eq. (11) by four and evaluating the elements of the matrix [F] from Eq. (8a), a comparison of the terms in (11) can be made with the one-dimensional exchange areas as presented in Hottel and Sarofim [5]. Adopting the notation convention presented in [5] for media to media exchanges ($\overline{g_i g_j}$) and surface to media exchanges ($\overline{g_i s_j}$), the following equivalences can be established

$$4F_{ij} = \overline{g_i g_j}, \tag{12}$$

$$4F_{ij} = \overline{g_j g_j}. \tag{13}$$

The terms in the column vectors of (11)(multiplied by four) involving E_3 are merely the gas to surface exchange areas ($\overline{g_i g_j}$) as presented in [5].

To complete this section representative results are presented for the distribution of emissive power between the plates (Fig. 3). In this figure the symbols represent results obtained for this problem as presented in [7]. For ease of comparison the results are plotted in terms of a nondimensional emissive power, $\overline{\phi}$, nondimensional distance Y/D and optical thickness $k_D = aD$, where ϕ is given by $\overline{\phi} = (\Theta^4 - 1.0/(\Theta_2^4 - 1.0)$.

For further details concerning the derivation of terms in the matrix [F] the reader is referred to Appendix A.

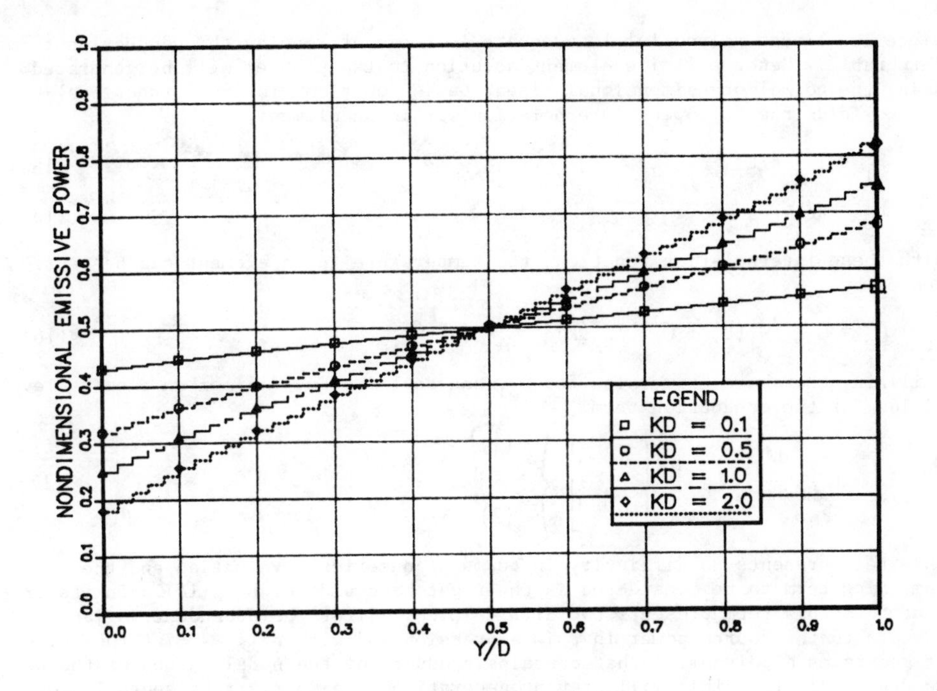

Fig. 3 Emissive Power Distribution Parallel Plates
50 Constant Temperature Elements

2.2. Conduction Included

When conduction is included the character of the problem changes significantly in that now second order derivatives appear in the equation and the dependent variable appears to both the first and fourth power--the problem becomes nonlinear, and Galerkins Procedure is utilized for deriving the finite element matrix equations.

The Galerkin discretized approximation is generated from Eq. (14) that follows. This equation results from the weak form of Eq. (2) that has been integrated by parts with a subsequent application of boundary conditions to yield

$$\int_0^{k_D} N \frac{d\Theta}{dk} \frac{dW_i}{dk} dk = -\int_0^{k_D} W_i[\Theta^4 - \frac{1}{2} E_2(k) - \frac{1}{2} \Theta_2 E_2(k_D-k) - \frac{1}{2} \int_0^{k_D} \Theta^4(k^*)E_1[|k-k^*|]dk^*]dk. \tag{14}$$

In this equation the W_i represent an appropriate basis function for representing the dependent variable Θ.

Again as in the previous section, a solution is sought in terms of piecewise polynomials and since the highest order derivatives in (14) are first, a piecewise linear polynomial is adequate in terms of keeping the conduction term integrable. Hence a finite element solution to the problem will be generated using the normal one-dimensional linear basis functions (or roof functions) which yields the following interpolation within an element

$$W_1 = 1 - \bar{k}/L \tag{15a}$$

$$W_2 = \bar{k}/L. \tag{15b}$$

With these interpolation functions the temperature in an element can be represented by

$$\bar{\Theta}_e = \bar{\Theta}_e^{(1)} W_1(\bar{k}) + \bar{\Theta}_e^{(2)} W_2(\bar{k}) \tag{16}$$

Utilizing the above expression for $\bar{\Theta}_e$, and applying Eq. (14) on an element level yields for the conduction term

$$\int_e N \frac{d\Theta}{dk} \frac{dW_i}{dk} dk = \frac{N}{L} \begin{bmatrix} 1 & -1 \\ -1 & 1 \end{bmatrix} \begin{Bmatrix} \bar{\Theta}_e^{(1)} \\ \bar{\Theta}_e^{(2)} \end{Bmatrix}. \tag{17}$$

This term presents no difficulty in terms of numerical evaluation and the only remaining term to be considered is the right hand side of Eq. (14). In its present form this term presents two difficulties. First the dependent variable appears to the fourth power in this expression and with a linear interpolation, it generates a polynomial that contains products of the nodal values of the dependent variable. This will prevent generation of a matrix representation of this term that can be written as a product of a coefficient matrix with a column vector of the unknown nodal variables. An alternative view that circumvents this problem is to consider the radiation term as a forcing function that is known from some initial guess or previous solution and utilize iteration for solution to the system of resulting equations. Pursuing this approach Eq. (14) generates the following equation for the finite element model of the system at the element level

$$[K_{COND}] \begin{Bmatrix} \bar{\Theta}_e^{(1)} \\ \bar{\Theta}_e^{(2)} \end{Bmatrix} = \frac{-1}{N} \begin{Bmatrix} \int_e W_1(\bar{k}) R_e(\bar{k}) d\bar{k} \\ \int_e W_2(\bar{k}) R_e(\bar{k}) d\bar{k} \end{Bmatrix}. \tag{18}$$

Here $R_e(\bar{k})$ is the value of the radiation terms on the right hand side of Eq.(14) at a point $\bar{k}$ within an element where $\bar{k}$ is measured from the local element coordinate system. This same quantity at a point k as measured from the global coordinate system is designated as R(k) where

$$R(k) = \Theta^4(k) - \frac{1}{2}E_2(k) - \frac{1}{2}\Theta_2{}^4 E_2(k_D - k)$$
$$- \frac{1}{2} \int_0^{k_D} \Theta^4(k^*) E_1[|k-k^*|] dk^*. \tag{19}$$

Physically the terms in the column vector on the right hand side of Eq. (18) represent the delegation of the weighted average of the net radiative flux into an element to the element's nodes.

The second difficulty in the evaluation of R(k) (or $R_e(\bar{k})$ in the local element coordinate system) stems from the presence of the integral term in R(k). At certain points of the solution domain $E_1[|k-k^*|]$ becomes infinite (at $k=k^*$). This behavior is demonstrated in Fig. 4. Shown in this figure is the solution domain divided into a number of finite elements along with a hypothetical temperature distribution. Writing the integral terms in R(k) as a sum of integrals over the complete solution domain,

$$\int_0^{k_D} \Theta^4(k^*)E_1[|k-k^*|]dk^* = \sum_{i=1}^{NEL} \int_e \Theta_e^{\,4}(k^*)E_1(|k-k^*|)dk^*, \tag{20}$$

it is easily seen that the integral over the element that brackets the discontinuity in $E_1[|k-k^*|]$ creates the problem. Physically this element integral represents the radiant heat flux per unit volume into point k of the element as a result of emission from the medium within the element itself. Fortunately for the linear approximation chosen a method for evaluating this integral can be formulated without recourse to special numerical techniques. This method consists of calculating the right hand side for a finite number of points within each element (4 were utilized to generate the following results) and utilizing the functional values of R(k) at these discrete points as representing the variation of R(k) over each element. To evaluate R(k) at the selected points, a coordinate system is erected at the point being considered and the integral term in the expression for R(k) is broken into two components

$$\int_0^{k_D} \Theta^4(k^*)E_1[|k-k^*|]dk^* = \int_0^{k} \Theta^4(k^*)E_1(k-k^*)dk + \int_k^{k_D} \Theta^4(k^*)E_1(k^*-k)dk^*. \tag{21}$$

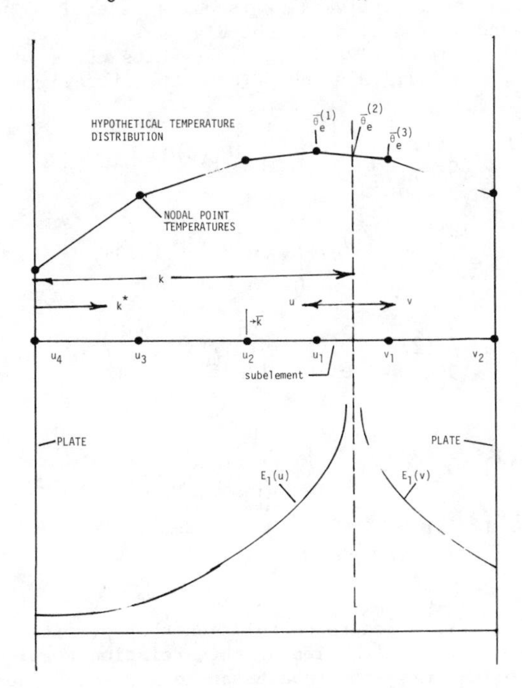

Fig. 4

The integral from 0 to k is transformed to an integral with u as the variable of integrations where u = k-k* and the integral from k to k_D is transformed to v variables where v = k*-k (see Fig. 4). Taking for example the integral from 0 to k in Eq. (21), applying the transformation and writing the integral as a sum of integrals over each finite element yields

$$\int_0^k \Theta^4(u)E_1(u)du = \underbrace{\int_0^{u_1} \Theta_{sub}^4(u)E_1(u)du}_{I_1(u)} + \int_{u_1}^{u_2} \Theta_e{}^4(u)E_1(u)du + \dots \quad (22)$$

The integral from 0 to u_1 (designated $I_1(u)$) represents an integration over a subelement and it is this integral that causes the difficulty due to the presence of the discontinuity in $E_1(u)$ at the lower limit of integration. This integral can be handled as follows. The linear interpolation for Θ over an element is transformed to a linear interpolation over the subelement and subsequently raised to the fourth power. This yields a polynomial in u/u_1 given by

$$\begin{aligned}\Theta_{sub}^4(u) = {} & [\overline{\Theta}_e{}^{(2)} - \overline{\Theta}_e{}^{(1)}]^4 (u/u_1)^4 - 4[\overline{\Theta}_e{}^{(2)}][\overline{\Theta}_e{}^{(2)} - \overline{\Theta}_e{}^{(1)}]^3 (u/u_1)^3 \\ & + 6[\overline{\Theta}_e{}^{(2)}]^2 [\overline{\Theta}_e{}^{(2)} - \overline{\Theta}_e{}^{(1)}]^2 (u/u_1)^2 \\ & - 4[\overline{\Theta}_e{}^{(2)}]^3 [\overline{\Theta}_e{}^{(2)} - \overline{\Theta}_e{}^{(1)}](u/u_1) + [\overline{\Theta}_e{}^{(2)}]^4.\end{aligned} \quad (23)$$

In this relation $\overline{\Theta}_e{}^{(2)}$ is the value of the dependent variable at the point within the element for which the radiative flux is being determined and $\overline{\Theta}_e{}^{(1)}$ is the nodal value at the end of the element (see Fig. 4). When Eq. (23) is substituted for $\Theta_{sub}^4(u)$ in $I_1(u)$ a sum of five integrals results whose integrands contain products of $(u/u_1)^j$, j = 0,1,2,3,4 and $E_1(u)$. Specifically

$$\begin{aligned}I_1(u) = {} & (\overline{\Theta}_e{}^{(2)} - \overline{\Theta}_e{}^{(1)})^4 \int_0^{u_1} (u/u_1)^4 E_1(u)du \\ & - 4\overline{\Theta}_e{}^{(2)}(\overline{\Theta}_e{}^{(2)} - \overline{\Theta}_e{}^{(1)})^3 \int_0^{u_1} (u/u_1)^3 E_1(u)du \\ & + 6[\overline{\Theta}_e{}^{(2)}]^2 [\overline{\Theta}_e{}^{(2)} - \overline{\Theta}_e{}^{(1)}]^2 \int_0^{u_1} (u/u_1)^2 E_1(u)du \\ & - 4[\overline{\Theta}_e{}^{(2)}]^3 [\overline{\Theta}_e{}^{(2)} - \overline{\Theta}_e{}^{(1)}] \int_0^{u_1} (u/u_1)E_1(u)du \\ & + [\overline{\Theta}_e{}^{(2)}]^4 \int_0^{u_1} E_1(u)du.\end{aligned} \quad (24)$$

Chandrasekhar [8] presents a recursion relation that permits integration of integrals of this form and utilization of this relation results in an expression that is a function of u_1 only--the subelement length (see Appendix B for further details). The remainder of the element integrals in Eq.

22 are well behaved and can be numerically integrated. A similar treatment for the integral from k to k_D (Eq. (21)) yields an evaluation procedure for the integral term in R(k). This procedure combined with an evaluation of the remaining terms for the forcing function produces a discrete distribution for the radiant heat loads when distributed to the element grid points through the use of Eq. (18) produce upon assembly from the local element system into the global system, a matrix equation of the form

$$[COND]\{\Theta\}^{[i+1]} = \frac{-1}{N}\{R\}^{[i]}. \tag{25}$$

where the [i] designates the forcing function evaluated from the $[i^{th}]$ iteration.

The previous discussion has centered about the evaluation of the integral term in the forcing function R(k) when the temperature is taken as a variable over each element. A simplification results if this temperature is taken to be constant in the integral term of Eq. (19). For this condition the quantity $\Theta_e^4(u)$ in each of the element integrals of Eq. (22) can be removed from the integral and each integral evaluated directly. For example, the integral over the subelement $I_1(u)$ becomes for this approximation

$$I_1(u) = \bar{\bar{\Theta}}_e^{\,4} \int_0^{u_1} E_1(u)du. \tag{26}$$

Here $\bar{\bar{\Theta}}_e^{\,4}$ (the constant nondimensional temperature) is taken to be the average of the fourth power of the nodal point temperatures of the element over which the integration is being performed. Equation (26) can be integrated directly to yield

$$I_1(u) = \bar{\bar{\Theta}}_e^{\,4}(1 - E_2(u_1)). \tag{27}$$

This relation is much simpler than the corresponding relation for $I_1(u)$ when the temperature is permitted to vary over each element (Eq. (24)). It is expected that this approximation will be reasonable if the variations, within an element, of the fourth power of the nondimensional temperature are small compared to variations in $E_1(u)$.

In the results that follow, solutions are presented for both constant and variable temperature elements.

3. NUMERICAL CONSIDERATIONS

All results presented in this paper were generated on an IBM Model 370/158 in single precision. For the inversion of the system of equations, a routine for tridiagonal systems based on Gaussian elimination and given in Carnahan, Luther and Wilkes [9] was utilized. All numerical integrations were performed using the IBM subroutine QSF.

For the type of iteration proposed for solution of the nonlinear system of equations that result from combined radiation and conduction, difficulty in obtaining convergence can occur for large values of the forcing function (small values of N--see Eq. (25)). To circumvent this problem, the temperature vector used for evaluating R(k) on each iteration was underrelaxed by

$$\{\Theta_{wt.}\}^{[i]} = (1 - \beta)\,\{\Theta\}^{[i]} = \beta\{\Theta\}^{[i-1]}, \tag{28}$$

where β is the underrelaxation parameter lying between 0 and 1. For the cases presented in this paper β was taken to be zero for values of N between infinity and .07 and varied between .7 and .95 for values of N between .07 and .01 (smallest value considered).

Convergence was determined by calculating the difference between successive solutions and prescribing, for iteration termination, a tolerance of 1.0×10^{-4} for the maximum allowable difference between elements of the solution vectors.

The number of iterations required for convergence varied depending upon the value of N chosen. For values of N greater than .10, 10 to 15 iterations were typical while at values of N approaching .01, 30 to 50 iterations might be required. A run requiring 50 to 60 iterations would typically require 5 minutes of CPU time.

4. RESULTS

The results presented in this paper are for calculated temperature distributions and heat fluxes. For comparison purposes a subset of the results presented in [10] has been selected for comparing the temperature calculated using finite elements. For heat flux calculations results in [1] have been chosen as a standard for comparison.

The calculated temperature distributions are shown in Figs. 5 through 8. The results represent solutions for an optical thickness (k_D) of one, and nondimensional wall temperature values of 1.0 and .10. For these values of optical thickness and boundary conditions, the temperature gradients between the plates can become large as N becomes small, and these conditions provide a good test of the method. The temperature distributions shown are for 5, 10, 20 and 29 variable temperature elements. The figures for 5, 10 and 20 elements are for equispaced nodes while for the 29 element case the mesh was graded. For this case,

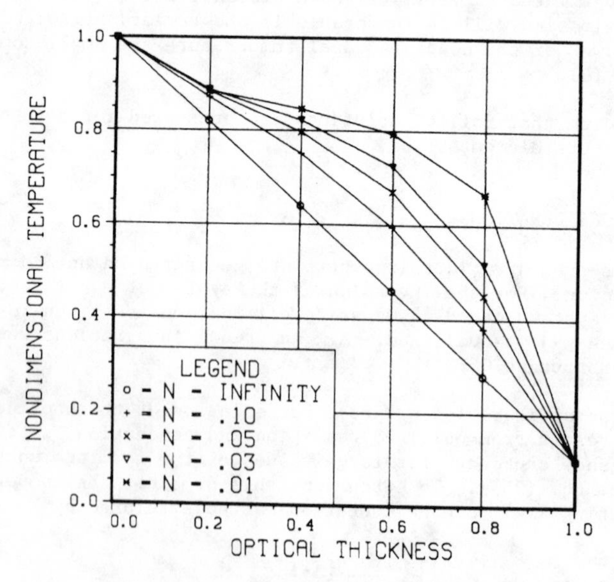

Fig. 5 Temperature vs. Optical Thickness
5 Variable Temperature Elements

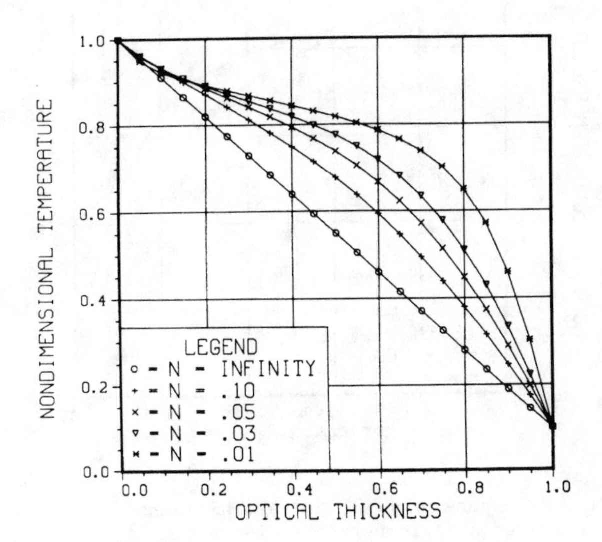

Fig. 6 Temperature vs. Optical Thickness
10 Variable Temperature Elements

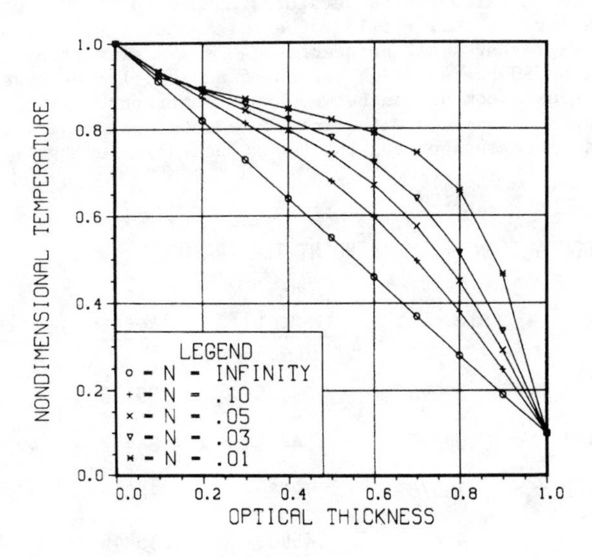

Fig. 7 Temperature vs. Optical Thickness
20 Variable Temperature Elements

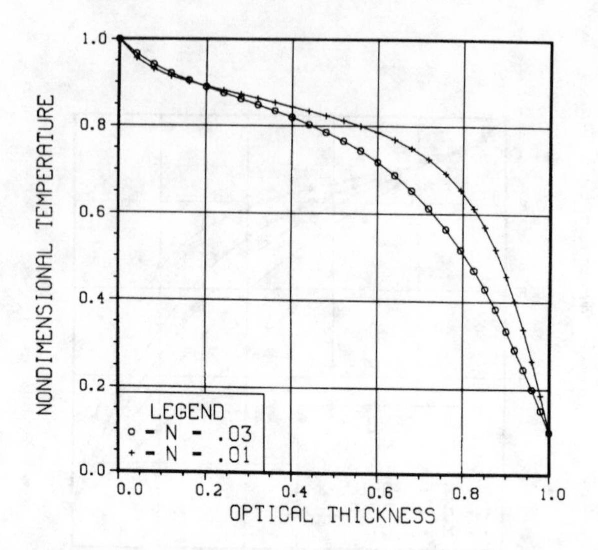

Fig. 8 Temperature vs. Optical Thickness
29 Variable Temperature Elements

the element lengths varied between .04 and .02 with elements graded in length from k = 0 to k = k_D. For the 29 element case, plots are presented only for N = .01, .02 and .03 since these conditions represent the cases for the steepest gradients. As a point of interest with respect to these temperature distributions, Table 1 shows nodal point temperatures common to 5, 10, 20, 29 and 40 element solutions for N = .01. It is to be noted that the nodal point temperature variations are rather small between the 40 and 5 element discretizations. For example, at k = .60 the solution for the 5 and 40 element cases vary by only 2.28%. Table 2 shows a comparison between the temperatures presented in reference [1] and those calculated with finite elements and comparison of the values shows good agreement between the two solution procedures.

TABLE 1
COMPARISON OF NODAL POINT TEMPERATURES

k	5 elements	10 elements	20 elements	29 elements	40 elements
.20	.89043	.89093	.89125	.89128	.89128
.40	.85409	.84516	.84459	.84452	.84442
.60	.80472	.78876	.78720	.78699	.78680
.80	--	.46201	.45900	.45845	.45817

TABLE 2

COMPARISON OF RESULTS FROM REFERENCE [10] (VISKANTA AND GROSH) AND FINITE ELEMENT SOLUTIONS TO ONE-DIMENSIONAL CONDUCTION-RADIATION EQUATION WITH 20 FINITE ELEMENTS

k	Reference [10] N = 1.00	Finite Element Solution 20 (elements) N = 1.00
0.0	1.000	1.0000
.10	.910 ± .003*	.91373
.20	.820 ± .003	.82883
.30	.740 ± .003	.74296
.40	.655 ± .003	.65613
.50	.570 ± .003	.56768
.60	.480 ± .003	.47746
.70	.387 ± .003	.38546
.80	.293 ± .003	.29175
.90	.198 ± .003	.19654
1.00	.1000	.10000

k	Reference [10] N = .100	Finite Element Solution N = .100
0.0	1.000	1.0000
.10	.925 ± .003	.93012
.20	.865 ± .003	.87092
.30	.810 ± .003	.81304
.40	.748 ± .003	.75055
.50	.685 ± .003	.67895
.60	.595 ± .003	.59481
.70	.500 ± .003	.49541
.80	.380 ± .003	.32946
.90	.248 ± .003	.24718
1.00	.1000	.1000

k	Reference [10] N = .01	Finite Element Solution N = .01
0.0	1.000	1.0000
.10	.920 ± .003	.92179
.20	.890 ± .003	.89125
.30	.865 ± .003	.86789
.40	.840 ± .003	.84459
.50	.815 ± .003	.81887
.60	.785 ± .003	.78720
.70	.740 ± .003	.73996
.80	.640 ± .003	.65018
.90	.450 ± .003	.45900
1.00	.1000	.10000

*Error results from determination of values from solution curves in Reference [10].

Comparison of results between the constant and variable temperature elements are presented in Table 3. The largest difference between the constant and variable element cases occurs for the 5 element case at a value of N = .01. For meshes finer than those generated by the 10 element case, no discernable differences occurred between the results generated by the two solution techniques.

The heat flux results are presented in Table 4. These results were calculated from the variable temperature element solutions using the following equation derived in [4]

$$\frac{q}{\sigma T_1^{\,4}} = -4N\frac{d\Theta}{dk}\Big|_{k=0} + 1 - 2\Big[\Theta_2^{\,4}E_3(k_D) + \int_0^{k_D} \Theta^4(k^*)E_2(k^*)dk^*\Big]. \qquad (29)$$

TABLE 3
COMPARISON BETWEEN CONSTANT TEMPERATURE ELEMENTS AND VARIABLE TEMPERATURE FINITE ELEMENTS

5 Finite Elements, N = 0.10

Optical Thickness	Temp. CTE	Temp. VTE	% Difference
0.00	1.000	1.000	--
0.20	0.814	.871	.34
0.40	.758	.752	.80
0.60	.604	.596	1.34
0.80	.386	.380	1.58
1.00	.100	.100	--

5 Finite Elements, N = 0.01

Optical Thickness	Temp. CTE	Temp. VTE	% Difference
0.00	1.000	1.000	--
0.20	.890	.884	.68
0.40	.854	.847	.83
0.60	.805	.795	1.26
0.80	.688	.667	3.15
1.00	.100	.100	--

10 Finite Elements, N = .10

Optical Thickness	Temp. CTE	Temp. VTE	% Difference
0.00	1.000	1.000	--
0.10	.930	.930	--
0.20	.872	.871	--
0.30	.814	.813	--
0.40	.752	.750	--
0.50	.681	.679	--
0.60	.597	.595	--
0.70	.497	.496	--
0.80	.381	.380	--
0.90	.248	.247	--
1.00	.100	.100	--

10 Finite Elements, N = .01

Optical Thickness	Temp. CTE	Temp. VTE	% Difference
0.00	1.000	1.000	--
0.10	.921	.919	.22
0.20	.892	.891	.11
0.30	.870	.868	.23
0.40	.847	.845	.23
0.50	.822	.820	.24
0.60	.791	.787	.51
0.70	.746	.743	.40
0.80	.659	.654	.76
0.90	.467	.462	1.08
1.00	.100	.100	--

TABLE 4
HEAT FLUXES

	5 elements	10 elements	20 elements	29 elements	40 elements	41 elements	42 elements	43 elements
	$\Theta_2 = .10,\ k_D = 1.0,\ N = .10$							
q_c	.25806	.27736	.29704	--	.30752	.31480	.31760	.31840
q_r	.64476	.64733	.64812	--	.64838	.64842	.64842	.64842
q_t	.90282	.92469	.94516	--	.95590	.96322	.96602	.96682
	$\Theta_2 = .10,\ k_D = 1.0,\ N = .01$							
q_c	.02191	.03225	.04129	.04381	.04824	.05384	.05600	.05712
q_r	.54899	.56897	.57208	.57247	.57298	.57315	.57316	.57316
q_t	.57090	.60122	.61337	.61628	.62122	.62699	.62915	.63028

The quantity on the left hand side of the above equation $(q/\sigma T_1^4)$ is the nondimensional heat flux and is represented in Table 4 by q_t. The quantity q_c in Table 4 represents the conduction flux while q_r gives the radiative flux,

$$q_c = -4N\frac{d\Theta}{dk}\Big|_{k=0}, \tag{30}$$

$$q_r = 1.0 - 2.0[\Theta_2^{\ 4}E_3(k_D) + \int_0^{k_D} \Theta^4(k^*)E_2(k^*)dk]. \tag{31}$$

The various fluxes for the test case are shown in Table 4. The 5, 10, 20 and 40 element cases all represent meshes with equispaced nodes while the 29, 41, 42 and 43 element solutions represent graded meshes. The 41, 42 and 43 element cases all represent discretizations that are graded at the wall. These three meshes correspond respectively to the following nodal locations to k = .025; 41 elements - k = 0.0, 0.01, 0.025; 42 elements - k = 0.00, 0.005, 0.010, 0.025; 43 elements - k = 0.00, 0.0025, 0.005, 0.010, 0.025. Beyond k = 0.25 the nodes were equispaced at k =.025, .050, .075, .100, .125....1.00. As Table 4 indicates, the convergence of the radiant fluxes is more rapid than the conductive fluxes and this, in turn, forces the mesh refinement at the wall if an accurate value of q_c is to be obtained. It is worth noting for N = .01 that even though the total flux shows little change between the 42 and 43 element case (.18%) the difference in the component heat fluxes indicates that the conductive flux changes are still at about 2%. This implies that the convergence of the heat fluxes should not be judged or determined by the convergence of the total flux alone. Both conduction and radiation fluxes should be examined as well as the relative sizes of the two fluxes and these in conjunction with the accuracy desired in the solution. If accurate conduction fluxes are required, mesh refinement near the wall is necessary, whereas if only accurate radiative fluxes are required, coarser meshes might be adequate. To conclude the results for the heat flux calculations discussed above, Fig. 9 shows temperature distributions for the 43 element mesh refinement at the wall at values of N = .10 and .01.

For purposes of comparison with other investigators, the results in Table 4a are presented. For these results, the boundary condition at k_D = 1.0 has been changed to Θ = .5 and the 43 element discretization was utilized for calculating the fluxes. The results generated using finite elements are compared to those presented in [1] and generated by using collocation. The results in the column headed Crosbie and Viskanta also come from [1] and the original reference for these results is [11]. Comparison of the results shows good agreement among the three investigators.

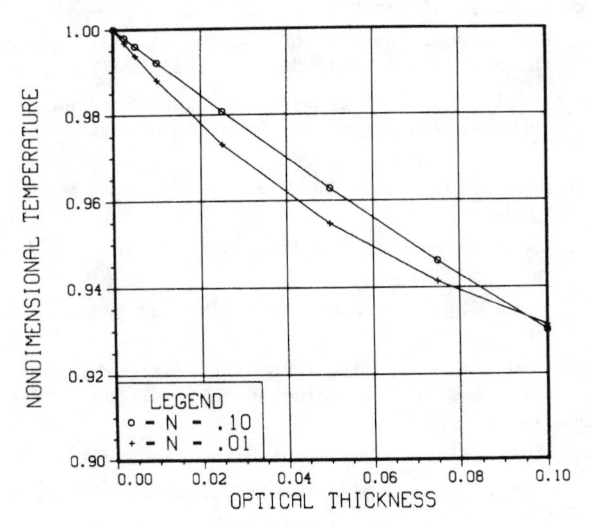

Fig. 9 Mesh Refinement at Wall
43 Variable Temperature Elements

TABLE 4a
Θ_2 = .50, k_D = 1.0

	Crosbie & Viskanta q_t	Chawla & Chan q_t	Finite Element q_t
N = 0.0	.7694	.7694	.7685
N = .010	.5675	.5675	.5665

5. SUMMARY AND CONCLUSIONS

This paper has presented the application of the finite element technique to a combined conduction-radiation problem in the presence of a participating medium.

For the case of pure radiation, application of the technique produces the one-dimensional exchange areas as defined by Hottel and Sarofim [5], and comparison of emissive power distributions between infinite parallel plates shows good agreement with the results of previous investigators.

For the case of combined conduction and radiation with linear elements, a procedure has been presented that combines analytical and numerical techniques for treating a singularity that occurs in the governing differential-integral equation. Temperature distributions have been presented for both a variable and a simplified, constant temperature element, and for meshes finer than those corresponding to 10 elements, the difference between the constant and variable element temperature distributions are practically negligible. The comparisons of temperature distributions and heat fluxes with those generated by previous investigators have all shown good agreement.

6. REFERENCES

1. Chawla, T.C. and Chan, S.H., Solution of radiation conduction problems with collocation method using B-splines as approximating functions, Int.J. Heat Mass Transfer 1979, Vol. 22, pp. 1657-1667.

2. Granger, Chui K., Gardon, Robert, Interaction of radiation and conduction in glass, Journal of the American Ceramic Society 1969, Vol. 52, No. 16, pp. 548-553.

3. Gardon, Robert, Calculation of temperature distributions in glass plates undergoing heat treatment, Journal of the American Ceramic Society 1958, Vol. 41, No. 6, pp. 200-208.

4. Siegel, Robert and Howell, John R., Thermal Radiation Heat Transfer, McGraw Hill 1972, pp. 628-660.

5. Hottel, H.C., and Sarofim, A.F., Radiative Transfer, McGraw Hill 1967, pp. 256-296.

6. Hildebrand, Frances B., Methods of Applied Mathematics, Prentice Hall Inc. 1965, pp. 222-336.

7. Usisken, C.M., and Sparrow, E.M., Thermal radiation between parallel plates separated by an absorbing-emitting nonisothermal gas, Int.J. Heat Mass Transfer, Vol. 1, pp. 28-36, 1960.

8. Chandrasekhar, S., Radiative Transfer, Dover, New York 1960, p. 373.

9. Carnahan, B., Luther, H.A., and Wilkes, J.O., Applied Numerical Methods, Wiley 1969, pp. 446.

10. Viskanta, R., and Grosh, R.J., Heat transfer by simultaneous conduction and radiation in an absorbing medium, J. Heat Transfer, Vol. 84, No. 1, 1962, pp. 63-72.

11. Crosbie, A.L., and Viskanta, R., Interaction of heat transfer by conduction and radiation in a nongray planar medium, Warme-Und Stroffuberlragung 4, 1971, pp. 205-212.

Due to space limitations, Appendices A and B have been omitted.

COMBUSTION AND FIRES

A Numerical Finite-Difference Study of the Oscillatory Behavior of Vertically Vented Compartments

K. SATOH*, J.R. LLOYD, K.T. YANG, and A.M. KANURY
Department of Aerospace and Mechanical Engineering
University of Notre Dame
Notre Dame, Indiana 46556

ABSTRACT

A numerical finite-difference study has been carried out in two and three dimensions for turbulent buoyant flow in a square compartment with floor and ceiling vents. A volumetric heat source is located either at the center of the floor or at the lower left corner of the compartment. Oscillatory behaviors have been found in the flow and temperature fields for the cases with center heat source, while for cases with heat source at the lower left corner, oscillations only occur during the initial transient period and are thereafter quickly damped out. The physical origin of these oscillations is noted. Results for one of the cases are also shown in terms of the effect of heat source strength on the frequency of oscillations.

1. INTRODUCTION

The importance of the effect of venting on the growth of compartment fires and removal of combustion gases from the compartment is now well recognized. Venting horizontally through vertical openings such as doorways and windows has been extensively studied since the pioneering work of Kawagoe [1]. Despite the general existence of ceiling and floor vents in compartments, studies on vertical venting through horizontal openings are essentially nonexistent. The correspon-ding venting characteristics could be quite different from those of horizontal venting since the general flow orientation through these vents is related to buoyancy generated by the compartment fire. A numerical study has recently been carried out to specifically address the vertical venting problem. Six geometries relative to various floor and ceiling vent combinations and locations of the fire source has been dealt with in the numerical study. Steady-state time-averaged results for a two-dimensional rectangular compartment with a volumetric heat source on the floor have been given in Ref. [2]. It has been found that in most of the cases studied, the long-time behaviors of the energy, flow, and pressure fields within the compartment are oscillatory.

Additional numerical experiments have been carried out herein to delineate the effects of vertical vent locations, heat source location and strength, and compartment aspect ratio as well as two and three dimensional effects on the oscillatory behaviors. The purpose of this paper is to present the results of these numerical experiments which can be used to develop coherent theories for the origin of the oscillations in vented compartment fires.

---

*Currently at Fire Research Institute, Tokyo, Japan

2. NUMERICAL EXPERIMENTS

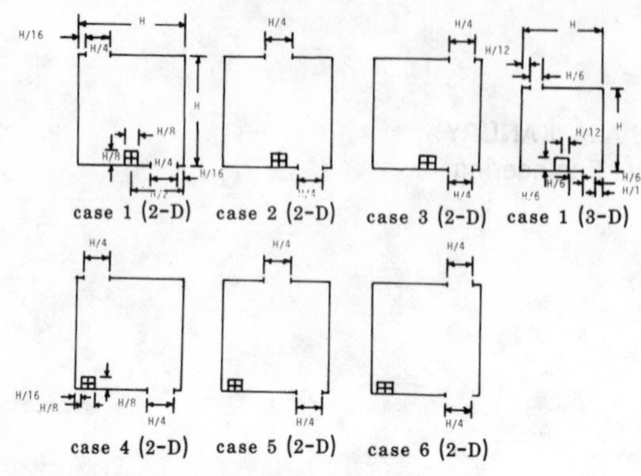

Fig. 1: Compartment Geometries

The basic square compartment and vent geometries and the location and size of the volumetric heat source used in the numerical experiments are shown in Fig. 1. Detailed numerical computations are based on a differential field model which takes into account strong buoyancy, turbulence, and compressibility. The finite-difference UNDSAFE-II computer code based on the use of primitive variables is utilized in the present study for the two-dimensional cases. Details are already given in Refs. [3-5] and hence only a brief outline will be presented herein.

For two-dimensional turbulent buoyant flow in a rectangular enclosure, the governing differential equations in the physical variables are known and have been given in Reference [3]. The equations may be reduced to dimensionless forms by introducing the following definitions:

$$\tilde{x} = \frac{x}{H}, \quad \tilde{y} = \frac{y}{H}, \quad \tilde{t} = \frac{U_R t}{H},$$
$$\tilde{u} = \frac{u}{U_0}, \quad \tilde{v} = \frac{v}{U_0}, \quad \tilde{T} = \frac{T}{T_0}, \tag{1}$$
$$\tilde{\rho} = \frac{\rho}{\rho_0}, \quad \tilde{\rho}_E = \frac{\rho_E}{\rho_0}, \quad \tilde{P} = \frac{P-P_E}{\rho_0 V_0^2},$$

where the subscripts 0 and E refer to reference quantities and the ambient condition, respectively. The governing equations may now be written as follows:

$$\frac{\partial\tilde{\rho}}{\partial\tilde{t}} + \frac{\partial}{\partial\tilde{x}}(\tilde{\rho}\tilde{u}) + \frac{\partial}{\partial\tilde{y}}(\tilde{\rho}\tilde{v}) = 0 \tag{2}$$

$$\frac{\partial}{\partial\tilde{t}}(\tilde{\rho}\tilde{u}) + \frac{\partial}{\partial\tilde{x}}(\tilde{\rho}\tilde{u}^2) + \frac{\partial}{\partial\tilde{y}}(\tilde{\rho}\tilde{u}\tilde{v}) = -\frac{\partial\tilde{p}}{\partial\tilde{x}} + \frac{\partial\tilde{\tau}_{xx}}{\partial\tilde{x}} + \frac{\partial\tilde{\tau}_{xy}}{\partial\tilde{y}} \tag{3}$$

$$\frac{\partial}{\partial\tilde{t}}(\tilde{\rho}\tilde{v}) + \frac{\partial}{\partial\tilde{x}}(\tilde{\rho}\tilde{u}\tilde{v}) + \frac{\partial}{\partial\tilde{y}}(\tilde{\rho}\tilde{v}^2) = -\frac{\partial\tilde{p}}{\partial\tilde{y}} - \frac{gH}{U_0^2}(\tilde{\rho}-\tilde{\rho}_E) + \frac{\partial\tilde{\tau}_{xy}}{\partial\tilde{x}} + \frac{\partial\tilde{\tau}_{yy}}{\partial\tilde{y}} \tag{4}$$

$$\frac{\partial}{\partial\tilde{t}}(\tilde{\rho}\tilde{T}) + \frac{\partial}{\partial\tilde{x}}(\tilde{\rho}\tilde{u}\tilde{T}) + \frac{\partial}{\partial\tilde{y}}(\tilde{\rho}\tilde{v}\tilde{T}) = -\nabla\cdot\tilde{q}_c + \nabla\cdot\frac{1}{Re_t Pr_t}\tilde{\nabla}\tilde{T} \tag{5}$$

where

$$\tilde{\tau}_{xx} = \frac{2}{Re_t}\frac{\partial \tilde{u}}{\partial \tilde{x}} , \quad \tilde{\tau}_{xy} = \frac{1}{Re_t}\left(\frac{\partial \tilde{u}}{\partial \tilde{y}} + \frac{\partial \tilde{v}}{\partial \tilde{x}}\right) , \quad \tilde{\tau}_{yy} = \frac{2}{Re_t}\frac{\partial \tilde{v}}{\partial \tilde{y}} \tag{6}$$

and

$$Re_t = \frac{\rho_0 U_0 H}{\mu_{eff}} , \qquad Pr_t = \frac{\mu_{eff} C_{p0}}{k_{eff}}$$

In the present study, an algebraic turbulence model for recirculating buoyant flows with large variations in the turbulence level is employed. In dimensionless form, it may be written as

$$\frac{\mu_{eff}}{\mu_0} = 1 + \frac{\left\{\left(\frac{\partial \tilde{u}}{\partial \tilde{y}}\right)^2 + \left(\frac{\partial \tilde{v}}{\partial \tilde{x}}\right)^2\right\}^{1/2} \left(\frac{\ell}{H}\right)}{2 + \frac{Ri}{Pr_t}} \tag{7}$$

where μ is the molecular viscosity and ℓ is the mixing length given by

$$\frac{\ell}{H} = k \frac{(\tilde{u}^2 + \tilde{v}^2)^{1/2}}{\left\{\frac{\partial \tilde{u}}{\partial \tilde{x}} + \frac{\partial \tilde{u}}{\partial \tilde{y}} + \frac{\partial \tilde{v}}{\partial \tilde{x}} + \frac{\partial \tilde{v}}{\partial \tilde{y}}\right\}^{1/2}} + \frac{\left\{\left(\frac{\partial \tilde{u}}{\partial \tilde{x}}\right)^2 + \left(\frac{\partial \tilde{u}}{\partial \tilde{y}}\right)^2 + \left(\frac{\partial \tilde{v}}{\partial \tilde{x}}\right)^2 + \left(\frac{\partial \tilde{v}}{\partial \tilde{y}}\right)^2\right\}^{1/2}}{\left\{\left(\frac{\partial^2 \tilde{u}}{\partial \tilde{x}^2}\right)^2 + \left(\frac{\partial^2 \tilde{u}}{\partial \tilde{y}^2}\right)^2 + \left(\frac{\partial^2 \tilde{v}}{\partial \tilde{x}^2}\right)^2 + \left(\frac{\partial^2 \tilde{v}}{\partial \tilde{y}^2}\right)^2\right\}^{1/2}} \tag{8}$$

and k is the von Kármán constant. Ri is the gradient Richardson number which is given by

$$Ri = \frac{Hg\left(\frac{\partial \tilde{T}}{\partial \tilde{y}}\right)}{U_0^2\left(\frac{\partial \tilde{u}}{\partial \tilde{y}}\right)^2} \tag{9}$$

where g is the gravitation constant.

With the turbulent Prandtl number taken to be unity, the effective turbulent conductivity is related to the turbulent viscosity by the following expressions:

$$\frac{k_{eff}}{\mu_0 C_{p0}} = \frac{1}{Pr} + \frac{1}{Pr_t}\left\{\frac{\mu_{eff}}{\mu_0} - 1\right\} \tag{10}$$

It suffices to give only a brief account of the numerical scheme, using the energy equation (5) as an example. The integral form of Equation (5) for a fixed control volume can be written as

$$\frac{d}{dt}\int_V \tilde{\rho}\tilde{T}dV = -\oint_S \tilde{\rho}\tilde{T}\tilde{U}_n dS - \oint_S \tilde{q}_c \cdot \underline{n}dS \tag{11}$$

where V and S denote the volume and surface of the dimensionless control volume, respectively, and $\tilde{U}_n$ is the normal velocity component and $\underline{n}$ is the outward unit normal vector. The finite-difference domain nomenclature is such that points P, E, W, N and S are located in the center of the cells' domain and points e, w, n and s are at domain boundaries.

By introducing the mass fluxes:

$$G_e = (\tilde{\rho}\tilde{u})_e \qquad G_w = (\tilde{\rho}\tilde{u})_w$$
$$G_n = (\tilde{\rho}\tilde{v})_n \qquad G_s = (\tilde{\rho}\tilde{v})_s \tag{12}$$

The upwind differencing scheme is used to determine the relationship between a node and its boundaries, e.g.

$$\tilde{T}_e = \begin{cases} \tilde{T}_P & \text{if} \quad G_e > 0 \\ \tilde{T}_E & \text{if} \quad G_e < 0 \end{cases} \tag{13}$$

The energy flux on the boundaries is given by

$$\tilde{T}_e G_e = \frac{1}{2}\tilde{T}_P (G_e + |G_e|) + \frac{1}{2}\tilde{T}_E (G_e - |G_e|) \tag{14}$$

and the conduction flux is given by a central difference, e.g.

$$(\tilde{q}_x)_e = -\frac{\tilde{u}_t}{Pr_t}\frac{(\tilde{T}_E - \tilde{T}_P)}{\Delta\tilde{X}} \tag{15}$$

The energy finite difference equation can be shown to have the following general form, similar to that of the momentum equations:

$$\left(A_P + \frac{\tilde{\rho}_P^o \Delta\tilde{X}\Delta\tilde{Y}}{\Delta\tilde{t}}\right)\tilde{T}_P = A_E\tilde{T}_E + A_W\tilde{T}_W + A_S\tilde{T}_S + A_N\tilde{T}_N + SU \tag{16}$$

when

$$A_E = \frac{1}{2}(|G_e| - G_e)\Delta\tilde{Y} + \frac{(\tilde{\mu}_t)_e\Delta\tilde{Y}}{Pr_t\Delta\tilde{X}}$$

$$A_W = \frac{1}{2}(|G_w| + G_w)\Delta\tilde{Y} + \frac{(\tilde{\mu}_t)_w\Delta\tilde{Y}}{Pr_t\Delta\tilde{X}}$$

$$A_N = \frac{1}{2}(|G_n| - G_n)\Delta\tilde{X} + \frac{(\tilde{\mu}_t)_n\Delta\tilde{X}}{Pr_t\Delta\tilde{Y}} \tag{17}$$

$$A_S = \frac{1}{2}(|G_S| + G_S)\Delta\tilde{X} + \frac{(\tilde{\mu}_t)_s\Delta\tilde{X}}{Pr_t\Delta\tilde{Y}}$$

$$A_P = A_E + A_W + A_N + A_S$$

3. NUMERICAL PROPERTIES

A concise criterion for numerical stability is difficult to obtain. In the present study, the following criterion based on the two-dimensional differencing scheme with upwind differencing for the convection terms [6] is used as a guideline for selecting the time step in the two-dimensional cases:

$$\Delta t \leq \frac{1}{\frac{2}{Re_t}\left\{\frac{1}{\Delta\tilde{x}^2} + \frac{1}{\Delta\tilde{y}^2}\right\} + \frac{|\tilde{u}|}{\Delta\tilde{x}} + \frac{|\tilde{v}|}{\Delta\tilde{y}}} \tag{18}$$

In addition, the limiting Courant number

$$\frac{|\tilde{u}_{max}|\Delta\tilde{t}}{\Delta\tilde{x}} \leq 1 \tag{19}$$

is also accomodated as a check. In the upwind differencing scheme used in the present study, numerical errors due to false diffusion can be expected at large cell Peclet numbers given by

$$Pe = \frac{\rho_o C_{po}|\tilde{u}|\Delta\tilde{x}}{k_{eff}} \quad \text{or} \quad \frac{\rho_o C_{po}|\tilde{v}|\Delta\tilde{y}}{k_{eff}} \tag{20}$$

However, due to the relatively large effective thermal diffusivity values which include the turbulent contribution, the cell Peclet numbers encountered range up to about 20 in the two-dimensional cases, and hence the effect of false diffusion is not expected to be serious. In the three-dimensional calculations, the velocity component in the third dimension becomes large only at the end-wall openings, and the flow moves essentially in the direction along the wall, thus also tending to minimize the false diffusion effects.

The same code has also been generalized to the three-dimensional cases with a simple turbulent viscosity model. For the two-dimensional compartment 16 cells by 16 cells (H x H) are used for the field calculations, while 12 cells by 12 cells by 12 cells (H x H x H) are utilized for the three dimensional compartment. Here H is the compartment height. Since the primary purpose of the three-dimensional calculations is to determine the validity of the basic two-dimensional numerical results, an attempt has been made to use a three-dimensional configuration which essentially conforms to that of the two-dimensional cases. More specifically, the heat source and the floor and ceiling vents all extend to the full width along the third dimension not shown in Fig. 1. For a compartment height of 2.44 meters and a reference temperature of 300°K, calculations have been made for the total volumetric heat-source strength levels of 50, 200, 400 and 600 kW. Also, for the study of the effect of compartment length on the oscillatory field behaviors, additional calculations have been carried out for a two-dimensional compartment in which the length is 3H, which is similar to the configuration utilized in the corresponding steady-state study [2].

4. NUMERICAL RESULTS

4.1 Mechanism of Oscillations:

At a heat input level of 50 kW, oscillatory behaviors have been found in all cases except Case 4, Fig. 1. Figure 2 shows the total heat outflow through the ceiling vent for Cases 1, 2 and 3. The total energy outflow for Case 1

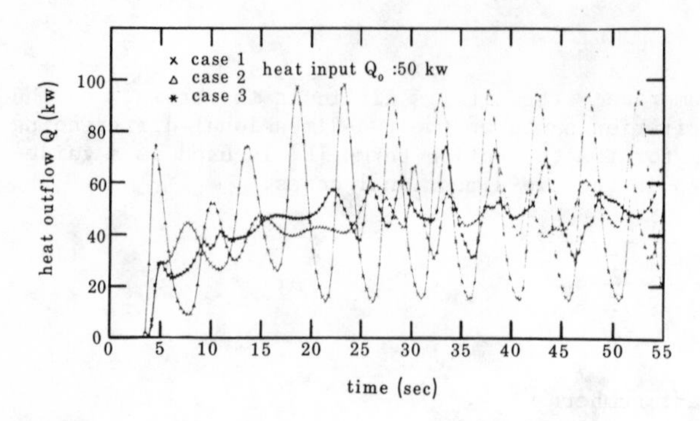

Fig. 2: Ceiling Vent Heat Outflow (2-D)

displays a regular periodicity about a mean value of 50 kW after a short initial transience. The frequency is about 0.208 cps and the amplitude is relatively large, about 40 kW. The origin of the oscillation is primarily due to the periodic growth of the vortices at the boundaries of the buoyant plume. When the left vortex grows to a size comparable to the compartment height, a burst of hot gases occurs through the ceiling vent, carrying along most of the hot gases formed on the right side. Since the buoyant plume essentially separates the compartment into two parts, the hot gas on the right cannot be vented readily. As a result, energy builds up until the bursting at the ceiling vent occurs. Shortly thereafter, fresh cool air is brought in through the floor opening to vent the entire compartment while the vortices develop again. This process of energy entrapment in the compartment and the subsequent venting is largely responsible for the high amplitude seen in Fig. 1. In reality, as discussed in a later section, three-dimensional effects are expected to reduce this amplitude due to better communication between the trapped hot gas and the ceiling vent in the direction of the third dimension.

4.2 Effects of Vent and Source Location:

For Cases 2 and 3, Fig. 2 shows that it takes longer, than for Case 1, to develop the oscillatory behavior. The oscillations are seen to be highly irregular and to possess high-order harmonics. The amplitudes are much lower than for Case 1 due primarily to the easier ventilation in Cases 2 and 3 where the ceiling vent is closer to the heat source. The irregular oscillation is believed to be caused by the relatively inactive region in the compartment to the left of the heat source and its interaction with the rest of the compartment.

Similar plots for Cases 4, 5 and 6 with a heat input of 50 kW are shown in Fig. 3. For these three cases the heat source is located close to the left corner of the compartment. Presence of the wall to the left of the heat source prevents the formation of a left vortex; and the buoyant flow traces a well defined flow path between the floor and ceiling vents. The heat outflow behavior for these latter three cases, as a consequence, is orderly. For Case 4 (the ceiling vent directly above the heat source) no oscillatory behavior is found, and the steady-state is achieved by about 10 seconds after the initiation of the energy input. During the transient start up period, damped oscillations can be seen for Cases 5 and 6, while the long time behaviors are steady. The stable conditions for all these three latter cases are largely due to the damping effects offered by the dominant flow path close to the solid boundaries represented by the floor, left wall and the ceiling.

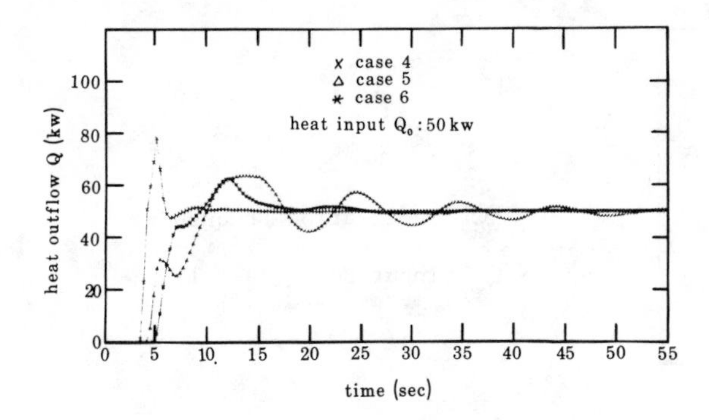

Fig. 3: Ceiling Vent Heat Outflow

4.3 Effect of Source Strength:

One of the most important physical parameters affecting the oscillatory behavior is the strength of the heat source. Numerical experiments have been carried out for a compartment with H = 2.44 meters and an ambient reference temperature T_o of 300 K at heat input levels of Q_o = 50, 200, 400 and 600 kW. Figure 4 shows the result of 2-d calculations for Case 1 relative to the total energy leaving through the ceiling vent, Q , expressed as a fraction of Q_o, for Q_o = 50 kW and 200 kW. Figure 5 shows the frequency as a function of strength. The frequency of oscillations is increased from 0.208 cps to 0.315 cps as Q_o increases from 50 kW to 200 kW. This is indeed expectable since the higher strength of the heat source hastens the growth of the vortices and the wash-out phenomenon at the ceiling vent. Figure 4 also indicates that the normalized amplitudes of the oscillations remain essentially the same for the two levels of heat source strength shown, indicating the fact that this amplitude is directly proportional to the heat source input.

4.4 Three-Dimensional Effects:

In the present study, the two-dimensional UNDSAFE computer code has also been modified to accomodate three-dimensional calculations to determine if the field oscillations are caused by the two-dimensional assumption. A simple turbulence model based on a turbulent viscosity 20 times the laminar viscosity is used in the three-dimensional calculations. The compartment is of dimensions H x H x H in which the heat source and the vents extend, as shown in Fig. 1, to the full width in the third dimension.

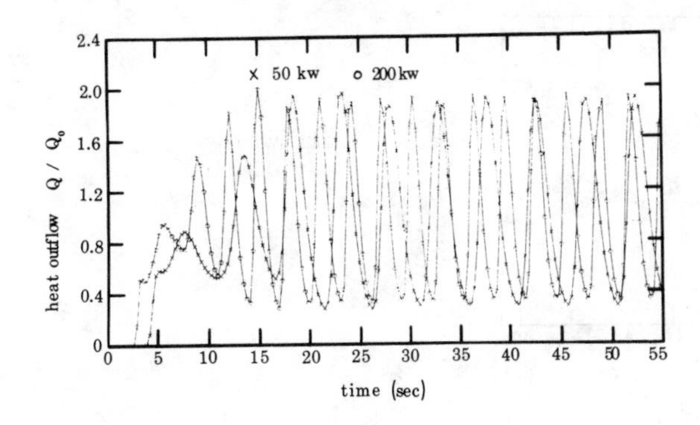

Fig. 4: Ceiling Vent Heat Outflow (case 1, 2-D)

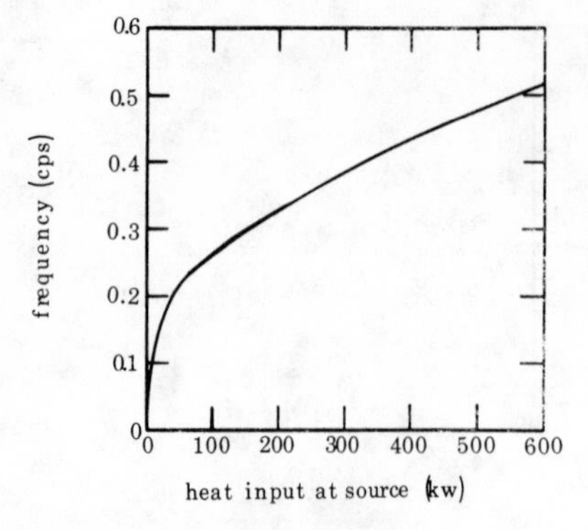

Fig. 5: Oscillation Frequency vs Input Heat (case 1)

To conserve computer storage, a grid system of 12 x 12 x 12 cells is utilized. Thus, this system involves geometrical configuration slightly different from that of the two-dimensional study. This difference is not expected to be critical for the intended purpose of the three-dimensional calculations. Results of the six cases are shown in Figures 6 and 7. The basic oscillatory behavior is exhibited by three-dimensional situations also. One can therefore conclude that these oscillations are physical in nature. The frequencies of oscillations in all cases except Case 4 remain essentially the same (Figure 8) in both the two-dimensional and three-dimensional calculations, another indication of the validity of the two-dimensional calculations in predicting the real phenomena. Amplitudes predicted by the three-dimensional calculations are smaller than those in the two-dimensional calculations. This is particularly pronounced in Case 1. As discussed previously, this reduction in amplitude is expected in view of the better flow communication between the ceiling vent and the rest of the compartment, as provided by flow passages in the third dimension. It is also interesting to note that for Cases 4, 5 and 6 the three-dimensional calculations also lead to the same long-time steady-state conditions. Finally, the amplitude of oscillations increases with heat input rate as in 2-d but this sensitivity is stronger in 3-d.

4.5 Mass Flow and Pressure Oscillations:

When the heat out-flow at the ceiling vent undergoes oscillation, other local physical variables experience cyclic changes also. For Case 1 with Q_o = 50 kW, the oscillatory variations in the mass out-flow at the ceiling vent

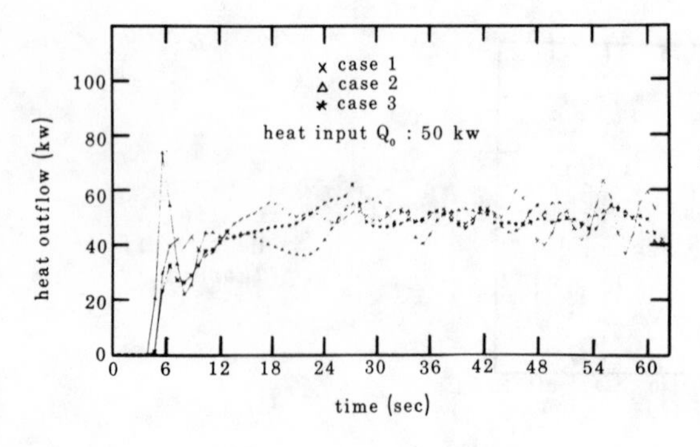

Fig. 6: Ceiling Vent Heat Outflow (3-D)

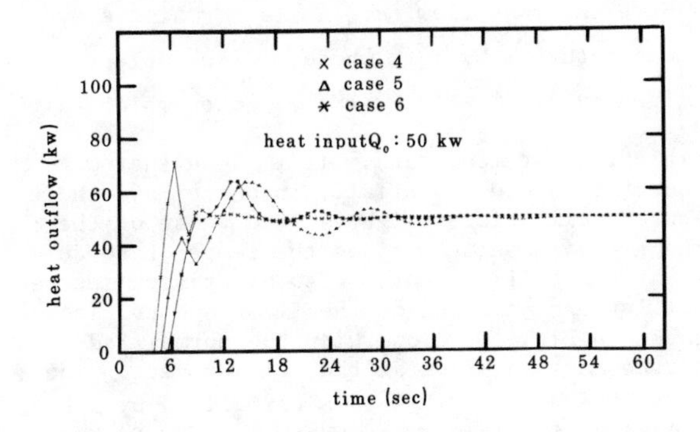

Fig. 7: Ceiling Vent Heat Outflow (3-D)

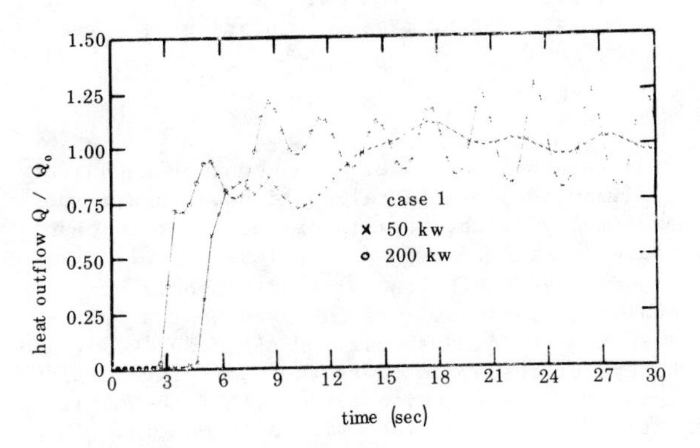

Fig. 8: Ceiling Vent Heat Outflow (3-D)

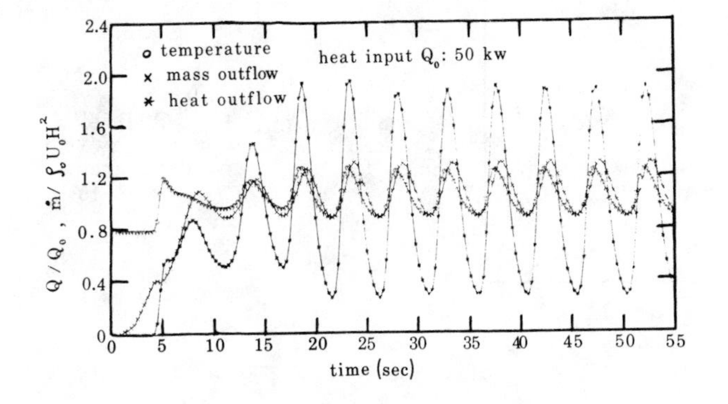

Fig. 9: Ceiling Vent Heat and Mass Outflow and Center Temperature (2-D, case 1)

and the hot gas temperature at the center of the ceiling opening are shown in Fig. 9 together with that for Q. Here the mass flow rate $\dot{m}$ is normalized by by the quantity $\rho_o U_o H^2$ and the temperature T by T_o, where ρ_o is ambient air density, U_o a reference velocity given by $5.128 \times 10^4 \nu_o/H$, ν_o the ambient air kinematic viscosity, and T_o the ambient air temperature. It is seen that oscilltions of these three physical quantities are essentially in phase, and there is an indication that the temperature oscillations slightly lead those of the other two variables. This is perhaps also expected, since the temperature definitely plays a more dominant role at the ceiling vent. Also of primary interest are the corresponding pressure oscillations just inside the floor and ceiling vents (along the vent centers), shown in Fig. 10, along with the normalized mass in-flow at the floor vent and the mass out-flow at the ceiling vent. The pressure difference over the ambient pressure, $p - p_o$, is normalized by $\rho_o U_o^2$. It is seen that the pressure oscillations in general lag behind those of the mass rates of flow, indicating that the pressures near the openings play only a passive role and are not responsible for the flows. The in-flow and out-flow oscillations are essentially in phase, a feature not entirely expected. One possible practical implication is that for a compartment with multiple vents it is very difficult to pressurize the compartment by mass accumulation as a result of having a fire or heat source in the compartment.

4.6 Sensitivity to Turbulence Models:

As mentioned previously, a simple turbulence model of a constant turbulent viscosity is utilized in the three-dimensional field calculations. An attempt has been made to determine the sensitivity of the oscillatory behavior to changing turbulent viscosity values. Based on the reference case (Case 1) with $Q_o = 50$ kW, H = 2 meters and $T_o = 300$ K, two turbulent viscosity models have been utilized in the two-dimensional calculations. One is based on the full algebraic model which is included in the two-dimensional UNDSAFE code [4,5], and a second model is based on a turbulent viscosity 20 times the laminar viscosity [3]. The results are shown in Fig. 11 and it is quite evident that the oscillatory behaviors are not too sensitive to the turbulent viscosity models. It is expected that this is also true in the three-dimensional calculations.

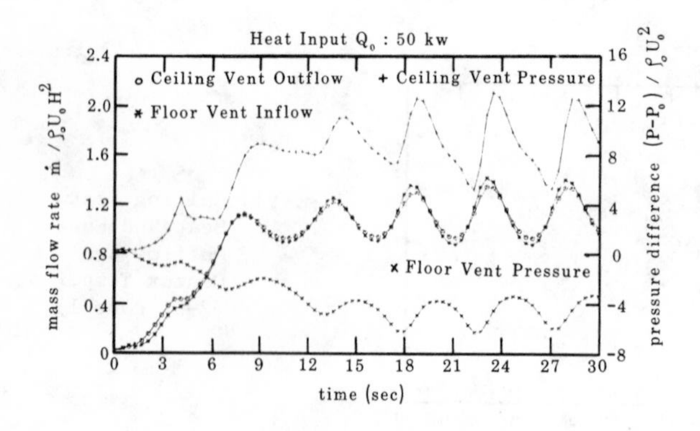

Fig. 10: Vent Opening Mass Flow Rate and Pressures (2-D, case 1)

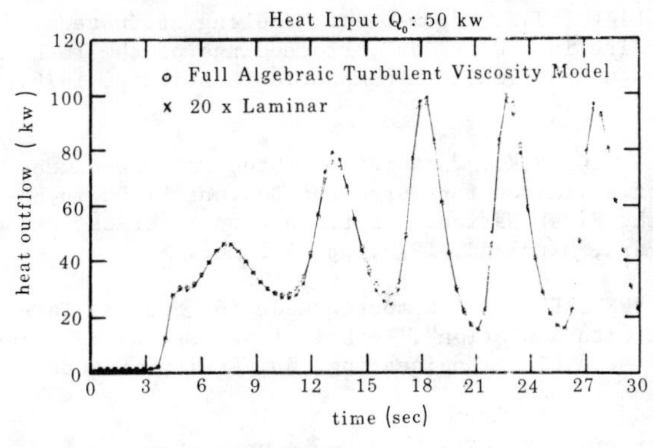

Fig. 11: Effect of Turbulent Viscosity Variation on Ceiling Vent Heat Outflow (2-D, case 1)

5. CONCLUDING REMARKS

In the present study numerical finite-difference two and three-dimensional calculations have been carried out to study the oscillatory behavior of the flow and temperature fields for six cases of a compartment with various combinations of floor and ceiling vents, and location and strength of the volumetric heat source. Long-time oscillatory behaviors are prevalent in those cases where the heat source is located at the floor center of the compartment. The origin of the oscillations lies in the growth of vortices on either side of the buoyant plume above the heat source and the subsequent wash-out of the hot gases at the ceiling vent opening. For cases where the heat source is located close to the left corner of the compartment, oscillations in the transient period are damped out quickly to achieve steady-state conditions at long times. Elimination of the vortex to the left of the buoyant plume and the stabilizing effects of the floor, left wall and ceiling boundaries in the dominant flow path are responsible for the lack of long-time oscillations for these latter cases. Three-dimensionable calculations have also been made to demonstrate that the oscillations observed in the two-dimensional calculations are physically real, and that the frequency of oscillations remains essentially the same as that in the two-dimensional calculations, even though the amplitude is much lower. This study is currently being continued to a quantitative predictive theory of the oscillatory behavior in a compartment with vertical vents.

ACKNOWLEDGEMENTS

The research reported herein is supported by Grant G7-9002 Mod. No. 2 to the University of Notre Dame from the NBS Center for Fire Research, the Fire Research Institute of Japan, the Science and Technology Agency of Japan, and the University of Notre Dame Computer Center.

REFERENCES

1. Kawagoe, K, "Fire Behavior in Rooms", Japan Ministry of Construction Building Research Institute Report No. 27, Tokyo, September, 1958.

2. Satoh, K., Lloyd, J.R., and Yang, K.T., "Turbulent Buoyant Flow and Smoke Layers in a Two-Dimensional Rectangular Compartment with Vertical Vents", Chemical and Physical Processes in Combustion, Proceedings of the 1980 Meeting of the Eastern Section of the Combustion Institute, paper No. 20, 1980.

3. Ku, A.C., Doria, M.L., and Lloyd, J.R., "Numerical Modeling of Unsteady Buoyant Flows Generated by Fire in a Corridor", Proceedings of the 16th Symposium (International) on Combustion, The Combustion Institute, 1976. pp. 1373-1384.

4. Lloyd, J.R., Yang, K.T., and Liu, V.K., "A Numerical Study of One-Dimensional Surface, Gas and Soot Radiation for Turbulent Buoyant Flows in Enclosures", Proceedings of the First National Conference on Numerical Methods in Heat Transfer, College Park, Maryland, 1979, pp. 142-161.

5. Yang, K.T., and Liu, V.K., "UNDSAFE-II A Computer Code for Buoyant Turbulent Flow in an Enclosure with Radiation", Technical Report TR-79002-78-3, Department of Aerospace and Mechanical Engineering, University of Notre Dame, 1978, 166 pages.

6. Roache, P.J., "Computational Fluid Dynamics", Hermosa Publishers, Albuquerque, New Mexico, 1972.

A Numerical Study of One-Dimensional Enclosed Flames

J.I. RAMOS
Department of Mechanical Engineering
Carnegie-Mellon University
Pittsburgh, Pennsylvania 15213

ABSTRACT

The propagation of a laminar flame in a closed container has been analyzed by means of nine finite-difference schemes. A lagrangian transformation has been used to eliminate the convection terms from the governing equations, giving rise to a system of integrodifferential reaction-diffusion equations. The chemistry has been modeled by one-step Arrhenius-type reaction. The numerical schemes evaluated include two methods of lines where the reaction terms are integrated point by point, an implicit predictor-corrector algorithm, a quasilinearization procedure, a linear block tridiagonal implicit algorithm, an operator splitting technique and the standard explicit, implicit and Crank-Nicolson schemes. All of the numerical methods use second order accurate spatial approximations and different temporal approximations. The results show that the explicit, implicit and Crank-Nicolson schemes underpredict the location of the flame front and the pressure, whereas the quasilinear, linear block and implicit predictor-corrector techniques overpredict them slightly. It is also shown that the explicit method is by far the most efficient in terms of computer time among the numerical algorithms considered. The numerical results also indicate that the flame front thickness is so small that the flame is almost a discontinuity. A qualitative discussion of an adaptive grid technique is presented, which will allow resolution of the flame front and avoid the large number of grid points required to resolve the flame front with the methods presented in this paper.

1. INTRODUCTION

The last decade has been characterized by the development of a large number of numerical methods aimed at analyzing the propagation of turbulent flames in internal combustion engines and gas turbine combustors [1-11]. Despite the large number of computations that have been performed in modeling the combustion processes, several areas have emerged in which much more work is required in order to predict the main characteristics of the flow. These areas can be classified in three major categories: numerical methods, turbulence modeling and chemical kinetics. In this paper we deal with numerical methods aimed at predicting the propagation of laminar flames in closed containers. More specifically, they are considered as possible techniques for modeling flame propagation in closed chambers containing a premixed fuel and oxidizer in the gaseous state.

The motion of a reactive gas medium must be properly accounted for, and in many geometries the full Navier-Stokes equations must be solved. The hydrodynamic equations are, however, coupled with the energy, continuity and chemical species equations. The heat released by the combustion process enters the model through the energy equation and depends on the chemical processes. Additionally, the various chemical species are transported by convection and diffusion. The equations governing the conservation of mass, momentum, energy and species are coupled and require proper spatial and temporal resolution. In general the complexities associated with the modeling of practical combustion devices is so large that investigators have made use of either a simple flow configuration where the simplicity of the flow field allows a more complete description of the chemical processes [12,13] or a more complex fluid dynamic behavior with very simple chemical kinetics processes [1,6].

The propagation of a one-dimensional, turbulent flame in an internal combustion engine has been analyzed by Sirignano [1] and Bellan and Sirignano [3, 5] who used a lagrangian transformation technique to eliminate the continuity equation and the convection terms from the governing equations. These investigators also assumed that the pressure was uniform throughout the combustor chamber. The resulting set of reaction-diffusion equations was solved using a quasilinear method. Boni, et al. [7] used a more comprehensive model in that the continuity, momentum, energy and species equations were solved to analyze the flow field in a divided-chamber stratified charge engine. Westbrook [14] used a generalization of the Implicit Continuous-Fluid Eulerian (ICE) technique for the calculation of fluid flows in the presence of rapid exothermic chemical reactions. His studies of one-dimensional flame propagation in a closed container showed that systematic errors occur in the conventional operator splitting solution technique. These errors were the result of a biasing in the order in which the ICE method solves the relevant conservation equations. Westbrook also concludes that the ICE method should be used only in those situations in which the fluid pressure variations are due principally to density variations.

The previous review of one-dimensional numerical schemes aimed at the prediction of laminar and turbulent flame propagation in closed chambers reveals that almost every investigator has his own numerical method and that the relative efficiencies of different numerical methods have not been previously assessed in the solution of the flame propagation phenomena which occur in a closed combustor. The reason for this approach seems to be due to the fact that the selection of a highly efficient solution procedure has not been essential for one-dimensional problems. However, as more complex chemical reaction schemes are introduced into the numerical problems, more efficient numerical schemes will be needed. Additionally, efficiency in one-dimensional models is important in that the procedure used in many multi-dimensional schemes is to reduce the problem to a sequence of one-dimensional calculations. For example, MacCormack [15] has developed a highly efficient explicit-implicit-characteristic method for solving the compressible Navier-Stokes equations. His method basically advances the solution in time by using a sequence of time-split, one-dimensional difference operators. MacCormack's scheme shows that more efficient numerical methods for the solution of one-dimensional problems are essential in the development of multi-dimensional models. The assessment of the efficiency of numerical methods should be carried out over a variety of different flow and chemical conditions and geometrical configurations. Such an assessment would be very costly for two- or three-dimensional test problems. For this reason a one-dimensional problem is considered in this study. The problem corresponds to the propagation of a laminar flame in a closed chamber where the chemistry obeys a one-step Arrhenius-type reaction. The relative efficiencies of nine different numerical schemes which use second-order accurate spatial approximations and different temporal approximations have been assessed for a particular geometry and chemical reaction. To the best knowledge of the author, such an assessment has not been made before for the propagation of laminar flames in closed chambers. The numerical methods, whose efficiencies have been investigated, include two methods of lines, an implicit predictor-corrector algorithm, a quasilinerization method, a linear block tridiagonal implicit technique, an operator splitting method and the standard explicit, implicit and Crank-Nicolson schemes. The governing equations have been solved in terms of lagrangian coordinates. Some of the techniques described and applied to the problem considered here have been previously considered in similar form to time-dependent flame calculations by various workers. Other techniques are adaptations of procedures developed for other applications. For example the method of lines has been used by Bledjian [13] in his studies of open laminar flame propagation. Margolis [12] has also used the method of lines in his studies of premixed laminar flames. He applied a lagrangian transformation to reduce the problem to a system of parabolic partial differential and introduced approximate B-spline (finite element) basis for the spatial variations. Otey and Dwyer [16] assessed the efficiency of the method of lines, operator splitting and linear block methods in their studies of reaction-diffusion equations, while Dwyer and Sanders [17] used the operator splitting method in the modeling of premixed, laminar flame propagation. Kee and Miller [18] applied the operator splitting method to a steady, laminar, jet diffusion flame. The linear block method has been successfully used to solve the compressible Navier-Stokes equations by Beam and Warming [19] and Briley and McDonald [20].

The list of the nine numerical methods studied herein does not include other very promising methods. For example, the use of adaptive grid methods shows great promise but it is still in the early stages of development [21]. However, the adaptive grid technique is qualitatively discussed in the section which presents the numerical results.

The efficiency and accuracy of the numerical methods is given in terms of computer time and comparisons of calculated temperature and pressure profiles. The relative efficiency of the various numerical methods was evaluated on a case-by-case basis by determining threshold values of the time step and convergence criteria which would yield converged solutions. The effect of the grid size in the relative efficiencies of the methods has not been investigated in this study, where an 82-point uniformly-spaced grid has been used.

2. THE GOVERNING EQUATIONS

The conservation equations for multicomponent reacting ideal mixtures can be found in [22]. These equations can be simplified by neglecting the thermal diffusion of the species (the Soret and Dufour effects), the pressure gradient diffusion, the bulk viscosity and radiation heat transfer.

In one-dimensional enclosed deflagrations, the Mach number is small and the pressure is almost spatially uniform. Under this assumption, the momentum equation and the viscous dissipation terms appearing in the energy equation can be dropped. Furthermore, by assuming that the species diffuse according to Fick's law with equal diffusion coefficients for all of them, that the Prandtl and Lewis numbers are equal to one, and that the species specific heats at constant pressure are equal and constant, the equations governing the propagation of laminar flames in closed containers ($0 \leq x \leq L$) can be written as

$$\frac{\partial \rho}{\partial t} + \frac{\partial}{\partial x} (\rho u) = 0, \tag{1}$$

$$\rho C_p\left[\frac{\partial T}{\partial t} + u\frac{\partial T}{\partial x}\right] = \frac{dp}{dt} + C_p\frac{\partial}{\partial x}\left(\rho D\frac{\partial T}{\partial x}\right) - \sum_{j=1}^{N} H_j^o\dot{m}_j \ , \tag{2}$$

$$\rho\left[\frac{\partial Y_j}{\partial t} + u\frac{\partial Y_j}{\partial x}\right] = \dot{m}_j + \frac{\partial}{\partial x}\left(\rho D\frac{\partial Y_j}{\partial x}\right) \ , \quad j=1,\ldots,N-1, \tag{3}$$

$$Y_N = 1 - \sum_{j=1}^{N-1} Y_j \ , \tag{4}$$

$$p = \rho\tilde{R}T\sum_{j=1}^{N}\frac{Y_j}{W_j} \ , \tag{5}$$

where ρ is the density, u the velocity, t the time, x the eulerian coordinate, C_p the specific heat at constant pressure, T the temperature, p the pressure, D the species mass diffusivity, $\dot{m}_j$ the reaction rate of species, H_j^o the enthalpy of formation of species j, Y the species mass fraction, N the number of species, $\tilde{R}$ the universal gas constant and W_j the species molecular weight. Eq. (2) can be simplified by assuming that the species specific heats at constant volume, C_v, are equal and constant. This assumption implies that the species molecular weights are equal and will be denoted by W. In addition, the ratio of specific heats, $\gamma = C_p/C_v$, is also a constant. Furthermore, introducing the transformation

$$\phi = T\,p^{(1-\gamma/\gamma)} \ , \tag{6}$$

into Eq. (2), the following transport equation is obtained

$$\rho\left[\frac{\partial\phi}{\partial t} + u\frac{\partial\phi}{\partial x}\right] = \frac{\partial}{\partial x}\left(\rho D\frac{\partial\phi}{\partial x}\right) - \frac{Q\,\dot{m}_1}{Cp\;p^{(\gamma-1/\gamma)}} \ , \tag{7}$$

where

$$\sum_{j=1}^{N} H_j^o\dot{m}_j = Q\,\dot{m}_1 \ , \tag{8}$$

and Q is the heat of reaction. Eqs. (1), (3) and (7) can be further simplified by introducing the following Spalding's transformation [23]

$$\rho = M\frac{\partial\xi}{\partial x} \ , \tag{9}$$

and

$$\rho u = -M\frac{\partial\xi}{\partial t} \ , \tag{10}$$

where

$$M = \int_0^L \rho\,dx \ . \tag{11}$$

In Eq. (11), M denotes the mass (per unit area) contained in a closed combustor of length L and is a constant.

Introducing Eqs. (9) and (10) into Eqs. (3) and (7) and assuming that $\rho^2 D$ is constant, i.e. $\alpha = \rho^2 D/M^2$ is constant, the equations governing the propagation of laminar flames in the domain $0 \le x \le L$ (or $0 \le \xi \le 1$) reduce to a system of reaction-diffusion equations which are presented in Table I. In these equations the unknowns are Y_j and ϕ. Once ϕ is obtained, the pressure can be calculated by integrating Eq. (5) from x = 0 to L and using Eqs. (6) and (9) to yield

TABLE I. THE GOVERNING EQUATIONS IN LAGRANGIAN COORDINATES

VECTOR EQUATION	$\frac{\partial U}{\partial t} = \alpha \frac{\partial^2 U}{\partial \xi^2} + F$
VARIABLES	$U = (Y_1, Y_2, \phi)^T$
REACTION TERMS	$F = \left\{\dot{m}_1/\rho, \dot{m}_2/\rho, - Q\dot{m}_1/(\rho C_p\, p^{(\gamma-1/\gamma)})\right\}^T$
	$\dot{m}_1 = - \frac{K}{32} \exp(- \frac{E}{\tilde{R}T})\, \rho^2 Y_1 Y_2$
	$\dot{m}_2 = \frac{160}{44} \dot{m}_1$
PRESSURE	$p = \frac{\tilde{R}M}{WL} \int_0^1 \phi d\xi$
TEMPERATURE	$T = \phi\, p^{(\gamma-1/\gamma)}$
DENSITY	$\rho = pW/(\tilde{R}T)$
SPECIES	$Y_3 = 1 - Y_1 - Y_2$
X-COORDINATE	$x = M \int_0^\xi (d\xi/\rho)$
VELOCITY	$u = - \frac{M}{\rho} \int_0^1 \frac{1}{\rho} \frac{\partial \rho}{\partial t}\, d\xi$

PHYSICO-CHEMICAL CONSTANTS

E=30,000 cal/mole	$\tilde{R}$ = 1.9871 cal/mole/°K	W_j = W = 28.91 gr/mole
C_p = 7 cal/mole/°K	γ = 1.4	$\rho^2 D$ = 2.1718x10^{-7} gr^2/cm^4/sec
Q = 11070 cal/gr	K = 10^{13} cm^3/gr/sec	L = 10 cm

$$p^{(1/\gamma)}\, L = \frac{\tilde{R}M}{W} \int_0^1 \phi d\xi \, . \tag{12}$$

The temperature and density are then calculated by using Eqs. (6) and (5) respectively. Once T and ρ are known the x-coordinate and the u velocity can be computed integrating Eqs. (9) and (1) respectively. The results of these computations are shown in Table I which also presents the governing equations in vector form.

3. THE CHEMICAL REACTION

In this study a one-step irreversible chemical reaction of the Arrhenius type

$$\text{Fuel (Species 1)} + \text{Oxidizer (Species 2)} \rightarrow \text{Products (Species 3)} \tag{13}$$

has been considered. Thus, N=3. The values of the reaction terms, $\dot{m}_j$, are given in Table I, which also lists the values of other physico-chemical parameters.

4. INITIAL AND BOUNDARY CONDITIONS

Initially the velocity was set to zero and the pressure was 1 atm. The species and temperature profiles were given by the following expressions

$$\left.\begin{aligned} T(0,\xi) &= 1500°K \\ Y_1(0,\xi) &= 0.01 \\ Y_2(0,\xi) &= 0.03652 \end{aligned}\right\} , \qquad 0 \le \xi \le 0.0438 , \tag{14}$$

and

$$\left.\begin{aligned} T(0,\xi) &= 300°K \\ Y_1(0,\xi) &= 0.06472 \\ Y_2(0,\xi) &= 0.23550 \end{aligned}\right\} , \qquad 0.0938 \le \xi \le 1.0 . \tag{15}$$

Linear temperature and species mass fraction profiles were used for $0.0438 \le \xi \le 0.0938$. It should be noted that these initial conditions correspond to the presence of burnt gases at the combustor left end. Thus, we do not consider the ignition phenomena. Under these conditions the density is calculated from Eq. (5), where $W_i=W$. The mass contained in the combustor can be calculated by integrating Eq. (9). The result can be written as

$$M = L \int_0^1 \frac{d\xi}{\rho} . \tag{16}$$

The combustor ends were assumed adiabatic and the following boundary conditions applied

$$\frac{\partial U}{\partial \xi}(t,0) = \frac{\partial U}{\partial \xi}(t,1) = 0 , \tag{17}$$

where $U = (Y_1, Y_2, \phi)^T$ is the column vector of the dependent variables as indicated in Table I.

5. DESCRIPTION OF THE NUMERICAL METHODS

The choice of a numerical method for a system of coupled reaction-diffusion equations is strongly influenced by the exponential nature of the non-linear reaction terms, and the steep temperature and species concentration profiles which exist at the flame front. Thus, the formulation of a solution technique in which the reaction terms can be integrated point-by-point seems to offer a promising approach. This will be a basic ingredient in the method of lines, the explicit method of lines and the operator splitting techniques discussed below. A point-by-point temporal integration technique of the reaction terms is also used in the implicit predictor-corrector method. The fifth method used in this study is called the quasilinear method, which consists of replacing the partial differential equations by their linearized difference equations. The linearization, however, is carried out only with respect to the dependent variable whose equation is being solved. In the sixth method, the partial differential equations are replaced by their linearized finite-difference forms, but where the linearization is carried out with respect to all the dependent variables. This results in a banded block tridiagonal matrix. The classical explicit, implicit and Crank-Nicolson methods were also used in the solution of the system of reaction-diffusion equations.

The steepness of the temperature and species concentration profiles plays a critical role in the numerical solution of laminar flame propagation in closed chambers. Therefore, spatial approximations and grid size are as important as the treatment of the temporal portion of the equations. In this paper we have used only second-order spatial approximations.

The mathematical development of the nine solution procedures, which have been used in the solution of the present problem, will be illustrated using the vector equation indicated in Table I

$$\frac{\partial U}{\partial t} = \alpha \frac{\partial^2 U}{\partial \xi^2} + F \quad . \tag{18}$$

5.1 The Method of Lines

The basic idea in the method of lines is to replace the spatial derivatives with an appropriate approximation which relates the dependent variables at neighboring grid points. This results in a set of time dependent coupled system of ordinary differential equations. Consider the following scheme

$$\frac{dU_i}{dt} = \frac{\alpha}{h^2} [U_{i+1} - 2U_i + U_{i-1}] + F_i \quad . \tag{19}$$

These equations can be written at each of the M grid points. This procedure reduces the system of three partial differential equations to a system of 3M coupled ordinary differential equations, which has been solved using a fourth-order Runge-Kutta method. The obvious disadvantage of the method is that the resulting set of coupled equations is ususally very large. It is worth noticing that Eq. (19), which gives the solution at the grid point i, involves the values of the dependent variables at grid points i-1 and i+1. This is avoided in the explicit method of lines which is discussed next.

5.2 The Explicit Method of Lines

The explicit method of lines is a very simple technique based on the method of lines described above. This technique evaluates the spatial derivatives at $t^{(n)}$. The resulting set of ordinary differential equations is integrated using a fourth-order Runge-Kutta method at each grid point over the interval $t^{(n)}$ to $t^{(n+1)}$. The equations can be written at each grid point as

$$\frac{dU_i}{dt} = \frac{\alpha}{h^2} [U_{i+1}^{(n)} - 2U_i^{(n)} + U_{i-1}^{(n)}] + F_i \quad . \tag{20}$$

Therefore, the explicit method of lines assumes that the diffusion terms are constant (they are evaluated at $t^{(n)}$) during the integration of Eq. (20) over the interval $\Delta t = t^{(n+1)} - t^{(n)}$. The spatial derivatives are reevaluated, after the solution of Eq. (20) has been found at $t^{(n+1)}$ and the process is repeated. This scheme is simpler than the method of lines and, in general, avoids the problems associated with the evaluation of large sets of coupled ordinary differential equations. However, it suffers in that the integration process must be interrupted to reevaluate the spatial derivatives frequently enough to satisfy the stability limitation imposed by the use of an explicit form for the diffusion terms. The method of lines, as well as the explicit method of lines, have the property of evaluating the reaction terms point-by-point.

5.3 The Operator Splitting Method

The operator splitting method used here is called majorant splitting method by Yanenko [24] and allows one term of Eq. (18) to be considered alone during each fractional step, while the remaining terms are ignored. In this study, the following fractional steps have been used:

- reaction operator: $L'_R : \frac{dU_i}{dt} = F_i$, (21)

- diffusion operator: $L'_d : \frac{\partial U_i}{\partial t} = \alpha \frac{\partial^2 U_i}{\partial \xi^2}$. (22)

Eq. (21) was solved using a fourth-order Runge-Kutta method, while Eq. (22) was differenced using a Crank-Nicolson scheme. It is to be noted that Eq. (22) yields a system of 3M uncoupled finite difference equations. The computation was carried out by integrating Eq. (21) over a time interval $\Delta t = t^{(n+1)} - t^{(n)}$. During this process, the time step used in the integration was varied as necessary to maintain the specified accuracy and was generally smaller than Δt. The solution thus obtained at each grid point was denoted by $\overline{U}_i$. The second fractional step involves the diffusion operator L'_d [Eq. (22)] and is executed implicitly solving the following Crank-Nicolson equations

$$\frac{U_i^{(n+1)} - \overline{U}_i}{\Delta t} = \frac{\alpha}{2h^2} [U_{i+1}^{(n+1)} - 2U_i^{(n+1)} + U_{i-1}^{(n+1)} + \overline{U}_{i+1} - 2\overline{U}_i + \overline{U}_{i-1}] . \quad (23)$$

Eq. (23) represents a set of 3M uncoupled tridiagonal finite difference equations, which was solved for the values of the dependent variables at $t^{(n+1)}$ by the method of Thomas [25]. Thus, the solution has been advanced one time step by the sequence

$$U^{(n+1)} = L'_d L'_R U^{(n)} . \quad (24)$$

The operator splitting method retains the advantage of evaluating the reaction terms [Eq. (21)] point-by-point, thus avoiding the difficulty of handling large sets of ordinary differential equations. Another advantage is that the diffusion operator has the stability characteristics normally associated with implicit methods. However, the accuracy of the operator-splitting method depends very much on the time step and grid size. Large time steps will tend to result in excessive uncoupling of the diffusion and reaction processes. This can lead to significant errors and, eventually, to a complete instability. Unlike the explicit method of lines, the operator splitting method does not allow diffusion to take place during the integration of the reaction terms [Eq. (21)].

5.4 The Implicit Predictor-Corrector Method

This method consists of projecting the value of the nonlinear reaction terms F [Eq. (18)], and then solving the resulting reaction-diffusion equations with these projected values. The predictor step was evaluated using the explicit method of lines. The values thus obtained were denoted by $\overline{U}$ and used to evaluate the reaction terms, $\overline{F} = F(\overline{U})$, in the corrector step. The following is a sequence of the two steps used in this method.

- predictor: $\frac{dU_i}{dt} = \frac{\alpha}{h^2} [U_{i+1}^{(n)} - 2U_i^{(n)} + U_{i-1}^{(n)}] + F_i$ (25)

- corrector: $\frac{U_i^{(n+1)} - U_i^{(n)}}{\Delta t} = \frac{\alpha}{2h^2} [U_{i+1}^{(n)} - 2U_i^{(n)} + U_{i-1}^{(n)} + U_{i+1}^{(n)} - 2U_i^{(n+1)} +$

$+ U_{i-1}^{(n+1)}] + \frac{1}{2} [F_i^{(n)} + \overline{F}_i]$, (26) where $\overline{F}_i$ stands for the value of the reaction terms evaluated with the solution of the predictor step.

The predictor step was evaluated using a fourth-order Runge-Kutta method, while the method of Thomas was used to solve the system of uncoupled finite-difference equations of the corrector step. It is worth noticing that the corrector step is basically a Crank-Nicolson scheme where the reaction terms at $t^{(n+1)}$ are substituted by the reaction terms evaluated with the values obtained in the predictor step.

5.5 The Quasilinear Method

Eq. (18) constitutes a set of nonlinear partial differential equations which may be easy to solve if they are linearized in some way. We will use the technique of quasilinearization first introduced by Bellman and Kalaba [26]. In this technique the nonlinear reaction terms are expanded in a Taylor series with respect to only that variable whose equation is being solved. The expansion of a variable is performed around the previously known value. Thus for Eq. (18), the nonlinear reaction terms, $F^{(n+1)}$, can be quasilinearized as

$$F^{(n+1)} = F^{(n)} + \left(\frac{\partial F}{\partial U}\right)^{(n)} I \; (U^{(n+1)} - U^{(n)}) \quad , \tag{27}$$

where $(\partial F/\partial U)^{(n)}$ is the jacobian matrix and I is the unit matrix. The matrix $(\partial F/\partial U)^{(n)} I$ is diagonal and indicates that the quasilinearization is carried out only with respect to the variable whose equation is being solved. The finite-difference form of the quasilinear method is

$$\frac{U_i^{n+1} - U_i^{n}}{\Delta t} = \frac{\alpha}{2h^2} [U_{i+1}^{(n+1)} - 2U_i^{(n+1)} + U_{i-1}^{(n+1)} + U_{i+1}^{(n)} - 2U_i^{(n)} + U_{i-1}^{(n)}]$$
$$+ \frac{1}{2} [F_i^{(n)} + F_i^{(n+1)}] \quad , \tag{28}$$

where the value of $F_i^{(n+1)}$ is substituted by that from Eq. (27). Eq. (28) has been solved using the method of Thomas. The quasilinear method is second-order accurate but has the disadvantage that the accuracy of the quasilinearization degrades as the time step increases. In general, the quasilinearization procedure will yield a system of uncoupled finite-difference equations. However, in this study because of the relationship between p and ϕ [Eq. (12)], the system is coupled and must be solved by iterations. The quasilinear method has the stability characteristics associated with implicit procedures.

5.6 The Linear Block Method

The linear block method is similar to the quasilinear method described above, but the linearization is carried out with respect to all dependent variables. This results in a banded block tridiagonal matrix. The method uses a Crank-Nicolson scheme

$$\frac{U_i^{(n+1)} - U_i^{(n)}}{\Delta t} = \frac{\alpha}{2h^2} [U_{i+1}^{(n+1)} - 2U_i^{(n+1)} + U_{i-1}^{(n+1)} + U_{i+1}^{(n)} - 2U_i^{(n)} + U_{i-1}^{(n)}]$$
$$+ \frac{1}{2} [F_i^{(n)} + F_i^{(n+1)}] \quad , \tag{29}$$

where $$F^{(n+1)} = F^{(n)} + (\partial F/\partial U)^{(n)} (U^{n+1} - U^{(n)}) \quad . \tag{30}$$

The linear block and quasilinear methods retain the stability characteristics associated with implicit methods. However, in the linear block method all the equations are coupled during the solution procedure.

5.7 The Implicit Method

The standard first-order accurate implicit method was used

$$\frac{U_i^{(n+1)} - U_i^{(n)}}{\Delta t} = \frac{\alpha}{h^2}\left[U_{i+1}^{(n+1)} - 2U_i^{(n+1)} + U_{i-1}^{(n+1)}\right] + F_i^{(n+1)} \quad , \tag{31}$$

where the nonlinear reaction terms were not linearized. The set of Eqs. (31) was solved by iterations using the tridiagonal matrix algorithm known as method of Thomas [25].

5.8 The Crank-Nicolson Scheme

The standard finite differences of the Crank-Nicolson method were used and solved by the method of Thomas.

$$\frac{U_i^{(n+1)} - U_i^{(n)}}{\Delta t} = \frac{\alpha}{2h^2}\left[U_{i+1}^{(n+1)} - 2U_i^{(n+1)} + U_{i-1}^{(n+1)} + U_{i+1}^{(n)} - 2U_i^{(n)} + U_{i-1}^{(n)}\right]$$

$$+ \frac{1}{2}\left[F_i^{(n)} + F_i^{(n+1)}\right] \quad . \tag{32}$$

5.9 The Explicit Method

The following first-order accurate explicit scheme was used

$$\frac{U_i^{(n+1)} - U_i^{(n)}}{\Delta t} = \frac{\alpha}{h^2}\left[U_{i+1}^{(n)} - 2U_i^{(n)} + U_{i-1}^{(n)}\right] + F_i^{(n)} \quad . \tag{33}$$

6. PRESENTATION AND DISCUSSION OF RESULTS

The calculations reported here were performed with an equally-spaced 82-point grid. The time step used in the computations was $\Delta t = 10^{-5}$ sec. The following convergence criterion was employed for all the methods

$$\left|p^{(K+1)} - p^{(K)}\right| / p^{(K)} \leq 10^{-4} \quad , \tag{34}$$

and

$$\left|T^{(K+1)} - T^{(K)}\right| / T^{(K)} \leq 10^{-4} \quad , \tag{35}$$

where K+1 and K denote iterations within the time step $\Delta t = t^{(n+1)} - t^{(n)}$. Figure 1 shows the temperature profiles versus the ξ-coordinate at different times. A flame characterized by a very steep temperature profile propagates from left to right in the combustor. The temperature of the unburnt gases is almost uniform and increases with time due to the pressure rise. Behind the flame the temperature is not uniform because of the adiabatic compression of the unburnt gases. In Fig. 2 we present the mass fraction profiles of fuel (Y_1) versus the ξ-coordinate at different times. The mass fraction of the unburnt gases is uniform and equal to its initial value. Behind the flame, the mass fraction of fuel is zero (a stoichiometric mixture was used in this study).

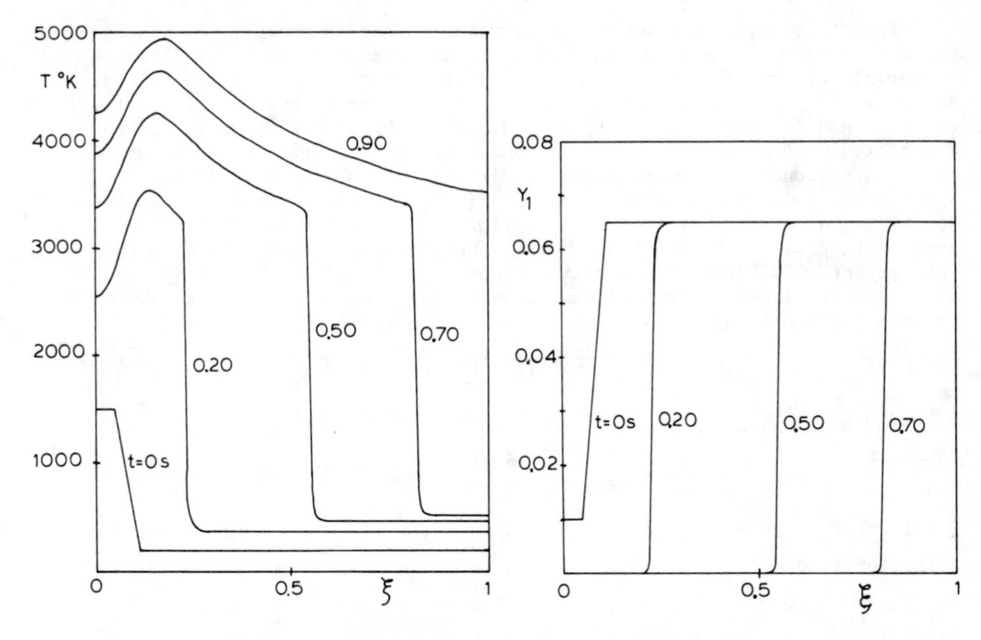

Fig. 1 Temperature profiles at different times as functions of the lagrangian coordinate ξ.

Fig. 2 Fuel mass fraction profiles at different times as functions of the lagrangian coordinate ξ.

Figures 1 and 2 indicate that the flame front is almost a discontinuity. The flame front thickness decreases with time because of the pressure and temperature increases. This point will be discussed later in this section.

Figure 3 shows the pressure as a function of time. The pressure is a monotonically increasing function of time until the flame reaches the right end of the combustor. Afterwards the temperature profiles are flattened because the reaction terms are zero and the problem is essentially controlled by diffusion and the pressure remains constant.

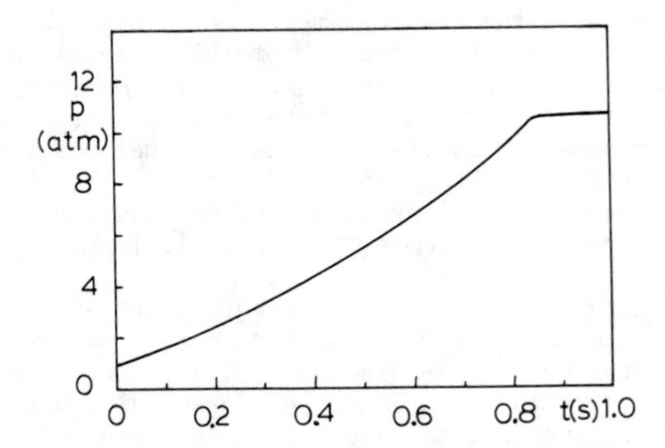

Fig. 3 Pressure as a function of time.

The efficiencies of the numerical methods used in solving the propagation of laminar flames in cartesian coordinates are presented in Table II in terms of normalized computation time. It is clear from this table that the explicit method is by far more efficient than the other eight methods. The least efficient method is the linear block method. The inefficiency of this method is due to two major reasons: first, a banded block tridiagonal matrix has to be inverted; second, the method requires iterations because the pressure term which appears in the reaction terms [Eq. (18)] depends on ϕ through an integral equation [Eq. (12)]. It is this iteration procedure together with the costly task of inverting a banded block matrix that makes the linear block method very inefficient. This need for iterations does not appear in the propagation of open laminar flames, or reaction-diffusion equations which are not subjected to integral nonlinearities such as those of Eq. (12).

TABLE II. NORMALIZED COMPUTATIONAL TIME FOR DIFFERENT NUMERICAL METHODS

METHOD	NORMALIZED COMPUTATIONAL TIME[1]
Explicit	1.00
Crank-Nicolson	1.23
Quasilinear	1.56
Method of Lines	1.64
Explicit Method of Lines	1.65
Implicit	1.70
Operator-Splitting	2.24
Implicit Predictor-Corrector	2.62
Linear Block	3.01

[1] A unity corresponds to 6020 sec. of CPU time in a DEC-20 computer for an 82-point grid.

For example, Otey and Dwyer [16] have shown that for reaction-diffusion equations, the linear block method is more efficient than the operator splitting method, the method of lines and the explicit method of lines. For integrodifferential reaction-diffusion equations, such as those studied here, the method of lines is more efficient than the explicit method of lines, the operator splitting method and the linear block method. From this comparison we can conclude that the efficiency of a method depends on the problem under consideration and its nonlinearities. In particular, methods which were found to be very efficient for open flames (or reaction-diffusion equations [16]) are very inefficient in the numerical solution of enclosed flames. This is also shown in Table III which compares the efficiencies of the methods for the problem considered here and that considered by Otey and Dwyer [16].

Table II also shows that the fourth-order accurate method of lines and explicit method of lines are more efficient than the operator splitting and the implicit predictor-corrector methods. This can be easily understood since these methods involve the solution of ordinary differential equations similar to those of the methods of lines and, in addition, they require the solution of additional equations of the corrector step in the implicit predictor-corrector method, and the solution of the diffusion operator in the operator splitting technique. The implicit method is slightly less efficient than the methods of lines. Note that in the implicit method, no linearization of the highly

TABLE III. COMPARISON OF EFFICIENCIES BETWEEN THE PRESENT WORK AND REFERENCE 16

METHOD	OTEY AND DWYER'S WORK (see Table 3 of [16])	PRESENT WORK
Linear Block	1.0	1.84
Operator-Splitting	1.3	1.37
Explicit Method of Lines	1.5	1.01
Method of Lines	1.9	1.00

nonlinear reaction terms was performed. Furthermore, the implicit equations were solved without relaxation. The quasilinear method is slightly more efficient than the method of lines and the implicit method. However, its accuracy deteriorates as larger time steps are taken or as the flame propagates through the combustor due to the accumulated errors associated with the linearization of the reaction terms. This point will become evident when we discuss the accuracy of the numerical methods. A significant feature of Table II is that the Crank-Nicolson method is more efficient than the quasilinear and implicit techniques. This is due to the evaluation of the reaction terms (Section 5). The Crank-Nicolson scheme evaluates the reaction terms at time $t^{(n+1/2)}$ as the average of the reaction terms at time $t^{(n)}$ (known) and $t^{(n+1)}$ (unknown), whereas the implicit method evaluates the reaction terms at time $t^{(n+1)}$.

The next question to be addressed is the relative accuracy of the different methods. As we have mentioned before, the term accuracy refers here to the temporal truncation error, since all the methods use second-order accurate spatial approximations. As we discussed in Section 5, the method of lines and the explicit method of lines are fourth-order accurate and are the most accurate methods used in the present work. This is clearly shown in Table IV which presents the values of the pressure in atmospheres at different times for all the numerical methods studied. This table indicates that the methods of lines are more accurate than the first-order-accurate explicit and implicit techniques, and the second-order-accurate Crank-Nicolson scheme. The accuracy of the operator splitting method is somewhere between that of the method of lines and the explicit method of lines. If we denote the solution given by the method of lines as numerically "exact", we can conclude that the explicit, implicit and Crank-Nicolson techniques, the explicit method of lines and the operator splitting technique underpredict the "exact" numerical values. The level of underprediction increases in the following order: operator splitting procedure, explicit method of lines, explicit, Crank-Nicolson and implicit methods. The relative differences between the results predicted by the operator splitting algorithm and the explicit method of lines are at most 0.1%. As one would have expected, the second order Crank-Nicolson method is more accurate than the first order implicit procedure. An interesting feature of Table IV is that the first-order explicit method is more accurate than the Crank-Nicolson scheme. Table IV also shows that the quasilinear, linear block and predictor-corrector methods overpredict the "exact" solution given by the method of lines. The relative differences between the results obtained with the method of lines and the linear block technique are less than 2.6%. The maximum difference occurs at t=0.3 sec. At first it would appear that the reason why the quasilinear and linear block methods overpredict the "exact" solution of the method of lines is the linearization process. This is partially true as computations carried out using a time step $\Delta t=10^{-6}$ sec showed that the solutions obtained with the quasilinear and linear block methods differed by less than 0.01% from those obtained with the method of lines. The same feature was observed in the implicit predictor-corrector method. As mentioned in Section 5.4, the predictor-corrector technique uses a Crank-Nicolson type scheme in the corrector step, but where

TABLE IV. THE VALUES OF THE PRESSURE (IN ATM) AT DIFFERENT TIMES FOR THE NUMERICAL METHODS INVESTIGATED

NUMERICAL METHOD*	TIME (sec) 0.1	0.2	0.3	0.4	0.5	0.6	0.7	0.8	0.9	1.0
Exp	1.77	2.54	3.43	4.44	5.57	6.83	8.12	9.62	10.49	10.49
Imp	1.76	2.53	3.42	4.42	5.54	6.77	8.01	9.31	10.23	10.24
C-N	1.77	2.54	3.43	4.44	5.56	6.82	8.09	9.58	10.45	10.45
MOL	1.77	2.54	3.44	4.44	5.57	6.83	8.22	9.63	10.49	10.49
EMOL	1.77	2.54	3.44	4.44	5.57	6.83	8.22	9.63	10.49	10.49
Quas	1.77	2.54	3.43	4.54	5.58	6.84	8.22	9.64	10.50	10.50
LB	1.77	2.54	3.43	4.54	5.58	6.84	8.23	9.64	10.50	10.50
IPC	1.77	2.54	3.44	4.45	5.57	6.83	8.22	9.63	10.50	10.50
O-S	1.77	2.54	3.44	4.44	5.57	6.83	8.22	9.63	10.49	10.49

*In this and subsequent tables the following nomenclature was used: Exp= explit, Imp=implicit, C-N=Crank-Nicolson, MOL=method of lines, EMOL=explicit method of lines, Quas=quasilinear, LB=linear block, IPC=implicit predictor-corrector, and O-S=operator splitting. The pressure was calculated from Eq. (12) using the trapezoidal rule.

the nonlinear reaction terms are evaluated as the mean of those obtained at $t^{(n)}$ and in the predictor step. This means that the reaction terms in the corrector step are known [Eq. (26)]. The error associated with the evaluation of these terms reduces with the decrease in the time step.

The differences between the temperature values obtained with the afore-mentioned nine numerical methods, are also shown in Tables V and VI, which present the temperatures at select grid points at t=0.3 and 0.7 secs, respectively. These grid points correspond to the location of the flame front. Table V indicates that quasilinear and linear block methods predict a faster flame than the other six methods at t=0.3 sec (see grid points 25, 26 and 27). The temperature differences between two particular methods are at most 50°K except at grid point 26, which defines the inflection point of the temperature profile. At t=0.5 sec all the numerical methods predict the same flame front location [27].

TABLE V. TEMPERATURE VALUES (IN °K) AT t=0.3 SEC FOR DIFFERENT NUMERICAL METHODS

GRID POINT	NUMERICAL METHODS Exp	Imp	C-N	MOL	EMOL	Quas	LB	IPC	O-S
20	3496	3487	3495	3498	3498	3524	3524	3499	3498
21	3456	3446	3454	3458	3458	3484	3484	3459	3458
22	3419	3407	3416	3421	3420	3445	3446	3421	3420
23	3383	3371	3380	3385	3384	3409	3410	3385	3385
24	3349	3336	3346	3350	3350	3375	3375	3350	3350
25	3299	3285	3296	3301	3301	3330	3330	3302	3301
26	1125	1055	1127	1279	1244	3253	3253	1308	1262
27	490	486	491	495	494	512	512	495	494
28	427	421	427	428	428	431	431	428	428
29	422	421	422	422	422	425	425	422	422
30	421	421	421	421	421	424	424	421	421
31	421	421	421	421	421	424	424	421	421
32	421	421	421	421	421	424	424	421	421
33	421	421	421	421	421	424	424	421	421

TABLE VI. TEMPERATURE VALUES (IN °K) AT t=0.7 SEC FOR DIFFERENT NUMERICAL METHODS

GRID	NUMERICAL METHODS								
POINT	Exp	Imp	C-N	MOL	EMOL	Quas	LB	IPC	O-S
57	3478	3385	3453	3489	3489	3490	3490	3488	3489
58	3464	3375	3438	3475	3475	3477	3476	3474	3475
59	3451	3373	3425	3462	3462	3462	3462	3461	3462
60	3437	3342	3413	3448	3448	3449	3449	3448	3448
61	3424	3307	3401	3435	3435	3434	3434	3434	3435
62	3401	3294	3381	3421	3421	3421	3421	3420	3421
63	1336	700	945	3397	3397	3396	3396	3396	3397
64	570	539	561	632	624	697	700	634	627
65	536	532	534	539	538	540	542	539	539
66	534	532	533	536	535	536	536	536	535
67	534	532	532	535	535	535	536	535	535
68	534	532	532	535	535	535	535	535	535
69	534	532	532	535	535	535	535	535	535

The major temperature underpredictions, however, appear in the implicit and Crank-Nicolson schemes at t=0.7 sec (Table VI). The explicit, implicit and Crank-Nicolson methods predict that the flame front is located at grid point 63, while the other methods predict it at grid point 64. This is in agreement with the previous findings on the pressure history presented in Table IV. The main features of these tables are the following. First, the implicit method underpredicts the temperature of the flame front (see grid points 62 and 63 in Table VI). Second, the explicit, implicit and Crank-Nicolson schemes predict slightly lower temperatures than the other six methods. This underprediction causes a slightly slower flame propagation as is to be expected by observing the pressure and temperature profiles (Tables IV, V and VI). These smaller pressure and temperature differences cannot be appreciated in Figures 1 and 2.

Although in this study we have only paid attention to the temporal resolution of the laminar flame propagation problem, several other aspects need further investigation. In particular, the resolution of the flame structure (a critical point if the prediction of radicals is to be made) requires larger number of grid points. Our calculations show that an 82-point grid has at most three grid points inside the flame. This is a totally unsatisfactory resolution of the flame front. Calculations were also carried out using 600 grid points and show that under these conditions 9 to 12 grid points were located at the flame front for a 10 cm combustor. This means that for a 10 cm combustor at least 10 grid points are required to predict the structure of a laminar flame. Other questions to be addressed are the effects of different spatial approximations. For example, Otey and Dwyer [16] have shown that the linear block method with fourth-order Pade spatial differences was more efficient than the method of lines, the explicit method of lines and the operator splitting technique in reaction-diffusion equations. However, these schemes will also require a large number of grid points, while, as shown in Figures 1 and 2, the region of sharp temperature and concentration profiles is very thin, whereas in front of and behind the flame these profiles are very smooth. This suggests the use of an adaptive grid technique that moves with the flame front and concentrates its grid points in the regions where largest changes occur. In this respect, the adaptive grid procedure developed by Dwyer and Sanders [21] seems a reasonable approach which will avoid large number of grid points while obtaining a high resolution of the flame front. The effects of higher order spatial approximations and the development of an adaptive grid technique for the solution of the integrodifferential reaction-diffusion equations which govern the propagation of laminar flames in closed containers are presently under study and will be reported elsewhere.

6. CONCLUSIONS

Nine numerical schemes which use second-order spatial approximations have been used to analyze the propagation of laminar flames in closed chambers, where the chemistry has been modeled with one-step irreversible Arrhenius-type reactions. The comparison among the numerical methods allows us to draw the following conclusions:

- The explicit method is by far more efficient (in terms of computer time) than the other eight numerical schemes.
- The linear block method is the least efficient algorithm for the integro-differential reaction-diffusion equations studied because of the required iterations and the inversion of a block tridiagonal matrix.
- The first-order accurate explicit and implicit methods, and the second-order accurate Crank-Nicolson scheme underpredict the pressure and temperature profiles. Therefore, they predict a slower flame than the method of lines.
- The accuracy of the operator splitting method is in between those of the method of lines and the explicit method of lines.
- For the same time step, the quasilinear, linear block and implicit predictor-corrector schemes overpredict the pressure and temperature profiles and predict a faster moving flame than the fourth-order accurate methods of lines. This is due to the linearization procedure and the evaluation of the reaction terms in the corrector step. A decrease in the time step causes these methods to be in agreement with the methods of lines.
- The steepness of the flame front and the almost uniform temperature profiles in front and behind the flame suggest that an adaptive grid method will reduce the number of grid points required to predict the flame structure and the formation of radicals at the flame front. In order to have 9 to 12 grid points in the flame front, at least 600 grid points are required to model the propagation of a laminar flame in a 10 cm long combustor.

ACKNOWLEDGMENTS

The author deeply appreciates the suggestions provided by Mr. A. Bagchi for his careful reading of the manuscript. Thanks are due to T. Rogers for the preparation of the manuscript.

REFERENCES

1. Sirignano, W.A. 1973. One-dimensional analysis of combustion in a spark-ignition engine. Combustion Sci. and Tech., Vol. 7, pp. 99-108.

2. Bracco, F.V. and Sirignano, W.A. 1973. Theoretical analysis of Wankel engine combustion. Combustion Sci. and Tech., Vol. 7, pp. 109-123.

3. Bellan, J.R. and Sirignano, W.A. 1973. A theory of turbulent flame development and nitric oxide formation in stratified charge internal combustion engines, Combustion Sci. and Tech., Vol. 8, pp. 51-68.

4. Lilley, D.G. 1974. Turbulent swirling flame prediction. AIAA J., Vol. 12, pp. 219-223.

5. Bellan, J.R. and Sirignano, W.A. 1976. Combustion and NO formation in a stratified-charge engine: a two-turbulent equations model. Combustion Sci. and Tech., Vol. 12, pp. 75-104.

6. Butler, T.D. and O'Rourke, P.J. 1977. A numerical method for two-dimensional unsteady reacting flows. Proc. 16th Symp. (Int.) on Combustion, The Combustion Institute, pp. 1503-1514.

7. Boni, A.A., Chapman, M., Cook, J.L. and Schneyer, G.P. 1977. Computer simulation of combustion in a stratified charge engine. Proc. 16th Symp. (Int.) on Combustion, The Combustion Institute, pp. 1527-1541.

8. Griffin, M.D., Diwaker, R., Anderson, J.D. and Jones, E. 1978. Computational fluid dynamics applied to flows in an internal combustion engine. AIAA paper no. 78-57, presented at the AIAA 16th Aerospace Sciences Meeting.

9. Syed, S.A. and Bracco, F.V. 1979. Further comparisons of computed and measured divided-chamber engine combustion. Paper no. 790247, presented at the 1979 SAE Congress and Exposition.

10. Gupta, H.C. 1980. A two-dimensional model for engine combustion: initial development, testing and application. Ph.D. Thesis, Princeton University.

11. Ramos, J.I. and Sirignano, W.A. 1981. Turbulent flow field in homogeneous-charge, spark-ignition engines. Proc. 18th Symp. (Int.) on Combustion, The Combustion Institute, pp. 1825-2835.

12. Margolis, S.B. 1978. Time-dependent solution of a premixed laminar flame. J. Comp. Phys., Vol. 27, pp. 410-427.

13. Bledjian, L. 1973. Computation of time-dependent laminar flame structure. Comb. Flame, Vol. 20, pp. 5-17.

14. Westbrook, C.K. 1978. A generalized ICE method for chemically reactive flows in combustion systems. J. Comp. Phys., Vol. 29, pp. 67-80.

15. MacCormack, R.W. 1978. An efficient explicit-implicit-characteristic method for solving the compressible Navier-Stokes equations. SIAM-AMS Proc., Vol. 11, pp. 130-155.

16. Otey, G.R. and Dwyer, H.A. 1979. A numerical study of the interaction of fast chemistry and diffusion, AIAA J., Vol. 17, pp. 606-613.

17. Dwyer, H.A. and Sanders, B.R. 1977. Modeling of unsteady combustion phenomena. AIAA Paper no. 77-136, presented at the AIAA 15th Aerospace Sciences Meeting.

18. Kee, R.J. and Miller, J.A. 1978. A split-operator finite difference solution for axisymmetric laminar jet diffusion flames. AIAA J., Vol. 16, pp. 169-176.

19. Beam, R.M. and Warming, R.F. 1978. An implicit factored scheme for the compressible Navier-Stokes equations. AIAA J., Vol. 16, pp. 393-402.

20. Briley, W.R. and McDonald, H. 1977. Solution of the multidimensional compressible Navier-Stokes equations by a generalized implicit method. J. Comp. Phys., Vol. 24, pp. 372-392.

21. Dwyer, H.A. and Sanders, B.R. 1977. Numerical modeling of unsteady flame propagation. Report no. SAND77-8275, Sandia National Lab., Livermore, CA.

22. Williams, F.A. 1965. Combustion Theory. Addison-Wesley Publishing Co., Reading, MA, pp. 1-17.

23. Spalding, D.B. 1956. The theory of flame phenomena with a chain reaction. Phil. Trans. Roy. Soc. (London), Vol. A249, pp. 1-25.

24. Yannenko, N.N. 1971. The Method of Fractional Steps. Springer-Verlag, New York, pp. 17-41.

25. Hornbeck, R.W. 1973. Numerical Marching Techniques for Fluid Flows With Heat Transfer. NASA SP-297, pp. 301-305.

26. Bellman, R.E. and Kalaba, R. 1965. Quasilinearization and Nonlinear Boundary Value Problems. American Elsevier, New York, pp. 111-124.

27. Ramos, J.I. 1981. The numerical solution of integrodifferential equations arising in combustion theory. Part I: cartesian coordinates. Report no. CO/81/5, Department of Mechanical Engineering, Carnegie-Mellon University, Pittsburgh, PA.

Index